Chapter	naeyc NAEYC's Professional Preparation Standards	DAP Developmentally Appropriate Practice (DAP) Guidelines	Common Core State Standards for Math (CCSSM)	Next Generation Science Standards (NGSS)
	3a. Understand the goals, benefits and uses of assessment, p. 64 **3b.** Use a variety of assessment tools and approaches, pp. 57–58 **3c.** Understand and practice responsible assessment, pp. 57–58, 64	**4B.** Focus assessment on children's progress toward goals that are developmentally and educationally significant, pp. 57–58 **4C.** Use the assessment information to guide what goes on in the classroom, pp. 57–58 **4D.** The methods of assessment are developmentally appropriate, pp. 57–58		
Chapter 3: Prekindergarten and Kindergarten Concepts and Skills	**5.** Use content knowledge to build meaningful curriculum, pp. 76–108 **5a.** Understand content knowledge and resources in math and science, pp. 76–108	**2C.** Know desired program goals, pp. 76–108 **3C.** Use the curriculum framework to ensure there is attention to important learning goals, pp. 76–108	**K.CCA 1** Count to 100 by ones and by tens, pp. 89–92 **K.CC.A.3** Write numbers 0 to 20, pp. 89–92 **K.MD.B.3** Classify objects into given categories; count the numbers of objects in each category, pp. 99–101 **K.MD.A.1** Describe measureable attributes of objects, such as length or weight, pp. 105–108 **K.MD.A.2** Directly compare two objects with a measureable attribute in common to see which object has more of or less of the attribute and describe the difference, pp. 107	**K-LS1-1** Scientists look for patterns and order when making observations about the world, pp. 76–108
Chapter 4: More Prekindergarten and Kindergarten Concepts and Skills: Early Geometry, Parts and Wholes, an d Applications of Fundamental Concepts to Science and Engineering	**5.** Use content knowledge to build meaningful curriculum, pp. 114–141 **5a.** Understand content knowledge and resources in math and science, pp. 114–141 **5c.** Design, implement, and evaluate developmentally meaningful and challenging curriculum for each child, pp. 114–141	**2C.** Know desired program goals, pp. 114–141 **3C.** Use the curriculum framework to ensure there is attention to important learning goals, pp. 114–141	**KGA2** Correctly name shapes regardless of their orientation or overall size, pp. 120–122 **MP1** Make sense of problems and persevere in solving them, pp. 114–136 **MP4** Model with mathematics, pp. 114–136	**K-2-ETS 1-1** Ask questions based on observations, pp. 136–141 **K-P3-1** Make observations to collect data that can be used to make comparisons, pp. 136–141
Chapter 5: Pre-K-K: Ordering, Measurement, and Data Collection and Analysis	**5.** Use content knowledge to build meaningful curriculum, pp. 146–183 **5a.** Understand content knowledge and resources in math and science, pp. 146–183 **5c.** Design, implement, and evaluate developmentally meaningful and challenging curriculum for each child, pp. 146–183	**2C.** Know desired program goals, pp. 146–183 **3C.** Use the curriculum framework to ensure there is attention to important learning goals, pp. 146–183	**MP1** Make sense of problems and persevere in solving them, pp. 146–155 **MP4** Model with mathematics, pp. 146–155 **K.MD.A.1** Describe measureable attributes of objects, such as length or weight, pp. 155–171 **K.MD.A.1** Directly compare two objects with a measurable attribute in common to see which object has more or less of the attribute, and describe the difference, pp. 160–162	**K-LS1-1** Scientists look for patterns and order when making observations about the world, pp. 172–183 **K-PS3-1** Make observations to collect data that can be used to make comparisons, pp. 172–183

Chapter	naeyc NAEYC's Professional Preparation Standards	DAP Developmentally Appropriate Practice (DAP) Guidelines	Common Core State Standards for Math (CCSSM)	Next Generation Science Standards (NGSS)
Chapter 6: Integrating the Curriculum	**2a.** Understand diverse family and community characteristics, pp. 194–203 **4b.** Understand and use effective strategies and tools for early education, including appropriate use of technology, pp. 188–200 **5a.** Understand content knowledge and resources in mathematics, and science, pp. 188–200	**3.D.1.** Teachers plan curriculum experiences that integrate children's learning, pp. 188–200	**MP1** Make sense of problems and persevere in solving them, pp. 194–196 **MP4** Model with mathematics, pp. 188–200	**K-ESS3-1** Use a model, pp. 188–200 **K-ESS3-2** Read grade-appropriate texts and/ or use media to obtain information, pp. 188–194 **K-ESS3-3** Communicate solutions with others in oral and/or written forms using models and/ or drawings, pp. 194, 195, 198, 199
Chapter 7: Transitioning from Preschool to Kindergarten to Primary	**5.** Use content knowledge to build meaningful curriculum, pp. 206–243 **5a.** Understand content knowledge and resources in math and science, pp. 206–243 **5c.** Design, implement, and evaluate developmentally meaningful and challenging curriculum for each child, pp. 206–243	**2C.** Know desired program goals, pp. 206–243 **3C.** Use the curriculum framework to ensure there is attention to important learning goals, pp. 206–243	**K.CC** Know number names and count sequence, pp. 206–215 **K.CC.1** Count to 100 by ones and by tens, pp. 206–215 **K.CC.2** Count forward beginning from a given number within the known sequence, pp. 206–215 **K.CC.3** Write numbers from 0 to 20, pp. 215–223 **K.OA** Understand addition and subtraction, pp. 225–226 **K.NBT** Work with numbers 11–19 to gain foundation for place value, pp. 225, 235	**K.LS1-1** Scientists look for patterns and order ok when making observations about the world, pp. 236–243 **K-PS2-1** Scientists Use different ways to study the world, pp. 236–243 **K-SS3-1** Use a model to represent relationships in the natural world, pp. 236–243
Chapter 8: Whole Number Operations, Patterns, and Fractions	**5.** Use content knowledge to build meaningful curriculum, pp. 248–278 **5a.** Understand content knowledge and resources in math and science, pp. 248–278 **5c.** Design, implement, and evaluate developmentally meaningful and challenging curriculum for each child, pp. 248–278	**2C.** Know desired program goals, pp. 248–278 **3C.** Use the curriculum framework to ensure there is attention to important learning goals, pp. 248–278	**1.0A.1** Represent and solve word problems involving addition and subtraction within 20, pp. 250, 252, 256, 258, 261 **1.0A 3** Apply properties of operations as strategies to add and subtract, pp. 248–257 **2.0A 1** Use addition and subtraction within 100 to solve one- and two-step word problems, pp. 248–257 **2.0A 2** Fluently add and subtract within 20 using mental strategies, By the end of grade 2, know from memory all sums of two one-digit numbers, pp. 248–257 **3.0A.A.1** Interpret products of whole numbers, pp. 257–260 **3.0A.A.3** Use multiplication and division within 100 to solve word problems, for example, by using drawings and equations with a symbol for the unknown number to represent the problem, pp. 257–260, 259–263	No Next Generation Science Standards in this chapter

Chapter	naeyc NAEYC's Professional Preparation Standards	DAP Developmentally Appropriate Practice (DAP) Guidelines	Common Core State Standards for Math (CCSSM)	Next Generation Science Standards (NGSS)
			3.OA.C.7 Fluently multiply and divide within 100, using strategies such as the relationship between multiplication and division or properties of operations. By the end of grade 3, know from memory all products of two one-digit numbers, pp. 257–260, 259–263 **3.OA.D.9** Identify arithmetic patterns, pp. 263–272 **3NFA.1** Understand a fraction 1/*b* as the quantity formed by 1 part when a whole is partitioned into *b* equal parts; understand a fraction *a/b* is the quantity formed by parts of size 1/*b*, pp. 272–278	
Chapter 9: Place Value, Geometry, Data Analysis, and Measurement	**5.** Use content knowledge to build meaningful curriculum, pp. 284–311 **5a.** Understand content knowledge and resources in math and science, pp. 284–311 **5c.** Design, implement, and evaluate developmentally meaningful and challenging curriculum for each child, pp. 284–311	**2C.** Know desired program goals, pp. 284–311 **3C.** Use the curriculum framework to ensure there is attention to important learning goals, pp. 284–311	**1.OA.1** Count to 120, starting at any number less than 120, pp. 284–292 **1.NBT.1** Understand that the three digits of a three-digit number represent amounts of 100s, 10s, and 1s, pp. 284–292 **3.NBT.A.2** Fluently add and subtract within 1000, pp. 284–292 **1.G.A.1** Distinguish between defining attributes versus non-defining attributes of shapes, pp. 295 **1.G.A.3** Partition circles and rectangles into two and four equal shares, pp. 294 **1.MDC4** Organize, represent, and interpret data with up to three categories, pp. 283, 299–303 **2.MD.A.1** Measure the length of an object using tools such as rulers, yardsticks, meter sticks and measuring tapes, pp. 302–307	**1-PS4-1, 2-PS-1, and 1-PS4-3** Plan and conduct investigations collaboratively to produce data to serve as the basis for evidence to answer a question, pp. 292, 213, 294, 216, 296, 299, 300 **1-PS4-4, 2-PS1-2** Use tools and material provided to design a device that solves a specific problem, pp. 295, 298–299, 310, 394
Chapter 10: Overview of Primary Science: Life Science and Physical Science	**5.** Use content knowledge to build meaningful curriculum, pp. 316–350 **5a.** Understand content knowledge and resources in math and science, pp. 316–350 **5c.** Design, implement, and evaluate developmentally meaningful and challenging curriculum for each child, pp. 316–350	**2C.** Know desired program goals, pp. 316–350 **3C.** Use the curriculum framework to ensure there is attention to important learning goals, pp. 316–350	**K.MD.B.3** Classify objects into given categories, count the number of objects in each category and sort the categories by count, pp. 316, 318–319, 321, 326, 328, 333, 340–41, 348, 350	**2-LS4-3-LS4** Biological Evolution: unity and diversity, pp. 318 **1-PS4** Waves and their applications in technologies for information transfer, pp. 339 **2-PS1** Matter and its interactions, pp. 339 **2-LS4-1** Making observations to collect data that can be used in comparisons, pp. 316, 318–319, 321–322, 325, 327, 330–334, 336–337, 340–350

Chapter	naeyc NAEYC's Professional Preparation Standards	DAP Developmentally Appropriate Practice (DAP) Guidelines	S Common Core State Standards for Math (CCSSM)	NGSS Next Generation Science Standards (NGSS)
Chapter 11: Earth and Space Sciences, Environmental Awareness, Engineering, Technology, and Science Applications	**5.** Use content knowledge to build meaningful curriculum, pp. 354–376 **5a.** Understand content knowledge and resources in math and science, pp. 354–376 **5c.** Design, implement, and evaluate developmentally meaningful and challenging curriculum for each child, pp. 354–376	**2C.** Know desired program goals, pp. 354–376 **3C.** Use the curriculum framework to ensure there is attention to important learning goals, pp. 354–376	No Common Core State Standards in this chapter	**1-ESS1-2** Make firsthand observations to collect data, pp. 354, 356, 359, 363, 373, 376, 377 **1-ESS1-1** Use firsthand observations to describe patterns in the natural world, pp. 357–358, 364–365, 367, 371, 374 **K-ESS-3** Communicate solutions that will reduce the impact of humans on the land, water, air, and/or other living things in the local environment, pp. 368–370, 372, 376–377
Chapter 12: Materials and Resources: Math and Science in the Classroom and the Home	**1c.** Create healthy, respectful, supportive, and challenging learning environments, pp. 382–391 **2a.** Know and understand diverse family and community characteristics, pp. 404–412 **2b.** Support and engage families and communities, pp. 404–412 **2c.** Involve families and communities in young children's development and learning, pp. 404–412 **4b.** Know and understand early education strategies and tools, including technology, pp. 391–404, 412 **5c.** Design, implement, and evaluate developmentally meaningful and challenging curriculum, pp. 391–404	**2E.** Promote each child's learning and development, pp. 382–412 **5D.** Acknowledge family's choices and goals respond with sensitivity and respect, pp. 404–408	**MP5** Use appropriate tools strategically, pp. 382–383, 390, 395, 398, 403, 406–407, 409	**3-PS2-1** Science and engineering practice: Science investigations use a variety of methods, tools, and techniques, pp. 382–392, 396, 399–401, 403–404, 411 **ETS 1.A** Define and delimit problems, pp. 391–392, 396–397, 403, 408–409 **ETS 1.B:** Develop possible solutions. Engineering, pp. 390–392, 398, 404, 409

MATH AND SCIENCE

FOR YOUNG CHILDREN

EIGHTH EDITION

This book is dedicated to the memory of a dear friend ADA DAWSON STEPHENS.

ROSALIND CHARLESWORTH
WEBER STATE UNIVERSITY

MATH AND SCIENCE

FOR YOUNG CHILDREN

EIGHTH EDITION

CENGAGE
Learning

Australia • Brazil • Canada • Mexico Singapore • Spain • United Kingdom • United States

Math and Science for Young Children,
Eighth Edition
Rosalind Charlesworth

Product Director: Marta E. Lee-Perriard

Product Manager: Mark Kerr

Content Developer: Kassi Radomski

Product Assistant: Julia Catalano

Marketing Manager: Chris Sosa

Content Project Manager: Samen Iqbal

Art Director: Marissa Falco

Manufacturing Planner: Doug Bertke

IP Analyst: Jennifer Nonenmacher

IP Project Manager: Brittani Hall

Production Service/Project Manager:
Lynn Lustberg, MPS Limited

Photo Researcher: Veerabaghu Nagarajan,
Lumina Datamatics Ltd.

Text Researcher: Nandhini Srinivasagopalan,
Lumina Datamatics Ltd.

Text and Cover Designer: Jeff Bane

Cover Image Credit: Comstock/Getty Images;
Ariel Skelley/Blend Images/Getty Images; Asia
Images Group/Getty Images; Brand X Pictures/
Stockbyte/Thinkstock; Vladimir Nenov/iStock/
Thinkstock; Jordan McCullough/iStock/
Thinkstock

Compositor: MPS Limited, Offshore

For product information and technology assistance, contact us at
Cengage Learning Customer & Sales Support, 1-800-354-9706
For permission to use material from this text or product,
submit all requests online at **www.cengage.com/permissions**
Further permissions questions can be emailed to
permissionrequest@cengage.com

Library of Congress Control Number: 2014946139

Student Edition:

ISBN: 978-1-305-08895-5

Loose-leaf Edition:

ISBN: 978-1-305-49689-7

Cengage Learning
20 Channel Center Street
Boston, MA 02210
USA

Cengage Learning is a leading provider of customized learning solutions with office locations around the globe, including Singapore, the United Kingdom, Australia, Mexico, Brazil, and Japan. Locate your local office at **www.cengage.com/global**

Cengage Learning products are represented in Canada by Nelson Education, Ltd.

To learn more about Cengage Learning Solutions, visit **www.cengage.com**

Purchase any of our products at your local college store or at our preferred online store **www.cengagebrain.com**

Printed in the United States of America
Print Number: 01   Print Year: 2015

BRIEF CONTENTS

CONTENTS

PART 3 APPLYING FUNDAMENTAL CONCEPTS

PREFACE

Math and Science for Young Children, Eighth Edition, is designed to be used by students in training and by teachers in service in early childhood education. To the student, it introduces the excitement and extensiveness of math and science experiences in programs for young children. For teachers in the field, it presents an organized, sequential approach to creating a developmentally appropriate math and science curriculum for preschool and primary school children. Further, it is designed in line with the guidelines and standards of the major professional organizations: National Association for the Education of Young Children (NAEYC), National Council of Teachers of Mathematics (NCTM), National Science Teachers Association (NSTA), and National Research Council (NRC).

Development of the Text

The text was developed and directed by the concept that the fundamental concepts and skills that form the foundation for mathematics and science are identical. Each edition has focused on these commonalities. As changes have emerged in each area, the text has been updated. Acquaintance with child development from birth through age 8 would be a helpful prerequisite.

Organization of the Text

The text is set up in a logical progression, and students should follow the text in sequence. Applying the assessment tasks and teaching one (or more) of the sample lessons will provide the student with hands-on experience relevant to each concept and each standard.

Activities are presented in a developmental sequence designed to support young children's construction of the concepts and skills essential to a basic understanding of mathematics and science. A developmentally appropriate approach to assessment is stressed in order to have an individualized program in which each child is presented at each level with tasks that can be accomplished successfully before moving on to the next level.

A further emphasis is placed on three types of learning: naturalistic, informal, and adult guided. Much learning can take place through the child's natural exploratory activities if the environment is designed to promote such activity. The adult can reinforce and enrich this naturalistic learning by careful introduction of information through informal and adult-guided experiences.

The test-driven practices that are currently prevalent have produced a widespread use of inappropriate instructional practices with young children. Mathematics for preschoolers has been taught as "pre-math," apparently under the assumption that math learning begins only with addition and subtraction in the primary grades. It also has been taught in both preschool and primary school as rote memory material using abstract paper-and-pencil activities. Science is often presented as discrete activities if at all. This text emphasizes the recognition by the National Council of Teachers of Mathematics and the National Research Council of the inclusion of mathematics at the pre-K level in its revised mathematics standards (CCSSM, NRC, 2010). A new Science Framework (NRC, 2012) and Next Generation Common Core Standards for Science (NGSS, NRC, 2013) cover K–12 science standards and emphasize science projects as ongoing endeavors integrated with the other curriculum areas. This text is designed to bring to the attention of early childhood educators the interrelatedness of math and science and the necessity of providing young children with opportunities to explore concretely these domains of early concept learning. Further integration is stressed with language arts, social studies, art, and music; the goal is to provide a totally integrated program. With the advent of STEM, efforts are being made to emphasize the relationships among science, technology, engineering, and mathematics. Also, the national Common Core state standards for mathematics and the New Generation Science Standards support an integrated, project approach to instruction. These standards are described in the relevant chapters. Also included are the relevant NAEYC Guidelines and Professional Development standards.

Part 1 sets the theoretical and conceptual foundation. Part 2 provides chapters on fundamental concepts: one-to-one correspondence, number sense and counting, logic and classifying, comparing, shape, spatial sense, parts and wholes, and application of these concepts to science. Each chapter is introduced with the relevant Common Core State Standards, followed by assessment; naturalistic, informal, and adult-guided activities; evaluation; and summary. Every chapter includes references and further reading and resources, brain connections, a suggested related video, and a technology connection. Most of the chapters in Parts 3, 4, and 5 follow the same format. Chapter 6 (in Part 3) sums up the application of process skills and important vocabulary and provides basic ideas for integrating math and science through dramatic play and thematic units and projects. Part 5 includes the major mathematics concepts for grades 1–3. Part 6 focuses on science investigations in the primary grades. Part 7 includes three areas: materials and resources, math and science in action, and math and science in the home. The appendices contain additional assessment tasks and lists of books, periodicals, and technology resources. A glossary and index are also included.

New to This Edition

Major revisions to the eighth edition include the following:

- **Learning Objectives** at the beginning of each chapter now correlate with main headings within the chapter and the Summary at the end of the chapter. The objectives highlight what students need to know to process and understand the information in the chapter. After completing the chapter, students should be able to demonstrate how they can use and apply their new knowledge and skills.

- **Improved integration of early childhood and primary grade professional standards** helps students make connections between what they are learning in the textbook and the standards. This edition now contains a list of standards covered at the beginning of each chapter, including NAEYC's Professional Preparation Standards (2010); Developmentally Appropriate Practice (DAP) Guidelines; Common Core Standards for Math; and Next Generation Science Standards. Throughout the text, these standards are also highlighted with icons, and a complete list of the standards addressed in this book can be found in the standards correlation chart on the inside front and back covers.

- **Digital Downloads** are downloadable and sometimes customizable practical and professional resources, which allow students to immediately implement and apply the textbook's content in the field. Students can download these tools and keep them forever, enabling preservice teachers to begin building a library of practical, professional resources. Look for the Digital Download label that identifies these items.

- **MindTap for Education** is a first-of-its kind digital solution that prepares teachers by providing them with the knowledge, skills, and competencies they must demonstrate to earn an education degree and state licensure, and to begin a successful career. Through activities based on real-life teaching situations, MindTap elevates students' thinking by giving them experiences in applying concepts, practicing skills, and evaluating decisions, guiding them to become reflective educators.

- **TeachSource Videos** feature footage from the classroom to help students relate key chapter content to real-life scenarios. Critical-thinking questions following each video provide opportunities for in-class or online discussion and reflection.

- **Brain Connection** boxes describe recent brain research related to the chapter topics.

- **Updated Technology for Young Children** boxes address the increasing role that technology tools are playing in children's education. Each box introduces resources for a particular topic or discusses related research.

- The text is streamlined for easier use, with 12 chapters rather than the 41 units that appeared in previous editions.

- Recent insights on instruction for special needs students help readers think about and determine how they will adapt their teaching style to include all children.

- Updated coverage of important topics in the field includes STEM/STEAM, with engineering now included in science and math chapters; multicultural and English Language Learner (ELL) classroom learning and strategies and multicultural integration; science performance expectations; and expanded discussion of constructivism.

- Science activities and projects are now divided into Next Generation and conventional approaches, as NGSS is just being introduced and may not be familiar to all readers.

- References have been updated throughout and are included at the end of the chapter, and the Further Readings and Resources list now includes just the most recent items and some classics.

Major Part-Specific Changes

Part 1

- Explanation and description of Science Framework and NGSS are included.

- CCSSM and new NCTM Principles and Actions are explained and described.

- Discussion of STEM and STEAM has been expanded.

- There is increased coverage of analysis of problem-solving processes.

- Chapter 1 contains content previously in Units 1, 2, 3, and 4.

- Chapter 2 includes the content from Units 5, 6, and 7.

Part 2

- Chapter 3 includes the content from Units 8–11.
- Chapter 4 includes the content from Units 12–14 and 16, and thus makes a closer connection between math and science.

Part 3

- Chapter 5 includes material from Units 17–21 and thus makes a closer connection between math and science.
- Chapter 6 includes material from Units 15 and 22, thus demonstrating how language, play, and projects can support learning across the curriculum.

Part 4

- New engineering examples are provided.
- Chapter 7 includes the material from Units 23–26 and thus provides a closer connection between math and science; in addition, it connects the more advanced concepts and skills that some children will learn by the end of kindergarten.

Part 5

- Chapter 8 includes material from Units 27–29.
- Chapter 9 includes material from Units 30–32.
- Math standards have been updated.

Part 6

- Chapter 10 includes material from Units 33–35.
- Chapter 11 includes material from Units 36–37 plus new material on engineering, technology, and science application.
- New project lesson plans based on NGSS standards are included for the primary grades.

Part 7

- Resource addresses have been updated.

Appendix A

- Tasks have been connected to new organization.
- Resources have been updated.

Appendix B

- A new section of technology resource sites has been included.
- New books have been added.

Supplement Package

- NEW MindTap™, The Personal Learning Experience, for Charlesworth's *Math and Science for Young Children*, 8th Edition, represents a new approach to teaching and learning. A highly personalized, fully customizable learning platform, MindTap, helps students to elevate thinking by guiding them to:
  - Know, remember, and understand concepts critical to becoming a great teacher;
  - Apply concepts, create tools, and demonstrate performance and competency in key areas in the course;
  - Prepare artifacts for the portfolio and eventual state licensure, to launch a successful teaching career; and
  - Develop the habits to become a reflective practitioner.

As students move through each chapter's Learning Path, they engage in a scaffolded learning experience designed to move them up Bloom's Taxonomy from lower- to higher-order thinking skills. The Learning Path enables preservice students to develop these skills and gain confidence in the following ways:

- Engaging them with chapter topics and activating their prior knowledge by watching and answering questions about TeachSource videos of teachers teaching and children learning in real classrooms
- Checking their comprehension and understanding through *Did You Get It?* assessments, with varied question types that are autograded for instant feedback
- Applying concepts through mini-case scenarios in which students analyze typical teaching and learning situations and create a reasoned response to the issue(s) presented in the scenarios
- Reflecting about and justifying the choices they made within the teaching scenario problem

MindTap helps instructors facilitate better outcomes by evaluating how future teachers plan and teach lessons in ways that make content clear and help diverse students learn, assessing the effectiveness of their teaching practice, and adjusting teaching as needed. The Student Progress App makes grades visible in real time so students and instructors always have access to current standings in the class.

MindTap for *Math and Science for Young Children* helps instructors easily set their course because it integrates into the existing Learning Management System and saves instructors time by allowing them to fully customize any aspect of the learning path. Instructors can change the order of the student learning activities, hide activities they don't want for the course, and—most importantly—add any content they do want (e.g., YouTube videos, Google docs, links to state education standards). Learn more at http://www.cengage.com/mindtap.

MindTap Moves Students Up Bloom's Revised Taxonomy

Create

Evaluate

Analyze

Apply

Understand

Remember & Know

Anderson, L. W., & Krathwohl, D. (Eds.). (2001). *A taxonomy for learning, teaching, and assessing: A revision of Bloom's taxonomy of educational objectives.* New York: Longman.

Online Instructor's Manual with Test Bank

An online Instructor's Manual accompanies this book. It contains information to assist the instructor in designing the course, including sample syllabi, discussion questions, teaching and learning activities, field experiences, learning objectives, and additional online resources. For assessment support, the updated test bank includes true/false, multiple-choice, matching, short-answer, and essay questions for each chapter.

PowerPoint Lecture Slides

These vibrant Microsoft PowerPoint lecture slides for each chapter assist you with your lecture by providing concept coverage using images, figures, and tables directly from the textbook.

Cognero

Cengage Learning Testing Powered by Cognero is a flexible online system that allows you to author, edit, and manage test bank content from multiple Cengage Learning solutions; create multiple test versions in an instant; and deliver tests from your LMS, your classroom, or wherever you want.

References

- Copple, C., & Bredekamp, S. (Eds.). (2009). *Developmentally appropriate practice in early childhood programs.* Washington, DC: National Association for the Education of Young Children.

- National Council of Teachers of Mathematics. (2014). *Principles to actions: Ensuring mathematical success for all.* Reston, VA: NCTM.

- National Governors Association Center for Best Practice Council of Chief State School Officers. (2010). *Common Core State Standards for mathematics.* Washington, DC: National Academies Press. www.corestandards.org.

- National Research Council (NRC). (2012). *A framework for K–12 science education,* Washington, DC: National Academies Press.

- National Research Council (NRC). (2013) *Next Generation Science Standards (NGSS),* Washington, DC: National Academies Press.

- *NAEYC standards for early childhood professional preparation programs.* (2012). Washington, DC: National Association for the Education of Young Children.

The authors and Cengage Learning make every effort to ensure that all Internet resources are accurate at the time of printing. However, the fluid nature of the Internet precludes any guarantee that all URLs will remain current throughout the life of this edition.

ACKNOWLEDGMENTS

The author wish to express her appreciation to the following individuals and Early Childhood and Development Centers:

- Special appreciation to Dr. Karen K. Lind for her years of collaboration and contributions to the past text revisions.

- Dee Radeloff, for her collaboration in the writing of *Experiences in Math for Young Children*, which served as the starting point for this book.

- Dr. Mark Malone of the University of Colorado at Colorado Springs, who contributed to the planning of this text. Dr. Malone also demonstrated great patience while introducing Dr. Charlesworth to the mysteries of word processing on a personal computer.

- Artist Bonita S. Carter, for the care and accuracy taken in her original art.

- Kate Charlesworth, for her tolerance of her mother's writing endeavors.

- Summer Sky Potter for her work sample contributions.

- Gaile Clement, for sharing her knowledge and expertise in the area of portfolio assessment with Dr. Charlesworth.

- The 30 East Baton Rouge Parish (Louisiana) K–3 teachers who participated in a six-week summer Mathematics/Child Development in-service workshop and to the other workshop faculty—Thelamese Porter, Robert Perlis, and Colonel Johnson—all of whom provided enrichment to Dr. Charlesworth's view of mathematics for young children.

- Shirley A. Leali, professor emerita of teacher education at Weber State University, for many helpful math conversations.

- The following teachers, who provided a place for observation and/or cooperated with our efforts to obtain photographs: Lois Rector, Kathy Tonore, Lynn Morrison, and Nancy Crom (LSU Laboratory Elementary School); Joan Benedict (LSU Laboratory Preschool); Nancy Miller and Candy Jones (East Baton Rouge Parish Public Schools) and 30 East Baton Rouge Parish School System K–3 teachers and their students; and Krista Robinson (Greatho Shryock), Maureen Awbrey (Anchorage Schools), Elizabeth Beam (Zachary Taylor), and Dr. Anna Smythe (Cochran, Jefferson County

Public Schools). Thanks to Mrs. Nancy Lindeman, Director; Mrs. Kacee Weaver, primary grade teacher; and her assistant, Miss Cindy Wahlen, at the Maria Montessori Academy in North Ogden, Utah, who allowed us to obtain photographs. We also thank Cami Bearden and Sherrie West who welcomed us into the WSU Children's School to take photographs. Photos were taken by Danielle Taylor, Rosalind Charlesworth, and Kate Charlesworth.

- Jill Hislop Gibson and her students at Polk Elementary School, who welcomed Dr. Charlesworth into their kindergarten and participated in math problem-solving activities.

- Anchorage Schools computer teacher Sharon Campbell and Rutherford Elementary computer teacher Phyllis E. Ferrell, who provided recommendations for using computers with young children.

- University of Louisville graduate students Shawnita Adams, Kate Clavijo, Phyllis E. Ferrell, Christy D. McGee, and Stephanie Gray, who provided assistance in researching and compiling information for earlier editions of the text.

- Phyllis Marcuccio, retired editor of *Science and Children* and director of publications for the National Science Teachers Association, for generously facilitating the use of articles appearing in *Science and Children* and other NSTA publications.

- The staff of Cengage Learning for their patience and understanding throughout my work with this project.

- Dr. David Jerner Martin for his contributions to this edition, particularly the science sections. Dr. Martin is Professor Emeritus of Science Education at Kennesaw State University where he won numerous outstanding professor awards for his teaching, his service, and his research and publications. He was the science education consultant for The Weather Channel's programs for schools. Dr. Martin has authored *Elementary Science Methods: A Constructivist Approach*, currently in its sixth edition, and *Constructing Early Childhood Science*, both of which help preservice teachers learn how to teach science meaningfully. He co-authored, with Dr. Kimberly S. Loomis, *Building Teachers: A Constructivist Approach to Introducing Education*, an introduction-to-education textbook currently in its second edition. Dr. Martin's textbooks are used widely in domestic colleges and universities and have been translated into Korean and Chinese for use in their respective countries.

■ The following reviewers, who provided many valuable ideas:

Sarah Allred, University of Southern Mississippi

Margaret Annunziata, Davidson County Community College

Marjory Ayala, Kennedy-King College

Teri Brannum, North Central State College

Sharon Carter, Davidson County Community College

Mary Jane Eisenhauer, Purdue University North Central

Kathleen Fasiq, Trevecca Nazarene University

Nancy Gallenstein, University of South Carolina Beaufort

Vivien Geneser, Texas A&M University-San Antonio

Marissa Happ, Waubonsee Community College

Holly Kirk, Itawamba Community College

Yvonne Liu-Constant, Lesley University

Paula McMurray-Schwarz, Ohio University Eastern Campus

Leslie Wasserman, Heidelberg University

ABOUT THE AUTHOR

Rosalind Charlesworth is professor emerita and retired department chair in the Department of Child and Family Studies at Weber State University in Ogden, Utah. During her tenure at Weber State University, she worked with the faculty of the Department of Teacher Education to develop continuity from preprimary to primary school in the program for students in the early childhood education licensure program. She also contributed as a guest presenter in the Elementary Mathematics Methods class.

Dr. Charlesworth's career in early childhood education has included experiences with both typical and atypical young children in laboratory schools, public schools, and day care and through research in social and cognitive development and behavior. She is also known for her contributions to research on early childhood teachers' beliefs and practices. She taught courses in early education and child development at other universities before joining the faculty at Weber State University. In 1995, she was named the Outstanding Graduate of the University of Toledo College of Education and Allied Professions. In 1999, she was the co-recipient of the NAECTE/Allyn & Bacon Outstanding Early Childhood Teacher Educator award. In 2014, she received the Legacy Award from the WSU Child and Family Studies Department in recognition of her contributions to early childhood education. She is the author of the popular Wadsworth text *Understanding Child Development*, has published many articles in professional journals, and has given presentations at major professional meetings. Dr. Charlesworth has provided service to the field through active involvement in professional organizations. She has been a member of the NAEYC Early Childhood Teacher Education Panel, a consulting editor for *Early Childhood Research Quarterly*, and a member of the NAECTE (National Association of Early Childhood Teacher Educators) Public Policy and Long-Range Planning Committees. She served two terms on the NAECTE board as regional representative and one as vice president for membership. She was twice elected treasurer and was elected as newsletter editor of the Early Childhood/Child Development Special Interest Group of the American Educational Research Association (AERA); is past president of the Louisiana Early Childhood Association; and was a member of the editorial board of the Southern Early Childhood Association journal *Dimensions*. She is currently on the editorial board of the *Early Childhood Education Journal*.

PART 1
CONCEPT DEVELOPMENT IN
MATHEMATICS AND SCIENCE
CHAPTER 1 Development, Acquisition, Problem Solving, and Assessment
CHAPTER 2 Basics of Science, Engineering, and Technology

CHAPTER

1

DEVELOPMENT, ACQUISITION,
PROBLEM SOLVING, AND ASSESSMENT

LEARNING OBJECTIVES

After reading this chapter, you should be able to:

1-1 Define concept development, and identify the concepts children are developing in early childhood.

1-2 Describe three types of learning experiences, and give an example of each.

1-3 Design lessons and activities using the six steps in instruction suggested in this chapter.

1-4 Explain the reasons for development of the National Assessment Standards.

STANDARDS ADDRESSED IN THIS CHAPTER

naeyc

NAEYC Professional Preparation Standards

1a. Know and understand children's characteristics and needs (0–8).

1b. Use developmental knowledge to create healthy learning environments for young children.

2a. Understand diverse family and community characteristics.

4c. Use developmentally appropriate teaching/learning approaches.

5a. Understand content knowledge and resources in mathematics and science.

5c. Design, implement, and evaluate developmentally meaningful and challenging curriculum for each child.

3a. Understand the goals, benefits, and uses of assessment.

3b. Use a variety of appropriate assessment tools and approaches.

3c. Understand and practice responsible assessment.

DAP Guidelines

3A2. Become familiar with state standards or other mandates.

2C. Know desired program goals.

3C. Use the curriculum framework to ensure there is attention to important learning goals.

4C. Use the assessment information to guide what goes on in the classroom.

4D. Ensure methods of assessment are developmentally appropriate.

Common Core State Standards for Math

MP1   Make sense of problems and persevere in solving them.

MP4   Model with mathematics.

Next Generation Science Standards

K-PS2-1   Plan and conduct an investigation.

K-PS-3   Make observations.

K-PS3-1   Use tools and materials.

K-ESS3-1   Use a model.

K-ESS3-2   Ask questions based on observations to obtain information.

K-ESS3-3   Communicate solutions.

DAP **naeyc**

1-1 CONCEPT DEVELOPMENT

In early childhood, children actively engage in acquiring fundamental concepts and learning fundamental process skills. **Concepts** are the building blocks of knowledge; they allow people to organize and categorize information. Concepts can be applied to the solution of new problems in everyday experience. As we watch children in their everyday activities, we can observe them constructing and using concepts. Some examples follow:

- *One-to-one correspondence.* Passing apples, one to each child at a table; putting pegs in pegboard holes; putting a car in each garage built from blocks.

- *Counting.* Counting the pennies from a penny bank, the number of straws needed for the children at a table, or the number of rocks in a rock collection.

- *Classifying.* Placing square shapes in one pile and round shapes in another; putting cars in one garage and trucks in another.

- *Measuring.* Pouring sand, water, pebbles, or other materials from one container to another.

As you proceed through this text, you will learn how young children begin to construct many concepts during the **preprimary or preschool/kindergarten** period (the years before children enter first grade). They also develop processes that enable them to apply their newly acquired concepts and to enlarge current concepts and develop new ones.

During the preprimary period, children learn and begin to apply concepts basic to both mathematics and science. As children enter the **primary** period (grades 1–3), they apply these early basic concepts to explore more abstract inquiries in science and to help them understand the operations of addition, subtraction, multiplication, and division as well as mathematical concepts such as measurement, geometry, and algebra.

As young children grow and develop physically, socially, and mentally, their concepts also grow and develop. **Development** refers to changes that take place as a result of growth and experience. Development follows an individual timetable for each child; it is a series or sequence of steps that each child takes one at a time. Different children of the same age may be weeks, months, or even a year or two apart in reaching certain stages and still be within the normal range of development. This text examines concept development in math and science from birth through the primary grades. For an overview of this development sequence, see **Figure 1-1**.

| Period | Concepts and Skills: Beginning Points for Understanding | | | |
	Section II Fundamental	Section III Applied	Section IV Higher Level	Section V Primary
Sensorimotor (Birth to age 2)	Observation Problem solving One-to-one correspondence Number Shape Spatial sense			
Preoperational (2 to 7 years)	Sets and classifying Comparing Counting Parts and wholes	Ordering, seriation, patterning Informal measurement: Weight Length Temperature Volume Time Sequence	Number symbols Groups and symbols	
Transitional (5 to 7 years)		Graphing Language Integration	Concrete addition and subtraction	Whole number operations
Concrete operations (7 to 11 years)			Number and Operations in Base 10: Algebraic Thinking; Problem Solving	Fractions Number facts Place value Geometry Measurement with standard units

FIGURE 1-1 The development of math and science concepts and process skills.

© Cengage Learning®

PHOTO 1-1 As infants crawl and creep to explore the environment, they develop a concept of space.

Name Mary

How many days until I see green sprouting up?

1	2	3	4	5	6	7	8	9	10	11	12
X	X	X									

FIGURE 1-2 Mary records each day that passes until her bean seed sprouts.

Concept growth and development begin in infancy. Babies explore the world with their **senses**. They look, touch, smell, hear, and taste. Children are born curious, wanting to know all about their environment. Babies begin to learn ideas of size, weight, shape, time, and space (**Photo 1-1**). As they look about, they sense their relative smallness. They grasp things and find that some fit in their tiny hands and others do not. Infants learn about weight when items of the same size cannot always be lifted. They learn about shape. Some things stay where they put them, whereas others roll away. Children learn time sequence. When they wake up, they feel wet and hungry. They cry. The caretaker comes. They are changed and then fed. Next they play, get tired, and go to bed. As infants begin to move, they develop spatial sense. They are placed in a crib, in a playpen, or on the floor in the center of the living room. As babies first look and then move, they discover space. Some spaces are big; some are small.

As children learn to crawl, stand, and walk, they are free to discover more on their own and learn to think for themselves. They hold and examine more things (**Photo 1-2**). They go over, under, and inside large objects and discover their size relative to them. Toddlers sort things. They put them in piles of the same color, the same size, the same shape, or that have the same use. Young children pour sand and water into containers of different sizes. They pile blocks into tall structures and see them fall and become small parts again. They buy food at a play store and pay with play money. As children cook imaginary food, they measure imaginary flour, salt, and milk. They set the table in their play kitchen, putting one of everything at each place, just as is done at home. The free exploring and experimentation of the first two years are the opportunity for the development of muscle coordination and the senses of taste, smell, sight, and hearing, skills children need as a basis for future learning.

As young children leave toddlerhood and enter the preschool and kindergarten levels of the preprimary period, exploration continues to be the first step in dealing with new situations; at this time, however, they also begin to apply basic concepts to collecting and organizing data to answer a question. Collecting data requires skills in observation, counting, recording, and organizing. For example, for a science investigation, kindergartners might be interested in the process of plant growth. Supplied with lima bean seeds, wet paper towels, and glass jars, the children place the seeds so that they are held against the sides of the jars with wet paper towels. Each day they add water as needed and observe what is happening to the seeds. They dictate their observations to their teacher, who records them on a chart. Each child also plants some beans in dirt in a small container, such as a paper or plastic cup. The teacher supplies each child with a chart for his or her bean garden. The children check off each day on their charts until they see a sprout (**Figure 1-2**). Then they count how many days it took for a sprout to appear and compare this number with those of the other class members and also with the time it takes for the seeds in the glass jars to sprout. Thus, the children have used the concepts of number and counting, one-to-one correspondence, time, and the comparison of the numbers of items in two groups. Primary children might attack the same problem. But they can operate more independently and record more information, use standard measuring tools (i.e., rulers), and do background reading on their own. Development guidelines charts for mathematics and science instruction are included in CCSSM (National Governors Association, 2010), NGSS (Lead States, 2010), and in NCTM/NAEYC, 2010.

PHOTO 1-2 Children learn though hands-on experience.

1-1a Relationships Between Science, Technology, Engineering, Math, and Art (Stem and Steam)

The same fundamental concepts, developed in early childhood, underlie a young child's understanding of math, science, engineering, and technology. Math and science integrate with technology and engineering to form STEM (see the *Science and Children* special issue, March 2010, and *A Framework for K–12 Science Education*, National Research Council, 2012). Much of our understanding of how and when this development takes place comes from research based on Jean Piaget's and Lev Vygotsky's theories of concept development. These theories are briefly described later in the chapter. The commonalities that link science, technology, engineering, math, and the arts are also described later in the chapter.

Working with problems and tasks in the STEM and STEAM areas, and particularly math, tends to cause anxiety for many adults and children. Those learning to teach math may allay those feelings by looking through Parts 5 and 7 and Chapter 12, which provide an overview of math materials and activities for young children. Similarly, those with anxieties about teaching science should refer to Parts 6 and 7 and Chapter 12.

STEM focuses on the interrelationships of science, technology, engineering, and mathematics (Moomaw & Davis, 2013); these fundamental mathematics concepts, such as comparing, classifying, and measuring, are simply called **process skills** when applied to science and engineering problems (see Chapter 2 for a more in-depth explanation). In other words, fundamental math concepts are needed to solve problems in science and engineering. The other science process skills (observing, communicating, inferring, hypothesizing, and defining and controlling variables) are equally important for solving problems in engineering, science, and mathematics. For example, consider the principle of the ramp, a basic concept in physics (DeVries & Sales, 2011). Suppose a 2-foot-wide plywood board is leaned against a large block so that it becomes a ramp. The children are given a number of balls of different sizes and weights to roll down the ramp. Once they have the idea of the game through free exploration, the teacher might pose some questions: "What do you think would happen if two balls started to roll at exactly the same time from the top of the ramp?" "What would happen if you changed the height of the ramp or had two ramps of different heights or of different lengths?" The students could guess (predict), explore what actually happens when using ramps of varying steepnesses and lengths and balls of various types, communicate their observations, and describe commonalities and differences. They might observe differences in speed and distance traveled contingent on the size or weight of the ball, the height and length of the ramp, or other variables. In this example, children could use math concepts of speed, distance, height, length, and counting ("How many blocks are propping up each ramp?") while engaged in scientific observation.

Block building also provides a setting for the integration of math, science, and engineering (Chalufour, Hoisington, Moriarty, Winokur, & Worth, 2004; Pollman, 2010). Pollman describes how block building is basic to developing an understanding of spatial relationships. Chalufour and colleagues identify the overlapping processes of questioning, problem solving, analyzing, reasoning, communicating, connecting, representing, and investigating as well as the common concepts of shape, pattern, measurement, and spatial relationships. For another example, suppose the teacher brings several pieces of fruit to class: one red apple, one green apple, two oranges, two grapefruit, and two bananas. The children examine the fruit to discover as much about it as possible. They observe size, shape, color, texture, taste, and composition (juicy or dry, segmented or whole, seeds or seedless, etc.). Observations may be recorded using counting and classification skills. ("How many of each fruit type? Of each color? How many are spheres? How many are juicy?") The fruit can be weighed and measured, prepared for eating, and divided equally among the students.

STEAM adds the arts to the STEM curriculum (Jones, Burr, Kaufman, & Beck, 2013). The arts provide a means for students to learn by doing. Many great scientists and mathematicians were (are) talented in the creative arts. For example, creating sculptures, paintings, architectural design, creating a song, and playing a musical instrument all apply math and science concepts (*The STEM classroom*, 2012). Geometry is integral to the visual arts when children make shape collages or draw and cut out shapes or build with blocks. Musical notes involve an understanding of fractions and recognition and discrimination of sounds.

As with these examples, it will be seen throughout the text that math and science concepts and skills can be acquired as children engage in traditional early childhood activities—such as playing with blocks, water, sand, and manipulatives during art, music, dramatic play, cooking, literacy, and outdoor activities (**Photo 1-3**).

PHOTO 1-3 **Children show their views of nature through their drawings.**

1-1b Rationale for Standards and Common Core Curriculum Guidelines

National professional organization members historically searched for guidelines or standards that could direct teaching in all subject areas focusing on what children should know and should be able to do at all ages and stages. The National Council of Teachers of Mathematics (NCTM) developed standards for mathematics, the National Research Council (NRC) for science, and the National Association for the Education of Young Children (NAEYC) for early childhood education. Further, using the standards as guides, educators across the country worked on the development of core curricula in each area, which provided for appropriate instructional guidelines in line with the professional standards. Although NCTM developed both standards for instruction and Core Curriculum State Standards for Math (CCSSM) for developmental placement of key concepts and skills, the National Science Teachers Association (NSTA) together with the National Academy of Sciences and the American Association for the Advancement of Science (AAAS) developed the Next Generation Science Standards (NGSS), which describe performance standards at each K–12 grade level for each primary science study area. NGSS standards development was guided by the 2012 Framework, which defined science as including the following disciplinary core ideas: Physical sciences, Life sciences, Earth and Space sciences, and Engineering, Technology, and Applications of science.

In 2002, NAEYC and NAECS/SDE (National Association of Early Childhood Specialists in State Departments of Education) published, in response to a growing standards-based movement, a joint position statement on early learning standards. Increasingly, individual states and the national Head Start were constructing lists of desired learning outcomes for young children. NAEYC and NAECS/SDE were concerned that early learning standards should be developmentally sound and applied fairly to all groups of young children. Some of the historical and current standards efforts are described next.

In 2009, NAEYC published a third edition of *Developmentally Appropriate Practice in Early Childhood Programs* (Copple & Bredekamp, 2009). In 2000, based on an evaluation and review of the previous standards' publications, NCTM published *Principles and Standards for School Mathematics* (NCTM, 2000). In 2014, NCTM moved further with the publication of *Principles to Actions: Ensuring Mathematical Success for All*, which describes eight research-supported teaching practices. In 2000, NCTM made a major change by the inclusion of preschool in its standards. In contrast, the Next Generation Science standards begin in kindergarten.

During the preschool years, young children's natural curiosity and eagerness to learn can be exploited to develop a joy and excitement in learning and applying mathematics concepts and skills. As in the previous standards, the recommendations in the current publication are based on the belief that "students learn important mathematical skills and processes with understanding" (NCTM, 2000, p. ix). In other words, rather than simply memorizing, children should acquire a true knowledge of concepts and processes. Understanding is not present when children learn mathematics as isolated skills and procedures. Understanding develops through interaction with materials, peers, and supportive adults in settings where students have opportunities to construct their own relationships when they first meet a new topic. Exactly how this takes place will be explained further in the text.

In 2002, the NAEYC and NCTM issued a joint position statement on early childhood mathematics (NCTM & NAEYC, 2002). This statement focuses on math for 3-to 6-year-olds, elaborating on the NCTM (2000) pre-K–2 standards. The highlights for instruction are summarized in "Math Experiences That Count!" (2002). In 2009, the NRC published a review of research and recommendations for instruction for pre-K and kindergarten mathematics (Cross, Woods, & Schweingruber, 2009), which will be described later in this chapter.

Principles of School Mathematics. The *Principles and Standards of School Mathematics* makes statements reflecting basic rules that guide high-quality mathematics education. The following six **principles** describe the overarching themes of mathematics instruction (NCTM, 2000, p. 11).

- *Equity*: High expectations and strong support for all students.

- *Curriculum*: More than a collection of activities; must be coherent, focused on important mathematics, and well articulated across the grades.

- *Teaching*: Effective mathematics teaching requires an understanding of what students know and need to learn, and then challenging and supporting them to learn it well.

- *Learning*: Students must learn mathematics with understanding, actively building new knowledge from experience and prior knowledge.

- *Assessment*: Assessment should support the learning of important mathematics and furnish useful information to both teachers and students.

- *Technology*: Technology is essential in teaching and learning mathematics; it influences the mathematics that is taught and enhances student learning (see Appendix B for a list of technology resources for children).

These principles should be used as a guide to instruction in all subjects, not just mathematics.

Standards for School Mathematics. **Standards** provide guidance as to what children should know and be able to do at different ages and stages. Ten standards are described for prekindergarten through grade 2, with examples of the expectations outlined for each standard. The first five standards are content goals for operations, algebra, geometry, measurement, and data analysis and probability. The next five standards include the processes of problem solving, reasoning and proof, connections, communication, and representation. These two sets of standards are linked, as the process standards are applied to learning the content. The standards and principles are integrated into the chapters that follow.

Standards for Science Education. In 2013, the NGSS was made public so individual states could decide whether to use the new standards, and, if so, how to use them. Each Standard has three dimensions: content; ways in which this content is used in science and engineering; and cross-cutting concepts (formerly known as interdisciplinary or multidisciplinary topics). Content is arranged into four overarching domains: the physical sciences, the life sciences, the earth and space sciences, and engineering, technology, and applications of science.

A prominent feature of the NGSS is a focus on *inquiry*. This term refers to the abilities students should develop in designing and conducting scientific investigations, as well as the understanding they should gain about the nature of scientific inquiry. Students who use inquiry to learn science engage in many of the same activities and thinking processes as scientists who are seeking to expand human knowledge. To better understand the use of inquiry, the NRC (2000) produced a research-based report, *Inquiry and the National Science Education Standards: A Guide for Teaching and Learning*, which outlines the case for inquiry, with practical examples of engaging students in the process. Addendums to the *National Science Education Standards* include *Classroom Assessment and the National Science Education Standards* (2001) and *Selecting Instructional Materials: A Guide for K–12* (1999). These will be discussed later in the text.

A national consensus has evolved around what constitutes effective science education. This consensus is reflected in two major national reform efforts in science education that affect teaching and learning for young children: the NRC's *National Science Education Standards* (1996) and the American Association for the Advancement of Science's (AAAS) Project 2061, which has produced *Science for All Americans* (1989) and *Benchmarks for Science Literacy* (1993). With regard to philosophy, intent, and expectations, these two efforts share a commitment to the essentials of good science teaching and have many commonalities, especially regarding how children learn and what science content students should know and be able to understand within grade ranges and levels of difficulty. Although they take different approaches, both the AAAS and NRC efforts align with the 2009 NAEYC guidelines for developmentally appropriate practice and the 2010 NCTM standards for the teaching of mathematics.

These national science reform documents are based on the idea that active, hands-on conceptual learning that leads to understanding—along with the acquisition of basic skills—provides meaningful and relevant learning experiences. The reform documents also emphasize and reinforce Oakes's (1990) observation that all students, especially underrepresented groups, need to learn scientific skills (such as observation and analysis) that have been embedded in a less-is-more curriculum that starts when children are very young.

The National Science Education Standards are directed to all who have interests, concerns, or investments in improving science education and in ultimately achieving higher levels of scientific literacy for all students. The standards intend to provide support for the integrity of science in science programs by presenting and discussing criteria for the improvement of science education.

The AAAS Project 2061 initiative constitutes a long-term plan to strengthen student literacy in science, mathematics, and technology. Using a less-is-more approach to teaching, the first Project 2061 report recommends that educators use three major themes that occur repeatedly in science to weave together the science curriculum for younger children: models and scale, patterns of change, and systems and interactions.

The second AAAS Project 2061 report, *Benchmarks for Science Literacy*, categorizes the science knowledge that students need to know at all grade levels. The report is not in itself a science curriculum, but it is a useful resource for those who are developing one.

NAEYC DAP Guidelines for Math and Science. The NAEYC Guidelines for Developmentally Appropriate Practice in Mathematics and Science Instruction (Copple & Bredekamp, 2009) indicate that mathematics begins for 3-year-olds with the exploration of materials such as building blocks, sand, and water, and for 4- and 5-year-olds, extends to cooking, observation of environmental changes, working with tools, classifying objects with a purpose, and exploring animals, plants, machines, and so on. For children ages 5 to 8, exploration, discovery, and problem solving are appropriate. Mathematics and science are integrated with other content areas such as social studies, the arts, music, and language arts. These current standards for mathematics and science curriculum and instruction take a constructivist view based on the theories of Jean Piaget and Lev Vygotsky (described in the next section).

1-1c The Movement Toward National Core State Curriculum Standards

As of 2010, 48 states supported the establishment of common K–12 curriculum standards (Gewertz, 2010a), and as of May 2011, 43 states adopted the Common Core State Standards (CCSS, 2011). More recently, a focus on standards for birth to age 5 is gaining attention. Early childhood educators are concerned that, like the K–12 standards, early childhood birth to age 5 standards might focus on math and literacy, leaving out science, art, social/emotional development, motor development, characteristics such as problem solving, curiosity, and persistence. It is also critical that birth to age 5 standards be age appropriate and developmentally and culturally appropriate. Several states, such as Utah and New York, have or are developing core standards for early childhood that focus on the prekindergarten years.

Common Core State Standards for Mathematics (National Governors Association, 2010) are available from the Common Core State Standards Initiative website and from NCTM. The math core standards are designed to make instruction more focused and to meet the goal of mathematical understanding. They are strongly influenced by the NCTM principles, content goals, and process standards described earlier and as included in this text in each chapter. In each mathematics unit, the K–3 standards, as well as standards for birth to age 5, are included.

The Next Generation Science Standards (NGSS) (NGSS, 2013) are based on the National Academy of Sciences' *A Framework for K–12 Science Education* (National Research Council, 2012). Four overarching content topics are included: Life Science, Earth and Space Science, Physical Science, and Engineering and Technology. At each grade level K–12 performance expectations are delineated for what students who demonstrate understanding can do. In addition to content, every NGSS standard addresses scientific and engineering practices and crosscutting concepts that require exploration into the world of integration of concepts both within science and with other disciplines.

1-1d National Standards for Professional Preparation

Standards for Professional Preparation outline what teachers should know and be able to do as learned and experienced during the teacher preparation program. NAEYC is a member of the National Council for Accreditation of Teacher Education (NCATE) and is the recognized specialized professional association (SPA) for early childhood teacher education. For early childhood teacher education (birth to age 8), the major standards for preparation are those developed by NAEYC (2012). The NAEYC preparation standards fall into six areas in which early childhood professionals need to be proficient:

1. Promoting Child Development and Learning

2. Building Family and Community Relationships

3. Observing, Documenting, and Assessing to Support Young Children and Families

4. Using Developmentally Effective Approaches to Connect with Children and Families

5. Using Content Knowledge to Build Meaningful Curriculum

6. Becoming a Professional

NAEYC Standard 5, Using Content Knowledge to Build Meaningful Curriculum, provides the requirements for knowledge of content areas and ability to plan developmentally appropriate curriculum. Mathematics, science, and visual arts are specifically listed as areas of important content knowledge (5a). Candidates need to know and use the central concepts, inquiry tools, and structures of content areas or academic disciplines (5b). Candidates must be able to use their own knowledge, appropriate early learning standards, and other resources to design, implement, and evaluate developmentally meaningful and challenging curriculum for each child (5c).

1-1e Constructivism

In studying how children learn, Jean Piaget came to the conclusion that knowledge is not transmitted from one person to another; instead, people construct their own understandings by attaching new experiences to experiences they already hold in such a way that the resulting conceptualizations make sense *to them*. This notion that people build their own knowledge is termed **constructivism** (Martin, 2012).

Piagetian Periods of Concept Development and Thought. Jean Piaget contributed enormously to understanding the development of children's thought. Piaget identified four periods of cognitive, or mental, growth and development. Early childhood educators are concerned with the first two periods and the first half of the third.

The first period identified by Piaget, called the **sensorimotor period** (from birth to about age 2), is described in the first part of this chapter. It is the time when children begin to learn about the world. They use all their sensory abilities—touch, taste, sight, hearing, smell, and muscular. They also use growing motor abilities to grasp, crawl, stand, and eventually walk. Children in this first period are explorers, and they need opportunities to use their sensory and motor abilities to learn basic skills and concepts. Through these activities, the young child assimilates (takes into the mind and comprehends) a great deal of information. By the end of this period, children have developed the concept of **object permanence**; that is, they realize that objects exist even when they are out of sight. They also develop the ability of **object recognition**, learning to identify objects by using the information they have acquired about features such as color, shape, and size. As children near the end of the sensorimotor period, they reach a stage where they can engage in **representational thought**; that is, instead of acting impetuously, they can think through a solution before attacking a problem. They also enter into a time of rapid language development.

The second period, called the **preoperational period**, extends through approximately ages 2 to 7. During this period, children begin to develop concepts that are more like those of adults, but these are still incomplete in comparison to what they will be like at maturity. These concepts are often referred to as **preconcepts**. During the early part of the preoperational period, language continues to undergo rapid growth, and speech is used increasingly to express concept knowledge. Children begin to use concept terms such as big and small (size), light and heavy (weight), square and round (shape), late and early (time), long and short (length), and so on. This ability to use language is one of the **symbolic behaviors** that emerges during this period. Children also use symbolic behavior in their representational play, where they may use sand to represent food, a stick to represent a spoon, or another child to represent father, mother, or baby. Play is a major arena in which children develop an understanding of the symbolic functions that underlie later understanding of abstract symbols such as numerals, letters, and written words.

An important characteristic of preoperational children is **centration**. When materials are changed in form or arrangement in space, children may see them as changed in amount as well. This is because preoperational children tend to center on the most obvious aspects of what is seen. For instance, if the same amount of liquid is put in both a tall, thin glass and a short, fat glass, preoperational children say there is more in the tall glass "because it is taller." If clay is changed in shape from a ball to a snake, they say there is less clay in the snake "because it is thinner." If a pile of coins is placed close together, preoperational children say there are fewer coins than they would say if the coins were spread out. When the physical arrangement of material is changed, preoperational children seem unable to hold the original picture of its shape in mind. They lack **reversibility**; that is, they cannot reverse the process of change mentally. The ability to hold or save the original picture in the mind and reverse physical change mentally is referred to as **conservation**, and the inability to conserve is a critical characteristic of preoperational children. During the preoperational period, children work with the precursors of conservation such as counting, one-to-one correspondence, shape, space, and comparing. They also work on **seriation** (putting items in a logical sequence, such as fat to thin or dark to light) and **classification or sorting** (putting things in logical groups according to some common criteria such as color, shape, size, or use).

During the third period, called **concrete operations** (approximately ages 7 to 11), children are becoming *conservers*. They are becoming more and more skilled at retaining the original picture in mind and making a mental reversal when appearances are changed. The time between ages 5 and 7 is one of transition to concrete operations. A child's thought processes are changing at his or her own rate, and so, during this time of transition, a normal expectation is that some children are already conservers and others are not. This is a critical consideration for kindergarten and primary teachers because the ability to conserve number (the coins problem) is a good indication that children are ready to deal with **abstract symbolic activities**. In other words, they will be able to mentally manipulate groups that are presented by number symbols with a real understanding of what the mathematical operations mean (see **Figure 1-3** for examples of conservation problems).

Original	Physical Change	Question	Nonconserving Answer	Conserving Answer
Same amount of drink		Is there still the same amount of drink?	No, there is more in the tall glass.	Yes, you just put the drink in different size glasses
Same amount of clay		Is there still the same amount of clay?	No, there is more clay in the snake because it is longer.	Yes, you just rolled it out into a different shape.
Same amount of pennies		Are there still the same number of pennies?	No, there are more in the bottom row because it is longer	Yes, you just moved the pennies closer together (points to top row).

FIGURE 1-3 Physical changes in conservation tasks.

Piaget's final period is called **formal operations** (approximately ages 11 through adulthood). During this period, children can learn to use the scientific method independently; that is, they learn to solve problems in a logical and systematic manner. They begin to understand abstract concepts and to attack abstract problems. They can imagine solutions before trying them out. For example, suppose a person who has reached the formal operations level is given samples of several colorless liquids and is told that some combination of these liquids will result in a yellow liquid. A person at the formal operations level would plan out how to systematically test to find the solution; a person still at the concrete operational level might start to combine the liquids without considering a logical approach to the problem, such as labeling each liquid and keeping a record of which combinations have been tried. Note that this period may be reached as early as age 11; however, it may not be reached at all by many adults without problem-solving training or brain-twister activities.

Piaget's View of How Children Acquire Knowledge. As mentioned earlier, Piaget believed that learners must construct meaning for themselves, individually. The only learning that can take place is that in which the learner attaches new knowledge to already existing knowledge, experiences, or conceptualizations Children do not wait to be instructed to do this; they are continually trying to make sense out of everything they encounter. Piaget divides knowledge into three areas.

- **Physical knowledge** includes knowledge about objects in the environment and their characteristics (color, weight, size, texture, and other features that can be determined through observation and are physically within the object).

- **Logico-mathematical knowledge** includes the relationships (same and different, more and less, number, classification, etc.) that each individual constructs to make sense out of the world and to organize information.

- **Social** (or conventional) **knowledge** (such as rules for behavior in various social situations) that is created by people.

The physical and logico-mathematical types of knowledge depend on each other and are learned simultaneously; that is, as the physical characteristics of objects are learned, logico-mathematical categories are constructed to organize information. In the popular story "Goldilocks and the Three Bears," for example, Papa Bear is big, Mama Bear is middle-sized, and Baby Bear is the smallest (seriation), but all three (number) are bears because they are covered with fur and have a certain body shape with a certain combination of features common only to bears (classification).

Constance Kamii, a student of Piaget's, has actively translated Piaget's theory into practical applications for the instruction of young children. Kamii emphasizes that, according to Piaget, **autonomy** (independence) is the aim of education.

Intellectual autonomy develops in an atmosphere where children feel secure in their relationships with adults and where they have an opportunity to share their ideas with other children. In such an environment, they should feel encouraged to be alert and curious, to come up with interesting ideas, problems and questions, to use initiative in finding the answers to problems, to have confidence in their abilities to figure out things for themselves, and to speak their minds. Young children need to be presented with problems that can be solved through games and other activities that challenge their minds. They must work with concrete materials and real problems, such as the examples provided earlier in this chapter.

In line with the NCTM focus on math for understanding, Duckworth (2006) explains that Piaget's view of understanding focuses on the adult paying attention to the child's point of view. In other words, we should not view "understanding" from our own perspective but should rather try to find out what the child is thinking. When the child provides a response that seems illogical from an adult point of view, the adult should consider and explore the child's logic. For example, if a child (when presented with a conservation problem) says that there are more objects in a spread-out row of 10 objects than in a tightly packed row of 10 objects, the teacher (or other adult) should ask the child for a reason.

TeachSource Video

5–11 YEARS: PIAGET'S CONCRETE OPERATIONAL STAGE

This video demonstrates the contrast between preoperational and concrete operational thought. Besides volume, also included are examples of conservation of mass and number.

1. Describe the differences in the responses of the preoperational and concrete operational children to the volume conservation problem.

2. How do the children's responses to the conservation of mass and number problems compare with their responses to the volume problem?

3. How do you believe their responses will relate to their math and science performances?

Vygotsky's View of How Children Learn and Develop. Like Piaget, Lev Vygotsky was also a cognitive development theorist. He was a contemporary of Piaget's, but Vygotsky died at the age of 38 before his work was fully completed. Vygotsky contributed a view of cognitive development that recognizes both developmental and environmental forces. Vygotsky believed that—just as people developed tools such as knives, spears, shovels, and tractors to aid their mastery of the environment—they also developed mental tools. People develop ways of cooperating and communicating as well as new capacities to plan and to think ahead. These mental tools help people to master their own behavior, mental tools that Vygotsky referred to as signs. He believed that speech was the most important sign system because it freed us from distractions and allowed us to work on problems in our minds. Speech both enables the child to interact socially and facilitates thinking. In Vygotsky's view, *writing and numbering* were also important sign systems.

Piaget looked at development as if it came mainly from the child alone, from the child's inner maturation and spontaneous discoveries, but Vygotsky believed this was true only until about the age of 2. At that point, culture and the cultural signs become necessary to expand thought. He believed that these internal and external factors interacted to produce new thoughts and an expanded menu of signs. Thus, Vygotsky put more emphasis than Piaget on the role of the adult (or a more mature peer) as an influence on children's mental development.

Whereas Piaget placed an emphasis on children as intellectual explorers making their own discoveries and constructing knowledge independently, Vygotsky developed an alternative concept known as the *zone of proximal development* (ZPD). The ZPD is the area between where the child is now operating independently in mental development and where she might go with assistance from an adult or more mature child. Cultural knowledge is acquired with the assistance or scaffolding provided by more mature learners. According to Vygotsky, good teaching involves presenting material that is a little ahead of development. Children might not fully understand it at first, but in time they can understand it, given appropriate scaffolding. Rather than pressuring development, instruction should support development as it moves ahead. Concepts constructed independently and spontaneously by children lay the foundation for the more scientific concepts that are part of the culture. Teachers must identify each student's ZPD and provide developmentally appropriate instruction. Teachers will know when they have hit upon the right zone because children will respond with enthusiasm, curiosity, and active involvement.

Piagetian constructivists tend to be concerned about the tradition of pressuring children. Vygotskian constructivists are concerned with children being challenged to reach their full potential. Today, many educators find that a combination of Piaget's and Vygotsky's views provides a foundation for instruction that follows the child's interests and enthusiasms while providing an intellectual challenge. The *learning cycle* view provides such a framework.

Bruner's and Dienes'. Jerome Bruner (Clabaugh, 2010) and Zoltan Dienes (Sriraman & Lesh, 2007) also contributed to theory and instruction in early childhood concept development. Bruner's interest in cognitive development was influenced by Piaget and Vygotsky. He also believed that learning was an active process during which children construct new knowledge based on their previous knowledge. He used math as an example of a context for learning. Bruner identified three stages of learning: enactive, iconic, and symbolic. The *enactive stage* is a period of manipulation and exploration. Learning activity centers on play. In the *iconic stage*, students can visualize the concrete. In the *symbolic stage*, students can move into abstract thinking. The adult role is to scaffold the students through these stages. Bruner emphasized discovery learning or guided discovery. Learning takes place in problem-solving situations. Instruction involves supporting the students' efforts to discover the problem's solution rather than forcing memorization.

Dienes's focus was on how children learn mathematics. He focused on materials and believed the initial stage of mathematics learning should center on free play. During free play, children enter a second stage where they see regularities that provide rules for mathematics games. In a third stage, they begin to compare the different games. In a fourth stage, they enter a period of abstraction where they use representations such as tables, coordinate systems, drawings, or other vehicles that can aid memory. During the fifth stage, they discover the use of symbols. At the sixth stage, students use formalized mathematical rules. Dienes is best known for the invention of multibase blocks, which are used to teach place value. Dienes taught mathematics in a number of cultures using manipulatives, games, stories, and dance. He supported the use of small groups working together in collaboration to solve problems.

The constructivist view provides a basis for the discussion of reform vs. traditional instruction (Bishop-Joseph & Zigler, 2011). A current thrust in mathematics and science instruction is the reform of classroom instruction, changing from the traditional approach of drill and practice memorization to the adoption of the constructivist approach. A great deal of tension exists between the traditional and reform approaches. *Telling* has been the traditional method of ensuring that student learning takes place. When a teacher's role changes to that of guide and facilitator, the teacher may feel a lack of control. The reform or constructivist approach is compatible with early childhood practice, but may be inappropriate for older children (Constructivist Versus Traditional Math, 2005). In the elementary grades, efficiency and accuracy are emphasized in the traditional program. There is evidence that children from constructivist programs are not prepared for algebra and other higher-level mathematics. On the other hand, the traditional "drill-and-kill" can deaden interest in math. Traditional math programs also tend to follow a one-size-fits-all approach in contrast to the constructivist differentiated curriculum. Many teachers have developed a mix of the two approaches. Finally, problems are presented when it comes to standardized testing. The required test may favor one method or the other. There needs to be a balance between teaching for understanding and teaching for accuracy and efficiency. Van de Walle (1999) believes the dilemma can be solved by using a problem-solving approach. Current research demonstrates that students in reform classrooms learn as well as or better than those in traditional classrooms. In this text, we have tried to achieve a balance between the traditional and reform approaches by providing a guide to ensuring that students have the opportunity to explore and construct their own knowledge while providing examples of developmentally appropriate adult-guided instruction. Our three-level instructional approach is compatible with the guidelines described by Ann S. Epstein in *The Intentional Teacher* (2014). Later in this chapter our three-level approach is described.

1-1f The Learning Cycle

The authors of the Science Curriculum Improvement Study (SCIS) materials designed a Piagetian-based learning cycle approach based on the assumption expressed by Albert Einstein and other scientists that "science is a quest for knowledge" (Renner & Marek, 1988). The scientists believed that, in the teaching of science, students must interact with materials, collect data, and make some order out of that data. The order that students make out of that data is (or leads to) a conceptual invention.

The **learning cycle** is viewed as a way to take students on a quest that leads to the construction of knowledge. It is used both as a curriculum development procedure and as a teaching strategy. Developers must organize student activities around phases, and teachers must modify their role and strategies during the progressive phases. The phases of the learning cycle are sometimes assigned different labels and are sometimes split into segments. However, the essential thrust of each of the phases remains: exploration, concept development, and concept application (Barman, 1989; Renner & Marek, 1988).

During the *exploration phase*, the teacher remains in the background, observing and occasionally inserting a comment or question (see the section on naturalistic and informal learning later in this chapter). The students actively manipulate materials and interact with each other. The teacher's knowledge of child development guides the selection of materials and how they are placed in the environment so as to provide a developmentally appropriate setting in which young children can explore and construct concepts.

For example, in the exploration phase of a lesson about shapes, students examine a variety of wooden or cardboard objects (squares, rectangles, circles) and make observations about the objects. The teachers may ask them to describe how they are similar and how they are different.

During the *concept introduction* phase, the teacher provides direct instruction, beginning with a discussion of the information the students have discovered. The teacher helps the children record their information. During this phase, the teacher clarifies and adds to what the children have found out for themselves by using explanations, print materials, videos, guest speakers, and other available resources (see the section on adult-guided learning experiences later in this chapter). For example, in this phase of the lesson, the children exploring shapes may take the shapes and classify them into groups.

The third phase of the cycle, the *application phase*, provides children with the opportunity to integrate and organize new ideas with old ideas and relate them to still other ideas. The teacher or the children themselves suggest a new problem to which the information learned in the first two phases can be applied. In the lesson about shape, the teacher might introduce differently shaped household objects and wooden blocks. The children are asked to classify these items as squares, rectangles, and circles. Again, the children are actively involved in concrete activities and exploration.

The three major phases of the learning cycle can be applied to the ramp-and-ball example described earlier in this chapter. During the first phase, the ramp and the balls are available to be examined. The teacher offers some suggestions and questions as the children work with the materials. In the second phase, the teacher communicates with the children regarding what they have observed. The teacher might also provide explanations, label the items being used, and otherwise assist the children in organizing their information; at this point, books and/or films about simple machines could be provided. For the third phase, the teacher poses a new problem and challenges the children to apply their concept of the ramp and how it works to the new problem. For example, some toy vehicles might be provided to use with the ramp(s).

Charles Barman (1989) describes three types of learning cycle lessons in *An Expanded View of the Learning Cycle: New Ideas About an Effective Teaching Strategy*. The lessons vary in accordance with the way data are collected by students and with the students' type of reasoning. Most young children will be involved in **descriptive lessons** in which they mainly observe, interact, and describe their observations. Although young children may begin to generate guesses regarding the reasons for what they have observed, serious hypothesis generation requires concrete operational thinking (*empirical-inductive lesson*). In the third type of lesson, students observe, generate hypotheses, and design experiments to test their hypotheses (*hypothetical-deductive lesson*). This type of lesson requires formal operational thought. However, this does not mean that preoperational and concrete operational children should be discouraged from generating ideas on how to find out if their guesses will prove to be true. Quite the contrary: They should be encouraged to take this step. Often they will propose an alternative solution even though they may not yet have reached the level of mental maturation necessary to understand the underlying physical or logico-mathematical explanation.

1-1g Adapting the Learning Cycle to Early Childhood

Bredekamp and Rosegrant (1992) adapted the learning cycle to early childhood education. The learning cycle for young children encompasses four repeating processes, as follows.

- **Awareness**. A broad recognition of objects, people, events, or concepts that develops from experience. The adult provides an environment that includes interesting materials.

- **Exploration**. The construction of personal meaning through sensory experiences with objects, people, events, or concepts. The adult facilitates exploration and extends children's play.

- **Inquiry**. Comparing their constructions with those of the culture, recognizing commonalities, and generalizing more like adults. The adult guides the children and helps them refine their understanding. The adult asks focused questions such as "What would happen if . . . ?"

- **Utilization**. Applying and using their understandings in new settings and situations. The adult provides settings for new applications.

Each time a new situation is encountered, learning begins with awareness and moves on through the other levels. The cycle also relates to development. For example, infants and toddlers will be at the awareness level, gradually moving into exploration. Children who are 3, 4, or 5 years old may move up to inquiry, whereas 6-, 7-, and 8-year-olds can move through all four levels when meeting new situations or concepts. For example, Bredekamp and Rosegrant (1992) provide an example in the area of measurement:

- Three- and 4-year-olds are aware of and explore comparative sizes;

- Four-, 5-, and 6-year-olds explore with nonstandard units, such as how many of their own feet wide is the rug;

- Seven- and 8-year-olds begin to understand standard units of measurement and use rulers, thermometers, and other standard measuring tools.

The authors caution that the cycle is not hierarchical; that is, utilization is not necessarily more valued than awareness or exploration. Young children may be aware of concepts that they cannot fully utilize in the technical sense. For example, they may be aware that rain falls from the sky without understanding the intricacies of meteorology. Using the learning cycle as a framework for curriculum and instruction has an important aspect: The cycle reminds us that children may not have had experiences that provide for awareness and exploration. To be truly individually

appropriate in planning, we need to provide for these experiences in school.

The learning cycle fits nicely with the theories of Piaget and Vygotsky. For both, learning begins with awareness and exploration, and both value inquiry and application. The format for each concept provided in the text is from naturalistic to informal to structured learning experiences. These experiences are consistent with providing opportunities for children to move through the learning cycle as they meet new objects, people, events, or concepts.

1-2 TYPES OF LEARNING EXPERIENCES

Children learn with understanding when the learning takes place in meaningful and familiar situations. As children explore their familiar environments, they encounter experiences through which they actively **construct** knowledge and discover new relationships. The adult's role is to build on this knowledge and support children as they move to higher levels of understanding. These initial child-controlled learning experiences can be characterized as naturalistic learning. Two other types of experiences are those characterized as informal learning and as adult-guided learning.

- **Naturalistic experiences** are those in which the child controls choice and action.

- **Informal** is where the child chooses the activity and action, but with adult intervention at some point.

- **Adult-guided** is where the adult chooses the experience for the child and gives some direction to the child's action (**Figure 1-4**).

Naturalistic experiences relate closely to the Piagetian **constructivist** view, and the informal and adult-guided experiences relate more to the Vygotskian view. The mathematics and science standards do not dictate teaching methods. We support a **constructivist** view of learning as described earlier in this chapter.

Referring to the learning cycle as described earlier in this chapter, it can be seen that these three types of experiences fit into the cycle. The learning cycle is basically a way to structure

TYPES OF ACTIVITY	INTERACTION EMPHASIZED
Naturalistic	Child/Environment
Informal	Child/Environment/Adult
Adult-guided	Adult/Child/Environment

FIGURE 1-4 Concepts are learned through three types of activity.

© Cengage Learning®

lessons so that all three ways of learning are experienced. Naturalistic experiences are encouraged at the awareness and the exploration levels. Informal experiences are added at the exploration, inquiry, and utilization levels. Adult-guided experiences are more likely to appear at the inquiry and utilization levels.

In providing settings for learning and types of instruction, keep in mind the variations in learning styles among groups of children and among different cultural and ethnic groups. Some of these types of variations are described later in the chapter.

1-2a Naturalistic Experiences

Naturalistic experiences are initiated spontaneously by children as they go about their daily activities (**Photo 1-4**). These experiences are the major mode of learning for children during the sensorimotor period. Naturalistic experiences can also be a valuable mode of learning for older children.

The adult's role is to provide an interesting and rich environment; that is, there should be many things for the child to look at, touch, taste, smell, and hear. The adult should observe the child's activity, note how it is progressing, and then respond with a glance, a nod, a smile,

a verbal description of the child's actions or elaboration of the child's comments, or a word of praise to encourage the child. The child needs to know when he is doing the appropriate thing.

Some examples of naturalistic experiences include the following:

- Ethan hands Dad two pennies, saying, "Here's your two dollars!"
- Tito is eating orange segments. "I got three" (holds up three fingers).
- In a walk around the school building, Elizabeth says, "Different plants have different shaped leaves."
- Aika (age 4) sits on the rug and sorts colored rings into plastic cups.
- Sam (age 5) is painting. He makes a dab of yellow and then dabs some blue on top. "Hey! I've got green now."
- Lila (age 6) draws a picture of the moon she saw last night.
- Mei (age 8) is experimenting with cup measures and containers. She notices that each cup measure holds the same amount, even though each is a different shape. She also notices that you cannot always predict how many cups of liquid a container holds just by looking at it; the shape can fool you.

1-2b Informal Learning Experiences

Informal learning experiences are initiated by the adult as the child is engaged in a naturalistic experience (**Photo 1-5**). These experiences are not preplanned for a specific time. They occur when the adult's experience and/or intuition indicates it is time to scaffold. This might happen for various reasons; for example, the child might need help or is on the right track

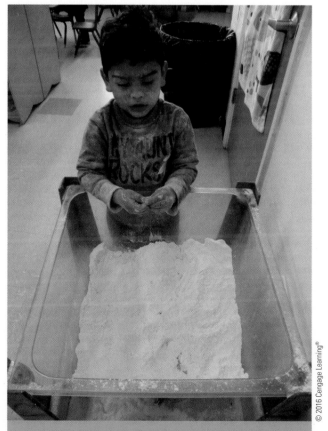

Photo 1-4 Children's naturalistic learning experiences include sensory exploration of environmental materials.

Photo 1-5 Informal learning experiences involve an adult who provides comments or asks or answers questions.

in solving a problem but needs a cue or encouragement. Or perhaps the adult has in mind some concepts that should be reinforced and takes advantage of a **teachable moment**. Informal learning experiences occur when an opportunity for instruction presents itself by chance. Some examples follow:

■ "I'm 6 years old," says 3-year-old Ava while holding up three fingers. Dad says, "Let's count those fingers. One, two, three fingers. How old are you?"

■ With arms outstretched at various distances, Daniel (age 4) asks, "Is this big? Is this big?" Mr. Brown says, "What do you think? What is *this* big?" Daniel looks at the distance between his hands with his arms stretched to the fullest. "This is a big person." He puts his hands about 18 inches apart. "This is a baby." He places his thumb and index finger about half an inch apart. "This is a blackberry." Mr. Brown watches with a big smile on his face.

■ Mia (age 4) has a bag of cookies. Mrs. Ramirez asks, "Do you have enough for everyone?" Mia replies, "I don't know." Mrs. R. asks, "How can you find out?" Mia says, "I don't know." Mrs. R. suggests, "How about if we count the cookies?"

■ Kindergartners Christopher and Anthony are playing with some small rubber figures called Stackrobats. Christopher links some horizontally, whereas Anthony joins his vertically. The boys are competing to see who can make the longest line. When Christopher's line reaches across the diameter of the table, he encounters a problem. Miss Jones suggests that he might be able to figure out another way to link the figures. He looks at Anthony's line of figures and then at his. He realizes that if he links his figures vertically he can continue with the competition.

■ Noah, a first grader, runs into Mrs. Red Fox's classroom on a spring day after a heavy rainstorm. He says, "Mrs. Red Fox! I have a whole bunch of worms." Mrs. Red Fox asks Noah where he found the worms and why there are so many out this morning. She suggests he put the worms on the science table where everyone can see them. Noah follows through and places a sign next to the can: "Wrms fnd by Noah."

■ Second-grader Chloe is working with blocks. She shows her teacher, Mr. Wang, that she has made three stacks of four blocks. She asks, "When I have three stacks of four, is that like when my big brother says 'three times four'?" "Yes," responds Mr. Wang. "When you have three stacks of four, that is three times four." Chloe has discovered some initial ideas about multiplication.

■ Third-grader Larry notices that each time he feeds Fuzzy the hamster, Fuzzy runs to the food pan before Logan opens the cage. He tells his teacher, who uses the opportunity to discuss anticipatory responses, why they develop, and their significance in training

PHOTO 1-6 Adult guided learning experiences are preplanned by an adult to meet specific learning objectives.

© 2016 Cengage Learning®

animals. He asks Logan to consider why this might happen so consistently and to think about other times he has noticed this type of response in other animals or humans. Several other children join the discussion. They decide to keep individual records of any anticipatory responses they observe for a week, compare observations, and note trends.

1-2c Adult-Guided Learning Experiences

Adult-guided experiences are preplanned lessons or activities (**Photo 1-6**). They can be done with individuals or small or large groups at a special time or an opportune time. They may follow the learning cycle sequence or consist of more focused adult-guided instruction. Following are examples of some of these adult-guided activities:

■ *With an individual at a specific time with a specific focus.* Alyssa is 4 years old. Her teacher decides that she needs some practice counting. She says, "Alyssa, I have some blocks here for you to count. How many are in this pile?"

■ *A learning cycle example.* Mrs. Red Fox sets up a new activity center in her room. A large tub is filled with balls of several different sizes, colors, and textures. The children all have had some experience with balls and are aware of them in the environment. Mrs. Red Fox points out the tub of balls to the students and tells them that they can explore the balls, looking at what is the same and different. She provides paper and markers that can be used to record what they learn. Each day the students gather for group reports about their daily activities. Those who have explored the balls report on their findings and share what they have recorded. Mrs. Red Fox asks questions and encourages the students to insert comments and questions. Finally, they discuss other things they might try to find out about the balls and other investigations they might make concerning the balls.

- *With an individual at an opportune time with a specific focus.* Mrs. Flores knows that Hannah needs help with the concept of shape. Hannah is looking for a game to play. Mrs. Flores says, "Try this shape-matching game, Hannah. There are squares, circles, and triangles on the big card. You find the little cards with the shapes that match."

- *With a group at an opportune time.* Mrs. Raymond has been working with the children on the concepts of "light" and "heavy." They ask her to bring out some planks to make ramps to attach to the packing boxes and the sawhorses. She brings out the planks and explains to the group, "These are the heavy planks. These are the light planks. Which are stronger? Where should they go?"

- *With a large group at a specific time.* The students have had an opportunity to explore a collection of bones that they brought from home. Ms. Hebert realizes classification is an important concept that should be applied throughout the primary grades because it is extremely important in organizing science data. Ms. Hebert puts out three large sheets of construction paper and has the students explore the different ways bones can be classified (such as chicken, turkey, duck, cow, pig, deer) or placed in subcategories (such as grouping chicken bones into wings, backs, legs, etc.).

Observe that, throughout the examples in this chapter, the adults ask a variety of questions and provide different types of directions for using the materials. It is extremely important to ask many different types of questions. Questions vary as to whether they are divergent or convergent, and they also vary as to how difficult they are.

- **Divergent questions and directions** do not have one right answer, but provide an opportunity for creativity, guessing, and experimenting. Questions that begin "Tell me about …"; "What do you think …?"; "What have you found out about …?"; "What can we do with …?"; "Can you find a way to …?"; "What would happen if …?"; "Why do you think …?"; and directions such as "You can examine these …"; or You may play with these …" are divergent.

- **Convergent questions and directions** ask for a specific response or activity. There is a specific piece of information called for, such as "How many …?"; "Tell me the names of the parts of a plant"; "Find a ball smaller than this one"; and so on.

Adults often ask only convergent questions and give convergent directions. Remember that children need time to construct their ideas. Divergent questions and directions encourage them to think and act for themselves. Convergent questions and directions can provide the adult with specific information regarding what the child knows, but too many of these questions tend to make the child think that there might be only one right answer to all problems. This can squelch creativity and the willingness to guess and experiment.

By varying the difficulty of the questions asked, the teacher can reach children of different ability levels. For example, in the office supply store center, pencils are 2¢ and paper is 1¢ per sheet. An easy question might be "If you want to buy one pencil and two sheets of paper, then how many pennies will you need?" A harder question would be "If you have 10¢, how many pencils and how much paper could you buy?"

1-2d Diverse Learning Styles

In planning learning experiences for children, consider individual and culturally determined styles of learning. Learning styles may relate to modalities such as auditory, visual, kinesthetic, or multisensory preferences. They may relate to temperamental characteristics such as the easygoing, serious student or the easily frustrated student. They also may relate to strengths in particular areas, such as those identified by Howard Gardner in his theory of multiple intelligences (Gardner, 1999). Gardner originally identified seven intelligences: (1) linguistic, (2) logical-mathematical, (3) bodily-kinesthetic, (4) interpersonal, (5) intrapersonal, (6) musical, and (7) spatial. More recently, he added that naturalist intelligence and existential intelligence have all the properties of a separate intelligence as described in his Theory of Multiple Intelligences. Gardner conceptualizes these intelligences as combined biological and psychological potentials to process information that can be used in a culture to solve problems or to create products that are valuable to the culture. Children must be provided with opportunities to solve problems using their strongest modalities and areas of intelligence. Too often, conventional learning experiences focus on the linguistic (language) and logical-mathematical intelligences while ignoring the other areas. Children who may have strength in learning through active movement and concrete activities (bodily-kinesthetic learners), or those who learn best through interacting with peers (interpersonal learners), or via one of the other modalities may lose out on being able to develop concepts and skills to the fullest. Incorporating peer tutoring and offering opportunities for group projects expands on the chances for success.

The variety of learning styles can be accommodated by integrating the various curriculum areas rather than teaching each area (mathematics, science, social studies, language arts, visual arts, musical arts, etc.) separately. Increasingly, attention is now being paid to integrated approaches to instruction (see Chapter 6). In this text, we focus on mathematics and science as the major focus, with other content areas integrated. However, any one of the content areas can be the hub at different times with different purposes. Integration is frequently pictured in a weblike structure similar to that constructed by spiders (**Figure 1-5**). The focus or theme of study is placed in the center, and the other content areas and/or major concepts are attached by the radials.

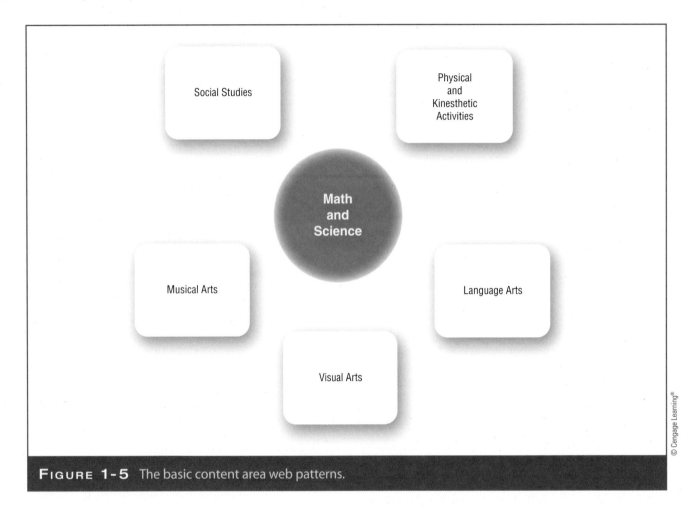

FIGURE 1-5 The basic content area web patterns.

In planning and instruction, consider not only diversity in modality-related learning styles, but also diversity in race, ethnicity, social class, gender, out-of-school experiences, and special needs. Whereas reform mathematics appears to have positive effects on achievement, research has not looked closely at how reform mathematics affects different groups. The reform classroom itself is a culture different from the traditional classroom. The reform movement is progressing from a linear, formal view of the teacher passing out knowledge to passive students toward a setting where mathematics and science are constructed, discussed, and questioned by active students. The reform mathematics and science classroom is an active productive culture. Unfortunately, developing this type of classroom is not easy because it requires the teacher to be tuned into each student's learning style and abilities. The Common Core State Standards emphasize understanding rather than just memorization.

Many fundamental concepts in mathematics and science are learned before the child enters school. Mathematics learned outside of school is referred to as **ethnomathematics** (Nunes, 1992). This type of mathematics is embedded in the out-of-school cultural activities whose primary purpose is not to learn mathematics, but rather to accomplish a culturally relevant task. Examples are activities such as counting out equal shares, setting the table, calculating a recipe, exchanging money, or measuring one's height or weight. Each culture has its own way of doing these tasks. The problem teachers face is how to capitalize on what children learn outside of school while considering that some of these tasks may apply mathematics and science differently than they are used in the classroom. Teachers must learn about the everyday lives of their students and how mathematics concepts may be applied on a day-to-day basis. To connect out-of-school to in-school experiences, mathematics, and science in school should be introduced by providing students with problems based on everyday experiences. For example, a science problem might ask the question "Why are cars covered with yellow stuff in the spring?" or "Why is the stagnant water found in the bend of a creek not safe to drink?" Teachers can then observe as students construct solutions based on their out-of-school life experiences. Once students have developed their own strategies, the conventional strategies or algorithms and formulas can be introduced as an alternative means of solving problems.

Teachers need to be responsive to the diverse cultural values and experiences of their students in order to identify each individual's zone of proximal development and build from where the children are operating independently to where their capabilities can take them with appropriate scaffolding. Multicultural education is not a topic to be presented in one week or one month and then forgotten; it should permeate the whole curriculum. Practice should be both developmentally and culturally appropriate (de Melendez & Beck, 2013). Across cultures, children develop in the same sequence physically, socially, and intellectually, but they experience varied cultural experiences within their environments. Child-rearing practices and environmental variation provide the content of children's knowledge and views of the world. Behavior that is considered normal within a culture may be viewed as unacceptable by a teacher from another culture. Teachers need to study the cultures of their students before making any behavioral decisions. In January 2008, NCTM published a position statement on equity in mathematics education (NCTM, 2008). The statement pledges that all students should have equal opportunity and equal access to quality mathematics instruction. There should be high expectations for all students' achievement and opportunities for challenging mathematics. Teachers should begin with each student's ethnomathematics (Gutierrez, Bay-Williams, & Kanold, 2008). Studies of Native American students indicate that starting with the beliefs and knowledge of the tribal elders is an effective approach to instruction (for example, Blending, 2008; Lipka, 1998; Lipka, Yanez, Andrew-Ihrke, & Adam, 2009; Tambe, Carrol, Mitchell, Lopez, Horsch, & St. John, 2007). Claudia Zaslavsky (1996) emphasizes the incorporation of math games from many cultures as a means for promoting multiculturalism in the mathematics curriculum.

English Language Learners (ELLs) also need special consideration (Santa Cruz, 2009). These students have the double challenge of learning mathematics and science language, concepts, and processes and English at the same time. In 2008, NCTM published a position statement on teaching mathematics to English language learners. NCTM called for the implementation of culturally relevant instruction. Others (e.g., Lee et al., 2008) suggest posting vocabulary walls where new science words are written and defined in English and in the languages of all ELLs. Above all, teachers should *not* consider children who are learning English to be inferior to those fluent in English; their only drawback is language (*not* understanding).

Equity also needs to be considered in relation to socioeconomic status (Clements & Sarama, 2002a). Research indicates that children from lower socioeconomic status (SES) homes lack important mathematics concepts. For example, counting might be limited to small groups and may not be accurate. Low-SES children who have had very little number experience at home might not be able to tell whether one amount is more than another. However, several researchers have developed early childhood instructional programs that improve the mathematics understanding of lower-SES children.

1-2e Helping Children with Special Needs

A great deal of research has documented the quantitative development of typical young children—information that can guide our instruction (Mix, Huttenlocher, & Levine, 2002)—but it is also important to consider the mathematical development and instruction of children with special needs. Wilmot and Thornton (1989) describe the importance of identifying appropriate mathematics instruction for special learners: those who are gifted and those with learning disabilities. Gifted students can be provided with enrichment experiences that go beyond numeracy and into probability, problem solving, geometry, and measurement. Children with disabilities may have any one or a combination of problems in memory, visual or auditory perception, discrimination deficits, abstract reasoning difficulties, or other difficulties that intrude on learning. Different approaches must be taken with each type of learner. Cooperative learning groups can be effective. Clements and Sarama (2002b) cite studies indicating that computer activities can help to increase all young children's mathematics skills and understanding. Providing positive experiences for young students with special needs can promote confidence as they move through school.

Geary (1996) describes how math anxiety and math disabilities can impede progress. Math anxiety results from a fear of mathematics, but it is hoped that a positive math experience in early childhood will prevent the development of math anxiety. About 6 percent of school-age children may have a **mathematics learning disorder (MLD)**. Some children cannot remember basic facts. Others cannot carry out basic procedures like solving a simple addition problem. Math disabilities may also result from brain injury. In his

---

 BRAIN CONNECTION

THE BRAIN AND MATH ANXIETY

In the book *Math Curse* (Scieszka & Smith, 1995), the math teacher tells the class, "You know, you can think of almost everything as a math problem." The student finds herself surrounded by problems resulting in stress and anxiety. Finally, the student solves all the problems and exits out of the math curse. Then the science teacher says, "YOU KNOW, you can think of almost anything as a science experiment." Although many people have a fear of math (or of science), that fear does not necessarily result in poor math performance. Brain scans show that the brains of some highly anxious people react differently from others. Students who were highly anxious, but performed well, showed high activity in the frontal and parietal regions of the brain. These areas of the brain are not directly connected to math, but are associated with cognitive control, focus, and regulation of negative emotions. Math interventions that focus on control of anxiety may be more successful than those directed directly on math.

S. D. Sparks, Brain Study Points to Potential Treatments for Math Anxiety, Education Week Blogs, October 20, 2011, http://blogs.edweek.org.

research, Geary found that about half of the students identified with MLD had no perceptual or neurological problem, but more likely lacked experience, had poor motivation, or suffered from anxiety. Procedural problems are usually related to slow cognitive development and usually clear up by the middle elementary grades. The fact-retrieval problem tends to continue. Some children have problems in reading and writing numbers and may also have problems in reading and writing words and letters. However, these problems usually are developmental and eventually disappear. Some children may have spatial relations problems, which show up when they misalign numbers in columns or reverse numbers. Geary concludes that early experiences that make necessary neural connections in the brain can lessen the chances of MLD. More recent research indicates that lack of development of number sense or the inability to estimate the size of numbers or numbers of objects is a major problem for many who have difficulties with mathematics (Sparks, June 17, 2011). Number sense is discussed in Chapter 3.

Gender is another issue of concern in the STEM areas. Girls are considered to be less capable, especially in math and science. It is suggested that STEM should be taught using methods that will engage girls as well as boys (Bazley & Madeira, 2013). Girls and boys should work together on projects in cooperative groups where they can each apply their respective strengths: boys being more hands-on and girls, more speaking and writing oriented. Efforts are being made to get girls more interested in STEM careers. For example, toys geared to girls suggest ways of processing information that might get them interested in engineering (Nicole, 2012). GoldieBlox is an effort at designing building toys designed for girls that are not just boys' toys colored pink.

Geary (1996, p. 285) suggests several ways to help children who have MLD.

- *Memory problems.* Don't expect the child to memorize the basic facts. Provide alternative methods.

- *Procedural problems.* Make sure the child understands the fundamental concepts. For example, be sure that he or she understands counting before being taught to count on. That is, when the child has counted several items and is provided with one or more additional items to add to the group, does he or she start with "one" or continue on from the original amount? Then have the child practice the procedures.

- *Visuospatial problems.* Provide prompts or cues that will help the child organize numbers so they are lined up correctly.

- *Problem-solving difficulties.* First, help the child with any basic skill difficulties. Have the child identify different types of word problems and help identify the steps needed to solve the problem.

Young children need to be carefully assessed and provided with extra practice and direct instruction if they don't seem to be developing and acquiring the fundamental concepts. Wright, Martland, Stafford, and Stanger (2002) provide a sequenced assessment and instruction method for teaching numbers to young children. Karp and Howell (2004) emphasize the importance of individualized approaches for children with learning disabilities. They describe four components of individualization:

- *Remove specific barriers.* For example, if a child has motor difficulties that make writing difficult, let him give his explanations orally and put his responses on tape.

- *Structure the environment.* Children with learning disabilities need a simple environment that is not overly stimulating. They also require transitions that are carefully planned and clearly set up.

- *Incorporate more time and practice.* Practice should be for frequent, short periods, avoiding "drill-and-kill."

- *Provide clarity.* Present problems clearly by using modeling, questioning, and presenting activities in small steps.

Ritz (2007) provides suggestions for supporting children with special needs in doing science. For example, many children have allergies or asthma. If a nonallergenic alternative material is not available for a science investigation, children might be supplied with protective gloves. A nature walk might be planned for a time of year when there is the least pollen and mold. Classroom accommodations for children with physical challenges should include the provision of easily accessible tables and areas. Teachers need to be responsive to each student's special needs and make appropriate accommodations.

1-2f Technology Today

In the twenty-first century, technology is advancing at a rapid rate. Technology will undoubtedly be an ever-increasing element in young children's learning in the future and will thus continue to present a multitude of challenges for adults who work with young children in both homes and schools. Although technology is becoming less expensive, much of it is still beyond the reach of many schools and homes. However, as television was available to most families by the end of the twentieth century, a variety of technology such as computers, tablets, and cell phones will probably be common in most homes by the end of the twenty-first century. Teachers, parents, and other caregivers are challenged to explore new technologies and their effectiveness as vehicles for children's learning. In special focus sections of *Young Children* (E-Learning for Educators, 2004; Technology and Young Children, 2013), the challenges for educators are described. Educators need to keep up with technological innovations in order to improve their own knowledge and that of their students (Charlesworth, 2014).

Television no longer dominates the media world (Brooks-Gunn & Donahue, 2008). Cell phones, touch tablets, computers, iPods, video games, instant messaging and email, interactive multiplayer video games, virtual reality sites, web social networks, and e-mail now compete with television. Most children have access to more than one type of media and are frequently media multitasking; that is, they are using more than one type of media at the same time. They might have the TV on and also be listening to an iPod while text messaging with friends. A cell phone or a touch tablet can be a camera, a television, an Internet portal, and a radio. Research does indicate that content influences children. Infants and toddlers need direct experience with people and things, so electronic media are not very effective for them without human involvement. With the right kind of presentation, by age 3, children can learn from electronic media. Achievement peaks in one to two hours. Prosocial behaviors such as altruism, cooperation, and tolerance can be increased via electronic media. Children continue to be influenced by electronic marketing and advertising. Parents must thus place limits on their children's use of electronic media (Charlesworth, 2014; Levin, 2013).

The Fred Rogers Center for Early Learning and Children's Media Center was established under the auspices of the NAEYC in 2001. The primary goal of the Center is "building bridges between early learning and children's media" (Fred Rogers Center, n.d.). The combined NAEYC and Fred Rogers Center published a position statement on technology in early childhood programs that reads in part (2011):

> *It is the position of NAEYC and the Fred Rogers Center that technology and interactive media are learning tools that, when used in intentional and developmentally appropriate ways and in conjunction with traditional tools and materials, can support the development and learning of young children. (p.1)*

Technology in the workplace is far ahead of technology in the school and home. The challenge for the future is to help our children become experienced in learning from and using technology so that they are ready to handle the technological requirements of their future occupations.

Calculators also provide a tool for learning. In Chapter 8, we describe some simple activities that young children can explore with calculators. An area of some concern centers on video games and whether children can learn through them (Sherman, 2007). Video games designed to teach basic concepts to young children are now on the market, and more are being designed. Classroom equipment and teaching have changed. In the flipped approach to teaching, homework may consist of online after-school lessons followed by in-class discussion and questioning. Students may sit at tables rather than in individual desks placed in rows. Teaching is becoming more child centered (Fairbanks, May 2013).

Assistive Technology. Assistive technology supports the learning of children with disabilities (Mulligan, 2003). Technology is available that can help children with develop-

mental challenges "express ideas, play with a toy, or demonstrate understanding of developmental concepts" (p. 50). High-tech tools, such as voice synthesizers, Braille readers, switch-activated toys, and computers, as well as low-tech tools can expand the experiences of children with special needs. Special handles can be put on pans and paintbrushes. Pillows and bolsters can help a child have a place in circle activities. A board with photos can be used as a means for a child to make choices. Selection of technology must consider the children served and their abilities, the environment, and cost. Further information can be obtained from the Division of Early Childhood (DEC) of the Council for Exceptional Children.

1-3 SIX STEPS IN INSTRUCTION

As the pathways of the development of mathematical knowledge from birth to age 8 gradually are mapped out, early childhood mathematics has received more attention and is now a priority in early childhood education (Hachey, 2013). The focus of instruction in science and mathematics should be problem solving and inquiry. Not only should teacher-developed problems and investigations be worked on, but child-generated problems and investigations should also be important elements in instruction. A problem-solving/inquiry focus emphasizes children working independently and in groups while the teacher serves as a facilitator and a guide (Ashbrook & Chalufour, 2013). For the program to succeed, teachers must know their students well so that they can support the students in reaching their full capacities within the zone of proximal development. This chapter outlines the basic instructional process and then describes the problem-solving inquiry approach to instruction as it applies to mathematics. In later chapters, science investigations serve as examples of problem solving. As described in the National Research Council's 2012 *Framework for K–12 Science Education*, a new view of inquiry is that it is one approach to scientific practice rather than the one main approach.

Problem solving is a major method for implementing the Common Core State Standards for Mathematics (Schwartz, 2013). In line with CCSS, problems should be based on real-world data and be nonroutine (discussed later). Schwartz describes a variety of tasks for K–2 that are congruent with CCSSM recommendations for teaching.

In planning, looking for and solving problems in the **STEM** era, it is essential to focus on creativity (Edutopia, 2013). Creativity is essential to STEM and is the concept that elaborates into **STEAM** by adding the Arts into STEM. Scientists, technologists, engineers, and mathematicians demonstrate creativity in identifying and solving problems. Play is at the basis of productive thought. Playing with concepts leads to new ideas and inventions. Children's STEAM creativity needs to be encouraged.

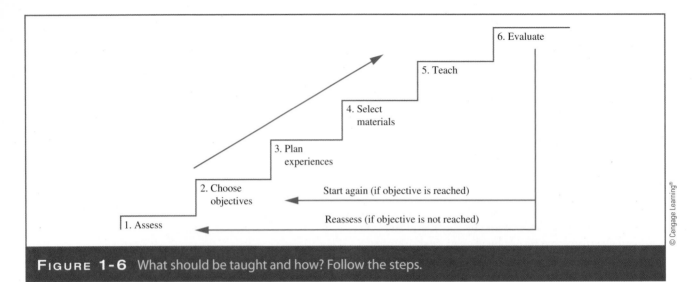

FIGURE 1-6   What should be taught and how? Follow the steps.

The steps involved in planning concept experiences are the same as those used for any subject area. Six questions must be answered (**Figure 1-6**).

- **Assess**. Where is the child now?

- **Choose objectives**. What should she learn next?

- **Plan experiences**. What should the child do to accomplish these objectives?

- **Select materials**. Which materials should be used to carry through the plan?

- **Teach**. Do the planned experiences with the child? Do the plan and the materials fit?

- **Evaluate**. Has the child learned what was taught (reached objectives)?

1-3a Assessing

Each child should be individually assessed. Two methods for this are used most frequently. Children can be interviewed individually using specific tasks, and they can be observed during their regular activities. The purpose of assessment is to find out what children know and what they can do before instruction is planned. The topic of assessment is covered in more detail later in this chapter.

Specific Task Assessment. Following are examples of some specific tasks that can be given to a child:

- Present the child with a pile of 10 counters (buttons, coins, poker chips, or other small things) and say, "Count these for me."

- Show the child two groups of chips: a group of three and a group of six. Ask, "Which group has more chips?"

- Show the child five cardboard dolls, each one a half inch taller than the next. Say: "Which is the tallest?" "Which is the shortest?" "Line them up from the shortest to the tallest."

- Provide a 6-year-old with an assortment of toy cars. Say: "Pretend you have a used car business. A customer wants to buy all your red cars and all your blue cars. Figure out how many of each he would be buying and how many he would be buying altogether. See how many ways you can solve this problem using the toy cars. You may also want to draw a picture or write about what you did."

- Provide a 7-year-old with a container of at least 100 counting chips. Say: "The zoo has a collection of 17 birds. They buy 12 more birds. Five birds get out of the aviary and fly away. How many birds do they have now? You can use the counters to figure it out. Then draw a picture and write about what you did."

- Place a pile of 30 counting chips in front of an 8-year-old. Say: "Find out how many different groups of two, three, five, and six you can make from this pile of chips, and record your findings."

Assessment by Observation. Here are some examples of observations that can be made as children play and/or work (**Photo 1-7**):

- Does the 1-year-old show an interest in experimenting by pouring things into and out of containers of different sizes?

PHOTO 1-7   Assessment can be done through observation of children using math materials.

- Does the 2-year-old spend time sorting objects and lining them up in rows?

- Does the 3-year-old show an interest in understanding size, age, and time by asking how big he is, how old he is, and "When will …" questions?

- Does the 4-year-old set the table correctly? Does she ask for help to write numerals, and does she use numbers in her play activities?

- Can the 5-year-old divide a bag of candy so that each of his friends receives an equal share?

- If there are five children and three chairs, can a 6-year-old figure out how many more chairs are needed so that everyone will have one?

- If a 7-year-old is supposed to feed the hamster two tablespoons of pellets each day, can he decide how much food should be left for the weekend?

- Four 8-year-olds are making booklets. Each booklet requires four pieces of paper. Can the children figure out how many pieces of paper will be needed to make the four booklets?

Through observation, the teacher can find out whether the child can apply concepts to real-life problems and activities. By keeping a record of these observations, the teacher builds up a more complete picture of the child's strengths and weaknesses. The current trend involves collecting samples of student work, photographs, audiotapes, and videotapes to construct a portfolio that represents student accomplishments over time.

1-3b Choosing Objectives

Once the child's level of knowledge is identified, objectives can be selected; that is, a decision can be made as to what the child should be able to learn next. For instance, look at the first task example in the previous section. Suppose a 5-year-old child counts 50 objects correctly. The objective for this child would be different from the one for another 5-year-old who can count only seven objects accurately. The first child does not need any special help with object counting. A child who counts objects at this level at age 5 can probably figure out how to go beyond 50 alone. The second child might need some help and specific activities with counting objects beyond groups of seven.

Suppose a teacher observes that a 2-year-old spends very little time sorting objects and lining them up in rows. The teacher knows that this is an important activity for a child of this age, one that most 2-year-olds engage in naturally without any special instruction. The objective selected might be that the child would choose to spend five minutes each day sorting and organizing objects. Once the objective is selected, the teacher then decides how to go about helping the child reach it.

1-3c Planning Experiences

Remember that young children construct concepts through naturalistic activities as they explore the environment. As they grow and develop, they feel the need to organize and understand the world around them. Children have a need to label their experiences and the things they observe. They notice how older children and adults count, use color words, label time, and so on. An instinctive knowledge of math and science concepts develops before an abstract understanding. When planning, adults must keep the following in mind:

- Naturalistic experiences should be emphasized until the child is into the preoperational period.

- Informal instruction is introduced during the sensorimotor period and increases in frequency during the preoperational period.

- Adult-guided experiences are used sparingly during the sensorimotor and early preoperational periods, and they are brief and sharply focused. The use of adult-guided experiences increases in kindergarten and primary grades.

- Follow the learning cycle format.

Abstract experiences can be introduced gradually during the preoperational and transitional periods and increased in frequency as the child reaches concrete exploratory operations, but they should always be preceded by concrete experiences. Keep these factors in mind when planning for young children. These points are covered in detail in the following section on selecting materials. In any case, the major focus for instructional planning is the promotion of individual and group problem solving and inquiry.

Planning involves deciding the best way for each child to accomplish the selected objectives. Will naturalistic, informal, and/or adult-guided experiences be best? Will the child acquire the concept best on her own? With a group of children? In a one-to-one setting with an adult? In a small group directed by an adult? Once these questions have been answered, the materials can be chosen. Chapters 3 through 7 tell how to plan these experiences for the concepts and skills that are acquired during the preoperational period.

1-3d Selecting Materials

Three things must be considered when selecting science and math materials. First, good materials have some general characteristics. They should be sturdy, well made, and constructed so that they are safe for children to use independently. They should also be useful for more than one kind of activity and for teaching more than one concept. Second, the materials must be designed for the acquisition of the selected concepts. In other words, they must fit the objective(s).

Third, the materials must fit the children's levels of development; that is, they must be developmentally appropriate. As stated, acquiring a concept begins with concrete experiences with real things. For each concept included in the curriculum, materials should be sequenced from concrete to abstract and from three-dimensional (real objects), to two-dimensional (cutouts or computer images), to pictorial, to paper and pencil. Too often, however, the first steps are skipped, and children are immersed in paper-and-pencil activities without the prerequisite concrete experiences and before they have developed the perceptual and motor skills necessary to handle a writing implement with ease. Five steps to be followed from concrete materials to paper and pencil are described as follows. Note that Step 1 is the first and last step during the sensorimotor period; during the preoperational period, the children move from Step 1 through Step 4; and during the transition and concrete operations periods, they move into Step 5.

- *Step 1.* Real objects are used for this first step. Children are given time to explore and manipulate many types of objects such as blocks, chips, stones, and sticks as well as materials such as sand, water, mud, clay, and playdough. Whether instruction is naturalistic, informal, or adult-guided, concrete materials are used.

- *Step 2.* Real objects are used along with pictorial representations. For example, blocks can be matched with printed or drawn patterns. When cooking, each implement to be used (measuring spoons and cups, bowls, mixing spoons, etc.) can be depicted on a pictorial sequenced recipe chart. Children can draw pictures each day showing the height of their bean sprouts.

- *Step 3.* Cutouts that can be manipulated by hand are introduced. For example, cardboard cutouts of different sizes, colors, and shapes can be sorted. Cutout dogs can be matched with cutout doghouses. Cutout human body parts can be put together to make a whole body. Although the materials have moved into two dimensions, they can still be manipulated. By manipulating the materials, the child can try a variety of solutions to the problem by trial and error and can engage in self-correction.

- *Step 4.* Pictures and virtual manipulatives are next. Virtual manipulatives from online or software sources can provide interesting experiences at this level. Many online games are also available. Commercially available pictorial materials, jigsaw puzzles, teacher-created or magazine pictures, and cut-up workbook pages can be used to make card games as well as sequencing, sorting, and matching activities. For example, pictures of people in various occupations might be matched with pictures of their work tools. Pictures of a person at different ages can be sequenced from baby to old age. Groups of objects drawn on a card can be counted and matched with the appropriate numeral. *Stop here if the children have not yet reached the transition stage.*

- *Step 5.* At this level, paper-and-pencil activities are introduced. When the teacher observes that the children understand the concept with materials at the first four levels, it is time for Step 5. If the materials are available, children usually start experimenting when they feel ready. Now they can draw and write about mathematics.

An example of sequencing materials using the five steps is presented next. Suppose one of the objectives for children in kindergarten is to compare differences in dimensions. One of the dimensions to be compared is length. Materials can be sequenced as follows:

- *Step 1: Real objects.* Children explore the properties of Unifix Cubes® and Cuisinaire Rods®. They fit Unifix Cubes together into groups of various lengths. They compare the lengths of the Cuisinaire Rods. They do measurement activities such as comparing how many Unifix Cubes fit across the short side of the table versus the long side of the table.

- *Step 2: Real objects with pictures.* The Unifix Cubes are used to construct rows that match pictured patterns of various lengths. Sticks are used to measure pictured distances from one place to another.

- *Step 3: Cutouts.* Unifix and Cuisinaire cutouts are used to make rows of various lengths. Cutouts of snakes, fences, and so on are compared.

- *Step 4: Pictures.* Cards with pictures of pencils of different lengths are sorted and matched. A picture is searched for the long and the short path, the dog with long ears, the dog with short ears, the long hose, the short hose, the tall person and the short person, and so on. On the Illuminations website (K–2), see the lesson "As People get Older, They Get Taller."
  Stop here if the children have not yet reached the transition stage.

- *Step 5: Paper-and-pencil activities.* For example, students might draw long and short things such as trees, horses, or school buses and goldfish, rabbits, or tricycles.

At the early steps, children might be able to make comparisons of materials with real objects or even with cutouts and picture cards, but they might fail if given just paper-and-pencil activities. In this case, the teacher might falsely assume that the children do not understand the concept when, in fact, the materials are inappropriate. Calculators, tablets, smartboards, and computers can be used at every step. Virtual manipulatives can be supportive of learning.

The chart in **Figure 1-7** depicts the relationship between the cognitive developmental periods—naturalistic, informal, and adult-guided ways of acquiring concepts—and the five levels of materials. Each chapter of this text has examples of various types of appropriate materials listed at the end. Chapter 12 contains lists and descriptions of many that are excellent teaching aids.

PERIODS OF DEVELOPMENT	HOW CONCEPTS ARE ACQUIRED		
	Naturalistic	**Informal**	**Adult Guided**
Sensorimotor	Real objects Objects and pictures Pictures	Real objects Objects and pictures Pictures	
Preoperational	Real objects Objects and pictures Cutouts Pictures	Real objects Objects and pictures Cutouts Pictures Calculators, computers and tablets	Real objects Objects and pictures Cutouts Pictures Calculators, computers and tablets
Transitional	Real objects Objects and pictures Cutouts Pictures	Real objects Objects and pictures Cutouts Pictures Paper and pencil Calculators, computers and tablets	Real objects Objects and pictures Cutouts Pictures Calculators, computers and tablets
Concrete Operations	Real objects Objects and pictures Cutouts Pictures	Real objects Objects and pictures Cutouts Pictures Paper and pencil Calculators, computers and tablets	Real objects Objects and pictures Cutouts Pictures Paper and pencil Calculators, computers and tablets

© Cengage Learning®

FIGURE 1-7 Two dimensions of early childhood concept instruction with levels of materials used.

1-3e Teaching

Epstein (2014) outlines a balanced approach to teaching that she calls **Intentional Teaching**. It balances child-guided and adult-guided teaching. It is teaching that, as described in this text, is guided by specific goals and objectives. Once the decision has been made as to what the child should be able to learn next and in what context the concept acquisition will take place, the next stage in the instructional process is the actual teaching. Teaching occurs when the planned experiences using the selected materials are put into operation. If the first four questions have been answered with care, the experience should go smoothly. A child will be interested and will learn from the activities because they match his level of development and style of learning. The child might even acquire a new concept or skill or extend and expand one already learned.

The time involved in the teaching stage might be a few minutes or several weeks, months, or even years, depending on the concept being acquired and on the age and ability of the child. For instance, time sequence is initially learned through naturalistic activity. From infancy, children learn that there is a sequence in their daily routines: sleeping; waking up wet and hungry; crying; being picked up, cleaned, fed, and played with; and sleeping again. In preschool, children learn a daily routine such as coming in, greeting the teacher, hanging up coats, eating breakfast, playing indoors, having a group activity time, snacking, playing outdoors, having a quiet activity, lunch, playing outdoors, napping, having a small group activity time, and going home. Time words are acquired informally as children hear terms such as *yesterday, today, tomorrow, o'clock, next, after,* and so on. In kindergarten, special events and times are noted on a calendar. Children learn to name the days of the week and months of the year and to sequence the numerals for each of the days. In first grade, they might be given a blank calendar page to fill in the name of the month, the days of the week, and the number for each day. Acquiring the concept of time is a complex experience and involves many prerequisite concepts that build over several years. Some children will learn at a fast rate, others at a slow pace. One child might learn that a week has seven days the first time the idea is introduced; another child might take all year to acquire that information. Some children need a great deal of structured repetition; others learn from naturalistic and informal experiences. Teaching developmentally involves flexible and individualized instruction.

Even with careful planning and preparation, an activity might not work well the first time. When this happens, analyze the situation by asking the following questions.

- Were the children interested?
- Was the task too easy or too hard?
- Did the children understand what they were asked to do?
- Were the materials right for the task?
- Were the materials interesting?
- Is further assessment needed?
- Was the teacher enthusiastic?
- Was it just a "bad day" for the children?

You might try the activity again using the same method and the same materials or with a change in the method and/or materials. In some cases, the child might have to be reassessed to ensure that the activity is appropriate for her developmental level.

1-3f Evaluating

The sixth question concerns evaluation: What has the child learned? What does he know, and what can he do after the concept experiences have been presented? The assessment questions are asked again. If the child has reached the objective, a new one can be chosen. The stages of planning, choosing materials, teaching, and evaluating are repeated. If the child has not reached the objective, the same activities can be continued, or a new method may be tried. For example, a teacher wants a 5-year-old to count out the correct number of objects for each of the number symbols from 0 to 10. She tries many kinds of objects for the child to count and many kinds of containers in which to place the things he counts, but the child is just not interested. Finally, she gives him small banks made from baby food jars and real pennies. The child finds these materials exciting and goes on to learn the task quickly and with enthusiasm.

Evaluation may be done using formal, structured questions as well as tasks and specific observations. Informal questions and observations of naturalistic experiences can also be used for evaluation. For example, when a child sets the table in the wrong way, it can be seen without formal questioning that she has not learned from instruction. She needs some help. Maybe organizing and placing a whole table setting is more than she can do now. Can she place one item at each place? Does she need to go back to working with a smaller number (such as a table for two or three)? Does she need to work with simpler materials that have more structure (such as pegs in a pegboard)? To look at these more specific skills, the teacher would then return to the assessment step. At this point, he would assess not only the child, but also the types of experiences and materials that he has been using. Sometimes assessment leads the teacher to the right objective, but the experience and/or materials chosen do not (as in the example) fit the child.

Frequent and careful evaluation helps both teacher and child avoid frustration. An adult must never take it for granted that any one plan or any one material is the best choice for a specific child. The adult must keep checking to be sure the child is learning what the experience was planned to teach him

1-3g Problem Solving and Inquiry

Problem solving and/or inquiry are included in the standards for both mathematics and science. These approaches promote thinking and reasoning in the children's approach to mathematics problems and science investigations.

Problem Solving and Inquiry in Science. The driving force behind problem solving in science is curiosity—an interest in

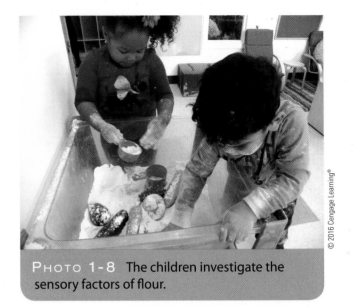

PHOTO 1-8 The children investigate the sensory factors of flour.

finding out, the desire to apply **inquiry** (**Photo 1-8**). (Inquiry is discussed further in Part VI of this book.) Problem solving is not as much a teaching strategy as it is a student behavior. The challenge for the teacher is to create an environment in which problem solving can occur. Encouragement of problem-solving and inquiry behaviors can be seen in the following examples:

- Ogue and Schmidt (2013) describe how kindergarten teachers notice that their students are curious about rocks. The children's pockets and cubbies are filled with collections from the playground, the park, and other outdoor places. The children develop their own rock vocabulary such as sparkly rocks, those that look like metal, like fossils, and so on. Some came from fairies, others from the moon. The children began asking each other questions about their rocks. This began an inquiry-based learning experience as the classes explored and collected information. Skillful questioning by the teachers supported students' investigations.

- Preschoolers work on physics problems in forces and motion (Ashley et al., 2013). A group works with a problem identified by one of the children: how to make a pathway that will make marbles go across the room. They identify the problem, develop a procedure of investigation, conduct the procedure, and draw conclusions. The teacher asks questions that help the children continue.

The asking and answering of questions is what problem solving is all about. When the situations and problems that the students wonder about are perceived as real, their curiosity is stimulated, and they want to find an answer.

Research indicates that working with concrete materials and drawing and/or writing explanations of solutions for problems are the best support for improving problem-solving skills. Keep in mind that the process skills discussed in Chapter 2 are essential to thinking and acting on a problem.

Four Steps in Science Problem Solving. Although people disagree about the exact number of steps it takes for a learner to solve a problem, four basic steps seem to be essential to the process:

1. *Identifying a problem and communicating it in a way that is understood.* This might involve assessing the situation and deciding exactly what is being asked or what is needed.

2. *Determining what the outcome of solving the problem might be.* This step involves the students in organizing a plan that will achieve their problem-solving goal(s).

3. *Exploring possible solutions and applying them to the problem.* In this step, the plan is executed using appropriate strategies and materials. Children must learn that their first approach to solving a problem might be erroneous, but that a solution will materialize if they keep trying. It is essential that children have the opportunity to explain their solutions to others; doing so helps clarify the problem and helps them be better able to explain the problem to themselves.

4. *Explain the possible solutions and revised solution* if they do not seem to work as well as hoped. Because there is no one correct answer or way to arrive at an answer, the results will vary. In fact, the problem may not have an answer.

Whether the lesson is part of the learning cycle, a culminating activity, or an unstructured experience, keep in mind that, first and foremost, student curiosity must be stimulated with problems that engage, intrigue, and motivate before problem solving can occur. As students understand and learn how to apply the basic steps of the problem-solving process, they will be able to make connections with their past experiences while keeping an open mind. The teacher's role is that of a facilitator, using instructional strategies to create a classroom rich with opportunities and where students are enthusiastic about learning and developing problem-solving skills that will last a lifetime.

Overview of Problem Solving and Inquiry in Mathematics. Earlier in this chapter, we outlined the process standards for school mathematics (NCTM, 2000 & 2014). These five standards include problem solving, reasoning and proof, communication, connections, and representation. **Problem solving** involves application of the other four standards. Although preoperational children's reasoning is different from that of older children and adults, it is logical from their own point of view. Pattern recognition and classification skills provide the focus for much of young children's reasoning. Adults should encourage children to make guesses and to explain their reasoning. Language is a critical element in mathematics (see Chapter 6). Children can explain how they approach problem solving by *communication* with language. Even the youngest students can talk about mathematics, and, as they grow older, they can write and draw about it.

The important connections for young mathematicians are those made between the out of school and in school informal mathematics and the formal mathematics of the school curriculum. The transition can be made with the use of concrete objects and by connecting to everyday activities such as table setting, finding out how many children are present in the class, and recognizing that when they surround a parachute they are forming a circle. Young children use several kinds of *representations* to explain their ideas: oral language, written language using invented and conventional symbols, physical gestures, objects, and drawings.

Problems should relate to and include the children's own experiences. From birth onward, children want to learn and naturally seek out problems to solve. Problem solving in school should build on the informal methods learned out of school. Problem solving through the prekindergarten years focuses on naturalistic and informal learning, which promotes exploration and discovery. In kindergarten and primary classes, a more adult-guided approach can be instituted. Every new topic should be introduced with a problem designed to afford children the opportunity to construct their own problem-solving strategies. For an overall look at implementing a problem-solving approach for kindergarten and primary students, read Skinner's book, *What's Your Problem?* (1990). Also refer to the resources listed at the end of this chapter.

Problem solving is a major focus in the Common Core State Standards in Mathematics (CCSSM) (Schwartz, 2013). As students enter the transition into concrete operations, they can engage in more complex problem-solving activities. These activities promote children's abilities to develop their own problems and translate them into a symbolic format (writing and/or drawing). This sequence begins with student questions and teacher responses. Teachers note students' interests and ask questions that get students thinking about problems. Problem solving became the focus of mathematics through the work of George Polya (O'Connor & Robertson, 2002). For Polya, problem solving was the study of heuristic or of providing oneself with a series of self-generated questions. O'Connor and Robertson provide the following quote from Polya:

The aim of heuristic is to study the methods and rules of discovery and invention. Hueristic as an adjective means "serving to discover." Its purpose is to discover the solution of the present problem ... What is good education? Systematically giving opportunity to the student to discover things by himself. (p. 4)

Polya is quoted further when speaking of teaching mathematics in the primary grades:

To understand mathematics is to do mathematics. And what does it mean doing mathematics? In the first place it means to do mathematical problems. (p. 5)

In regard to teaching, Polya refers to it as an art. It is not a science because there is no proven best way. Teaching must be active, its main point being to develop the tactics of problem solving. Polya defined four main phases in mathematics problem solving (Hall, 1957): (1) Understand the problem; (2) devise a plan; (3) carry out the plan; and (4) look back.

In mathematics, there are two major types of problems: **routine** and **nonroutine**. Consider the following descriptions of students working on problems.

- Brent and the other children in his class have been given the following problem by their teacher, Mr. Wang. "Derrick has 10 pennies. John has 16 pennies. How many pennies do they have altogether?" Brent notes the key words, "How many altogether?" and decides that this is an addition problem. He adds 10 and 16 and finds the answer: 26 pennies.

- Mr. Wang has also given them the following problem to solve. "Juanita and Lai want to buy a candy bar that costs 35 cents. Juanita has 15 pennies, and Lai has 16 pennies. Altogether, do they have enough pennies to buy the candy bar?" Brent's attention is caught by the word *altogether*, and again he adds 15 and 16. He writes down his answer: 31 pennies.

- Brent has five sheets of 8½ × 11-inch construction paper. He needs to provide paper for himself and six other students. If he gives everyone a whole sheet, two people will be left with no paper. Brent draws a picture of the five sheets of paper, and then he draws a line down the middle of each. If he cuts each sheet in half, there will be 10 pieces of paper. Because there are seven children, this would leave three extra pieces. What will he do with the extras? He decides that it would be a good idea to have the three sheets in reserve in case someone makes a mistake.

The first problem is a *routine problem*. It follows a predictable pattern and can be solved correctly without actually reading the whole question carefully. The second is called a *nonroutine problem*. There is more than one step, and the problem must be read carefully. Brent has focused on the word *altogether* and stopped with the addition of the two girls' pennies. He misses the question asked, which is, "Once you know there are 31 pennies, is that enough money to buy a 35¢ candy bar?" The current focus in mathematics problem solving is on providing more opportunities for solving nonroutine problems, including those that occur in naturalistic situations, such as the problem

in the third example. Note that the third problem is multistepped: subtract five from seven; draw a picture; draw a line down the middle of each sheet; count the halves; decide whether there are enough; subtract seven from 10; and decide what to do with the three extras. This last problem really has no single correct answer. For example, Brent could have left two of the children out, or he could have given three children whole sheets and four children halves. Real problem-solving skills go beyond simple one-step problems.

Note that, when dealing with each of the problems, the children went through a process of self-generated questions. This process is referred to as **heuristics**. There are three common types of self-generated questions:

- Consider a similar but simpler problem as a model.

- Use symbols or representations (build concrete representations; draw a picture or a diagram; make a chart or a graph).

- Use means-ends analysis, such as identifying the knowns and the unknowns, working backward, and setting up intermediate goals.

We often provide children with a learned idea or heuristic such as a series of problem-solving steps. Unfortunately, if the rules are too specific, they will not transfer (note Brent's focus on the key word). Yet if the rules are too general, how will you know whether the idea has been mastered? The teacher must recognize that applying a heuristic—such as developing the relevant charts, graphs, diagrams, or pictures, or performing needed operations—requires a strong grounding in such basics as counting, whole number operations, geometry, and the like.

Researchers have investigated not only whether heuristics can be taught, but also what successful problem solvers do that leads to their success. It has been found that general heuristics cannot be taught. When content is taught with heuristics, content knowledge improves, but not problem-solving ability. The study of successful problem solvers has shown that they know the content and organize it in special ways. Therefore, content and problem solving should be taught together, not first one and then the other. Good problem solvers think in ways that are qualitatively different from poor problem solvers. Children must learn how to think about their thinking and manage it in an organized fashion. Heuristics is this type of learning; it is not simply learning a list of strategies that might not always work. Children need to learn to apply consciously the following steps as described by Polya (which are similar to the steps in a science investigation):

1. Assess the situation and decide exactly what is being asked.

2. Organize a plan that is directed toward answering the question.

3. Execute the plan using appropriate strategies.

4. Verify the results; that is, evaluate the outcome of a plan.

Children must deal with real problems that might not have clearly designated unknowns, that might contain too much or too little information, that can be solved using more than one method, that have no one right answer (or even no answer), that combine processes, that have multiple steps necessitating some trial and error, and that take considerable time to solve. Unfortunately, most textbook problems are of the routine variety: The unknown is obvious; only the necessary information is provided; the solution procedure is obvious; there is only one correct answer; and the solution can be arrived at quickly. It is essential that students have the opportunity to share possible solutions with their peers. If children have the opportunity to explain solutions to others, they will clarify the problem and be better able to explain problems to themselves.

Formal problem solving can be introduced using **contrived problems**, that is, problems devised or selected by teachers. This procedure provides an opportunity for the teacher to model problem-solving behavior by posing the problem and then acting out the solution. The children can then be asked to think of some variations.

Skinner (1990) presented the first problems to her 5-year-olds in book form to integrate mathematics and reading/language arts. The tiny books were on sturdy cardboard with an illustration and one sentence on a page. They were held together with spiral binding. Skinner encouraged students to use manipulatives such as Unifix Cubes to aid in solving problems or to act out their solutions. Eventually, the students moved into dictating problems and then into writing. By age 7, they were creating most of their own problems. Research indicates that working with concrete materials and drawing and/or writing explanations of solutions for problems are the best experiences for improving problem-solving skills.

Assessment. The assessment of children's problem-solving expertise is not an easy task. It demands that teachers be creative and flexible. Development of problem-solving skills is a long-term activity; it is not learned in one lesson. It must be focused on the process of problem solving, not solely on the answers. Therefore, you must provide children with problem-solving situations and observe how they meet them, interview students, have small groups of children describe how they solved problems, and have students help each other solve problems.

Observe the following as students work on problems:

- Do they attack the problem in an organized fashion; that is, do they appear to have a logical strategy?

- If one strategy does not work, do they try another?

- Are they persistent in sticking with the problem until they arrive at what they believe is a satisfactory solution?

- How well do they concentrate on the problem-solving task?

- Do they use aids such as manipulatives and drawings?

- Do their facial expressions indicate interest, involvement, frustration, or puzzlement?

Behaviors noted can be recorded with anecdotal records or on checklists. Their solutions can be analyzed as to whether they understood or partially understood the problem, whether they planned a solution or had a partial plan, and whether they obtained a correct or partially correct answer.

Interviews will be emphasized as a format for assessment throughout this text. The interview is also an excellent way to look at problem-solving behavior. Present the child with a problem, or have the child invent a problem and let her find a solution, describing what she is thinking as she works. Make a recording or take notes.

Instruction. Researchers agree that children should experience a variety of problem-solving strategies so that they do not approach every problem in the same stereotyped way. They should be given problems that are at their developmental level. Natural and informal methods of instruction should begin the exploration of problem solving. For example, ask how many children are in the classroom today, how many glasses of juice we will need at Kate's table, and so on.

To be effective problem solvers, children need time to mull over problems, to make mistakes, to try various strategies, and to discuss problems with their friends. When teaching in the kindergarten and primary grades, if you must use a textbook, then check the problems carefully. If you find that most of the problems are routine, you will have to obtain some nonroutine problems or devise some yourself. You may use the following criteria.

- Devise problems that contain extra information or that lack necessary information.

    George paid 10¢ a bag for two bags of cookies with six cookies in each bag. How many cookies did George buy? (Price is extra information.)

    John's big brother is 6 feet tall. How much will John have to grow to be as big as his brother? (We don't know John's height.)

- Devise problems that involve estimation or that do not have clearly right or wrong answers.

    Vanessa has $1. She would like to buy a pen that costs 49¢ and a notebook that costs 39¢. Does she have enough money? (Yes/no rather than numerical answer.)

    How many times can you ride your bike around the block in 10 minutes? In one hour? In a week? In a month? (Estimation)

- Devise problems that apply mathematics in practical situations such as shopping, cooking, or building.

- Base problems on things children are interested in, or make up problems that are about students in the class (giving them a personal flavor).

- Devise problems that require more than one step and provide opportunities for application of logic, reasoning, and the testing out of ideas.

- Ask questions that will require the children to make up a problem.

- Design problems whose solutions will provide data for decision making, for example:

    There are 25 students in the third-grade class. The students are planning a party to celebrate the end of the school year. They need to decide on a menu, estimate the cost, and calculate how much money each of them will have to contribute.

Collect resources that children can use for problem solving. Gather statistics that children can work with (such as the weather information from the daily newspaper). Use children's spontaneous questions. ("How far is it to the zoo?") Literature (see Chapter 6) provides a wealth of information for problem solving. Have children write problems that other children can try to solve. Calculators can be helpful tools for problem solving: Children can try out more strategies because of time saved that might otherwise be spent in tedious hand calculations.

Computers can also be used for problem solving. LOGO programming is a problem-solving activity in itself. Remember, have children work in pairs or small groups. Technology opportunities are described and referred to in each of the chapters on mathematics and science content in this textbook.

The conventional problem-solving strategies taught follow Polya's four-step procedure (Reys, Lindquist, Lambdin, Smith, & Suydam, 2004) and have been as follows:

- Understand the problem.

- Devise a plan for solving it.

- Carry out your plan.

- Look back to examine the solution obtained.

However, start by letting children develop their own solutions. They will gradually become more direct in their approaches. Through modeling, new strategies can be introduced. Reys and colleagues (2004) suggest several such strategies:

1. *Act out the problem.* Use real objects or representations to set up the problem and go through the steps of finding a solution. This is the type of activity used to introduce whole number operations.

2. *Make a drawing or a diagram.* The pictures must be extremely simple and should include only the important elements. For example:

    George wants to build a building with his blocks that is triangular-shaped with seven blocks in the bottom row. How many blocks will he need?

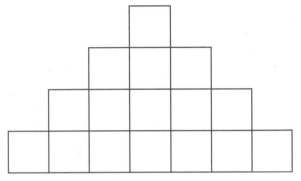

Theresa's mother's van has three rows of seats. One row holds three passengers, the next row holds two, and the back row holds four. Can 10 passengers and the driver ride comfortably?

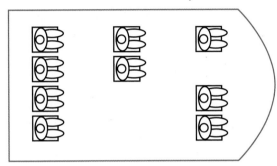

The van holds eight passengers and the driver. Ten passengers and the driver would be crowded.

3. *Look for a pattern* (see Chapter 8).

4. *Construct a table* (see Chapter 9).

5. *Account systematically for all possibilities.* In other words, as different strategies are tried or different calculations are made, keep track of what has been used.

    The following map shows all the roads from Jonesville to Clinton. Find as many different ways as you can to get from Jonesville to Clinton without ever backtracking.

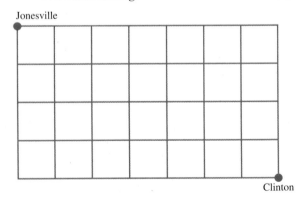

Jonesville

Clinton

6. *Guess and check.* Make an educated guess based on attention to the detail of the problem and past experience. Some problems demand trial and error and a best guess to solve. Sudoku has become popular with both children and adults. Problems follow

the pattern below (*Sudoku for Kids!*, 2008). Using only the numbers 1–9, fill the squares so that the sum in every row and column is 15.

7. *Work backward.* In some problems, the endpoint is given and the problem solver must work backward to find out how the endpoint was reached. A maze is a concrete example of this type of problem.

    Chan's mother bought some apples. She put half of them in her refrigerator and gave two to each of three neighbors. How many apples did she buy?

8. *Identify wanted, given, and needed information.* Rather than plunging right into calculations or formulating conclusions, the problem solver should sort out the important and necessary information from the extraneous factors and may need to collect additional data. Taking a poll is a common way of collecting data to make a decision.

    Trang Fung says that most of the girls would like to have pepperoni pizza at the slumber party. Sara claims that most of the girls prefer hamburger. To know how much of each to order, they set up a chart, question their friends, and tally their choices.

9. *Turn a word problem into an equation or number sentence.*

    Mary gives Johnny half of her allowance. With the rest of her money, she uses half to buy an ice cream cone for $2. How much allowance did Mary receive? Number sentence: $2 \times \$2 = \$4 \times 2 = \$8$ allowance.

    This process is not easy for students, but too frequently it is the only strategy included in a textbook.

10. *Solve a simpler or similar problem.* Sometimes large numbers or other complications get in the way of seeing how to solve a problem; so making a similar problem may help the child discover the solution. For example, in the following problem, the amounts could be changed to "Derrick has $4 and Brent has $6."

    If Derrick has saved $4.59 and Brent has saved $6.37, how much more money has Brent saved?

    Sometimes problems have to be broken down into smaller parts. Also, a strategy may be clarified if a problem is put into the child's own words.

11. *Change your point of view.* Is the strategy based on incorrect assumptions?

    Stop and ask, "What is really being said in this problem?"

All these strategies will not be learned right away. They will be introduced gradually and acquired throughout the elementary grades. Prekindergarten through fourth grade play a crucial role in providing the foundations for problem solving.

Estimation. Estimation is arriving at an approximation of the answer to a problem. Estimation should be taught as a unique strategy. Estimation is mental and should not be checked to see how accurate it is. Later on, children can apply estimation after computation to help them decide whether a computed answer is a reasonable one. First, however, the concept must be developed. At the primary level, the most common problems for applying estimation involve length or numerosity and are solved through visual perception. Children might guess how wide the rug is or how many objects are in a container. Computational estimation is usually introduced near the end of the primary period (i.e., in the third grade).

A number of strategies can be used for estimation (**Photo 1-9**). At the introductory levels, students work with concrete situations. For example, they might explore by estimating how many trucks could be parked in their classroom or how many shoes will fit in the closet. Children can select some benchmarks for measurement, such as a body part; that is, they could estimate how many hands wide the hallway is. Another example would be estimating how many beans would fill a jar using a 1-cup measure that holds 100 beans as the benchmark. Keeping the same jar and changing the size or type of objects placed in it will help children build on their prior knowledge and increase their estimation skills.

Photo 1-9 Children can estimate the temperature each day they get outside to play.

Three strategies might be used for more advanced estimation. The *front-end strategy* is one that young children can use. This strategy focuses on the first number on the left when developing an estimate. For example:

37   To estimate the sum, focus on the left column first.
43   Note that there are nine 10s, which would be 90.
+24 Then look at the right column. Obviously, the answer is more than 90, and noting that the right column adds up to more than 10, an estimate of $90 + 10 = 100$ is reached.

Another strategy is called *clustering*. Clustering can be used when numbers are close in value. For example, estimate the total attendance in class for the week.

Class Attendance

Monday	27		1.	There were about 30 students each day.
Tuesday	29			
Wednesday	31			
Thursday	32			
Friday	30		2.	$5 \times 30 = 150$, the estimated total for the week.

Rounding is a strategy that is helpful for mental computation. Suppose you wondered how many primary-grade children had eaten lunch at school this week. You found out that there were 43 first graders, 38 second graders, and 52 third graders.

Number of Primary Students Eating Lunch

		Round	Add
First graders	43	40	40
Second graders	38	40	40
Third graders	52	50	50
			130
			(estimate)

Two additional strategies are much more complex and would be used by more advanced students beyond the elementary grades. The *compatible numbers* strategy involves more complex rounding. *Special numbers* strategy overlaps several strategies. For the most part, primary-grade children will be using only the noncomputational and the front-end strategies. The important point is that children begin early to realize that mathematics is not just finding the one right answer, but can also involve making good guesses or estimates.

Estimation is frequently used in science inquiries as a means of checking that the investigation procedure is correct. For example, suppose the class wants to know how many children are wearing colored sneakers. It is worthwhile to estimate the number before counting to be sure they are on the right track (the number cannot be any larger than the number of children in the class).

Multicultural Problem Solving. Zaslavsky (1996) suggests games from many cultures as fun ways to teach mathematics while learning about other cultures. Games offer challenges to children. Problem-solving skills are developed as students think through strategies, think ahead, and evaluate their selections of moves. Older children can teach the games to younger children, and games can be related to the customs of cultures. Games can be played by men or by women, by children or adults, on special occasions or at any time. Young children like to change the rules of the game, which changes the strategies to be used.

Helping Children with Special Needs. As with other children, instruction for children with special needs must be individualized and related to how children best learn (Bowe, 2010). Children with special needs tend to lose ground and get farther behind in each year of school. Meeting their unique needs and teaching them the required academic skills and knowledge presents an enormous challenge. Each type of disability provides a different instructional challenge. Planning is required to be individualized for each child and documented in an **IFSP** (individualized family service plan) for infants and toddlers and an **IEP** (individualized educational plan) for older children. Children with disabilities require much more individualized instruction than do other children. Approaches to instruction in **ECSE** (early childhood special education) tend to be behaviorist based, in contrast to the constructivist-based approaches used in regular **ECE** (early childhood education). However, there is no evidence that suggests all ECSE students do best with behaviorist instructional approaches. Special education requirements for the youngest children focus on learning in the family and in other natural environments that include outdoor activities, experiences with animals, experiences with art materials, and other opportunities recommended for all children. Instruction is embedded in the activities through verbal descriptions, questions, and descriptive statements. Children with disabilities may need ancillary services such as physical therapy, occupational therapy, and/or speech-language therapy. Children with disabilities learn math and science through the same types of activities as described in this textbook for other children, but with adaptations and accommodations as needed. Teaching needs to be from the concrete to the abstract, as described earlier in this chapter. Teaching in an inclusive classroom is an enormous challenge due to the wide variety of approaches needed to meet each child's needs.

The needs of English language learners (**ELL**) can also be addressed by special instructional approaches. Teachers must maintain a close relationship with the ELL students' families and learn as much as possible about the students' home countries, languages, and customs. Pair language with visual communication using objects, pictures, and gestures. Be sure that these students are situated where they can see and hear everything. Vocabulary is critical in both math and science. Bilingual vocabulary, both visual and oral, can be very helpful.

1-4 NATIONAL ASSESSMENT STANDARDS

Children's levels of concept development are determined by seeing which concept tasks they are able to perform independently. The first question in teaching is "Where is the child now?" To find the answer to this question, the teacher assesses. The purpose of *assessment* is to gather information and evidence about student knowledge, skills, and attitudes (or dispositions) regarding mathematics and science. This evidence is then used to *plan* a program of instruction for each child and to *evaluate* each child's progress and the effectiveness of instruction. According to NAEYC (2003), assessment has two major purposes:

1. Supporting learning and instruction
2. Identifying students who may need additional services

Assessment should be tied to children's daily activities. Assessment may be done through observation, through questioning as the child works on a problem or investigation, and/or through interviews in which the child is given a specific task to perform. This information is used to guide the next steps in teaching. The long-term objective for young children is to be sure that they have a strong foundation in basic concepts that will take them through the transition into the concrete operational stage, when they begin to deal seriously with abstract symbols in math and independent investigations in science. Following the methods and sequence in this text helps reach this goal and at the same time builds:

- A positive feeling in the child toward math and science.
- Confidence in the child that he can do math and science activities.
- A questioning attitude in response to children's curiosity regarding math and science problems.

The National Council of Teachers of Mathematics (NCTM) assessment principle (2000, p. 22) states "**assessment** should support the learning of important mathematics and furnish useful information to both teachers and students." It should be an integral part of instruction, not just something administered at the end of instruction. Assessment should include the following elements:

- It should enhance children's learning by being a part of everyday instruction.
- Assessment tasks that are similar or identical to instructional tasks can indicate to students exactly what they should be able to know and do.
- Student communication skills can be enhanced when assessment involves observations, conversations, interviews, oral reports, and journals.

- Evaluation guides (or rubrics) can clarify for the students exactly what their strengths and weaknesses are and so enable their self-assessment.

Assessment should be integrated into everyday activities so that it is not an interruption, but rather a part of the instructional routine. Assessment should provide both teacher and student with valuable information. There should not be overreliance on formal paper-and-pencil tests; instead, information should be gathered from a variety of sources. "Many assessment techniques can be used by mathematics teachers, including open-ended questions, constructed-response tasks, selected response items, performance tasks, observations, conversations, journals, and portfolios" (NCTM, 2000, p. 23). In this text, the focus is on observations, interviews, and portfolios of children's work, which may include problem solutions, journal entries, results of conversations, photos, and other documentation. Also, take heed of the equity principle and diversify assessment approaches to meet the needs of diverse learners such as English language learners, gifted students, and students with learning disabilities.

The NCTM (1995) also advocates decreased attention to a number of traditional assessment elements:

- Assessing what students do not know, comparing them with other students, and/or using assessments to track students relative to apparent capability.
- Simply counting correct answers on tests for the sole purpose of assigning grades.
- Focusing on the assessment of students' knowledge of only specific facts and isolated skills.
- Using exercises or word problems requiring only one or two skills.
- Excluding calculators, computers, and manipulatives from the assessment process.
- Evaluating teacher success only on the basis of test scores.

The NCTM (1989) has this to say about the assessment of young children: "Methods should consider the characteristics of the students themselves ... At this stage, when children's understanding is often closely tied to the use of physical materials, assessment tasks that allow them to use such materials are better indicators of learning" (p. 202).

The National Research Council (NRC) created standards for assessment in science education (NRC, 1996). According to the NRC, assessment is primarily a way to obtain feedback. For young children, the feedback tells how well students are meeting the expectations of teachers and parents and tells teachers how effective their instruction is. Through assessment, data are collected for use in planning teaching and guiding learning. The important areas for data collection focus on students' achievement and attitudes (dispositions). For young children, the important assessment methods in science are much the same as in mathematics: performance testing, interviews, portfolios, performances, and observations. A variety of methods should be used to get an accurate assessment picture. Furthermore, methods should be authentic; that is, they should match the intended science outcomes and be situations that match how scientists actually work. Assessment must provide the best possible picture of what children know and how they think. "The notion of assessing what children really know in the areas of the program they are being taught is termed **authentic assessment**" (Martin, 2012. Five science assessment standards are designed for K–12; the following are modified to meet pre-K–3.

- *Assessment Standard A.* The assessments must be consistent with the decisions they are designed to inform. There should be a clear purpose that assesses specific knowledge, skills, and attitudes. Decisions are made on the basis of the assessment data.

- *Assessment Standard B.* Achievement in science must be assessed. Assessments and instruction should be guided by the science content standards. Assessment should provide information on the student's ability to inquire; to know and understand facts, concepts, and principles; to reason scientifically; and to communicate about science.

- *Assessment Standard C.* The technical quality of the data collected is well matched to the decisions and actions taken on the basis of their interpretation. Assessments actually measure what they say they are measuring, tasks are authentic, an individual student's performance is similar on at least two tasks designed to measure the same concept(s), and students have adequate opportunity to demonstrate their achievements.

- *Assessment Standard D.* Assessment practices must be fair. Tasks must be modified to accommodate the needs of students with physical disabilities, learning disabilities, or limited English proficiency. Assessment tasks must be set in a variety of contexts, be engaging to students with different interests and experiences, and must not assume the perspective or experience of a particular gender, racial, or ethnic group.

- *Assessment Standard E.* The inferences made from assessments about student achievement must be sound. In other words, decisions should be made in an objective manner.

Following these standards will enable teachers to collect information for improving classroom practice, planning curricula, developing self-directed learners, and reporting student progress.

The 1996 National Science Education Standards (NSES Standards) were developed over the course of four years and involved tens of thousands of educators and scientists in extensive comment and review. The resultant standards offered a vision of effective science education for all students. However, more guidance was needed in some areas to sufficiently develop the deep understanding of key topics needed for classroom implementation. Groups of experts were convened with an appropriate balance of viewpoints, experience, and expertise in the research to develop addendums to the NSES Standards in the identified areas. As a result of this effort, the report Classroom Assessment and the National Science Education Standards (NRC, 2001) was developed. This document takes a closer look at the ongoing assessment that occurs each day in classrooms between teachers and students and provides vignettes of classroom activity wherein students and teachers are engaged in assessment. Highlights of these findings are integrated into Chapter 2 and throughout the parts of this book that address science content (Chapters 4, 10, and 11). In September 2013, a meeting to address assessment and NGSS was convened at Educational Testing Service. Reports can be found on the NSTA website.

The recent development of common core curriculum standards for math (CCSSM, 2010) and Next Generation Standards for Science (NGSS Lead States, 2013) still rely on the standards described above for guiding assessment. At the end of April 2011, a conference was held to discuss the need for assessment guidelines that align with CCSSM (Moving Forward Together, 2011). Recommendations were made for the development of assessments that align with the standards. Because many parts of the assessments will be online, there is much concern with developing technology that will be equitable and accurately scored. The National Research Council (Pellegrino, Wilson, Koenig, & Beatty, 2013) publication *Developing Assessment for the Next Generation Science Standards* presents guidelines for science assessment that align with the *Framework* and with *NGSS*. Classroom assessments are defined as those designed by or selected by teachers and integrated into classroom instruction. Observations, products, and formal testing are examples. State and national tests will be developed.

DAP **naeyc**

1-4a Assessment Methods

Observation and interview are assessment methods that teachers use to determine a child's level of development. Examples of both of these methods were included earlier in this chapter, and more are provided in this part of the chapter. Sample math assessments are included in each math chapter and in Appendix A. Assessment is most appropriately done through conversations, observation, and interviews using teacher-developed assessment tasks (Glanfield, Bush, & Stenmark, 2003; Komara & Herron, 2012). Commercial instruments used for initial screening may also supply useful information, but their scope is too limited for the everyday assessment needed for planning. Initial screening instruments usually cover a broad range of educational assessments and provide a profile that indicates overall strengths and weaknesses. These strengths and weaknesses can be looked at in more depth by the classroom teacher to glean information needed for making normal instructional decisions or by a diagnostic specialist (i.e., a school psychologist or speech and language therapist) when an initial screening indicates some serious developmental problem. Only individually administered screening instruments should be used with young children. Child responses should require the use of concrete materials and/or pictures, verbal answers, or motoric responses such as pointing or rearranging some objects. Paper and pencil should be used only for the assessment of perceptual motor development (i.e., tasks such as name writing, drawing a person, or copying shapes). Booklet-type paper-and-pencil tests administered to groups or individuals are inappropriate until children are well into concrete operations, can deal with abstract symbols, and have well-developed perceptual motor skills.

Observational Assessment. Observation is used to find out how children use concepts during their daily activities (**Photo 1-10**). Observation can occur during naturalistic, informal, and adult-guided activities. The teacher has in mind the concepts the children should be using. Whenever she sees a concept reflected in a child's activity, she writes down the incident and places it in the child's record folder. This helps her plan future experiences.

© Cengage Learning®

Photo 1-10 Assessment information can be obtained through observation of children working with materials to solve problems and inquiry into their questions.

Throughout this book, suggestions are made for behaviors that should be observed. The following are examples of behaviors as the teacher would write them down for the child's folder:

- "Brad (18 months old) dumps all the shape blocks on the rug. He picks out all the circles and stacked them up. He can sort and organize."

- "Rosa (4 years old) carefully set the table for lunch all by herself. She remembered everything. She understands one-to-one correspondence."

- "Chris (3 years old) and Kai (5 years old) stood back to back and asked Rosa to check who was taller. Good cooperation—it is the first time Chris has shown an interest in comparing heights."

- "Mary (5 years old), working on her own, put the right number of sticks in juice cans marked with the number symbols 0–20. She is ready for something more challenging."

- "Last week I set out a tub of water and a variety of containers of different sizes in the mathematics and science center. The children spent the week exploring the materials. Trang Fung and Sara seemed especially interested in comparing the amount of liquid that could be held by each container. I gave each of them a standard 1-cup measure and asked them to estimate how many cups of water would fill each container. Then I left it up to them to measure and record the actual amounts. They did a beautiful job of setting up a recording sheet and working together to measure the number of cups of water each container would hold. They then lined up the containers from largest to smallest volume, which demonstrated their understanding of ordering or seriation."

- "Today I read Chin's (second grader) math journal. Yesterday's entry included a chart showing the names and amounts of each type of baseball card in his collection. He also wrote his conclusions about which players and teams were his favorites as evidenced by the number of cards. Chin is skilled at organizing data and drawing conclusions, and he understands the concepts of more and less."

- "Ann and Jason (8-year-olds) argue about which materials will float and sink. They asked their teacher if they could test their theories. They got the water, collected some objects, and set up a chart to record their predictions and then the names of the items that sink and those that float. This demonstrates understanding of how to develop an investigation to solve a problem."

Observational information may also be recorded on a **checklist**. For example, concepts can be listed, and then, each time the child is observed demonstrating one of the behaviors, the date can be put next to that behavior. Soon

CONCEPT ACTIVITY OBSERVATION CHECKLIST

Child's Name _____ Birth Date _____

School Year _____ Grade/Group _____

Concept Activities *(Concepts and activities are described in the text)*	Dates Observed
Selects math center	
Selects science center	
Selects cooking center	
Selects math concept book	
Selects science book	
Selects sand or water	
Sets the table correctly	
Counts spontaneously	
Sorts play materials into logical groups	
Uses comparison words (i.e., *bigger, fatter,* etc.)	
Builds with blocks	
Works with part/whole materials	
Demonstrates an understanding of order and sequence	
Points out number symbols in the environment	
Demonstrates curiosity by asking questions, exploring the environment, and making observations	
Uses concept words	

© Cengage Learning®

FIGURE 1-8 Concept observation checklist.

Digital Download

there will be a profile of the concepts the child demonstrates spontaneously (**Figure 1-8**).

Assessment Through Informal Conversations. As children explore materials, the teacher can informally make comments and ask them questions about their activity to gain insight into their thinking. Glanfield and colleagues (2003, p. 56) suggest several types of questions that can prompt students to share their thinking:

- "Tell me more about that."
- "Can you show me another way?"
- "Help me understand."

- "Why did you...?"
- "How did you know what to do next?"
- "What else do you know about...?"
- "What were you thinking when you...?"

Interview Assessment. The individual interview is used to find out specific information in a direct way. These informal assessments are teacher created, tied to classroom curriculum, and used for monitoring of math skills (Komara & Herron, 2012) (**Photo 1-11**). The teacher can present a task to the child and observe and record how the child works on the task, as well as the solution she arrives at for the problem the task presents (**Photo 1-12**). The accuracy of the answers is not as important as how the child arrives at the answers. Often a child starts out on the right track but gets off somewhere in the middle of the problem. For example, Kate (age 3) is asked to match four saucers with four cups. This is an example of one-to-one correspondence. She does this task easily. Next she is asked to match five cups with six saucers: "Here are some cups and saucers. Find out if there is a cup for every saucer." She puts a cup on each saucer. Left with an extra saucer, she places it under one of the pairs. She smiles happily. By observing the whole task, the teacher can see that Kate does not feel comfortable with the concept of one-more-than. This is normal for a preoperational 3-year-old. She finds a way to "solve" the problem by putting two saucers under one cup. She understands the idea of matching one to one but cannot have things out of balance. Only by observing the whole task can the teacher see the reason for what appears to be a "wrong" answer.

Another example: Tim, a first grader, has been given 20 Unifix Cubes, 10 red and 10 blue. His teacher asks him to count the red cubes and then the blue cubes, which he does with care and accuracy. Next, she asks him to see how many combinations of 10 he can make using the red cubes and the blue cubes. To demonstrate she counts out 9 blue

PHOTO 1-12 The observer takes note of the children exploring the sounds of rhythm sticks.

cubes and adds 1 red cube to her group to make 10. She tells him to write and/or draw each combination that he finds. His teacher watches as he counts out 8 blue cubes and 2 red cubes. He then draws on his paper 8 blue squares and 2 red squares.

Finally, in the second-grade class, Emily's teacher, Mr. Martin, notices that she is not very accurate in her work. The class is working on two-digit addition and subtraction with no regrouping, and the teacher is concerned that Emily will be totally lost when they move on to regrouping. He decides to assess her process skills by having her show him with Unifix Cubes how she perceives the problems. For 22 + 31 she takes 22 cubes and 31 cubes and makes a pile of 53. For 45 − 24 she takes a pile of 45 and adds 24 more cubes. Mr. Martin realizes that Emily is not attentive to the signs for plus and minus. Mr. Martin also decides she needs to work on place value and grouping by 10s and 1s.

An important factor in the one-to-one interview is that the interviewer (teacher, parent volunteer, teacher aid, or college methods student) must do it in an accepting manner. The interviewer must value and accept the child's answers regardless of whether they are right or wrong from the adult point of view. If possible, the interview should be done in a quiet place where nothing else might take the child's attention off the task. The interviewer should be warm, pleasant, and calm. Let the child know that he is doing well with smiles, gestures (nods of approval, a pat on the shoulder), and specific praise ("You are very careful when you count

PHOTO 1-11 An individual interview can provide insight into a child's thinking about math.

the cubes"; "I can see you know how to match shapes"; "You work hard until you find an answer"; etc.).

If someone other than a teacher (such as a parent volunteer, teacher aid, or college student intern) does the assessment interview, the teacher should be sure that the assessor spends time with the children before the interviews. Advise a person doing an interview to sit on a low chair or on the floor next to where the children are playing. Children are usually curious when they see a new person. One may ask, "Who are you? Why are you here?" The children can be told, "I am Mr. X. Someday I am going to give each of you a turn to do some special work with me. It will be a surprise. Today I want to see what you do in school and learn your names." If the interviewer pays attention to the children and shows an interest in them and their activities, they will feel comfortable and free to do their best when the day comes for their assessment interviews.

1-4b Assessment Tasks

The assessment tasks included in each content chapter and in Appendix A address the concepts that must be acquired by young children between birth through the primary grades. Most of the tasks require an individual interview with the child. Some tasks are observational and require recording of activities during playtime or class time. The infant tasks and observations assess the development of the child's growing sensory and motor skills. As previously discussed, these sensory and motor skills are basic to all later learning.

The assessment tasks are divided into nine developmental levels. *Levels 1–2* are tasks for the child in the sensorimotor stage. *Levels 3–5* include tasks of increasing difficulty for the prekindergarten child. The *Level 6* tasks are things that most children can do upon entering kindergarten between the ages of 5 and 6; this is the level that children are growing toward during the prekindergarten years. Some children will be able to accomplish all these tasks by age 5; others, not until 6 or over. *Level 7* summarizes the math words that are usually a part of the child's natural speech by age 6. *Level 8* is included as an assessment for advanced prekindergartners and for children enrolled in a kindergarten program. Children who are about to enter first grade should be able to accomplish the tasks at Levels 6 and 8 and should also be using most of the concept words (Level 7) correctly. *Level 9* includes tasks to be accomplished during the primary grades.

Example of an Individual Interview. **Table 1-1** recounts part of the Level 5 assessment interview as given to Bob (4½ years old). A corner of the storage room has been made into an assessment center. Mrs. Ramirez comes in with Bob. "You sit there, and I'll sit here, Bob. We have some important things to do." They both sit down at a low table, and Mrs. Ramirez begins the interview.

An interview need not include any special number of tasks. For the preoperational child, teachers can begin with matching and proceed through the ideas and skills one at a time; so each interview can be quite short if necessary.

1-4c Assessment Task File

Each child and each group of children is different. Teachers need to have on-hand questions to fit each age and stage she might meet in individual young children. Teachers also need to add new tasks as they discover more about children and their development. A computer file, card, or loose-leaf notebook of assessment tasks should be set up. This has three advantages:

- Teachers have a personal involvement in creating and selecting their own assessment tasks, and they are more likely to use them, understand them, and value them.

- The file computer file, paper file, or loose-leaf notebook format makes it easy to add new tasks to and to revise or remove old ones.

- There is room for teachers to use their creativity by adding new questions and making materials.

Use the tasks in each chapter and in Appendix A to begin the file. Other tasks can be developed as you proceed through the chapters in this book and during your future career with young children. Most of the tasks require the use of concrete materials and/or pictures. Concrete materials can be items found around the home and classroom. Pictures can be purchased or cut from magazines and readiness-type workbooks and glued on cards. **Virtual materials** and **activities** are pictorial versions of concrete materials as depicted online. Virtual activities using virtual materials, which could be used for assessment, are also available online (such as those found at NCTM's Illuminations website or Utah State University's National Library of Virtual Manipulatives). The movement in assessment is toward tests with problems that include using virtual manipulatives and performance tasks (Shaughnessy, May 2011). These virtual activities with virtual materials are best suited for children who are well advanced in the preoperational stage or have solidly entered into the concrete operation stage of cognitive development before any formal use of virtual materials. Children should have experiences with real objects before using virtual materials.

In Appendix A, each assessment task is set up for digital download. Observe that, for each task, what the adult says to the child is always printed in a lowercase, bold font so that the instructions can be found and read easily. The tasks are set up developmentally from the sensorimotor level (birth to age 2) to the preoperational level (ages 2 to 7), to early concrete operations (ages 6 to 8). The ages are flexible relative to the stages and are given only to serve as a guide for selecting the first tasks to present to each child.

Each child is at his or her own level. If the first tasks are too hard, the interviewer should go to a lower level. If the first

TABLE 1-1 Assessment Interview

Mrs. Ramirez:	Bob's Response:
How old are you?	"I'm four." (He holds up four fingers.)
Count to 10 for me, Bob. (Mrs. Ramirez nods her head up and down.)	"One, two, three, four, five, six, seven, eight, nine, ten…I can go some more. Eleven, twelve, thirteen, twenty!"
Here are some blocks. How many are there? (She puts out 10 blocks.)	(He points, saying) "One, two, three, four, five, six, seven, eight, nine, ten, eleven, twelve." (He points to some more than once.)
Good, you counted all the blocks, Bob. Now count these. (She puts out 5 blocks.)	(He counts, pushing each one he counts to the left.) "One, two, three, four, five."
(She puts the blocks out of sight and brings up five plastic horses and riders.) **Find out if each rider has a horse.**	(Bob looks over the horses and riders. He lines up the horses in a row and then puts a rider on each.) "Yes, there are enough."
Fine, you found a rider for each horse, Bob. (She puts the riders and horses away. She takes out some inch cube blocks. She puts out two piles of blocks: five yellow and two orange.)	
Does one group have more?	"Yes." (He points to the yellow.)
Okay. (She puts out four blue and three green.)	
Does one group have less?	(He points to the green blocks.)
Good thinking.	
(She takes out five cutouts of bears of five different sizes.) **Find the biggest bear.**	"Here it is." (He picks the biggest.)
Find the smallest bear.	(He points to the smallest.)
Put all the bears in a row from biggest to smallest.	(Bob works slowly and carefully.) "All done." (Two of the middle bears are reversed.)
(Mrs. Ramirez smiles.)	
Good for you, Bob. You're a hard worker.	

© Cengage Learning®

tasks are relatively easy for the child, the interviewer should go to a higher level. **Figure 1-9** is a sample recording sheet format that could be used to keep track of each child's progress. Some teachers prefer an individual sheet for each child; others prefer a master sheet for the whole class. The names and numbers of the tasks to be assessed are entered in the first column. Several columns are provided for entering the date and the level of progress (+, accomplished; ✓, needs some help; −2, needs a lot of help) for children who need repeated periods of instruction. The column on the right is for comments on the process used by the child that might give some clues as to specific instructional needs.

1-4d Record Keeping and Reporting

The records of each child's progress and activities are kept in two separate folders: a **record folder** and a **portfolio**. The record folder contains anecdotal records and checklists, as already described. The portfolio is a purposeful collection of student work that tells the story of the student's efforts, progress, and achievements. It is a systematic collection of material designed to provide evidence of understanding and to monitor growth. Portfolios provide a vehicle for "authentic" assessment, that is, examples of student work done in many real-world contexts. Students and teacher work together to gather work, reflect on it, and evaluate it.

The physical setup for portfolios is important. A box or file with hanging folders is a convenient place to begin. As work accumulates, it can be placed in the hanging folders. At regular intervals, teacher and child go through the hanging files and select work to place in the portfolio. An expanding legal-size file pocket makes a convenient portfolio container. Each piece of work must be dated so that growth can be tracked. Sticky notes or self-stick mailing labels can be used to write notations on each piece of work. Labels should include the date, the type of activity, and the reason for selecting each sample.

An essential attribute of a portfolio is that items are *selected* through regularly scheduled student/teacher

DEVELOPMENTAL TASKS RECORDING SHEET

Child's Name _____ Birth Date _____

School Year _____ School _____ Teacher _____

Grade/Group _____ Person Doing Assessment _____

Levels: +, accomplishes; √, partial; −, cannot do task

Task	Levels			Comments
	Date	Date	Date	

Comments:

FIGURE 1-9 Recording sheet for developmental tasks.

© Cengage Learning®

Digital Download

conferences. Teachers have always kept folders of student work, but portfolios are more focused and contain specially selected work that can be used for assessment. A portfolio offers a more complete picture than does traditional assessment, because the former provides a vehicle for student reflection and self-evaluation.

Here are some examples of items that might be included in a portfolio:

- Written or dictated descriptions of the results of investigations
- Pictures—drawings, paintings, photographs of the child engaged in a significant activity; teacher or student sketches or photos of products made with manipulatives or construction materials such as unit blocks, Unifix Cubes, buttons, and so on
- Dictated (from younger children) or written (from older children) reports of activities, investigations, experiences, ideas, and plans
- Diagrams, graphs, videos or other recorded data
- Excerpts from students' math, science, and/or social studies journals
- Samples of problem solutions, explanations of solutions, problems created, and the like
- Video and/or audio recordings
- Journal entries
- CDs or DVDs

Technology for Young Children

Many young children arrive at school with technology knowledge. Even preschoolers have had experiences with technology, such as computers, tablets, iPhones, Xbox, Wii, Nintendo, video games, interactive websites, and electronic media systems such as Leapfrog. Preschool teachers need to become acquainted with the popular technology and develop a plan for incorporating technology in their classrooms (Maldonado, 2009–2010). It is also important to consider the change that technology is bringing about in the area of human contact (Turkle, 2013). Online conversations are not the same as face-to-face exchanges. Children are missing the nuances of face-to-face exchanges

Current technology can be used to document children's activities and work (Parnell & Bartlett, 2012). Parnell and Bartlett describe how smartphones and tablets can be used as documentation devices. Using a smartphone or tablet, you can first make videos of children being engineers as they build with unit blocks. Then download the video into the class's video-sharing account, and create a blog entry to which you can add photos. At home, families can view the classroom blog. In class, children can build online portfolios that their parents can access. Teachers can begin with one piece of technology at a time and gradually get into more complex documentation. If the teachers can team up with a tech expert, they can learn the documentation process more easily.

W. Parnell & J. Bartlett, iDocument, Young Children, 67(3), 2012, 50–57.

This material is invaluable for evaluation and for reporting progress to parents. When beginning portfolio assessment, start small. Pick one focus, such as mathematics or science, or focus on one particular area (e.g., problem solving, data from thematic investigations, artwork, writing, etc.). Beginning with a scope that is too broad can make the task overwhelming.

Evaluating a portfolio involves several steps. First, develop a rubric. A **rubric** is a list of qualities that you think are important and should be evaluated. Rubrics should be developed based on what you are looking for in your class—not on isolated skills, but rather on broad criteria that reflect understanding. The statements will vary with the content focus of the portfolio. **Figure 1-10** provides a general format and sample statements. Next, a summary providing an overview should be written (**Figure 1-11**). If grades must be assigned, then there is a final step: the **holistic evaluation** (**Figure 1-12**). For a holistic evaluation, the portfolios are grouped into piles such as strong, average, and weak (or very strong, strong, high average, low average, somewhat weak, and very weak), based on the rubric and the summary. This comparative analysis can then guide grading. See the reference list for publications that offer additional ideas regarding the development of portfolio assessment practices. Glanfield and colleagues (2003) and Komara and Herron (2012) suggest rubrics for evaluation of K–2 work samples and checklists for recording results.

SAMPLE PORTFOLIO RUBRIC

	Strong, Well Established	Beginning to Appear	Not Yet Observed
1. Can organize and record data			
2. Explores, analyzes, looks for patterns			
3. Uses concrete materials or drawings to aid in solving problems			
4. Investigations and activities help develop concepts			
5. Persistent, flexible, self-directed			
6. Works cooperatively			
7. Enjoys math and science			

© Cengage Learning®

FIGURE 1-10 General format for a rubric.

Digital Download

PORTFOLIO SUMMARY ANALYSIS

CHILD'S NAME _____ DATE _____

OVERALL EVALUATION

STRENGTHS AND WEAKNESSES

FURTHER RECOMMENDATIONS

© Cengage Learning®

FIGURE 1-11 Format for portfolio summary analysis.

Digital Download

4	Strong on all the characteristics listed in the rubric.
3	Consistent evidence of the presence of most of the characteristics.
2	Some presence of the characteristics, but incomplete communication or presence of ideas, concepts, and/or behaviors.
1	Little or no presence of desired characteristics.

© Cengage Learning®

FIGURE 1-12 Sample of a holistic scoring format.

naeyc DAP

1-4e Maintaining Equity

As already mentioned, equity must be maintained in assessment. Assessment must be done in a manner appropriate to culture, gender, language, and disabilities. Gather information from multiple sources (de Melendez & Beck, 2013). Document observations by teachers, family members, and any specialists the child sees. Anecdotal records, photos, and audio and video recordings can be extremely valuable. Conversations with children and parents, home visits, and interviews with family members and with other professionals can provide important information. Compile portfolios of work products and information from checklists. Authentic assessment tools such as portfolios are recommended for equitable assessment. Children's pictorial number representations can provide a window into their cultural views of themselves (McCulloch, Marshall, & DeCuir-Gunby, 2009). Completing an assignment to make a sign that would provide visitors with information about their class, McCulloch and colleagues found that some kindergarten and first- and second-grade students graphed their peers by skin color. One student who had many experiences in counting coins depicted 21 students as two dimes and one penny. Paper-and-pencil booklet tests and worksheets are not developmentally appropriate.

Formal testing, if used at all, should be just one source of information and should never constitute the sole criteria for making high-stakes decisions. De Melendez and Beck underscore the importance of making modifications and adaptations for children with special needs or with cultural and linguistic differences. Assessment of English Language Learners is a major focus as the Latino population in the United States increases. Selecting the appropriate language for assessment depends on the purpose of the assessment (NAEYC, 2005). If the purpose is program evaluation, the assessment should be done in language and dialect in which the child is most proficient. If this factor is unclear, the child should be assessed in both his home language and English. If the assessment is to be used to guide instruction, a dual language approach is recommended. The home language may be preferred by students for assessments in mathematics.

For young children with special needs, assessment should be "multi- or transdisciplinary, multidimensional, multimethod, multisource, multicontext, culturally appropriate, proactive, and involve ongoing information exchange and collaboration" (Gargiulo & Kilgo, 2011, p. 106). A team of professionals and family members does the assessment of young children with disabilities. However, day-to-day assessment is the responsibility of the individual teacher. As with other children, the assessment must be authentic. Teachers and parents need to know when to request assessments by specialists, such as the physical therapist or the speech-language therapist. Equity requires that appropriate materials be used for instruction to allow for fair assessment. In addition, adequate time must be allowed for students with disabilities to complete tasks. Gargiulo and Kilgo (2011) emphasize the importance of regular and systematic collection of assessment information. The goals included in the IFSP or IEP must be checked for progress. Information regarding appropriate assessment of children with disabilities can be obtained from the Division of Early Childhood (DEC, 2007).

Assessment will result in the identification of a wide variety of achievement levels within a classroom. Instruction should be differentiated to meet the needs of diverse learners (Grimes & Stevens, 2009). Common elements in diverse classrooms are student responsibility, student choice, peer tutoring, flexible grouping, and modified instruction.

Intervention to assist children who are having difficulties with all or any subject is sometimes needed. NCTM (2011) endorses "the use of increasingly intensive and effective instructional interventions for students who struggle in mathematics" (p.1). Interventions may be carried out in the classroom, in groups outside of the classroom or in tutoring sessions.

Response to Intervention (RTI). **RTI** is a widely used intervention approach (DEC, NAEYC, and NHSA [National Head Start Association], 2013). DEC, NAEYC, and NHSA developed a joint framework for RTI as it relates to early childhood education as an evolving practice. These are the common principles across RTI practice:

- Specification of a multitiered system of supports
- Early provisions of support or intentional teaching/ caregiving with sufficient intensity to promote positive outcomes and prevent later problems
- Use of child data to inform teaching and responsive caregiving practices
- Use of research-based, scientifically validated practices to the maximum extent possible (p. 3)

Because RTI for older children may not be appropriate for children below school age, a definition and features of RTI frameworks for young children was developed. The framework includes three tiers of instruction from universal to targeted, to highly individualized instruction and outcomes. In early childhood, progress is continuously monitored. Middle-tier children's misconceptions can be reached through the use of diagnostic interviews (Hodges, Rose, & Hicks, 2012). Maintenance of equity requires thorough diagnosis and follow-up planning of instruction.

SUMMARY

1-1 Concept Development

Concept development begins in infancy and grows through four periods throughout a lifetime. The exploratory activities of the infant and toddler during the sensorimotor period are the basis of later success. As they use their senses and muscles, children learn about the world. STEM is a coordinated area of science, technology, engineering, and mathematics. STEAM integrates the arts into STEM. Both mathematics and science instruction should be guided by principles and standards developed by the major professional organizations in each content area and by the national core curriculum guidelines. Mathematics is also guided by curriculum focal points and the recommendations of the National Research Council report. The text presents the major concepts, skills, processes, and attitudes that are fundamental to mathematics and science for young children as their learning is guided in light of these principles and standards. Constructivism grows out of the theories of Piaget, Vygotsky, and Bruner; children develop the basic concepts and skills of science, mathematics, technology, and engineering. They move toward intellectual autonomy through independent activity, which serves as a vehicle for the construction of knowledge. Between the ages of 5 and 7, children enter the concrete operations period; they learn to apply abstract ideas and activities to their concrete knowledge of the physical and mathematical world. The learning cycle lesson is an example of a developmentally inspired teaching strategy. The Learning cycle is a Piagetian-based constructivist approach to instruction. The cycle consists of four learning/teaching phases: awareness, exploration, inquiry, and utilization.

1-2 Types of Learning Experiences

We have described and defined three types of learning experiences. Through practice, the teacher and parent learn how to make the best use of naturalistic, informal, and adult-guided experiences so that the child has a balance of free exploration and specific planned activities. When planning activities, the children's learning styles and areas of strength should be considered. Culture, socioeconomic status, special needs, and previous experience are all important factors in learning. Gender is another consideration, as girls are less likely to be interested in STEM. Technology—in the form of computers, tablets, cell phones, calculators, and so on—provides valuable tools for learning math and science concepts. Classrooms are being equipped with interactive whiteboards and other newer technology. Teaching is becoming more child centered.

1-3 Six Steps in Instruction

This chapter has described six steps that provide a guide for what to teach and how to teach it. Following these steps can minimize guesswork. The steps are (1) assessing, (2) choosing objectives, (3) planning experiences, (4) selecting materials, (5) teaching with intention, and (6) evaluating.

Problem solving and inquiry are the major processes that underlie all instruction in mathematics and science. Problem solving and inquiry emphasize the process rather than the final product (or correct answer). The important factor is that, during the early childhood years, children gradually learn a variety of problem-solving strategies, as well as when and where to apply them. For young children, problems develop out of their everyday naturalistic activities. Children must also be afforded the opportunity to investigate science problems in areas of interest. Assessment and evaluation should each focus on the process rather than on the answers. Observation and interview techniques may both be used.

Games can provide a multicultural problem-solving experience. Children with disabilities need more individualized instruction than do other children. English language learners need work with objects, pictures, and gestures.

1-4 National Assessment Standards

The focus of assessment in mathematics and science is on assessment integrated with instruction during naturalistic classroom activities and during activities that involve performance of concrete, hands-on problem solving, and child-directed investigations. Performance and understanding should be demonstrated. The major ways to assess the developmental levels of young children are observation, informal conversation, questioning, interviewing, checklists and rubrics, and the collection of materials in a portfolio. Observation is the most useful when looking at how children use concepts in their everyday activities. The interview with one child at a time gives the teacher an opportunity to look at specific ideas and skills. Interview assessment tasks are included in content chapters and in Appendix A. They provide a format for individual assessment. We have given guidelines for conducting an interview and a summary of the nine levels of developmental tasks (in Appendix A). A sample of part of an interview shows how the exchange between interviewer and child might progress. We described a system for record keeping, reporting, and evaluation using a record folder and a portfolio. Increasingly technology is being used to document children's learning. A holistic approach to evaluation is recommended. We have emphasized the importance of equitable systems and methods of assessment. RTI (Response to Intervention) is an assessment method widely used to intervene with children who need extra help.

FURTHER READING AND RESOURCES

Charlesworth, R., & Leali, S. A. (2012). Using problem solving to assess young children's mathematics knowledge. *Early Childhood Education Journal, 39*(6), 373–382.

Froschauer, L. (2013). The role of science standards in early childhood education. In A. Shillady (Ed.), *Exploring Science* (pp. 72–74). Washington DC: National Association for the Education of Young Children.

Koestler, C., Felton, M. D., Bieda, K. N., & Otten, S. (2013). *Connecting the NCTM process standards & the CCSSM practices.* Reston, VA: National Council of Teachers of Mathematics.

Science for all. (2014), *Science and Children* [Focus Issue] *51*(5).

REFERENCES

American Association for the Advancement of Science. (1989). *Science for all Americans: A Project 2061 report on literacy goals in science, mathematics and technology.* Washington, DC: Author.

American Association for the Advancement of Science. (1993). *Benchmarks in science literacy.* Washington, DC: Author.

American Association for the Advancement of Science. (2001). *Atlas of science literacy.* Washington, DC: Author.

Ashbrook, P., & Chalufour, I. (2013). Spotlight on young children: Exploring science. In A. Shillady (Ed.), *Exploring Science* (pp. 1–4). Washington, DC: National Association for the Education of Young Children.

Ashley, J. S., Hamilton, Y., Oxley, E., Eastman, A. M., & Brent, R. (2013). Young thinkers in motion. In A. Shillady (Ed.), *Exploring Science* (pp. 29–49). Washington, DC: National Association for the Education of Young Children.

Barman, C. R. (1989). *An expanded view of the learning cycle: New ideas about an effective teaching strategy* (Council of Elementary Science International Monograph No. 4). Indianapolis: Indiana University Press.

Bazley, K., & Madeira, C. (2013). Addressing a gender gap in academic performance. *Focus on Elementary, 25*(3).

Bishop-Joseph, S. J., & Zigler, E. (2011). The cognitive/academic emphasis versus the whole child approach. In E. Zigler, W. S. Gilliam, W. S. Barnett (Eds.). *The Pre-K Debates.* Washington, DC: NAEYC and Baltimore, MD: Brookes.

Blending western, traditional science for success. (2008). *NSTA Reports, 19* (December).

Bowe, F. G. (2010). *Early childhood special education: Birth to eight.* Belmont, CA: Wadsworth Cengage Learning.

Bredekamp, S., & Rosegrant, T. (1992). *Reaching potentials: Appropriate curriculum and assessment for young children* (vol. 1). Washington, DC: National Association for the Education of Young Children.

Brooks-Gunn, J., & Donahue, E. H. (2008). Children and electronic media. *The Future of Children, 18*(1), 3–10.

Chalufour, I., Hoisington, C., Moriarty, R., Winokur, J., & Worth, K. (2004). The science and mathematics of building structures. *Science and Children, 41*(4), 31–34.

Charlesworth, R. (2014). *Understanding child development*, 9th ed. Belmont, CA: Wadsworth Cengage Learning.

Clabaugh, G. K. (Ed.). (2010). The educational theory of Jerome Bruner: A multidimensional analysis. New-Foundations. www.newfoundations.com.

Clements, D. H., & Sarama, J. (2002a). Mathematics curricula in early childhood. *Teaching Children Mathematics, 9*(3), 163–166.

Committee on Science Learning, Kindergarten Through Eighth Grade. Board on Science Education, Center for Education. (2007). *Taking science to school: Learning and teaching science in grades K–8*. Washington, DC: National Academies Press.

Common Core State Standards. (2011, May 20). www.commoncore.org.

Common Core State Standards for Mathematics. (2010, July). www.corestandards.org

Constructivist versus traditional math. (2005). Retrieved January 10, 2010, from www.readingtoparents.org.

Copple, C., & Bredekamp, S. (Eds.). (2009). *Developmentally appropriate practice in early childhood programs serving children birth through age eight*, 3rd ed. Washington, DC: National Association for the Education of Young Children.

de Melendez, W. R., & Beck, V. (2013). *Teaching young children in multicultural classrooms*, 4th ed. Belmont, CA: Wadsworth Cengage Learning.

DEC. (2007). *Promoting positive outcomes for children with disabilities: Recommendations for curriculum, assessment, and program evaluation*. Missoula, MT: Author.

DEC, NAEYC, & NHSA. (2013, February 7). Frameworks for response to intervention in early childhood: Description and implications. Washington, DC: Authors. www.naeyc.org.

DeVries, R., & Sales, C. (2011). *Ramps and pathways*. Washington, DC: National Association for the Education of Young Children.

Duckworth, E. (2006). *The having of wonderful ideas*, 3rd ed. New York: Teachers College Press.

E-learning for educators. (2004). *Young Children, 59*(3), 10–44.

Edutopia. (2013, August 21). Creativity is the secret sauce in STEM. www.edutopia.org/blog/creativity-secret-sauce-in-stem-ainissa-ramirez.

Epstein, A. (2014). *The Intentional teacher*, revised ed. Washington, DC: National Association for the Education of Young Children & Ypsilanti, MI: HighScope.

Fairbanks, A. M. (2013, May 22). Digital trends shifting the role of teachers. *Education Week*. www.edweek.org.

Gardner, H. (1999). *Intelligence reframed*. New York: Basic Books.

Garfield et al., 2003. From p.

Gargiulo, R., & Kilgo, J. (2011). *Young children with special needs*, 3rd ed. Belmont, CA: Wadsworth Delmar Cengage Learning.

Geary, D. C. (1996). *Children's mathematical development*. Washington, DC: American Psychological Association.

Gewertz, C. (2010, April 6). Both value and harm seen in K–3 common standards. *Education Week*. www.edweek.org.

Glanfield, F., Bush, W. S., & Stenmark, J. K. (Eds.). (2003). *Mathematics assessment: A practical handbook for grades K–2*. Reston, VA: National Council of Teachers of Mathematics.

Grimes, K. J., & Stevens, D. D. (2009). Glass, bug, mud. *Phi Delta Kappan, 90*(9), 677–680.

Gutierrez, R., Bay-Williams, J., & Kanold, T. D. (2008). Beyond access and achievement: Equity issues for mathematics teachers and leaders. *NCTM News Bulletin, 45*(3), 5.

Hachey, A. C. (2013). The early childhood mathematics revolution. *Early Education and Development, 24*, 419–430.

Hall, A. (1957). Common-Sense Questions—Polya (1957). Learning and Mathematics. Drexel University School of Education. http://mathforum.org.

Hodges, E., Rose, T. D., & Hicks, A. D. (2012). Interviews as RTI tools. *Teaching Children Mathematics, 19*(1), 30–41.

Jones, J. P., Burr, S, Kaufman, L., & Beck, J. (2013). Beyond the fluff: Integrating fine arts in the common core classroom. *Focus on Inclusive Education, 10*(4), 7 pp.

Karp, K., & Howell, P. (2004). Building responsibility for learning in students with special needs. *Teaching Children Mathematics, 11*(3), 118–126.

Komara, C., & Herron, J. (2012). Implementing formative mathematics assessments in prekindergarten. *Childhood Education, 88*(3), 162–168.

Lee, O., Deaktor, R., Enders, C., & Lambed, J. (2008). Impact of a multi-year professional development intervention on science achievement of culturally and linguistically diverse elementary students. *Journal of Research on Science Teaching, 42*(6), 726–747.

Levin, D. E. (2013). *Beyond remote controlled childhood.* Washington, DC: National Association for the Education of Young Children.

Lipka, J. (1998). *Transforming the culture of schools: Yupik Eskimo examples.* Mawah, NJ: Lawrence Erlbaum Associates.

Lipka, J., Yanez, E., Andrew-Ihrke, D. & Adam, S. (2009). A two-way process for developing effective culturally based math. In B. Greer, S. Mukhopadhyay, A. B. Powell, & S., Nelson-Barber (Eds.), *Culturally responsive mathematics education.* New York: Routledge, 257–280.

Maldonado, N. S. (2009–2010). How much technology knowledge does the average preschooler bring to the classroom? *Childhood Education, 86*(2), 124–126.

Martin, D. J. (2012). *Elementary Science Methods: A Constructivist Approach.* Belmont, CA: Wadsworth Cengage Learning.

Math experiences that count! (2002). *Young Children, 57*(4), 60–61.

McCulloch, A. W., Marshall, P. L., & & DeCuir-Gunby, J. T. (2009). Cultural capital in children's number representation. *Teaching Children Mathematics, 16*(3), 184–189.

Mix, K. S., Huttenlocher, J., & Levine, S. C. (2002). *Quantitative development in infancy and early childhood.* New York: Oxford University Press.

Moomaw, S., & Davis, J. A. (2013). STEM comes to preschool. In A. Shillady (Ed.). *Exploring science* (pp. 7–22). Washington, DC: National Association or the Education of Young Children.

Moving forward together: Curriculum & assessment and the CCSSM. (2011, April 29–May 1). Summary prepared by Erin Krupa. www.mathismore.net.

Mulligan, S. A. (2003). Assistive technology: Supporting the participation of children with disabilities. *Young Children, 58*(6), 50–51.

National Association for the Education of Young Children (NAEYC). (2003). Early childhood curriculum, assessment, and program evaluation: Position statement. www.naeyc.org.

National Association for the Education of Young Children (NAEYC). (2005). From p. 105.

National Association for the Education of Young Children. (2009). *NAEYC standards for early childhood professional preparation programs.* Washington, DC: Author.

National Association for the Education of Young Children (NAEYC). (2012, September). *NAEYC standards for early childhood professional preparation programs: A position statement.* Washington, DC: Author.

National Association for the Education of Young Children. (2005). *Screening and assessment of young English language learners.* Position Statement. Washington, DC: Author.

National Association for the Education of Young Children & the National Association of Early Childhood Specialists in State Departments of Education. (2002). *Early learning standards: Creating conditions for success.* Washington, DC: Authors.

National Council of Teachers of Mathematics (NCTM). (1989). *Curriculum and evaluation standards for school mathematics.* Reston, VA: Author.

National Council of Teachers of Mathematics (NCTM). (1995). *Assessment standards for school mathematics.* Reston, VA: Author.

National Council of Teachers of Mathematics (NCTM). (2000). *Principles and standards for school mathematics.* Reston, VA. Author.

National Council of Teachers of Mathematics (NCTM). (2011). *Intervention: A position.* Reston, VA: Author.

National Council of Teachers of Mathematics (NCTM). (2014). *Principles to actions: Executive summary.* www.naeyc.org.

National Council of Teachers of Mathematics & National Association for the Education of Young Children. (2002). NCTM position statement: Early childhood mathematics: Promoting good beginnings. *Teaching Children Mathematics, 9*(1), 24.

National Governors Association Center for Best Practices, Council of Chief State School Officers. (2010). Common Core State Standards for Mathematics. Washington, DC: Author.

National Research Council (NRC). (1996). *National science education standards.* Washington, DC: National Academies Press.

National Research Council (NRC). (1999). Selecting instructional materials: A guide for K–12. Washington, DC: National Academies Press.

National Research Council (NRC). (2000). *Inquiry and the national science education standards: A guide for teaching and learning.* Washington, DC: National Academies Press.

National Research Council (NRC). (2001). *Classroom assessment and the national science education standards.* Washington, DC: National Academies Press.

National Research Council (NRC). (2007). *Taking science to school: Learning and teaching science in grades K–8.* Washington, DC: National Academies Press.

National Research Council. (2012). *A Framework for K–12 Science Education: Practices, crosscutting concepts, and core ideas.* Washington, DC: National Academies Press.

Next Generation Science Standards (NGSS) Lead States (2013). *The Next Generation Science Standards: For states, by states.* Washington, DC: National Academies Press.

Nicole, K. (2012, October 15). Beauty, brains and business: Engineering girls for a man's world. *Forbes.* www.forbes.com.

Nunes, T. (1992). Ethnomathematics and everyday cognition. In D. A. Grouws (Ed.), *Handbook of research on mathematics teaching and learning.* New York: Macmillan, 557–574.

Oakes, J. (1990). *Lost talent: The underparticipation of women, minorities, and disabled persons in science.* Santa Monica, CA: Rand.

O'Connor, J. J., & Robertson, E. F. (2002). George Polya. www-history.mcs.st-and.ac.uk.

Ogu, U., & Schmidt, S. R. (2013). Kindergartners investigate rocks and sand. In A. Shillady (Ed.), *Exploring Science* (61–67). Washington, DC: National Association for the Education of Young Children.

Parnell, W., & Bartlett, J. (2012). iDocument, *Young Children, 67*(3), 50–57.

Pellegrino, J. W., Wilson, M. R., Koenig, J. A., & Beatty, A. S. (Eds.). (2013). *Developing assessments for the next generation science standards.* Washington, DC: National Academies Press.

Pollman, M. J. (2010). *Blocks and beyond.* Baltimore, MD: Brookes.

Renner, R. W., & Marek, E. A. (1988). *The learning cycle and elementary school science teaching.* Portsmouth, NH: Heinemann.

Reys, R. E., Lindquist, M. M., Lambdin, D. V., Smith, N. L., & Suydam, M. N. (2004). *Helping children learn mathematics, 7th ed.* New York: Wiley.

Ritz, W. C. (Ed.). (2007). *Head start on science.* Arlington, VA: National Science Teachers Association.

Rogers, F. (n.d.). Fred Rogers Center Mission Statement. www.fredrogerscenter.org/about/mission-statement.

Santa Cruz, R. M. (2009). Giving voice to English language learners in mathematics. *NCTM News Bulletin* (January/February). www.NCTM.org.

Schwartz, S.L. (2013). *Implementing the Common Core State Standards through mathematical problem solving.* Reston, VA: National Council of Teachers of Mathematics.

Scieszka, J, & Smith, L. (1995). *Math curse.* New York: Viking.

Shaughnessy, M. (2011, May). CCSSM and curriculum and assessment: NOT business as usual. *NCTM Summing Up,* 1–2.

Sherman, D. (2007, March 16). More video games, fewer books at schools? http://uk.reuters.com.

Shores, E. F., & Grace, C. (1998). *The portfolio book.* Beltsville, MD: Gryphon House.

Skinner, P. (1990). What's your problem? Portsmouth, NH: Heinemann.

Sparks, S. D. (2011, June 17). Study helps pinpoint math disability. *Education Week.* www.edweek.org.

Sparks, S. D. (2011, October 20). Brain study points to potential treatments for math anxiety. *Education Week Blogs.* http://blogs.edweek.org.

STEM: Science, technology, engineering and mathematics. (2010). *Science and Children* (special issue), *47*(7).

The arts in STEM: STEAM. (2012, October). The *STEM Classroom.* www.magnetmail.net.

Sriraman, B., & Lesh, R. (2007, September). A conversation with Zoltan P. Dienes. *The Montana Mathematics Eenthusiast,* Monograph 2, 151–167. www.math.umt.edu.

Sudoku for Kids! (2008). www.activityvillage.co.uk/sudoku-for-kids.

Tambe, P., Carroll, B., Mitchell, H., Lopez, L., Horsch, E., & St. John, M. (2007). *Effective educational practices in mathematics for Native American learners: A conference summary.* Inverness, CA: Inverness Research Associates. www.inverness-research.org.

Technology and young children (special section). (2012). *Young Children, 67*(3),

Turkle, S. (2013, August 6). Screen time warning. *ExchangeEveryDay.* www.childcareexchange.com/eed.

Van de Walle, J. A. (1999). Reform mathematics vs. the basics: Understanding the conflict and dealing with it. Presentation at the 77th Annual Meeting of NCTM. http://mathematicallysane.com.

Wilmot, B., & Thornton, C. A. (1989). Mathematics teaching and learning: Meeting the needs of special learners. In P. R. Trafton & A. P. Shulte (Eds.), *New directions for elementary school mathematics* (pp. 212–222). Reston, VA: National Council of Teachers of Mathematics.

Wright, R. J., Martland, J., Stafford, A. K., & Stanger, G. (2002). *Teaching number: Advancing children's skills and strategies.* Thousand Oaks, CA: Chapman.

Zaslavsky, C. (1996). *The multicultural math classroom.* Portsmouth, NH: Heinemann.

BASICS OF SCIENCE, ENGINEERING,
AND TECHNOLOGY

LEARNING OBJECTIVES

After reading this chapter, you should be able to:

2-1 Describe the importance of the science framework and standards, the relationship of science and literacy, science as inquiry and as engineering design, and the content areas of science.

2-2 Explain how science concepts are developed and learned.

2-3 Assess, Plan, Teach, and Evaluate science instruction in line with national standards.

STANDARDS ADDRESSED IN THIS CHAPTER

naeyc

NAEYC Professional Preparation Standards

1a. Know and understand children's characteristics and needs (0–8).

1b. Use developmental knowledge to create healthy learning environments for young children.

4c. Use developmentally appropriate teaching/learning approaches.

5. Use content knowledge to build meaningful curriculum.

5a. Understand content knowledge in mathematics and science.

5c. Design, implement, and evaluate developmentally meaningful and challenging curriculum for each child.

3a. Understand the goals, benefits, and uses of assessment.

3b. Use a variety of appropriate assessment tools and approaches.

3c. Understand and practice responsible assessment.

DAP Guidelines

3A. Identify and articulate desired goals in learning and development.

3A2. Become familiar with state standards or other mandates.

2F. Effectively promote each child's learning and development at that moment.

2C. Know desired program goals.

3C. Use the curriculum framework to ensure there is attention to important learning goals.

4A. Assess that children's progress and achievements are ongoing, strategic, and personal.

4B. Focus assessment on children's progress toward goals that are developmentally and educationally significant.

4C. Use the assessment information to guide what goes on in the classroom.

4D. Ensure methods of assessment are developmentally appropriate.

Next Generation Science Standards

K-ESS3-2   Ask questions based on observations to obtain information.

1-PS4-1   Begin science investigations with a question.

2-LS4-1   Make observations to collect data that can be used to make comparisons.

3-LS3-2   Use evidence to support an explanation.

NGSS

2-1 THE FRAMEWORK AND STANDARDS FOR SCIENCE EDUCATION

With the advent of STEM (see Chapter 1), science is now divided into four areas of disciplinary core ideas: Physical Sciences, Life Sciences, Earth and Space Sciences, and Engineering, Technology, and Applications of Science (National Research Council, 2012). The *Framework for K–12 Science Education Practices* (National Research Council, 2012) was developed to guide creation of *The Next Generation Science Standards* (NGSS) (NGSS Lead States, 2013). The integration of engineering and technology in the Science Framework and the *Next Generation Science Standards* is a major conceptual change (NSTA, 2013). The NGSS includes student performance expectations. It is not a curriculum. The methods of instruction are left up to the teacher.

When people think of science, they generally think first of the content of science. Science is often viewed as an encyclopedia of discoveries and technological achievements. Formal training in science classes often promotes this view by requiring the memorization of seemingly endless science concepts. Science has been compiling literally millions of discoveries, facts, and data over thousands of years. We are now living in an age that has been described as the knowledge explosion. Consider that the amount of scientific information amassed between 1900 and 1950 equals what was learned from the beginning of recorded history until the year 1900. Since 1950, the rate of newly discovered scientific information has increased even more. Some scientists estimate that the total amount of scientific information produced now doubles every two to five years.

If you tried to teach all that has been learned in science—starting in preschool and continuing daily straight through high school—you could make only a small dent in the body of knowledge. Learning everything is simply impossible. Nevertheless, far too many teachers approach the task of teaching children science as if it were a body of information that anyone can memorize.

In fact, it is nearly impossible to predict what specific information taught to preschool and primary grade students today will be of use to them as they pursue a career in the twenty-first century. Very possibly, today's body of scientific, engineering, and technological knowledge will change before a child graduates from high school. Scientists and engineers are constantly looking at data in different ways and arriving at new conclusions. Thus, it cannot be predicted with any certainty which facts will be the most important for students to learn in the years to come. What is known is that individuals will always be facing new problems that they will attempt to solve. Life, in a sense, is a series of problems. Those who are most successful in future decades will be the ones who are best equipped to solve the problems they encounter.

According to the National Research Council Framework for Science and Engineering education, education should focus on a limited number of core ideas and cross-cutting concepts that apply to both science and engineering (to be discussed in later chapters) and basic practices (2012).

This discussion is intended to put the essence of science in perspective. Science in preschool through college should be viewed more as a verb than as a noun. It is not so much a body of knowledge as it is a way of thinking and acting, a way of trying to discover the nature of things. Engineering is a means for solving problems. The attitudes and thinking skills that have moved science and engineering forward through the centuries are the same attitudes and skills that enable individuals to solve the problems they encounter in everyday life.

An approach to science and engineering teaching that emphasizes the development of thinking and the open-minded attitudes of science would seem to be most appropriate for the instruction of young children. It is also important to make the exploration of science and engineering topics enjoyable, an approach that supports a lifelong learning of science as well as a lifelong interest in solving engineering problems. This chapter covers science processes, attitudes, content planning, and organizing for instruction. The content standards are useful for identifying what children at different ages and stages should know and be able to do in the area of science. The standards describe appropriate content for children in kindergarten through high school and also identify the practices needed to successfully understand science and engineering.

NGSS

2-1a Science as Inquiry and Engineering Design

Inquiry, a longstanding basic instructional approach in science, is a learning process based on children's questions (Gadzikqwski, 2013). At the preschool level the topics of study can be totally emergent from children's interests. In kindergarten and primary school, the topics of study are usually provided by the state, but the method of instruction is inquiry, which is divided into abilities children need for sound scientific inquiry and understandings they should have about scientific inquiry. Inquiry is presented as a step beyond such process learning skills as observing, inferring, and predicting. These skills are required for inquiry, but students must combine them with scientific knowledge as they use scientific reasoning and critical thinking to develop understanding. Engaging students in inquiry serves five essential functions:

- Assists in the development of understanding of scientific and engineering concepts

- Helps students "know how we know" in science and engineering

- Develops an understanding of the nature of science and engineering

- Develops the skills necessary to become independent inquirers about the natural world
- Develops the dispositions to use the skills, abilities, and habits of mind associated with science and engineering

Inquiry-oriented instruction, often contrasted with expository methods, reflects the constructivist model of learning and is often referred to as *active learning*. As described in Chapter 1, the constructivist model of learning is the result of ongoing changes in our mental frameworks as we attempt to make meaning out of our experiences. To develop scientific inquiry skills, preschool, kindergarten, and primary grade children need the following skills:

- Planning and conducting a simple investigation
- Employing simple equipment and tools to gather data
- Using data to construct reasonable explanations
- Communicating the results of the investigations and giving explanations

Additional strategies that encourage students in the active search for knowledge are discussed later in this chapter.

2-1b Processes of Inquiry

Science **process skills** are those that allow students to process new information through concrete experiences (**Figure 2-1**). They are also progressive, building on and overlapping one another. The skills most appropriate for preschool and primary students are the basic skills of **observing, comparing, classifying, measuring,** and **communicating.** Sharpening these skills is essential for coping with daily life as well as for future study in science and mathematics. As students move through the primary grades, mastery of these skills will enable them to perform intermediate process skills that include gathering and organizing information, **inferring,** and **predicting.** If students have a strong base of primary and intermediate process skills, by the time they reach the intermediate grades, they will be prepared to apply those skills to the more sophisticated and abstract skills, such as forming **hypotheses** and separating **variables,** that are required in experimentation.

Grade-level suggestions for introducing specific science process skills are given as a general guide for their appropriate use. Because students vary greatly in experience and intellectual development, you may find that your early childhood students are ready to explore higher-level process skills sooner. In such cases, you should feel free to stretch their abilities by encouraging them to work with more advanced science process skills. For example, four- and five-year-olds can begin with simple versions of intermediate process skills, such as making a reasonable guess about a physical change (What will happen when the butter is heated?) as a first step toward predicting. They can gather and organize simple data (such as counting the days until the chicks hatch) and make simple graphs like those described in Chapters 5 and 9. Giving preoperational children the opportunity to engage in inferring and predicting allows them to refine these skills. Teachers understand that young children need repeated experiences before they can become proficient.

Basic Process Skills

1. *Observing.* Using the senses to gather information about objects or events.
2. *Comparing.* Looking at similarities and differences in real objects. In the primary grades, students begin to compare and contrast ideas, concepts, and objects.
3. *Classifying.* Grouping and sorting according to properties such as size, shape, color, use, and so on.
4. *Measuring.* Quantitative descriptions made by an observer either directly through observation or indirectly with a unit of measure.
5. *Communicating.* Communicating ideas, directions, and descriptions orally or in written form such as pictures, maps, graphs, or journals so others can understand what you mean.

Intermediate Process Skills

6. *Inferring.* Based on observations, but suggests more meaning about a situation than can be directly observed. When children infer, they recognize patterns and expect these patterns to recur under similar circumstances.
7. *Predicting.* Making reasonable guesses or estimations based on observations and prior knowledge and experiences.

Advanced Process Skills

8. *Hypothesizing.* Devising a statement, based on observations, that can be tested by experiment. A typical form for a hypothesis is, "*If* water is put in the freezer overnight, *then* it freezes."
9. *Defining and controlling variables.* Determining which variables in an investigation should be studied or should be controlled to conduct a controlled experiment. For example, when we find out if a plant grows in the dark, we must also grow a plant in the light.

FIGURE 2-1 Scientific process skills.

2-1c Science Process Skills Used in Inquiry

Knowledge and concepts are developed through the use of the processes used in inquiry. With these processes and skills, individuals think through and study problems and begin to develop an understanding about scientific inquiry. Process skills are applied during naturalistic, informal, and adult-guided experiences.

Observing. The most fundamental of the scientific thinking process skills is observation. Only through this process are we able to receive information about the world around us. The senses of sight, smell, sound, touch, and taste are the means by which our brains receive information and give us the ability to describe something. As young children use their senses in a firsthand exploratory way, they are using the same skills that scientists and engineers extend to construct meaning and knowledge in the world.

Sometimes we *see* but do not properly *observe.* Teaching strategies that reinforce observation skills require children to observe carefully to note specific phenomena that they might ordinarily overlook. For example, when Mr. Wang's class observes an aquarium, he guides them by asking, "Which fish seems to spend the most time on the bottom of the tank? In what way do the fish seem to react to things like light or shadow or an object in their swimming path?"

Observation is the first step in gathering information to solve a problem. Students need opportunities to examine size, shape, color, texture, and other observable properties in objects. Teacher statements and questions facilitate the use of this process: "Tell me what you see." "What do you hear?" "What does this feel like?" "How would you describe the object?"

Comparing. As children develop skills in observation, they will naturally begin to compare and contrast and to identify similarities and differences. The comparing process, which sharpens their observation skills, is the first step toward classifying.

Teachers can encourage children to find likenesses and differences throughout the school day. A good example of this strategy can be seen when, after a walk through a field, Mrs. Red Fox asks her first graders, "Which seeds are sticking to your clothes?" and "How are these seeds alike?"

The comparing process builds on the process of observing. In addition to observing the characteristics of an object such as a leaf, children learn more about the leaf by comparing it to other leaves. For example, a child finds a leaf and brings it to class to compare with other leaves in the leaf collection. Statements and questions can facilitate the comparing process: "How are these alike?" "How are these different?" "Which of these is bigger?" "Compare similarities and differences between these two leaves." Begin by having children tell you about the characteristics of the objects. Next, have the children compare objects and discuss how and why they feel the objects are similar or different.

Classifying. *Classifying* begins when children group and sort real objects. The grouping and sorting are done based on the observations they make about the objects' characteristics. To *group*, children need to compare objects and develop subsets. A **subset** is a group that shares a common characteristic unique to that group. For example, the jar may be full of buttons, but children are likely to begin grouping by sorting the buttons into subsets of red buttons, yellow buttons, blue buttons, and other colors.

Mrs. Jones has her kindergarten children collect many kinds of leaves. They place individual leaves between two squares of wax paper. Mrs. Jones covers the wax paper squares with a piece of smooth cloth and presses the cloth firmly with a warm steam iron. The leaf is now sealed in and will remain preserved for the rest of the year.

Once the leaves are prepared, the children choose a leaf to examine, draw, and describe. They carefully observe and compare leaves to discover each leaf's unique characteristics. Then the children classify the leaves into subsets of common characteristics. Once the children have completed their classifications, have them explain how they made their decisions. The discussion generated will give the teacher insight into a child's thinking.

Children initially group by one property, such as sorting a collection of leaves by color, size, shape, and so on. As children grow older and advance in the classification process,

objects or ideas are put together on the basis of two or more characteristics that are inherent in the items. For example, brown-colored animals with four legs can be grouped with all brown-colored animals (regardless of the number of legs) or with four-legged animals (regardless of color). Scientists from all disciplines use organization processes to group and classify their work, whether that work involves leaves, flowers, animals, rocks, liquids, or rockets. Again, statements and questions facilitate this process: "Put together all of the animals that belong together." "Can you group them in another way?" "How are these animals organized?" "Identify several ways that you used to classify these animals."

Measuring. *Measuring* is the skill of quantifying observations. This can involve numbers, distances, time, volumes, and temperature, which may or may not be quantified with standard units. Nonstandard units are involved when children say that they have used two "shakes" of salt while cooking or a "handful" of rice and a "couple" of beans when creating their collage.

Children can also invent units of measure. For example, when given beans to measure objects, Vanessa may state that the book is "12 beans long," although Ann finds that the same book is "11 beans long." An activity such as this helps children see a need for a standard unit of measure. Questions that facilitate the measuring process include "How might you measure this object?" "Which object do you think is heavier?" "How could you find out?"

Communicating. All humans communicate in some way. Gestures, body postures and positions, facial expressions, vocal sounds, words, and pictures are some of the ways we communicate with each other and express feelings. Through communication, scientists share their findings with the rest of the world. Scientists compare and discuss their findings and negotiate the meaning of their findings. Children can learn to negotiate through four phases (Kuhn & Dermott, 2013):

- Self-Negotiation: Students reflect on their personal understanding of what they observed.

- Peer-to-Peer Negotiation: In small groups, students share and compare data.

- Check with Experts: Students compare their own ideas with those found in textbooks or other resources.

- Write to Learn: Individually, students reflect and write.

In early childhood science explorations, communicating is the skill of describing a phenomenon. A child communicates ideas, directions, and descriptions orally or in written form, such as in pictures, dioramas, maps, graphs, journals, and reports. Communication requires that information be collected, arranged, and presented in a way that helps others understand your meaning.

Teachers encourage communication when they ask children to keep logs, draw diagrams or graphs, or otherwise record an experience they have observed. Children respond well to tasks such as recording daily weather by writing down the date and time of day and drawing pictures of the weather that day. They will enjoy answering questions about their observations, such as "What was the temperature on Tuesday?" "Was the sun out on Wednesday?" "What did you see?" "Draw a picture of what you see."

Inferring. When children *infer*, they make a series of observations, categorize them, and then try to give them some meaning. An inference is arrived at indirectly (not directly, as with simple observations). For example, you look out the window, see the leaves moving on the trees, and infer that the wind is blowing. You have not experienced the wind directly, but—based on your observations and prior knowledge and experience—you know that the wind is blowing. In this case, your inference can be tested simply by walking outside.

The process skill of inferring requires a reasonable assumption of prior knowledge. It requires children to infer something that they have not yet seen—either because it has not happened or because it cannot be observed directly. For this reason, the inferring process is the most appropriate for middle-level grades and the science content associated with those grades. However, science content and inferences associated with past experiences can be appropriate for older primary grade children. For instance, younger children can make inferences about what animals made a set of tracks, the loss of water from plants, and the vapor in air.

In another example, a teacher prepares four small opaque bottles by filling them with different substances such as sand, chalk, stones, marbles, and paper clips. As the students observe the closed canisters, the teacher asks: "What do you think is inside these canisters?" "What did you observe that makes you think that?" "Could there be anything else in the canister?" "How could you find out?"

Predicting. When you predict, you are making a statement about what you expect to happen in the future. You make a reasonable guess or estimation based on observations of data. Keep in mind that this process is more than a simple guess. Children should have the prior knowledge necessary to make a reasonable prediction. Children enjoy simple prediction questions.

After reading Seymour Simon's *Science in a Vacant Lot* (1970), children can count the number of seeds in a seed package and then predict how many of the seeds will grow into plants. As they prepare to keep a record of how two plants grow (one has been planted in topsoil, the other in subsoil), they are asked, "Which plant do you think will grow better?"

The ability and willingness to take a risk and form a prediction (e.g., "If you race the metal car with the wooden car, the metal car will go faster.") is of great importance in developing an awareness and understanding of cause and effect. This awareness can be developed and refined in many situations into the related skill of perceiving a pattern emerging and predicting accurately how it will continue. For example, if children are investigating changes in the shape of a piece of clay as more weight is added, they can be encouraged to look for patterns in their results, which can be recorded by drawing or measuring, and to predict each succeeding result. The more predictions children are able to make, the more accurate they become. Always ask children to explain how they arrived at their prediction. By listening to their reasoning, you may find that children know more than you think.

Hypothesizing and Controlling Variables = Investigation. To be called an *experiment*, an investigation must contain a hypothesis and control variables. A *hypothesis* is a more formal operation than the investigative questions that young children explore in the preschool and primary grades. A hypothesis is a statement of a relationship that might exist between two variables. A typical form of a hypothesis is, "If . . ., then . . . ." With young children, a hypothesis can take the form of a question such as, "What happens if the magnet drops?"

In a formal experiment, variables are defined and controlled. Although experiments can be attempted with primary grade children, experimental investigations are most appropriate in the middle and upper grades.

The question of what a hypothesis is has probably caused more confusion than other science processes. *Hypotheses* can be described as simply the tentative answers or untried solutions to the questions, puzzles, or problems that scientists are investigating. The major types of hypotheses are varied in character, but they correspond to the types of knowledge or understanding that the investigation aims to develop. Strategies for creating an environment that encourages investigation can be found in section 2-2 of this chapter.

2-1d Developing Scientific Attitudes Used in Inquiry

In some ways, attitudes toward a subject or activity can be as important as the subject itself. Examples are individuals who continue to smoke, even though they know the habit could kill them; people who don't wear seat belts, even though they know that doing so would greatly improve their chances of surviving an automobile accident; or people who text while driving, even though they know the distraction is dangerous. The same is true with scientific attitudes.

The scientific attitudes of **curiosity**, **skepticism**, **positive self-image**, and **positive approach to failure** are listed together with other relevant attitudes in **Figure 2-2**.

Curiosity	Checking evidence
Withholding judgment	Positive approach to failure
Skepticism	Positive self-image
Objectivity	Willingness to change
Open-mindedness	Positive attitude toward change
Avoiding dogmatism	Avoiding superstitions
Avoiding gullibility	Integrity
Observing carefully	Humility
Making careful conclusions	

FIGURE 2-2 Scientific attitudes.

© Cengage Learning®

Curiosity. Preschool and primary students are obviously not mentally developed to a point where they can think consciously about forming attitudes for systematically pursuing problems. However, they can practice behaviors that will create lifelong habits that reflect scientific attitudes.

Curiosity is thought to be one of the most valuable attitudes that anyone can possess. It takes a curious individual to look at something from a new perspective, question something long believed to be true, or look more carefully at an exception to the rule. This approach, which is basic to science, is natural to young children. They use all their senses and energies to find out about the world around them. Often, this valuable characteristic is squelched by years of formalized school experiences that allow little time for exploration and questioning. Educational experiences that incorporate first-hand inquiry experiences, as characterized by the learning cycle described in Chapter 1 and in section 2-2 of this chapter, exploit a child's natural curiosity instead of suppressing it.

Skepticism. Do you hesitate to believe everything you see? Are you skeptical about some things that you hear? Good! This attitude reflects the healthy skepticism required by both science and the child's environment. Children need to be encouraged to question, wonder, ask "Why?" and be cautious about accepting things at face value. Experiences designed to incorporate direct observation of phenomena and gathering data naturally encourage children to explore new situations in an objective and open-minded fashion. This type of experience can do much toward developing confidence and a healthy skepticism.

Positive Approach to Failure and Self-Image. A positive approach to failure and a positive self-image are closely related attitudes. Students need the opportunity to ask their own questions and to seek their own solutions to problems. At times this may mean that they will pursue dead ends, but often much more is learned in the pursuit than in the correct answer. Children who are conditioned to expect adult authority figures to identify and solve problems will have a difficult time approaching new problems—both as students and as adults.

For the last 20 years, some educators have believed that children should not be allowed to experience failure. Educational situations were structured so that every child could be successful nearly all the time. It was reasoned that the experience of failure would discourage students from future study. In the field of science, however, finding out what does not work is as important as finding out what does. In fact, real advances in science tend to occur when solutions do not fit the predictions. Although students should not be constantly confronted with frustrating learning situations, a positive attitude toward failure may better serve them in developing problem-solving skills. After all, in much of science inquiry, there are no right or wrong answers.

The remaining science attitudes, *willingness to change, positive attitude toward change, withholding judgment, avoiding superstitions, integrity,* and *humility,* are important both for science and for functioning as a successful adult. These attitudes can be encouraged in science teaching by the teacher's exhibiting them and acknowledging students who demonstrate them. All of these attitudes that support the enterprise of science are also valuable tools for young students in approaching life's inevitable problems.

2-1e Engineering Design

The integration of science and engineering into science education is accomplished by raising engineering design to the level of scientific inquiry (NGSS Lead States, 2013). Engineering design grows out of young children's natural desire to build as they create sand castles and construct caves and forts out of cardboard boxes. At the primary level, this creative energy can be channeled to solve problems and achieve goals. The process of **design technology** usually proceeds through three stages.

- *Defining the problem* begins in kindergarten as children begin to realize that if people want to change something it can be viewed as a problem to be solved. By the end of second grade, children should be able to ask questions and make observations and gather information that will help them envision an object or a tool that will solve the problem.

- *Developing possible solutions* follows from the problem definitions. Children should not rush to a solution but should make sketches and models before trying out a solution.

- *Comparing different solutions* is a phase where students try out two or more solutions to the problem to see which works best to meet their goal.

In kindergarten students are expected to design and build simple devices. In first grade, students use tools and materials to solve a simple problem. They then test and compare different solutions. In second grade students define more complex problems. They then develop, test, and analyze data to compare different solutions. When they leave second grade, they should be able to proceed through all three stages and understand the interrelated processes of engineering design.

DAP **naeyc**

2-1f Science Content Knowledge and Learning and the Development of Literacy

An often-heard question is, "Why bother teaching science to young children?" Many teachers believe that they have too much to do in a day and that they cannot afford to take the time to teach science. The argument for teaching science is, "You cannot afford *not* to teach science." Piaget's theory leaves no question as to the importance of learning through activity. The Council for Basic Education reports that there is impressive evidence that hands-on science programs aid in the development of language and reading skills. Some evidence indicates that achievement scores increase as a result of such programs, a statement that is supported by many researchers. Following are possible explanations for this improvement:

- In its early stages, literacy can be supported by giving children an opportunity to manipulate familiar and unfamiliar objects. During science experiences,

THINKING SKILLS USED DURING SCIENCE EXPERIENCES	THINKING SKILLS NEEDED FOR READING AND WRITING
Matching similar and logical characteristics	Comparing information and events
Discriminating physical observations and data	Discriminating letters and sounds
Sequencing procedures	Arranging ideas and following sequential events
Describing observations	Communicating ideas
Classifying objects	Distinguishing concepts

© Cengage Learning®

FIGURE 2-3 Science and reading connection.

children use the thinking skills of science to match, discriminate, sequence, describe, and classify objects. These perceptual skills are among those needed for reading and writing (**Figure 2-3**). A child who is able to make fine discriminations between objects will be better prepared to discriminate between letters and words of the alphabet. As children develop conventional reading and writing skills, they can apply their knowledge to facilitate their explorations in science by reading background material and recording hypotheses, observations, and interactions.

■ What better way to allow for children to develop communication skills than to participate in the "action plus talk" of science! Depending on the age level, children may want to communicate what they are doing to the teacher and to other students. They may even start talking about themselves. Communication by talking, drawing, painting, modeling, constructing, drama, puppets, and writing should be encouraged. These are natural communication outcomes of hands-on science.

■ Reading and listening to stories about the world is difficult when you do not have a base of experience. If story time features a book about a hamster named Charlie, it might be difficult to understand what is happening if you have not seen a hamster. However, the communication gap is bridged if children have knowledge about small animals. Once a child has contact with the object represented by the written word, meaning can be developed. Words do not make a lot of sense when you do not have the background experience to understand what you read.

■ The relationship of language developed in the context of the direct experiences of science is explored in section 2-3 of this chapter. Ideas for working with experience charts, tactile sensations, listening, writing, and introducing words are included in curriculum integration.

■ Science also provides various opportunities to determine cause-and-effect relationships. A sense of self-esteem and of control over their lives develops when children discover cause-and-effect relationships and when they learn to influence the outcome of events. For example, a child can experience a causal relationship by deciding whether to add plant cover to an aquarium. Predicting the most probable outcome of actions gives children a sense of control, which is identified by Mary Budd Rowe (1978) as fate control. She found that problem-solving behaviors seem to differ according to how people rate on measures of fate control: Children scoring high on these measures performed better at solving problems.

■ Keep in mind that the child who is academically advanced in math and reading is not always the first to solve a problem or assemble the most interesting collection or build the most complex block structure. If sufficient time to work with materials is provided, children with poor language development may exhibit good reasoning. Correlating language skills with mental ability is a mistake.

2-1g Appropriate Science Content

The science content for preschool is not specified in the national standards but is in some states that have preschool state standards. Therefore the area of study for preschool can follow the students' interests. The content for kindergarten through high school is specified in NGSS and in the science framework. As previously mentioned, how science is taught is probably far more important than the science content itself. The four main areas of science emphasized in the primary grades are life science; physical science; earth, space and environmental science; and engineering, technology, and science applications. Appropriate science areas of study for the early childhood years can be found throughout the text and specifically in the chapters dealing with science content. The content at each grade level will be further described in later chapters.

Life Science. Life science focuses on the patterns, processes, and relationships of living organisms (National Research Council, 2012). Four core life science ideas have been identified (National Research Council, 2012):

- From Molecules to Organisms: Structures and Processes focuses on how organisms are structured and how they function.

- Ecosystems: Interactions, Energy, and Dynamics focuses on the interactions within ecosystems.

- Heredity: Inheritance and Variation of Traits Across Generations focuses on the life cycles of living organisms.

- Biological Evolution: Unity and Diversity looks at how populations of organisms change over time.

The observations and skills needed to gain an understanding of life science in the primary grades and beyond begin with the observations and investigative explorations of prekindergarten children.

Science teaching at the prekindergarten level is traditionally dominated by life science experiences—not because it is most appropriate, but rather because of tradition. Many programs and materials for young children concentrate much time on life science to the exclusion of other science content. This can be attributed to teachers seeking to take advantage of children's interest in what makes up their world. Children are natural observers and enjoy finding out about the living world around them. Still, although life science is an important part of the curriculum for young children, it should not be the entire curriculum.

Life science investigations lend themselves quite readily to simple observations, explorations, and classifications. As with all science content at this level, hands-on experiences are essential to the development of relevant concepts, skills, and attitudes. The areas of content typically covered with preschool children are plants, animals, and ecology. These experiences should build a foundation for students' understanding of environmental problems and solutions in higher grade levels and in adult life. Intelligent decision making regarding the interaction of science, technology, and the environment may well be a critical factor for survival in the twenty-first century. Examples of strategies for teaching appropriate life science content at the kindergarten and prekindergarten levels are found in Chapters 4 and 5 and at the primary level are found in Chapters 10 and 11.

Physical Science. In physical science, children in kindergarten through grade 4 are expected to develop an understanding of the properties of objects and materials; position and motion of objects; and light, heat, electricity, and magnetism. Prekindergarten children are able to learn basic concepts and skills as they become familiar with the materials needed to prepare them for higher-level thinking. The physical sciences, physics and chemistry, underlie all natural and human-created phenomena.

Young children enjoy pushing levers, making bulbs light, working with magnets, using a string-and-can telephone, sending objects down ramps, and changing the form of matter. This is the study of physical science: forces, motion, energy, and machines. Teachers will enjoy watching a child assemble an assortment of blocks, wheels, and axles into a vehicle that really works. Physical science activities are guaranteed to make a child's face light up and ask, "How did you do that?" It may take years for children to fully understand systems and levers, but children of all ages recognize that gears must make physical contact with each other to form a working system.

Sometimes the content of this area is overlooked, which is unfortunate because physical science lends itself quite well to the needs of young children. One advantage of physical science activities is that they are more foolproof than many other activities. For example, if a young child is investigating the growth of plants, many things can go wrong that will destroy the investigation. Plants can die, get moldy, or take so long to give the desired effect that the children lose interest. Physical science usually has a quicker pace. If something damages the investigation, it can always be repeated in a matter of minutes. Repeatability of activities is a significant advantage in developing a process orientation to science.

Four physical science core ideas have been identified (National Research Council, 2012):

- Matter and Its Interactions
- Motion and Stability: Forces and Interactions
- Energy
- Waves and Their Applications in Technology for Information Transfer

Principles of chemistry are interrelated with the other physical science principles. The core ideas will be expanded upon in Chapters 4, 5, 10, and 11.

Keep in mind that children are growing up in a technological world. They interact daily with technology. Future lifestyles and job opportunities are likely to depend on skills related to the realm of physical science.

Earth and Space Sciences. In earth and space science, students gain an understanding of properties of earth materials, objects in the sky, and changes in the earth and sky. The study of earth and space science also allows many opportunities to help children develop process skills. Children are eager to learn about weather and how soil is formed. Air, land, water, and rocks, as well as the sun, moon, and stars, are all a part of earth science. Although these topics are attention grabbers; to be effective, the teacher of young children must be certain to make the phenomena concrete for them. Hands-on experiences need not be difficult. Try making fossil cookies, weather and temperature charts, parachutes, and rock and cloud observations to teach a concept. Three core ideas are designated for earth and space science (National Research Council, 2012):

- Earth's Place in the Universe: stars, solar system, and earth history.

- Earth's Systems: materials; system interactions; the role of water, weather, and climate; biogeology.

- Earth and Human Activity: natural resources, natural hazards, human impacts on earth systems, and global climate change.

These core ideas will be elaborated upon in later chapters.

Chapter 11 gives a number of examples of how the earth sciences can be made meaningful for young children. Refer to Chapters 11 and 12 for environmental education ideas.

Engineering, Technology, and Applications of Science. The content standard for science, engineering, and technology focuses on establishing connections between the natural and designed worlds and by providing opportunities for children to develop their decision-making skills. Two core ideas represent the engineering, technology, and applications of science area (National Research Council, 2012):

- Engineering Design: identifying and delimiting an engineering problem, developing possible solutions, optimizing the design solution
- Links Among Engineering, Technology, Science, and Society: interdependence of science, engineering, and technology and the influence of engineering, technology, and science on society and the natural world

Strategies for using science, engineering, and technology education are integrated throughout the text, but they are emphasized in Chapters 7, 11, and 12.

2-1h Important Developmental Factors

Taking Science to School (Committee on Science Learning, 2007) highlights four themes that cut across all discussions of knowledge growth after preschool. These themes will be elaborated on in the section 2-2 of this chapter.

1. Primary grade children are building on the products of preschool knowledge growth. It is clear that an individual's cognitive achievements while an infant and a toddler provide the foundation for further understanding in later years.

2. A great deal of developmental science learning in elementary school involves learning about more detailed aspects of mechanisms and facts that were explored in earlier years. Whether the subject is gear action or notions of digestion, primary grade children use concrete thinking to explore the details learned in preschool and infancy.

3. As children develop more concrete models of thinking, they will form many misconceptions—some of them dramatic. However, this is not necessarily a step backward. Moving through a series of misconceptions may be the only way to progress toward developing more accurate notions.

4. Keep in mind that the primary and elementary years include further periods of conceptual change for children. New insights can change the way a concept is understood, and there is a growing awareness of both the similarities and differences between children's and scientists' concept development.

naeyc DAP

2-2 CONCEPT UNDERSTANDING IN YOUNG CHILDREN

Young children try very hard to explain the world around them. Do any of the following statements sound familiar?

- "Thunder is the sound of the angels bowling."
- "Chickens lay eggs, and pigs lay bacon."
- "Electricity comes from a switch on the wall."
- "The sun follows me when I take a walk."

These are the magical statements of intuitive thinkers. Children use their senses or intuition to make judgments. Their logic is unpredictable, and they frequently prefer to use magical explanations to account for what is happening in their world. Clouds become the "smoke of angels," and rain falls because "it wants to help the farmers." These comments are typical of the self-centered view of intuitive children. They think that the sun rises in the morning just to shine on them. It never occurs to them that there may be another explanation. They also have a difficult time remembering more than one thing at a time.

Statements and abilities such as these inspired Jean Piaget's curiosity about young children's beliefs (see Chapter 1). His search for answers about how children think and learn has contributed to our understanding that learning is an internal process. In other words, the child brings meaning to the world, not vice versa. A child's misconceptions are normal. This is what the child believes; thus, this is what is real to the child.

The temptation is to try to move children out of their magical stage of development. This is a mistake. Although some misconceptions can be corrected, others must wait for more advanced thinking to develop. Students cannot be pushed, pulled, or dragged through developmental stages. Instead, the goal is to support the development of young children at their present level of operation. In this way, they have the richness of experiences to take with them when the next level of development naturally occurs.

2-2a Enhancing Awareness

When teaching concepts that are too abstract for children to fully understand, try to focus on aspects of the concept that can be understood. This type of awareness can be enhanced by the use of visual depictions, observing, drawing, and discussion.

Although some aspects of weather might remain a mystery, understanding can be developed by recording the types of weather that occur in a month. Construct a large calendar and put it on the wall. Every day, have a student draw a picture that represents the weather for the day. When the month is completed, cut the calendar into individual days. Then, glue the days that show similar weather in columns to create a bar graph. Ask the children to form conclusions about the month's weather from the graph. In this way,

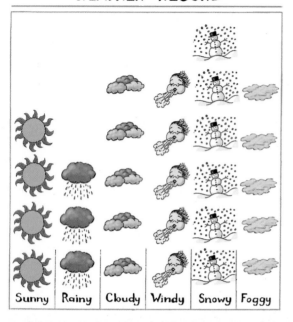

WEATHER RECORD

Sunny | Rainy | Cloudy | Windy | Snowy | Foggy

FIGURE 2-4 "How many cloudy days were there this month?"

▶❚❚ **TeachSource Video**

DATA COLLECTION AND VISUALIZATION IN THE ELEMENTARY CLASSROOM

Data collection tools, such as spreadsheets, are valuable applications students can use to support their learning. In this second-grade classroom students perform activities like scientist do as they collect and report weather data.

1. In the teacher interview what does the teacher explain about the children's activities?

2. In the classroom video, what questions does the teacher ask the students to get them set to do the next step in their study of weather?

3. What steps do the students progress through in order to create their spreadsheets?

children can relate to weather patterns and visualize that these patterns change from day to day (**Figure 2-4**).

Perhaps the best tool for children's understanding of awareness is observation. To enhance awareness and to be effective, observations should be done in 10 minutes or less, conducted with a purpose, and brought together by discussions. Unconnected observations do not aid in concept formation. For example, if a purpose is not given for observing two flickering, different-sized candles, then children will lose interest within minutes. Instead of telling children to "go look" at two burning candles, ask them to look and find the difference between the candles. Children will become excited with the discovery that the candles are not the same size (**Figure 2-5**).

Discussions that follow observations heighten a child's awareness of that observation. A group of children observing a fish tank to see where the fish spends most of its time will be prepared to share what they saw in the tank. However, the children may not agree.

Differences of opinion about observations stimulate interest and promote discussion. Children are likely to return to the tank to see for themselves what others say they saw. This would probably not happen without the focusing effect of discussion.

Drawing provides excellent opportunities for observation and discussion. An effective use of drawing to enhance concept development is to have children draw a tiger from memory before going to the zoo. Strategies like this usually reveal that more information is needed to construct an accurate picture. After visiting the zoo, have the children draw a tiger and compare it with the one drawn before the field trip. Discussion should focus on the similarities and differences between the two drawings. Children will be eager to observe details that they might not otherwise notice about the tigers in the zoo (**Figure 2-6**).

FIGURE 2-5 Children notice that the candles are not the same size.

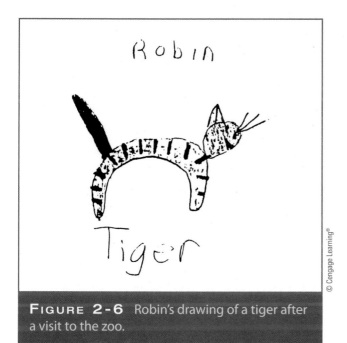

FIGURE 2-6 Robin's drawing of a tiger after a visit to the zoo.

2-2b Teacher Magic and Misconceptions

Children need time to reflect and absorb ideas before they fully understand a concept. Misconceptions can occur at any stage. Be sure to give them plenty of time to manipulate and explore. For example, when a teacher mixes yellow and blue paints to create green, children might think the result is teacher magic. However, if given the paints and the opportunity to discover green, they might remember that yellow and blue mixed together make green. Because children cannot carry out most operations mentally, they need to manipulate materials in order to develop concepts. Teachers can enhance a child's understanding by making comments or asking questions that draw attention to a particular event. Using the previous color example, a teacher might ask, "Why do you think that happened?" or "How did you do that?"

Misconceptions can occur at any stage of development. Some children in the primary grades may be in a transitional stage or may have moved into the concrete operation stage of development. Although these students will be able to do much logical thinking, the concepts they work with must still be tied to concrete objects that they can manipulate. Firsthand experiences with materials continue to be essential for learning.

The child in this developmental stage no longer looks at the world through magical eyes. Explanations for natural events are influenced by other natural objects and events. For example, a child may now say, "The rain comes from the sky" rather than "It rains to help farmers." This linking of physical objects first appears in the early concrete development stages. Do not be misled by an apparent new awareness. The major factor in concept development is still contingent on children's abilities to manipulate, observe, discuss, and visually depict things to understand what is new and different about them.

2-2c Self-Regulation and Concept Attainment

Have you ever seen someone plunge a turkey skewer through a balloon? Did you expect the balloon to burst? What was your reaction when it stayed intact? Your curiosity was probably piqued: You wanted to know why the balloon did not burst. Actually, you had just witnessed a **discrepant event** and entered the process of self-regulation. This is when your brain responds to interactions between you and your environment. Gallagher and Reid (1981) describe **self-regulation** as the active mental process of forming concepts. Knowing a little bit about how the brain functions in concept development will help to explain this process. Visualize the human mind as thousands of concepts stored in various sections of the brain—much like a complex system of mental pigeonholes, a postal sorting system, or a filing cabinet filled with individual file folders. As children move through the world and encounter new objects and phenomena, they assimilate and accommodate new information and store it in the correctly labeled mental category in their minds.

Charlesworth (2014) describes the brain as functioning like a postal worker, naturally classifying and storing information in the appropriate pigeonholes (**Figure 2-7**). New information is always stored close to all the related, previously stored information. These groupings of closely related facts and of phenomena related to a particular concept make up the **cognitive structure**. In other words, all we know about the color red is stored in the same area of the brain. Our concept of red is developed further each time we have a color-related experience. The word *red* becomes a symbol for what we understand and perceive as the color red.

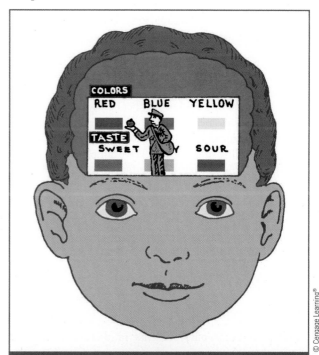

FIGURE 2-7 The brain functions like a postal worker.

Our understanding of the world is imperfect because, sooner or later, true understanding ends, and misconceptions exist but go unquestioned. This is because incorrect interpretations of the world are stored alongside correct ones.

Continuing the postal worker analogy: If the information doesn't quite fit into an existing pigeonhole, then another pigeonhole must be made. A point can also be reached where new information conflicts with older information stored in a given concept file. When children realize that they do not understand something they previously thought they understood, they are said to be in what Piaget calls a state of **disequilibrium**. This is where you are when the balloon does not burst: The balloon does not behave as you expected, and things no longer fit neatly together.

This is the teachable moment. When children are perplexed, their minds will not rest until they can find some way to make the new information fit. Because existing structures are inadequate to accommodate all of the existing information, they must continually modify or replace it with new concepts. When in this state, children actively seek out additional information to create the new concept. They ask probing questions, observe closely, and inquire independently about the materials at hand. In this state, they are highly motivated and receptive to learning. When children have gathered enough information to satisfy their curiosity and to create a new concept that explains most or all of the facts, they return to a state of **equilibrium**, where everything appears to fit together. As children move from disequilibrium to equilibrium, two mental activities take place. When confronted with something they do not understand, children fit it into a scheme, something they already know. If this does not work for them, they modify the scheme or make a new one. This is called **accommodation**. **Assimilation** and accommodation work together to help students learn concepts.

To make use of the process of self-regulation in your classroom, find out at what point your students misunderstand or are unfamiliar with the topic you are teaching. Finding out what children know can be done in a number of ways. In addition to referring to the assessment units in this book, listen to children's responses to a lesson or question, or simply ask them to describe their understanding of a concept. For example, before teaching a lesson on animals, ask, "What does an animal look like?" You'd be surprised at the number of young children who think that a life form must have legs to be considered an animal. Using this process will allow you to present information contrary to or beyond your students' existing cognitive structure and thus put them in a state of disequilibrium, where learning occurs.

DAP **naeyc**

2-2d Discrepant Events

A discrepant event puts students in disequilibrium and prepares them for learning. They are curious and want to find out what is happening. Take advantage of the natural learning process to teach children what you want them to understand. The following scenes might give you some ideas for discrepant events that might improve lessons you plan to teach.

> Mr. Wang's second-grade class is studying the senses. His students are aware of the function of the five senses, but they may not know that the sense of smell plays as large a role in appreciating food as does the sense of taste. His students work in pairs, with one child blindfolded. The blindfolded students are asked to pinch their noses shut and taste several foods, such as bread, raw potatoes, or apples, to see whether they can identify them.

> Students switch roles and try the same investigation with various juices, such as apple, orange, tomato, and so on. Most students cannot identify juices. Having experienced this discrepant event, the students will be more interested in finding out about the structures of the nose related to smell. They may be more motivated to conduct an investigation about how the appearance of food affects its taste.

> Mrs. Fox fills two jars with water while her first-grade class watches. She fills one jar to the rim and leaves about an inch of space in the other jar. She puts a lid on each jar and places it on a tray in the schoolyard on a cold winter day. Her students return later in the day and find that both have frozen, but that the completely filled jar has burst. Students are eager to find out why.

> Kindergarten students Ann and Vanessa have been instructed to place two ice cubes in a glass and then fill it to the brim with water. The ice cubes float on the water and extend about half an inch above the edge of the glass. Ms. Hebert asks them what will happen when the ice cubes melt. Vanessa thinks the water will overflow because there will be more water. Ann thinks the water level will drop because the ice cubes will contract when they melt. They watch in puzzlement as they realize that the water level stays the same as the cubes melt (**Figure 2-8**).

DAP **naeyc**

2-2e Using the Learning Cycle to Build Concepts

You can assist your students in creating new concepts by designing learning experiences in a manner congruent with how children learn naturally. One popular approach is the application of the learning cycle. The learning cycle, described in Chapter 1, is based on the cycle of equilibration

FIGURE 2-8 Ann and Vanessa check their predictions.

originally described by Piaget. The learning cycle, which is used extensively in elementary science education, combines aspects of naturalistic, informal, and structured activity methods—suggested elsewhere in this book—into a method of presenting a lesson.

As you have learned, the discrepant event is an effective device for motivating students and placing them in disequilibrium. The learning cycle can be a useful approach to learning for many of the same reasons. Learning begins with a period of free exploration. During the **exploration phase**, the children's prior knowledge can be assessed. Teachers can assess inquiry skills and gain clues to what the children know about a science concept as they explore the materials.

Refer to the "Strategies That Encourage Inquiry" section in this chapter for more information on assessing inquiry. Additionally, any misconceptions the children may have are often revealed during this phase. Exploration can be as simple as giving students the materials to be used in a day's activity at the beginning of a lesson so that they can play with them for a few minutes. Minimal or no instructions should be given other than those related to safety, breaking the materials, or logistics in getting the materials. By letting students manipulate the materials, they will explore and very likely discover either something they did not know before or something other than what they expected. The following example, "Making the Bulb Light," utilizes all three steps of the learning cycle.

MAKING THE BULB LIGHT

Exploration Phase

Mr. Wang placed a wire, a flashlight bulb, and a size-D battery on a tray. Each group of three students was given a tray of materials and told to try to figure out a way to make the bulb light. As each group successfully lit the bulb, he asked them if they could find another arrangement of materials that would make the bulbs light. After about 10 minutes, most groups had found at least one other way to light the bulb.

Concept Introduction Phase

After the children played with the wires, batteries, and bulbs, Mr. Wang had them bring their trays and form a circle on the floor. He asked the students if they had found out anything interesting about the materials. Jamie showed the class one arrangement that worked to light the bulb. To introduce the class to the terms *open, closed,* and *short circuit,* Mr. Wang explained to the class that an arrangement that lights is called a closed circuit. Annabelle showed the class an arrangement that she thought would work but did not. Mr. Wang explained that this is an open circuit. Chloe showed the class an arrangement that did not light the bulb but made the wire and battery very warm. Mr. Wang said this was a short circuit. Then he drew an example of each of the three types of circuit on the board and labeled them.

Concept Application Phase

Next, Mr. Wang showed the class a worksheet with drawings of various arrangements of batteries and bulbs. He asked the children to predict which arrangements would not light and form an open circuit; which would form a closed circuit by lighting; and which would heat up the battery and wire, forming a short circuit. After recording their predictions independently, the children returned to their small groups to test each of the arrangements. They recorded the actual answers beside their predictions (**Figure 2-9**).

After the students completed the task, Mr. Wang called them together. They discussed the results of their investigation, sharing which arrangements of batteries, wire, and bulbs they predicted correctly and incorrectly. Then Mr. Wang reviewed the terms learned during the lesson and asked the students to read a short section of their science text that talked about fire and electrical safety. The reading discussed the dangers of putting metal objects in wall sockets or fingers in light sockets and suggested precautions when flying kites near power lines.

After reading the section aloud, Mr. Wang asked the class whether they could see any relationship between the reading and the day's activity. Chloe responded that flying a kite into an electrical power line or sticking a dinner fork in a wall socket were similar to what he did when he created a short circuit with the battery and wire. Other students found similar relationships between the reading activity and their lives.

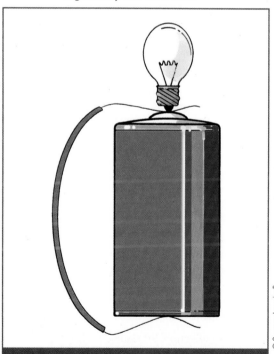

FIGURE 2-9 Battery prediction sheet.

In the preceding activity, you have seen a functioning model of Piaget's theory of cognitive development implemented in the classroom. The exploration phase invites assimilation and disequilibrium; the concept development phase provides for accommodation; the **concept application** phase expands the concept, and strategies for retaining the new concept are provided.

Using Part of the Learning Cycle to Build Concepts. Although a formal investigation using the learning cycle is an excellent way to present lessons to children, teaching all lessons in this manner is not desirable. At times, exploration and observation might be the full lesson. Giving students an opportunity to practice their skills of observation is often sufficient for them to learn a great deal about unfamiliar objects or phenomena. In the following scenarios, teachers made use of exploration observations to create lessons.

Mr. Brown constructed a small bird feeder and placed it outside the window of his prekindergarten room. One cold winter day, his efforts were rewarded. Students noticed and called attention to the fact that several kinds of birds were at the feeder. Brad said that they all looked the same to him. Noah pointed out different characteristics of the birds to Brad. Ella and Hailey noticed that the blue jay constantly chased other birds away from the feeder and that a big cardinal moved away from the feeder as soon as any other bird approached. Students wondered why the blue jay seemed to scare all the other birds and why the cardinal seemed to be afraid of even the small birds. They spent several minutes discussing the possibilities.

Miss Collins decided that the class should make a microwave cake to observe the effects of heating and cooling on cake batter. The students helped Miss Collins mix the ingredients and commented on the sequence of events as the cake cooked for seven minutes in the microwave. Jackson was the first to observe how bubbles started to form in small patches. Then George commented that the whole cake was bubbling and getting bigger. After removing the cake from the microwave, many children noticed how the cake shrank, got glossy, and then lost its gloss as it cooled.

Some lessons can be improved by having children do more than just observing and exploring. These exploration lessons include data collection as an instructional focus. **Data collection** and interpretation are important to real science and real problem solving. Although firsthand observation will always be important, most breakthroughs in science are made by analyzing carefully collected data. Scientists usually spend much more time searching through stacks of data than peering down the barrel of a microscope or through a telescope.

Data collection for young children is somewhat more abstract than firsthand observation. Therefore, students must have sufficient practice in making predictions, speculations, and guesses with firsthand observations before they begin to collect and interpret data. Nevertheless, young students can benefit from early experience in data collection and interpretation. Initial data collections are usually pictorial in

© 2016 Cengage Learning®

PHOTO 2-1 First graders identify and list appropriate winter clothes.

form. Long-term patterns and changes that children cannot easily observe in one setting are excellent beginnings for data collection.

- Records such as those discussed previously can expose children to patterns during any time of the year. After charting the weather with drawings or attaching pictures that represent changing conditions, have children decide which clothing is most appropriate for a particular kind of weather (Photo 2-1). Drawing clouds, sun, rain, lightning, snow, and so on that correspond to the daily weather and relating that information to what is worn can give students a sense of why data collection is useful.

- Growing plants provide excellent opportunities for early data collection. Mrs. Fox's first grade class charted the progress of bean plants growing in paper cups on the classroom windowsill. Each day, students cut a strip of paper the same length as the height of their plant and glued the strips to a large sheet of newsprint. Over a period of weeks, students could see how their plants grew continuously even though they noticed few differences by just watching them. After pondering the plant data, Ethan asked Mrs. Fox if the students could measure themselves with a strip of paper and chart their growth for the rest of the year. Thereafter, Mrs. Fox measured each student once a month. Her students were amazed to see how much they had grown during the year.

Another technique for designing science lessons is to allow students to have input into the process of problem solving and designing investigations. This might be called a *concept introduction lesson* because it utilizes the **concept introduction phase** of the learning cycle as the basis for a lesson. Although initial investigation and problem-solving experiences may be designed by the teacher, students eventually will be able to contribute to planning their own investigations. Most students probably will not be able to choose a topic and plan the entire investigation independently until they reach the intermediate grades, but their input into the process of planning gives them some ownership of the lesson and increases their confidence to explore ideas more fully. When solving real problems, identifying the problem is often more critical than the skills of attacking it. Students need practice in both aspects of problem solving.

The following examples depict students giving input into the problem to be solved and then helping to design how the problem should be approached.

Mr. Wang's second-grade class had some previous experience in charting the growth of plants. He told his class, "I'd like us to design an investigation about how fast plants grow. What things do you think could affect how fast a plant grows?" Mr. Wang used the whiteboard to list his students' suggestions, which included such factors as the amount of water, fertilizer, sunshine, and temperature as well as the type of seed, how much the plants are talked to, whether they are stepped on, and so forth. Students came up with possibilities that had never occurred to Mr. Wang. Next, he divided the class into small groups and told each group that it could have several paper cups, seeds, and some potting soil. Each group was asked to choose a factor from the list that it would like to investigate. Then, Mr. Wang helped each group plan its investigation.

Caleb and Jack decided to study the effect of light on their plant. Mr. Wang asked them how they would control the amount of light their plants receive. Jack suggested that they bring a lightbulb to place near the plants so that they could leave the light on all day. Caleb said that he would put the plants in a cardboard box for the hours they were not supposed to receive light. Mr. Wang asked them to think about how many plants they should use. They decided to use three: One plant would receive light all day; one plant would receive no light; and one plant would receive only six hours of light.

2-2f Strategies That Encourage Inquiry

The fundamental abilities and concepts that underlie science as inquiry establish the groundwork for developing and integrating strategies that encourage inquiry. Young children should experience science in a form that engages them in the active construction of ideas and explanations and that enhances their opportunities to develop the skills of doing science. In the early years, when children investigate materials and properties of common objects, they can focus on the process of doing investigations and develop the ability to ask questions. The following strategies can be used to engage students in the active search for knowledge (Gadzikowski, 2013, and others):

- *Ask a question about objects, organisms, and events in the environment.* Children should be encouraged to answer their questions by seeking information from their own observations and investigations and from reliable sources of information. When possible, children's answers can be compared with what scientists already know about the world.

- *Do preliminary research on the question.* Children compile knowledge relevant to the question from their own experience and by looking at books and asking adults about what they know.

- *Construct a hypothesis.* The children make their best guess as to the answer to their question.

- *Plan and conduct a simple investigation.* When children are in their earliest years, investigations are based on systematic observation. As children develop, they may design and conduct simple investigations to answer questions. (However, the fair tests necessary for experimentation may not be possible until the fourth grade.) Types of investigations that are appropriate for younger children include describing objects, events, and organisms; classifying them; and sharing what they know with others.

- *Employ simple equipment and tools to gather data and extend the senses.* Simple skills such as how to observe, measure, cut, connect, switch, turn on/off, pour, hold, and hook—together with simple instruments such as rulers, thermometers, magnifiers, and microscopes—should be used in the early years. Children can use simple equipment and can gather data by, for example, observing and recording attributes of the daily weather (**Photo 2-2**). They can also develop skills in the use of computers, tablets, and calculators.

- *Use data to construct a reasonable explanation.* In inquiry, students' thinking is emphasized as they use data to formulate explanations. Even at the earliest grade levels, students can learn what counts as evidence and can judge the merits of the data and explanations.

- *Communicate investigations and explanations.* Students should begin developing the abilities to communicate, critique, and analyze their work and the work of other students. This communication could be spoken or drawn as well as written.

The natural inquiry of young children can be seen as they observe, group, sort, and order objects. By incorporating familiar teaching strategies, such as providing a variety of objects for children to manipulate and talking to children as they go about what they are doing with objects, teachers can help children to learn more about their world. Children

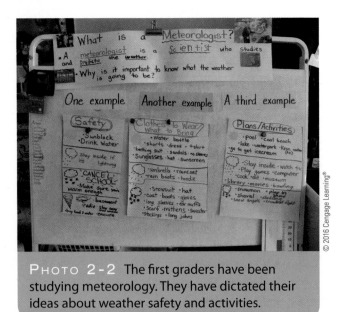

PHOTO 2-2 The first graders have been studying meteorology. They have dictated their ideas about weather safety and activities.

also can learn about their world through observations and discussions about those observations. When opportunities are provided for children to work individually at constructing their own knowledge, they gain experiences in organizing data and understanding processes. A variety of activities that let children use all of their senses should be offered. In this way, children may explore at their own pace and self-regulate their experiences.

Assessing and Evaluating Inquiry Learning. Observation is vital for the teacher as she assesses children's progress. It is essential that the teacher watch carefully as the children group and order materials. Are the materials ordered in a certain way? Do the objects in the group have similar attributes? Are the children creating a random design, or are they making a pattern? Clues to children's thinking can be gained by watching what children do and having them explain, to each other or to you, what they are doing. In the following example, the teacher assesses the students' abilities to do scientific inquiry by making use of an activity that invites children to manipulate objects.

> *Mrs. Raymond's classroom contains a variety of objects with a number of characteristics (size, color, texture, and shape) for children to group and sort. She has enough sets of keys, buttons, beans, nuts and bolts, fabric swatches, and wooden shapes for each child to work alone. To expose children to science content, she also has sets of leaves, nuts, bark, twigs, seeds, and other objects related to the science content that she wants to emphasize. As the children group and sort the objects, either by a single characteristic or in some other way, Mrs. Raymond observes them carefully and asks them to tell her about how they are organizing the objects. The teacher moves around and listens to the individual children as they make decisions. She makes notes in the anecdotal records she is keeping and talks with the children: "Can you put the ones that go together in a pile?" "How did you decide to put this leaf in the pile?"*

2-3 INTEGRATING SCIENCE INTO THE CURRICULUM

Children are more likely to retain concepts that are presented in a variety of ways and extended over a period of time. For example, after a trip to the zoo, extend the collective experience by having children dictate a story about their trip or by having them build their own zoo and demonstrate the care and feeding of the animals. The children can also depict the occupations found at the zoo. Other activities can focus on following up on previsit discussions that directed children to observe specifics at the zoo, such as differences in animal noses. Children might enjoy comparing zoo animal noses with those of their pets by matching pictures of similar noses on a bulletin board. In this way, concepts can continue to be applied and related to past experiences as the year progresses.

Additional integrations might include drawing favorite animal noses, creating plays about animals with specific types of noses, writing about an animal and its nose, and creating smelling activities. You might even want to introduce reasons an animal has a particular type of nose. One popular idea is to purchase plastic animal noses, distribute them to children, and play a game similar to "Mother may I." Say, "If you have four legs and roar, take two steps back. If you have two legs and quack, take three steps forward."

Think of how much more science students can learn if we make connections to other subjects. This requires preparing planned activities and taking advantage of every teachable moment that occurs in your class to introduce children to science.

Opportunities abound for teaching science in early childhood. Consider actively involving children with art, blocks, dramatic play, woodworking, language arts, math, and creative movement. Interest centers are one way to provide excellent integration and opportunities for assessment (centers are discussed in Chapter 12). The following ideas are meant to encourage your thinking about possible learning centers.

- *Painting.* Finger painting helps children learn to perceive with their fingertips and demonstrates the concept of color diffusion as they clean their hands. Children can learn to recognize shapes by painting with familiar objects.

- *Water center.* Children begin to grasp concepts such as volume and conservation when they measure with water and sand. They can explore buoyancy with boats and with sinking and floating objects.

- *Blocks.* Blocks are an excellent way to introduce children to friction, gravity, and simple machines and other engineering concepts. Leverage and efficiency can be reinforced with woodworking.

- *Books.* Many books introduce scientific concepts while telling a story. Books with pictures give views of unfamiliar things as well as an opportunity to explore detail and to infer and discuss.

- *Music and rhythmic activities.* These let children experience the movement of air against their bodies. Air resistance can also be demonstrated by dancing with a scarf. Movement teaches about body parts and what they can do.

- *Manipulative center.* Children's natural capacities for inquiry can be seen when they observe, group, sort, and order objects during periods of play. Children can pair objects such as animals and can use fundamental skills such as one-to-one correspondence.

- *Creative play.* Dressing, moving, and eating like an animal will provide children with opportunities for expressing themselves. Drama and poetry are a natural integration with learning about living things.

- *Playground.* The playground can provide an opportunity to predict weather, practice balancing, and experience friction. Children's natural curiosity will lead them to many new ideas and explorations.

- *Literacy.* The concrete world of science integrates especially well with reading and writing. Basic words, object guessing, experience charts, writing stories, and working with tactile sensations all encourage early literacy development.

2-3a Children Learn in Different Ways

It is important to provide children with a variety of ways to learn science. Even very young children have developed definite patterns in how they learn. Observe a group of children engaged in free play: Some prefer to work alone quietly; others do well in groups. Personal learning style also extends to a preference for visual or auditory learning (**Photo 2-3**). The teacher in the following scenario keeps these individual differences in mind when planning science experiences.

> *Ms. Hebert knows that the children in her kindergarten class exhibit a wide range of learning styles and behaviors. For example, Ann wakes up slowly. She hesitates to jump in and explore, and she prefers to work alone. On the other hand, Vanessa is social, verbal, and ready to go first thing in the morning. As Ms. Hebert plans activities to reinforce the observations of flamingos that her class made at the zoo, she includes experiences that involve both group discussion and individual work. Some of the visual, auditory, and small- and large-group activities include flamingo number puzzles, drawing and painting flamingos, and acting out how flamingos eat, rest, walk, and honk. In this way, Ms. Hebert meets the diverse needs of the class and integrates concepts about flamingos into the entire week. Organizing science lessons in the context of subject matter correlations ensures integration. The following section outlines ways to plan science lessons and investigations.*

PHOTO 2-3 These boys investigate sounds.

© 2016 Cengage Learning®

NGSS

2-3b Organizing for Teaching Science

To teach effectively, teachers must organize what they plan to teach. How they organize depends largely on their teaching situation. Some school districts require that a textbook series or curriculum guide be used when teaching science. Some have a fully developed program to follow, and others have no established guidelines. Currently many states are adopting the Framework (NRC, 2012) and NGSS Lead States (2013) as the guides for K–12 instruction. Some states and the NAEYC provide guidance for Pre-K science. Regardless of state or district directives, the strategies discussed in this chapter can be adapted to a variety of teaching situations.

Planning for Developing Science Concepts. After assessing what your students know and want to know about a science topic, the first questions to ask when organizing for teaching are, "What is the appropriate science content that the children need to know?" and "What is the best way to organize learning experiences?" You might have a general topic in mind, such as air, but do not know where to go from there. One technique that might help organize your thoughts is webbing, a strategy borrowed from literature. A web depicts a variety of possible concepts and curricular experiences that you might use to develop concepts. By visually depicting your ideas, you will be able to tell at a glance the concepts covered in your unit. As the web emerges, projected activities can be balanced by subject area (e.g., social studies, movement, art, drama, and math) and by a variety of naturalistic, informal, or adult guided activities.

Start your planning by asking the students what they know and what they would like to know about the topic. Next research what are important ideas children should know about a topic. For example, the topic of air contains many science concepts (**Photo 2-4**). Four concepts about air

PHOTO 2-4   This boy experiments with the topic of air as he runs with the streamer flying in the wind.

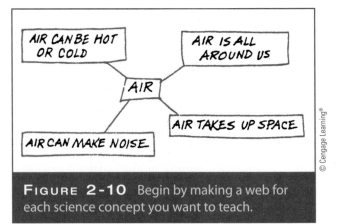

FIGURE 2-10   Begin by making a web for each science concept you want to teach.

that are commonly taught to young children begin the web depicted in **Figure 2-10** and are as follows:

1. Air is all around us.
2. Air takes up space.
3. Air can make noise.
4. Air can be hot or cold.

After selecting the concepts to develop, begin adding appropriate activities to achieve your goal. Look back at section 2-2 in this chapter, and think of some of these strategies that will best help you teach about air. Remember that "messing around" time and direct experience are both vital for learning.

The developed web in **Figure 2-11** shows at a glance the main concepts and activities that could be included in this investigation. You may not want to use all of these activities, but you will have the advantage of flexibility when you make decisions.

Next, turn your attention to how you will evaluate children's learning. Preschool and primary grade children will not be able to verbalize their true understanding of a concept. They simply have not advanced to more formal stages

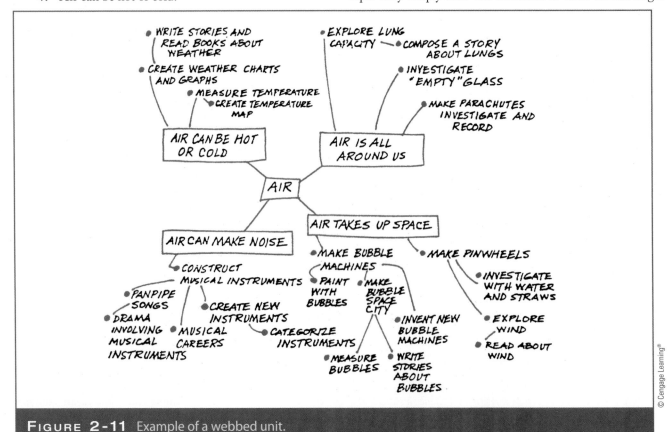

FIGURE 2-11   Example of a webbed unit.

```
ACTION VERBS
Simple Action Words

arrange       design        match
attempt       distinguish   measure
chart         explain       name
circle        formulate     order
classify      gather        organize
collect       graph         place
compare       identify      point
compile       include       report
complete      indicate      select
contrast      label         sort
count         list          state
define        locate        tell
describe      map
```

FIGURE 2-12 Verbs that indicate action.

```
INSTRUCTIONAL PLANNING
TOPIC/CONCEPT   What is the topic or concept?
GOAL            Where are you headed?
OBJECTIVE       How do you plan to achieve
                your goal?
ADVANCED        What do you need to have
                prepared in order to teach?
PREPARATION
MATERIALS       What will you need?
ACTIVITIES      What will you and the children
                do?
EVALUATION      What did the students learn as
                reflected from the evidence you
                obtained?
```

FIGURE 2-13 Components in instructional planning.

of thinking. Instead, have students show their knowledge in ways that can be observed, encouraging them to explain, predict, tell, draw, describe, construct, and so on (**Figure 2-12**). These verbs indicate actions. For example, as students explain to you why they think the bubble wrap makes a noise when popped, be assured that the facts are there and so are the concepts; one day, they will come together in a fully developed concept statement. Concept development takes time and cannot be rushed.

The webbed plan that you have developed is a long-term plan for organizing science experiences around a specific topic. Formal plans usually contain overall goals and objectives, a series of lessons, and an evaluation plan. **Goals** are the broad statements that indicate where you are heading with the topic or outcomes you would like to achieve. **Objectives** state how you plan to achieve your goals. Practical teaching direction is provided by daily lesson plans. An evaluation plan is necessary to assess student learning and your own teaching. These components can be organized in a variety of ways, but **Figure 2-13** outlines the essential ingredients. Refer to the "Assessment Strategies" section of this chapter for suggestions on how to build on children's existing knowledge when designing learning experiences.

Planning. The activity plan is a necessary component of the investigation, helping you plan the experiences that will aid in concept development. The following plan is adaptable and focuses on developing a science concept, manipulating materials, and extending and reinforcing the concept with additional activities and subject area integrations. Refer to **Figures 2-14** and **2-15**, the bubble machine, for an example of this activity plan format.

Basic Science Activity Plan Components.

- *Concept.* Concepts are usually the most difficult part of an activity plan. The temptation is to write an objective or topic title. However, to really focus your teaching on the major concept to be developed, you must find the science in what you intend to teach. For example, ask yourself, "What do I want the children to learn about air?"

- *Objective.* Then ask, for example, "What do I want the children to do in order to help them understand that air takes up space?" When you have decided on the basic experience, be sure to identify the process skills that children will use. In this way, you will be aware of both content and process.

  Define the teaching process in behavioral terms. State what behavior you want the children to exhibit. This will make evaluation easier because you have stated what you expect the children to accomplish. Although many educators state behavioral objectives with conditions, most teachers find that beginning a statement with "The child should be able to . . .," followed by an action verb, is an effective way to state objectives. Some examples follow:

  - The child should be able to describe the parts of a flower.

  - The child should be able to construct a diorama of the habitat of a tiger.

  - The child should be able to draw a picture that shows different types of animal noses.

- *Materials.* If children are to manipulate materials, you must decide which materials should be organized

CONCEPT: "Air takes up space. Bubbles have air inside of them."

OBJECTIVE: Construct a bubble-making machine by manipulating materials and air to produce bubbles. Observe and describe the bubbles.

MATERIALS: Bubble solution of eight tablespoons liquid detergent and one quart water (expensive detergent makes stronger bubbles), straws, four-ounce plastic cups.

ADVANCED PREPARATION:

1. Collect materials.
2. Cut straws into small sections.
3. Mix bubble solution.

PROCEDURE:

Initiating Activity: Demonstrate an assembled bubble machine. Have children observe the machine and tell what they think is happening.

How to do it: Help children assemble bubble machines. Insert straw into the side of the cup. Pour the bubble mixture to just below the hole in the side of the cup. Give children five minutes to explore blowing bubbles with the bubble machine. Then ask children to see how many bubbles they can blow. Ask: "What do your bubbles look like? Describe your bubbles." Add food coloring for more colorful bubbles.

"What happens to your bubbles? Do they burst? How can you make them last longer?"

"What do you think is in the bubbles? How can you tell? What did you blow into the bubble? Can you think of something else that you blow air into to make larger?" (balloon)

EVALUATION:

1. Were the children able to blow bubbles?
2. Did they experiment with blowing differing amounts of air?
3. Did the children say things like, "Look what happens when I blow real hard"?

EXTENSION:

1. Have students tell a story about the bubble machine as you record it on chart paper.
2. Encourage children to make bubble books with drawings that depict their bubbles, bubble machines, and the exciting time they had blowing bubbles. Encourage the children to write or pretend to write about their pictures. Threes and fours enjoy pretending to write; by five or six, children begin to experiment with inventing their own spellings. Be sure to accept whatever they produce. Have children read their books to the class. Place them in the library center for browsing.
3. Make a bubbles bulletin board. Draw a cluster of bubbles and have students add descriptive words about bubbles.
4. Challenge students to invent other bubble machines. (Chapter 10 of this book contains activities that teach additional concepts of air and bubbles.)

© Cengage Learning®

FIGURE 2-14 The bubble machine lesson.

Digital Download

in advance of the lesson experience. Ask, "What materials will I need to implement this experience?"

■ *Advanced preparation.* These are the tasks that the teacher needs to complete prior to implementing the plan with the children. Teachers should ask themselves, "What do I need to have prepared to implement this activity?"

■ *Procedure.* The procedure section of a lesson plan provides the step-by-step directions for completing the activity with the children. When planning, try the procedure yourself and ask, "How will this experience be conducted?" You must decide how you will initiate the experience with children, present the learning experience, and relate the concept to

© Cengage Learning®

FIGURE 2-15 Laticia makes a bubble machine.

the children's past experiences. Questions that encourage learning should be considered and included in the lesson plan.

Begin the lesson with an initiating experience. This experience could be the messing-around-with-materials stage of the learning cycle, a demonstration or discrepant event, or a question sequence that bridges what you intend to teach with a previous activity or experience. The idea is that you want to stimulate and engage the children in what they are going to do during the activity.

- *Extension.* To ensure maximum learning of the concept, plan ways to keep the idea going. This can be done by extending the concept and building on students' interest with additional learning activities, integrating the concept into other subject areas, preparing interest centers, and so on.

2-3c Assessment Strategies

To teach effectively, you must plan for assessment. There is no point in continuing with another more advanced activity before you know what students understand from the current activity. Engaging in ongoing assessment of your own teaching and of student progress is essential to improving teaching and learning. Bear in mind that your major role is to help students build concepts, use process skills, and reject incorrect ideas. To do this, students should be engaged in meaningful experiences and should have the time and tools needed to learn. Recall that the assessment of students' progress and the guidance of students toward self-assessment are at the heart of good teaching.

The content and form of an assessment task must be congruent with what is supposed to be measured. The task

of establishing the complexity of the science content while addressing the importance of collecting data on all aspects of student science achievement can be challenging.

A variety of assessment formats have been suggested that will help in determining what students understand and are able to do with their knowledge as well as how they will apply this knowledge. Examples of effective strategies include the use of teacher-recorded observations that describe what the students are able to do and the areas that need improvement. Interviews or asking questions and interacting with children are effective assessment strategies. Portfolios contain examples of individual student work that indicate progress, improvement, and accomplishments; and science journal writing captures yet another dimension of student understanding. **Performance-based assessment** involves assigning one or more students a task that will reveal the extent of their thinking skills and their level of understanding of science concepts. Regardless of the assessment strategy used, enough information has to be provided so that both the student and teacher know what needs to happen for improvement to take place. Additional strategies are discussed in Chapter 1, earlier in this chapter, and throughout the text.

Assessment that takes place before teaching is diagnostic in nature and occurs when you assess the children's experiences and ideas about a science concept. For example, when you ask children where they think rain comes from, you are assessing what they know about rain and discovering any misconceptions.

An effective strategy for science learning is to build on children's existing knowledge and to challenge students' preconceptions and misconceptions. Before you begin teaching, find out what your students already know, or think they know, about a science topic. A popular method for finding out what students already know is the K-W-L strategy, described by Ogle (1986) for literacy and adapted for use in science, in which children are asked what they know (K), what they want to know (W), and what they learned (L). Most teachers begin by recording the children's brainstormed responses to the first two questions on a large piece of paper that has been divided into three columns, each headed by one of the K-W-L questions. As the responses are recorded, some difference of opinion is bound to occur. Such disagreement is positive and can provide a springboard for student inquiry. At this point, potential investigations, projects, or inquiry topics can be added to the curriculum plan.

As teachers assess student progress during teaching, changes in teaching strategies are decided. If one strategy is not working, try something else. As children work on projects, you will find yourself interacting with them on an informal basis. Listen carefully to children's comments, and watch them manipulate materials. You cannot help but assess how things are going. You might even want to keep a record of your observations or create a chart that reflects areas of concern to you, such as the attitudes of or the interactions between students. When observations are written down in an organized way, they are called *anecdotal records* (**Figure 2-16**).

RECORDED OBSERVATIONS

Things to record when observing, discussing, or keeping anecdotal records

Cognitive:

How well do the children handle the materials?

Do the children cite out-of-school examples of the science concept?

Is the basic concept being studied referred to as the children go about their day?

Attitude and skill:

Do the children express like or dislike of the topic?

Are there any comments that suggest prejudice?

Do children evidence self-evaluation?

Are ideas freely expressed in the group?

Are there any specific behaviors that need to be observed each time science is taught?

© Cengage Learning®

FIGURE 2-16 Keeping anecdotal records.

If you decide to use anecdotal records, be sure to write down dates and names and to tell students you are keeping track of things that happen. A review of your records will be valuable when the investigation is complete. Recording observations can become a habit and provides an additional tool for assessing children's learning and your teaching strategies. Anecdotes are also invaluable resources for parent conferences. Refer to Chapter 1 and section 2-2 of this chapter for examples of assessing prior knowledge and keeping anecdotal notes.

Responses to oral questions can be helpful in evaluating while teaching. Facial expressions are especially telling. Everyone has observed the blank look that usually indicates a lack of understanding, which may be the result of asking a question that was too difficult. When this occurs, ask an easier question or present your question in a different manner for improved results. Or have the students discuss the question with a partner.

One way to assess teaching is to ask questions about the investigation in an activity review. Some teachers write main idea questions on the chalkboard. Then, they put a chart next to the questions and label it "What We Found Out." As the investigation progresses, the chart is filled in by the class as a way of showing progress and reviewing the problem.

Another strategy is to observe children applying the concept. For example, as the *Three Billy Goats Gruff* (Rounds, 1993) is being read, Joyce comments, "The little billy goat walks just like the goat that we saw at the zoo." You know from this statement that Joyce has some idea of how goats move (refer to Chapter 1).

"Always do the activity first."

© Cengage Learning®

FIGURE 2-17 The golden rule.

Sometimes students have difficulty learning because an activity just doesn't work. One basic rule when teaching science is always to do the activity yourself first. This includes noting questions or possible problems you may encounter. If you have trouble, the students will, too (**Figure 2-17**).

2-3d Evaluating the Investigation Plan

How well was the investigation designed? Reflect and **evaluate** the plan before you begin the investigation, and ask yourself some questions, such as the following, to help evaluate your work. These questions pull together the major points of this investigation:

1. Is the plan related to the children's prior knowledge and past experiences?

2. Are a variety of science process skills used in the lessons?

3. Is the science content developmentally appropriate for the children? How will you know?

4. Have you integrated other subject areas with the science content of the investigation?

5. When you use reading and writing activities, do they align with the science content and relate to hands-on learning?

6. Do you allow for naturalistic, informal, and adult-guided activities?

7. Have you included a variety of strategies to engage students in the active search for knowledge? (This is covered earlier in this chapter.)

8. What opportunities are included for investigation and problem solving?

9. Are both open ended and narrowly focused questions included?

10. Will the assessment strategies provide a way to determine whether children can apply what they have learned?

11. What local resources are included in the plan?

When publishers design a plan, they usually field-test it with a population of teachers. In this case, you are field-testing the plan as you teach your students. Keep notes and records on what worked well and what needs to be modified when the plan is used again. After the investigation is completed, it is suggested that you take time to reflect on the experience and use assessment data that you have gathered to guide in making judgments about the effectiveness of your teaching. Consider the following categories when making judgments about curricula:

- Developmental appropriateness of the science content
- Student interest in the content
- Effectiveness of activities in producing the desired learning outcomes
- Effectiveness of the selected examples
- Understanding and abilities students must have to benefit from the selected activities and examples

2-3e Three Basic Types of Science Investigations and Units

Some teachers like to develop *resource files*. The resource file is an extensive collection of activities and suggestions focusing on a single science topic. The advantage of a resource file is the wide range of appropriate strategies available to meet the needs, interests, and abilities of the children. As the investigation proceeds, additional strategies and integrations are usually added. For example, Mrs. Jones knows that she is going to have the children investigate the properties of seeds and plants in her kindergarten class. She collects all of the activities and teaching strategies that she can find. When she is ready to begin the investigation, she selects the activities that she believes are most appropriate. Although certain topics may be designated in K–12, in pre-K children's questions and interests can usually direct investigations. Examples may be found in Shillady, 2013.

Teachers who design a *teaching* plan develop a science concept, objectives, materials, activities, and evaluation procedures for a specific group of children. This plan is less extensive than a resource file and contains exactly what will be taught, a timeline, and the order of activities. Usually, general initiating experiences begin the investigation, and culminating experiences end it. The specific teaching plan has value and may be used again with other classes after appropriate adaptations have been made. For example, Mr. Wang has planned a two-week unit on batteries and bulbs. He has decided on activities and planned each lesson period of the two weeks.

Extending the textbook in a *textbook unit* is another possibility. The most obvious limitation of this approach is that the school district might change textbooks. A textbook unit is designed by outlining the science concepts for the unit and checking the textbook for those already covered in the book or teacher's manual. Additional learning activities are added for concepts not included in the text or sometimes to replace those in the text. Initiating activities to spark students' interest in the topic might be needed. One advantage of this type of unit is using the textbook to better advantage. For example, after doing animal activities, use the text as a resource to confirm or extend knowledge. On the other hand, the topics may not be of interest to the children.

Open-Ended and Narrow Questions. Asking questions can be likened to driving a car with a stick shift. When teaching the whole class, start in low gear with a narrow question that can be answered by yes or no, or start with a question that has an obvious answer. This usually puts students at ease. They are happy; they know something. Then, try an open-ended question that has many answers. Open-ended questions stimulate discussion and offer opportunities for thinking. However, if the open-ended question is asked before the class has background information, the children might just stare at you, duck their heads, or exhibit undesirable behavior. Do not panic; quickly shift gears and ask a narrow question. Then work your way back to what you want to find out. Teachers who are adept at shifting between narrow and open-ended questions are probably excellent discussion leaders and have little trouble with classroom management during these periods.

Open-ended questions are excellent interest builders when used effectively. For example, consider Ms. Hebert's initiating activity for a lesson about buoyancy. Ms. Hebert holds a rock over a pan of water and asks a narrow yes-or-no question: "Will this rock sink when dropped in water?" Then she asks an open-ended question: "How can we keep the rock from sinking into the water?" The children answer: "Tie string around it." "Put a spoon under it." "Grab it."

As the discussion progresses, the open-ended question leads the children into a discussion about how they can find out whether their ideas will work. The teacher provides materials such as plastic containers, clay, and other items for them to use in designing a device that will float the rock.

Good questions excite and motivate children. When questions are posed that are open-ended and do not depend on yes-or-no answers, children will begin to expand their own capacity for problem solving and inquiry learning.

SUMMARY

2-1 The Framework and Standards for Science Education

The Framework for Science Education and the NGSS provide guidance for science curriculum planning. The Framework includes descriptions of the four primary science areas: Physical Science, Life Science, Earth and Space Science, and Engineering, Technology, and Science Applications. Each area includes core ideas. Our major goal in science education is to develop scientifically literate people who can think critically. To teach science to tomorrow's citizens, process skills and attitudes must be established as major components of any science content lesson. Facts alone will not be sufficient for children who are born into a technological world. Children interact daily with science. Their toasters pop; their can openers whir; and televisions, recording devices, and computers are commonplace. Preparation to live as productive individuals in a changing world should begin early in a child's life.

Science as Inquiry. Inquiry is a major focus of the science learning process. It is a constructivist approach that bases learning on children's interests and their questions about the world. Process skill application is at the center of inquiry. The learning cycle described in Chapter 1 is a mode of inquiry instruction.

Science Content Knowledge and Learning and the Development of Literacy. Science content in each of the core areas is described in the Framework and in the NGSS. The manipulation of science materials, whether initiated by the child or the teacher, creates opportunities for language and literacy development.

Appropriate Science Content. Appropriate science content is outlined in the Framework. Content at each grade level is included NGSS.

2-2 Concept Understanding in Young Children

For all the preschool and primary grade developmental stages described by Piaget, keep in mind that children's views of the world and concepts are not the same as yours. Their perception of phenomena is from their own perspective and experiences. Misconceptions arise; so help children explore the world to expand their thinking, and always be ready for the next developmental stage. Teach children to observe with all of their senses and to classify, predict, and communicate so that they can discover other viewpoints.

Self-Regulation and Concept Attainment. Through self-regulation concepts are built. The cognitive structure is modified through the processes of disequilibration, equilibration, accommodation, and assimilation.

Discrepant Events. Discrepant events put students in disequilibrium and prepare them for learning. Natural events can set the stage for learning.

Using the Learning Cycle to Build Concepts. There are many possible ways to design science instruction for young children. The learning cycle is an application of the theory of cognitive development described by Piaget; it can incorporate a number of techniques into a single lesson, or each of the components of the learning cycle can be used independently to develop lessons.

Strategies That Encourage Inquiry. A sequence of strategies can support children's learning, from the initial questions to evaluation of data and information collected.

2-3 Integrating Science into the Curriculum

Children are more likely to retain science concepts that are integrated with other subject areas. Making connections between science and other aspects of a child's school day requires that opportunities for learning be well planned and readily available to children. Learning science in a variety of ways encourages personal learning styles and ensures subject integration.

Organizing for Teaching Science. The key to effective teaching is organization. Planning provides a way to make clear what and how you want children to learn. A planning web is a useful technique for depicting ideas, outlining concepts, and integrating content. The three basic types of planning approaches are resource files in support of investigations, teaching plans that focus on a selected topic, and textbook units. Teachers utilize whichever approach best suits their classroom needs. By asking open-ended and narrow questions, teachers develop science concepts and encourage higher-order thinking skills in their students.

FURTHER READING AND RESOURCES

Bredekamp, S., & Rosegrant, T. (1992). *Reaching potentials: Appropriate curriculum and assessment for young children* (vol. 1). Washington, DC: National Association for the Education of Young Children.

Bredekamp, S., & Rosegrant, T. (1995). *Reaching potentials: Transforming early childhood curriculum and assessment* (vol. 2). Washington, DC: National Association for the Education of Young Children.

Duschl, R., & Grandy, R. (Eds.) (2008). *Teaching scientific inquiry: Recommendations for research and implementation.* Rotterdam: Sense Publishers.

Harlan, J., & Rivkin, M. (2007). *Science experiences for the early childhood years: An integrated affective approach,* 9th ed. Upper Saddle River, NJ: Merrill/Prentice-Hall.

Lederman, N. G., Lederman, J. S., & Bell, R. L. (2005). *Constructing science in elementary classrooms.* Boston: Allyn & Bacon.

NSTA, National Science Teachers Association. (Member Draft, December 2013). *NSTA Position statement: Early Childhood Science Education.* www.nsta.org.

NSTA, National Science Teachers Association. (2002, July). *Position statement: Elementary School Science.* www.nsta.org.

Weiss, T. H. (2013, Summer). Any questions? *Science and Children, 50*(9), 36–41.

REFERENCES

Charlesworth, R. (2014). *Understanding child development,* 9th ed. Belmont, CA: Wadsworth Cengage Learning.

Committee on Science Learning, Kindergarten Through Eighth Grade. Board on Science Education, Center for Education. (2007). *Taking science to school: Learning and teaching science in grades K–8.* Washington, DC: National Academies Press.

Gadzikowski, A. (2013). Preschool and kindergarten strategies for the young scientist. In A. Shillady (Ed.), *Exploring Science,* 48–54. Washington, DC: National Association for the Education of Young Children.

Gallagher, J. M., & Reid, D. K. (1981). *The learning theory of Piaget and Inhelder.* Monterey, CA: Brooks/Cole.

Kuhn, M., & McDermott, M. (2013, Summer). Negotiating the way to inquiry. *Science and Children,* 50(9), 52–57.

National Research Council. (2012). *A Framework for K–12 Science Education.* Washington, DC: The National Academies Press.

NGSS Lead States. (2013). *Next Generation Science Standards: For states, by states.* Washington, DC: The National Academies Press.

NSTA (National Science Teachers Association). (2013, November). Position Statement: The next generation science standards. www.nsta.org.

Ogle, D. M. (1986). K-W-L: A teaching model that develops active reading of expository text. *The Reading Teacher,* 39(6), 564–570.

Rounds, G. (1993). *Three billy goats gruff.* New York: Holiday House.

Rowe, M. B. (1978). *Teaching science as continuous inquiry: A basic,* 2nd ed. New York: McGraw-Hill.

Shillady, A. (Ed.). (2013). *Exploring science.* Washington, DC: National Association for the Education of Young Children.

Simon, S. (1970). *Science in a vacant lot.* New York: Viking Press.

PART 2
FUNDAMENTAL CONCEPTS AND SKILLS

CHAPTER 3 Prekindergarten and Kindergarten Concepts and Skills

CHAPTER 4 More Prekindergarten and Kindergarten Concepts and Skills: Early Geometry, Parts and Wholes, and Applications of Fundamental Concepts to Science and Engineering

CHAPTER 3

PREKINDERGARTEN AND KINDERGARTEN CONCEPTS AND SKILLS

LEARNING OBJECTIVES

After reading this chapter, you should be able to:

3-1 Assess, plan, teach and evaluate one-to-one-correspondence concept lesson activities following national standards.

3-2 Describe, assess, plan, teach, and evaluate number and number sense concept lesson activities following national standards.

3-3 Assess, plan, teach, and evaluate logic and classification concept lesson activities following national standards.

3-4 Assess, plan, teach, and evaluate comparison concept lesson activities following national standards.

STANDARDS ADDRESSED IN THIS CHAPTER

NAEYC Professional Preparation Standards

5. Use content knowledge to build meaningful curriculum.

5a. Understand content knowledge and resources in mathematics.

DAP Guidelines

2C. Know desired program goals.

3C. Use the curriculum framework to ensure there is attention to important learning goals.

 COMMON CORE STATE STANDARDS

Common Core State Standards for Math

K.CC.A.1 Count to 100 by 1s and by 10s.

K.CC.A.3 Write numbers 0 to 20.

Logic and classification

K.MD.B.3 Classify objects into given categories; count the numbers of objects in each category.

Comparing

K.MD.A.1 Describe measureable attributes of objects, such as length or weight.

K.MD.A.2 Directly compare two objects with a measureable attribute in common to see which object has more of or less of the attribute, and describe the difference.

NGSS

Next Generation Science Standards

K-LS1-1 Scientists look for patterns and order when making observations about the world.

3-1 ONE-TO-ONE CORRESPONDENCE

One-to-one correspondence is not specifically mentioned in CCSSM. However, the National Council of Teachers of Mathematics (NCTM, 2000), whose guidelines guided the development of the CCSSM, state expectations for **one-to-one correspondence** as it relates to **rational counting** (attaching a number name to each object counted), as is described later in this chapter. Placing items in one-to-one correspondence, as is described in this chapter, is a supportive concept and skill for rational counting.

One-to-one correspondence is a focal point for number and operations at the prekindergarten level (NCTM, 2006) and is used in connection with solving such problems as having enough (cups, dolls, cars, etc.) for all members of a group.

One-to-one correspondence is the most fundamental component of the concept of number. It is the understanding that one group has the same number of things as another. For example, each child has a cookie; each foot has a shoe; each person wears a hat. It is preliminary to counting and basic to the understanding of equivalence and to the concept of conservation of number described in Chapter 1. As with other mathematics concepts, it can be integrated across the curriculum (**Figure 3-1**).

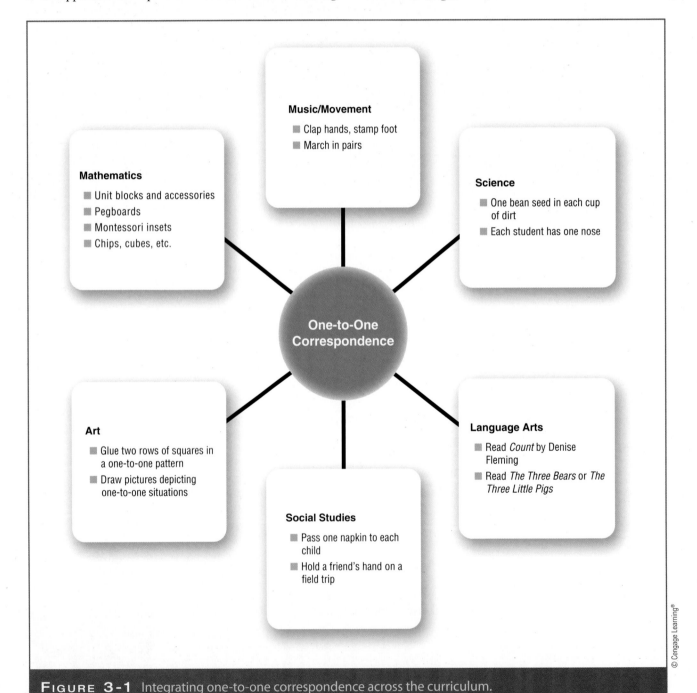

FIGURE 3-1 Integrating one-to-one correspondence across the curriculum.

3-1a Pre-Assessment Observation

To obtain information of an informal nature, note the children's behavior during their work, play, and routine activities. Look for one-to-one correspondence that happens naturally. For example, when the child plays train, he may line up a row of chairs so that there is one for each child passenger. When she puts her mittens on, she shows that she knows there should be one for each hand; when painting, he checks to be sure he has each paintbrush in the matching color of paint. Tasks for interview assessment are provided in Appendix A.

For their initial naturalistic, informal, and adult-guided exploratory activities, children use what are called "tools" or "manipulatives" to develop problem solutions. Tools come in many varieties. Paper and pencils, crayons and markers, color cubes, beads and base-10 blocks are a few examples of tools. Digital tools are also available (Van De Walle, Karp, & Bay-Williams, 2013). Applets or virtual manipulatives are available online on the website for the National Library of Virtual Manipulatives or the Illuminations website.

SAMPLE ASSESSMENT TASK

3A   PREOPERATIONAL AGES 2–3

ONE-TO-ONE CORRESPONDENCE: CHAPTER 3

METHOD Observation, individuals or groups.

SKILL Child demonstrates one-to-one correspondence during play activities.

MATERIALS Play materials that lend themselves to one-to-one activities, such as small blocks and animals, dishes and eating utensils, paint containers and paintbrushes, pegs and pegboards, sticks and stones, and so on.

PROCEDURE Provide the materials, and encourage the children to use them.

EVALUATION Note whether the children match items one to one, such as putting small peg dolls in each of several margarine containers or on top of each of several blocks that have been lined up in a row. Record on checklist with anecdote and/or photo or video.

INSTRUCTIONAL RESOURCE
R. Charlesworth, *Math and Science for Young Children*, 8th ed., San Francisco, CA: Cengage Learning, 2016.

`Digital Download`

SAMPLE ASSESSMENT TASK

6A   PREOPERATIONAL AGES 5–6

ONE-TO-ONE CORRESPONDENCE: CHAPTER 3

METHOD Interview.

SKILL The child can place two groups of 10 items each in one-to-one correspondence.

MATERIALS Two groups of objects of different shapes and/or colors (such as pennies and cube blocks or red chips and white chips). Have at least 10 of each type of object.

PROCEDURE Place two groups of 10 objects in front of the child. **"Find out whether there is the same amount [number] in each group [bunch, pile]."** If the child cannot do the task, try it with two groups of five objects.

EVALUATION The children should arrange each group so as to match the objects one to one, or they might count each group to determine equality. Record on checklist.

INSTRUCTIONAL RESOURCE
R. Charlesworth, *Math and Science for Young Children*, 8th ed., San Francisco, CA: Cengage Learning, 2016.

`Digital Download`

3-1b Activities

Naturalistic Activities. One-to-one correspondence activities develop from an infant's early sensorimotor activity. The infant's first tools are whatever she can grasp (**Photo 3-1**). She finds out that she can hold one thing in each hand but can put only one object at a time in her mouth.

As a toddler, she discovers that five peg dolls will fit, one each, in the five holes of her toy bus. Quickly she learns that one person fits on each chair; one shoe goes on each foot; and so on. The 2-year-old spends a great deal of her playtime in one-to-one correspondence activities. She lines up containers such as margarine cups, dishes, or boxes and puts a small toy animal in each one. She pretends to set the table for lunch. First she sets one place for herself and one for her bear, with a plate for each. Then she gives each place a spoon and a small cup and saucer. She plays with her large plastic shapes and discovers there is a rod that will fit through the hole in each shape.

Informal Activities. There are many daily opportunities for informal one-to-one correspondence activities. Often

PHOTO 3-1   The infant reaches out for the object with one hand.

PHOTO 3-2   This pegboard provides one-to-one correspondence and color matching.

things must be passed out to a group: food items, scissors, crayons, paper, napkins, paper towels, or notes to take home. Each child should do as many of these things as possible. Checking on whether everyone has accomplished a task or has what students need is another chance for informal one-to-one correspondence. "Does everyone have a chair to sit on?" "Does everyone have on two boots or two mittens?" "Does everyone have on a coat?" "Does each person have a cup of milk or a sandwich?" Children can check by matching: "Larry, find out whether everyone has a pair of scissors, please." One-to-one correspondence helps to solve difficulties. For instance, the children are washing rubber dolls in soapsuds. Jeanie is crying: "Petey has two dolls, and I don't have any." Mrs. Carter comes over. "Petey, more children want to play here now, so each one can have only one baby to wash." One-to-one correspondence is often the basis for rules such as "Only one person on each swing at a time" or "Only one piece of cake for each child today." Other informal activities occur when children select from a variety of materials and activities made available during learning center time. These kinds of materials include pegboards, felt shapes on a flannelboard, bead and inch-cube block patterns, shape sorters, formboards, lotto games, and other commercial materials (**Photo 3-2**). If tablets and smartboards are available, games can be selected that involve one-to-one correspondence. The teacher can also make materials to serve the same purposes. Most of the materials described in the next section can be made available for informal exploration both before and after they have been used in adult-guided activities.

Adult-Guided Activities. The extent and variety of materials that can be used for one-to-one correspondence activities is almost endless. Remember the six steps from concrete to abstract materials covered in Chapter 1. These steps are especially relevant when selecting one-to-one correspondence materials. In addition, consider these five characteristics when selecting materials: whether they are perceptual, number of items, concreteness, whether they are physically

joined, and whether groups are the same number. Teachers can vary or change one or more of the five characteristics and can use different materials. In this way, more difficult tasks can be designed (**Figure 3-2**).

Perceptual qualities are critical in matching activities. Materials can vary a great deal with regard to how similar or how different they look, and the way the materials look is important in determining how hard it will be for the child to match them. Materials are easier to match if the groups are different. To match animals with cages or to find a spoon for each bowl is easier than making a match between two groups of blue chips. In choosing objects, the task can be made more difficult by picking out objects that look more similar.

The number of objects to be matched is important. The more objects in each group, the more difficult it is to match. Groups with fewer than five things are much easier than groups with five or more. In planning activities, start with small groups (fewer than five), and work up, step by step, to groups of nine. A child who is able to place groups of 10 in one-to-one correspondence has a well-developed sense of the concept.

Concreteness refers to the extent to which materials are real (**Figure 3-3**). Remember from Chapter 1, instruction should always begin with concrete real objects. The easiest and first one-to-one correspondence activities should involve the use of real things such as small toys and other familiar objects. Next, objects that are less familiar and more similar (e.g., cube blocks, chips, popsicle sticks) can be used. The next level is cutout shapes, such as circles and squares, cowboys and horses, or dogs and doghouses, to be followed by pictures of real objects and pictures of shapes. Real objects and pictures of objects or people can also be employed.

Computers, tablets, and their accompanying resources can be used by young children who need practice in one-to-one correspondence. Learning to hit the computer keys or the tablet icons one at a time with one finger is a one-to-one

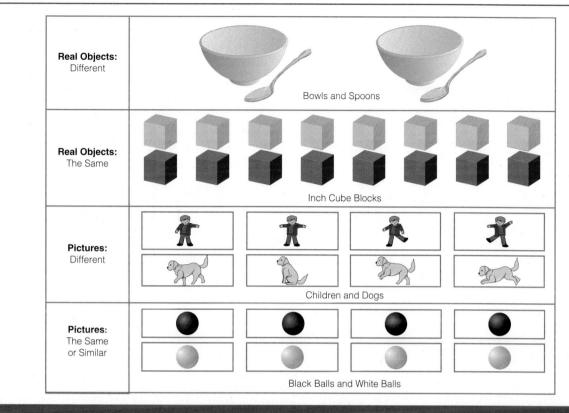

FIGURE 3-2 Examples of groups with different perceptual difficulty levels.

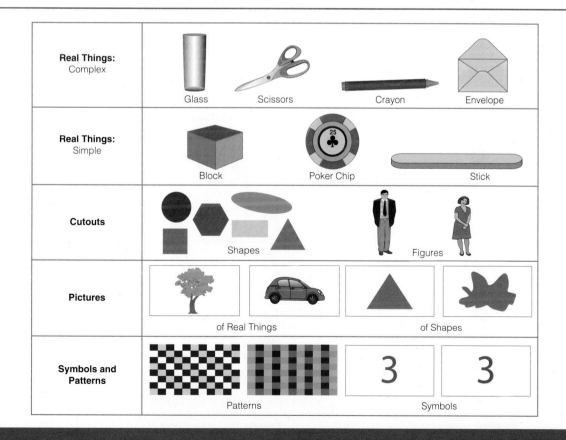

FIGURE 3-3 Concreteness: How close to real?

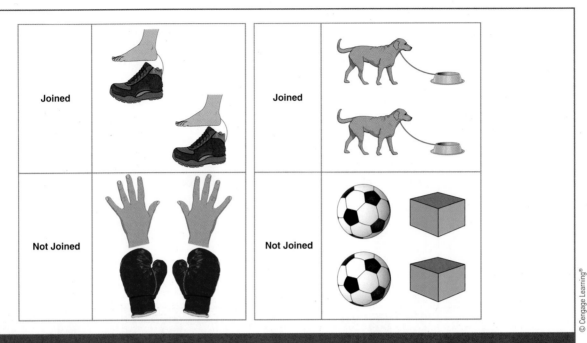

FIGURE 3-4 Joined groups and groups that are not joined.

experience in both the kinesthetic and perceptual-motor domains. The following online resources serve this purpose:

- PBS Kids website: *Matching Games* (Forty matching games starring PBS characters.)
- Nick Jr. website: 51 math games such as Peter Rabbit Nut catch game

When using objects or pictures of objects, it is easier to see one-to-one correspondence if the objects are joined than if they are not joined. For example, it is easier to tell whether there are enough chairs for each child if the children are sitting in them than if the chairs are on one side of the room and the children are on the other. In beginning activities, the objects can be hooked together with a line or a string so that the children can more clearly see whether there is a match. In **Figure 3-4**, each foot is joined to a shoe and each animal to a bowl; neither the hands and mittens nor the balls and boxes are joined.

Placing unequal groups in one-to-one correspondence is harder than placing equal groups. When the groups have the same number, children can check to be sure they have used all the items. When one group has more, they do not have this clue (**Figure 3-5**).

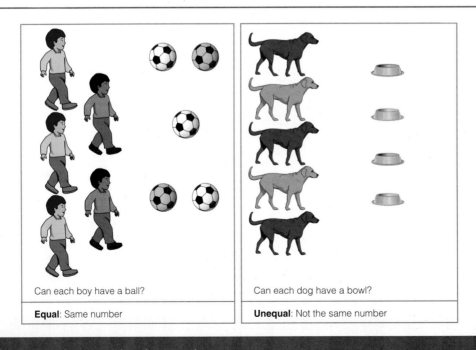

Can each boy have a ball?

Equal: Same number

Can each dog have a bowl?

Unequal: Not the same number

FIGURE 3-5 Matching equal and unequal parts.

ONE-TO-ONE CORRESPONDENCE—DOGS AND PEOPLE

Objective:	To match joined groups of three objects.
Naturalistic and Informal Activity:	In learning centers provide materials that lend themselves to naturalistic and informal one-to-one correspondence experiences: unit blocks and accessories, dishes and tableware, adult and child animals, and so forth. Observe and ask questions and make comments as appropriate.
Materials:	Two sets of three objects that normally would go together. For example, doll people holding toy dogs on leashes.
Structured Activity:	**Here are some people and some dogs. The dogs are on leashes. Does each person have a dog? Show me how you can tell.** Note if the children can show or explain that the leashes connect the dogs and people.
Follow-Up:	Use other groups of objects such as cats and kittens, cups and saucers, houses and roofs, etc. Increase the number of items in each group as the three-to-three task becomes easy.

© Cengage Learning®

FIGURE 3-6 One-to-one correspondence activity card—Dogs and people: Matching objects that are perceptually different.

Digital Download

The sample lessons presented in **Figures 3-6** through **3-11** illustrate some basic types of one-to-one correspondence activities. Note that they also show an increase in difficulty by varying the characteristics just described. Each activity begins by presenting the students with a problem to solve.

3-1c Helping Children with Special Learning Needs

One-to-one correspondence games with objects or picture cards can support the learning of perceptual-motor skills and vocabulary. For children with a language disability or

ONE-TO-ONE CORRESPONDENCE—THE THREE PIGS

Objective:	To match joined groups of three items.
Naturalistic and Informal Activity:	Read the story "The Three Little Pigs." In the literacy center place the three pigs, wolf, houses, straw, sticks, and bricks. These might be flannelboard figures or puppets. Observe how the children use the materials. Do they play out the story matching each pig with the appropriate house building material and house? Ask questions or make comments as appropriate.
Materials:	Two sets of cutouts for the bulletin board. Three pieces of yarn. Make three pig cutouts and three house cutouts: straw, sticks, and bricks. Put them on bulletin board and connect each pig to his house with thick yarn.

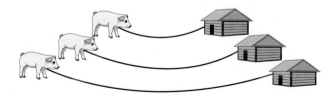

Structured Activity:	**Who are these fellows? (Children answer) Yes, the three little pigs. Is there a house for each pig?** Have one of the children show you how he knows there is by tracing from each pig to his house along the yarn "path." Leave the display up for use by the children during center time.
Follow-Up:	Make a set of pigs, houses, and a wolf for the flannelboard. Both teachers and children can use these for storytelling.

© Cengage Learning®

FIGURE 3-7 One-to-one correspondence activity card—matching the three little pigs to cutouts that are perceptually different.

Digital Download

ONE-TO-ONE CORRESPONDENCE—PENNIES FOR TOYS

Objective:	To match groups of two and more objects.
Naturalistic and Informal Activity:	Set up a store center such as toys, groceries, or clothing. Provide play money pennies. Put a price of 1¢ on each item. Discuss with the students what they might do in the store. Observe and note if they exchange one penny for each item. Make comments and ask questions as appropriate.
Materials:	Ten pennies and ten small toys (for example, a ball, a car, a truck, three animals, three peg people, a crayon).
Structured Activity:	**Let's pretend we are playing store. Here are some pennies and some toys.** Show the child(ren) two toys. Place two pennies near the toys. **Do I have enough pennies to buy these toys if each one costs one penny? Show me how you can find out.**
Follow-Up:	Use more toys and more pennies as the children can match larger and larger groups.

FIGURE 3-8 One-to-one correspondence activity card—Pennies for toys: Matching real objects.

© Cengage Learning®

Digital Download

English language learners (ELLs), one-to-one correspondence experiences can provide vocabulary support. When playing a matching game, the adult can label the examples. For example:

- When matching toy animals: "**This is a cat. Find another cat.**"

- When passing out materials: "**Give each friend some playdough.**"

- When using a pegboard: "**Put a peg in each hole. You put a red peg in the hole.**"

- Or ask questions that encourage speech: "**What should you look for to match this picture?**"

Finger plays can promote one-to-one correspondence. For example, "Where is Thumbkin?" requires the recognition of one finger at a time. ELL students whose primary language is Spanish can learn popular Latin American fingerplays in Spanish and English (Orozco & Kleven, 1997).

3-1d Informal Post-Evaluation

Informal evaluation can be accomplished by noticing each child's response during adult-guided activities. Also observe

---

ONE-TO-ONE CORRESPONDENCE—PICTURE MATCHING

Objective:	To match groups of pictured things, animals, or people.
Naturalistic and Informal Activity:	Place card sets as described below on a table in one of the classroom learning centers. Observe what the students do with the picture card sets. Do they sort them, match them, and so on? Make comments and ask questions as appropriate.
Materials:	Make or purchase picture cards that show items familiar to young children. Each set should have two groups of ten. Pictures from catalogs, magazines, or readiness workbooks can be cut out, glued on cards, and covered with clear Contac or laminated. For example, pictures of ten children should be put on ten different cards. Pictures of ten toys could be put on ten other cards.
Structured Activity:	Present two people and two toys. **Does each child have a toy? Show me how you can find out.** Increase the number of items in each group.
	Make some more card sets. Fit them to current science or social studies units. For example, if the class is studying jobs, have pilot with plane, driver with bus, etc.

FIGURE 3-9 One-to-one correspondence activity card—Picture matching.

© Cengage Learning®

Digital Download

ONE-TO-ONE CORRESPONDENCE—SIMILAR OR IDENTICAL OBJECTS

Objective:	To match two through ten similar and/or identical objects.
Naturalistic and Informal Activity:	Each day in the math center provide opportunity to explore manipulatives such as inch cube blocks, Unifix Cubes, Lego, and so on. Observe what the students do with the materials. Note if they do any one-to-one correspondence as they explore. Make comments and ask questions as appropriate.
Materials:	Twenty objects such as poker chips, inch cube blocks, coins, cardboard circles, etc. There may be 10 of one color and 10 of another or 20 of the same color (more difficult perceptually).
Structured Activity:	Begin with two groups of two, and increase the size of the groups as the children are able to match the small groups. **Here are two groups (bunches, sets) of chips (blocks, sticks, pennies, etc.). Do they have the same number, or does one group have more? Show me how you know.** Have the children take turns using different sizes of groups and different objects.
Follow-Up:	Glue some objects to a piece of heavy cardboard or plywood. Set out a container of the same kinds of objects. Have this available for matching during center time. Also, place baggies with groups of objects of varied amounts in the math center where students can select pairs of objects for matching.

© Cengage Learning®

FIGURE 3-10 One-to-one correspondence activity card—Similar or identical objects.

Digital Download

each child during learning center play to see whether he or she can pass out toys or food to other children, giving one at a time. On the shelves in the housekeeping area, paper shapes of each item (dishes, cups, tableware, purses, etc.) may be placed on the shelf where the item belongs. Hang pots and pans on a pegboard with the shapes of each pot drawn on the board. Do the same for blocks and other materials. Notice which children can put materials away by making the right match. Using the same procedures as in the assessment tasks, a more formal check can be made regarding what the children have

ONE-TO-ONE CORRESPONDENCE—OBJECTS TO DOTS

Objective:	To match zero to nine objects with zero to nine dots.
Naturalistic and Informal Activity:	In the math center provide sets of picture and conventional dominoes and other materials that lend themselves to one-to-one correspondence. Observe what the students do with the materials. Note if they do any one-to-one correspondence as they explore. Make comments and ask questions as appropriate.
Materials:	Ten frozen juice cans or other identical containers, with dots (filled circles) painted in a dark color on each from zero to nine:

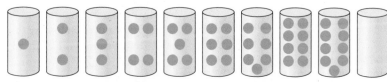

Forty-five tongue depressors or ice cream bar sticks.

Structured Activity:	Give each child a can. Put all the sticks in a container where the children can reach them. **Look at the dots on your can. Put the same number of sticks in your can as there are dots on your can.** Have the children check with each other.
Follow-Up:	Put the can and sticks out during free play. Encourage children who have had a hard time in the group to practice on their own.

© Cengage Learning®

FIGURE 3-11 One-to-one correspondence activity card—Matching the number of objects to the number of dots.

Digital Download

learned. Once children can do one-to-one matching with 10 objects, try more—see how far the children can go.

Technology for Young Children

Try one of the following:

1. If possible, observe a young child interacting with an online activity such as those found at PBS Kids, Nick Jr., Illuminations, or an activity downloaded to a tablet or computer. See whether the activity appears to support the child's ability to engage in one-to-one correspondence.

2. Select instructions for a one-to-one correspondence activity from the Internet. Assemble any materials needed, and use the activity with a small group of pre-K or kindergarten students.

COMMON CORE STATE STANDARDS

3-2 NUMBER SENSE AND COUNTING STANDARDS AND DESCRIPTION

According to CCSSM, by the end of kindergarten, children should be able to count to 100 by 1s and 10s, write numbers from 0 to 20, count 20 objects, and compare groups of objects by matching or counting (CCSSM, 2010). Children in prekindergarten through second grade are also expected to develop an understanding of the relative position and size of whole numbers, ordinal numbers, and cardinal numbers as well as of their connections to each other. Finally, they are expected to develop a sense of whole numbers and be able to represent and use them in many ways. These expectations should be achieved through real-world experiences and by using physical materials. Number sense and counting can be integrated into other content areas (**Figure 3-12**).

DAP NCTM and NAEYC published a joint position statement on early childhood mathematics (NAEYC & NCTM, 2010). The typical knowledge, skills, and sample teaching strategies for ages 3 to 6 were delineated:

- Preschoolers should move from counting four items to counting to 100 by groups of 10.

- They should be able to quickly identify groups of one to three items.

- They should be able to move up to six patterned items.

- They should be able to move from simple subtraction with one to three items and do simple addition using groups of less than 10 (Chapter 7).

3-2a Number Sense and Its Relationship to Counting

The concept of number or understanding number is referred to as **number sense**, which makes the connection between quantities and counting. It underlies the understanding of more and less, relative amounts, the relationship between space and quantity (i.e., number conservation), and parts and wholes of quantities. Number sense enables children to understand important benchmarks, such as 5 and 10, as they relate to other quantities. The concept also helps children estimate quantities and measurements. Counting assists children in understanding quantity. A critical fundamental concept is grasping that the last number named is the quantity in the group. Number sense is the understanding of the oneness of 1, the twoness of 2, and so on (Marshal, 2006). Number sense in first grade predicts later academic success (Neergaard, 2013; Feigenson, Libertus, & Halberda, 2013). Infant studies indicate that number sense in terms of estimating quantities without counting is hard-wired in the brain at birth.

When shown a group, the ability to see "how many" instantly is called **subitizing**. There are two types of subitizing: perceptual and conceptual. **Perceptual subitizing** is when one can state how many items are in a group without actually counting them. Young children usually learn to subitize up to four items perceptually. In other words, when shown a group of one, two, three, or four items, they can tell you "one, two, three, or four" without counting. Perceptual subitizing is thought to be the basis for counting and **cardinality** (understanding that the last number named is the amount in a group).

Conceptual subitizing involves seeing number patterns within a group, such as the larger dot patterns on dominos. The viewer may break down the eight-dot pattern into two groups of four, which make up the whole. This ability develops from counting and patterning and helps in developing number sense and arithmetic skills. Preschoolers can subitize perceptually. Conceptual subitizing for small quantities usually begins in first grade. Clements (1999) suggests some games for kindergarten play that can bridge into conceptual subitizing. Fosnot and Cameron (2007) provide a means of developing number sense through games. Their games are open ended and thus allow for the use of more than one strategy; they are also cooperative and noncompetitive.

Children first recognize quantities from one to four or five. Infants can perceive the difference between these small quantities, and children as young as 2½ or 3 years may recognize these small amounts so easily that they seem to do so without counting. The concept of number is constructed bit by bit from infancy through the preschool years and gradually becomes a tool that can be used in problem solving.

Rote and Rational Counting. Number's partner, counting, includes two operations: rote counting and rational counting. **Rote counting** is the reciting of the names of the numerals

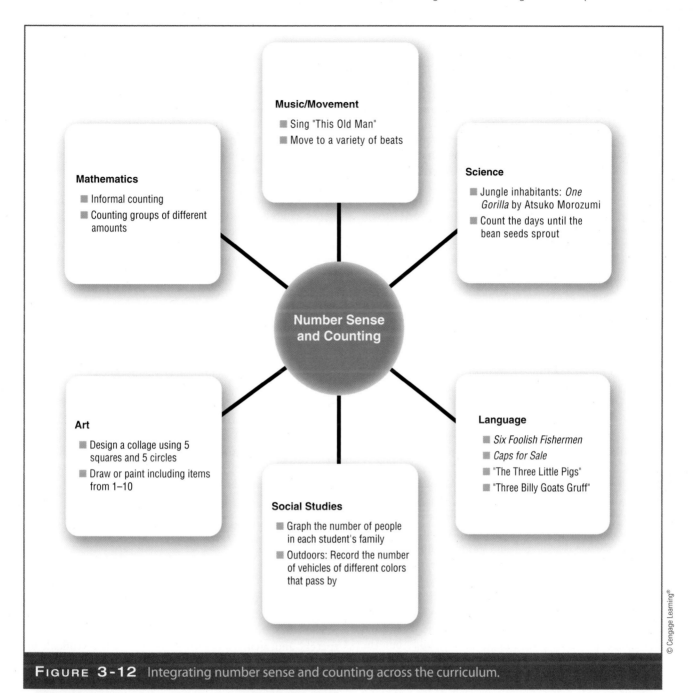

FIGURE 3-12 Integrating number sense and counting across the curriculum.

in order from memory. The child who says, "One, two, three, four, five, six, seven, eight, nine, ten" has correctly counted in a rote manner from 1 to 10. **Rational counting** is matching each numeral name in order to an object in a group. Rational counting builds on children's understanding of one-to-one correspondence; it is a heightened level of one-to-one correspondence. Reys, Lindquist, Lambdin, Smith, and Suydam (2004) identify four principles of rational counting.

1. Only one number name may be assigned to each of the objects to be counted.

2. There is a correct order for assigning the number names (i.e., one, two, three, etc.).

3. Counting can start with any of the items in the group.

4. The *cardinality rule* states that the last number name used is the number of objects in the group.

As an example, Maria has some pennies in her hand. She takes them out of her hand, one at a time, and places them on the table. Each time she places one on the table, she says the next number name in sequence: "one" (places first penny), "two" (places another penny), "three" (places another penny). Maria has successfully done rational counting of three objects. Rational counting to at least 20 is an essential pre-first-grade skill that predicts first-grade math scores (Rasicot, 2012).

BRAIN CONNECTION

NUMBER SENSE AND COUNTING

Building number sense in the brain is a complex activity that depends on the connection between the front language center and the side quantity region of the brain (Tsang, 2013). For preschoolers to have a complete understanding of number, we must support them so they think about all the different aspects of number at the same time. For example, they should play games in which they concurrently (1) count, (2) associate number names with several representations such as groups, movements, or distances, and (3) think about "more" and "less" and other math vocabulary. For example, count groups over and over, but with the items in different orders, and use vocabulary such as *more* and *less, nearer* and *farther,* and *bigger* and *smaller.* Finger counting is widespread but follows different patterns in diverse cultures (Burns, 2012). There is an evolutionary link between hands and counting. The human brain gradually evolved from a simple group of nerve cells to complex groups of specialized cells. The cells that evolved into representing our fingers were recruited to represent our concept of number. As man evolved, finding the need to count fingers became connected to counting. In our brains, our fingers were recruited to serve as counting aids. Even though we may not be using them, our fingers are activated when we do numerical tasks. Children with good finger awareness are better at performing quantitative-type tasks than those with less finger sense.

C. Burns, What Does the Way You Count on Your Fingers Say About Your Brain? Science Blog, June 26, 2012, www.theguardian.com.
J. Tsang, Building Number Sense in the Brain: More Than Just Counting to Ten. Kidadaptive's Blog, March 15, 2013, http://blog.kidadaptive.com.

A basic understanding of accurate rote counting and one-to-one correspondence comprises the foundation of rational counting. The ability of rational counting assists children in understanding the concept of number by enabling them to check their labeling of a quantity as being of a specific amount. It also helps them to compare equal quantities of different things—such as two apples, two children, and two chairs—and to realize that the quantity two is *two,* regardless of what makes up a group. Marshall (2006) emphasizes the importance of understanding that numbers are abstractions and that each refers to its unique amount regardless of what is included in a group. Number, counting, and one-to-one correspondence all serve as the basis for developing the concept of number conservation, which is usually mastered by age 6 or 7. Too often, the preprimary mathematics program centers on counting with repeated teacher-directed drill and practice. Children need repeated and frequent practice to develop counting skills, but the practice should be of short duration and should center on naturalistic and informal instruction. Adult-guided activities should include many applications, such as the following examples of data collection:

- "How many children in the class have brothers? Sisters? Neither?"

- "How many days will it be until the first seed sprouts? Let's make some guesses, and then we'll keep track and see who comes close."

- "How many days did we mark off before the first egg hatched?"

- "How many carrots do we need so that each rabbit will get one?"

- "How many of the small blocks will balance the big block on the balance scale?"

Normally, rote counting develops ahead of rational counting. A 2- or 3-year-old who has a good memory might rote-count to 10 but be able to rational-count only one, two, or three objects accurately. For example, when given a group of more than three to count, a young child might perform as follows: Six blocks are placed in front of a 2½-year-old, who is asked, "How many blocks do you have?" Using her pointer finger, she counts out loud as she points.

- "One, two, three, four, five, six, seven, eight" (pointing at some blocks more than once and some not at all).

- "One, two, four, six, three, ten" (pointing to each block only once but losing track of the correct order).

Rational counting is a fairly complex task. To count objects accurately, the child must know the number names in the correct order and be able to coordinate eyes, hands, speech, and memory (**Photo 3-3**). The task is difficult for

PHOTO 3-3 By age 3 or 4, most children can rational-count small groups.

© 2016 Cengage Learning®

a 2- or 3-year-old because she is still in a period of rapid growth in coordination. She is also limited in her ability to stick to a task. The teacher should not push a child to count more things than he can count easily and with success. Most rational counting experiences should be naturalistic and informal.

By age 4 or 5, children's rate of physical growth is slowing. Their coordination of eyes, hands, and memory is maturing. Rational counting skills should begin to catch up with rote counting skills. Adult-guided activities can be introduced, and naturalistic and informal activities should continue.

During the kindergarten year, children usually become skilled at rote and rational counting. Many kindergartners are ready to play more complex games with quantities, such as counting backward and counting on from a given quantity. Counting backward and counting on lay the foundation for the whole-number operations of addition and subtraction. Estimation activities can begin with prekindergartners playing simple games such as "Guess how many beans are in a small jar?" or "How many paper clips wide is the table?" Questions like these should be followed by checking the children's guesses by counting the beans and paper clips.

In *Number in Preschool and Kindergarten* (1982), Kamii emphasizes that the need to be aware of the coordination of one-to-one correspondence and counting in the development of the concept of number. Four levels of development in counting have been identified by asking children to put out the same number of items as an adult does in groups of four to eight.

1. Children cannot understand what they are supposed to do.

2. They do a rough visual estimation or copy (i.e., they attempt to make their group look like the model).

3. They do a methodical one-to-one correspondence. Children seldom reach this stage before age 5½.

4. They count. They count the items in the model and then count out another group with the same amount. Children usually reach this stage at about age 7.

To develop the coordination of the two concepts, children must be able to count and do one-to-one correspondence using movable objects. Obviously, among their other weaknesses, the use of workbook pages precludes moving the objects to be counted and/or matched. In addition, opportunities should be provided for children to work together so that they can discuss and compare ideas. As the children work individually and/or with others, watch closely and note the thinking process that seems to take place as they solve problems using counting and one-to-one correspondence. The objects selected for counting are important (Petersen & McNeil, 2013). Petersen and McNeil found that perceptually rich unfamiliar objects are most effective for children's performance.

3-2b Informal Pre-Assessment

The adult should note the child's regular activity. Does she recognize groups of zero to four without counting? "Mary has no cookies"; "I have two cookies"; "John has four cookies." Does she use rational counting correctly when needed? "Here, Mr. Black, six blocks for you." (Mr. Black has seen her count them out on her own.) For formal assessment, see the tasks on pages 77, 88, 98 and 105, and those in Appendix A. Be sure to record naturalistic and informal events.

DAP **naeyc**

3-2c Activities

Young children use a great deal of number sense and counting skills in their everyday activities. Once these are in a child's thoughts and activity, he will be observed often engaging in number and counting activities.

Naturalistic Activities. A child may practice rote counting often during regular activities. She may run up to her teacher or parent saying, "I can count—one, two, three." She may be watching a TV program and hear "one, two, three, four, …," after which she repeats "one, two, …" At first she may play with the number names, saying "one, two, five, four, eight, …" to herself in no special order. Over time, listen carefully, and note that gradually she gets more and more of the names in the right order.

The number concept appears often in the child's activities once he has the idea in mind. A child is eating crackers and says, "Look at all my crackers. I have two crackers." One and two are usually the first amounts used by 2- and 3-year-old children. They may use one and two for quite a while before they go on to larger groups. Number names are used for an early form of division. For example, a child has three cookies, which he divides equally with his friends: "One for you, one for you, and one for me." Looking at a picture book, the child says, "There is one daddy and two babies." The child wants another toy: "I want one more little car, Dad."

Informal Activities. The alert adult can find a multitude of ways to take advantage of opportunities for informal instruction. For example, the child is watching a children's TV program while a parent is sitting next to her. A voice from the TV rote-counts by singing, "One, two, three, four, five, six." The parent says to the child, "That's fun, let's count, too." They then sing together: "One, two, three, four, five, six." Or a teacher and children are waiting for the school bus to arrive. "Let's count as far as we can while we wait. One, two, three …" Because rote counting is learned through frequent but short periods of practice, such informal activities should be used most for teaching.

Everyday activities also offer many opportunities for informal rational counting and number activities. For instance, the teacher is helping a child get dressed after his nap. "Find your shoes and socks. How many shoes do you have? How many socks? How many feet?" "Do you have the same

DAP **naeyc**

SAMPLE ASSESSMENT TASK

4G PREOPERATIONAL AGES 3–6

ROTE COUNTING: CHAPTER 3

METHOD Interview, individual.

SKILL Demonstrates the ability to rote-count.

MATERIALS None.

PROCEDURE "Count as far as you can. One, two, what's next?"

EVALUATION Note how far the child counts and the accuracy of the counting.

Young children often lose track (i.e., "One, two, three, four, five, six, ten, seven, …"), or they miss a number name. Children ages 2 and 3 may be able to count only to their ages, whereas 4-year-olds usually can count accurately to 10 and might try the teens and even beyond. By age 5 or 6, children usually begin to understand the commonalities

in the 20s and beyond, and they move on toward counting to 100. At each age level, young children vary a great deal, so it is important to find where each individual is and to move along from there.

INSTRUCTIONAL RESOURCE
R. Charlesworth, *Math and Science for Young Children*, 8th ed., San Francisco, CA: Cengage Learning, 2016.

Digital Download

DAP **naeyc**

SAMPLE ASSESSMENT TASK

4H PREOPERATIONAL AGES 3–6

RATIONAL COUNTING: CHAPTER 3

METHOD Interview, individual, or small group.

SKILL Child demonstrates the ability to rational-count.

MATERIALS Thirty or more objects such as cube blocks, chips, or Unifix Cubes.

PROCEDURE Place a pile of objects in front of the child (about 10 for a 3-year-old, 20 for a 4-year-old, 30 for a 5-year-old, and as many as 100 for older children). "**Count**

these for me. How many can you count?"

EVALUATION Note how accurately the child counts and how many objects he attempts to count. While observing, note the following.

1. Does the child use just his eyes, or does he actually touch each object as he counts?

2. Does the child use an organizational system, such as lining

up the objects in rows or moving the ones counted to the side?

3. Compare the child's rational-counting accuracy with his rote-counting ability.

INSTRUCTIONAL RESOURCE
R. Charlesworth, *Math and Science for Young Children*, 8th ed., San Francisco, CA: Cengage Learning, 2016.

Digital Download

---

number of feet and shoes?" Some children are meeting at the door. The teacher says, "We are going to the store. There should be five of us. Let's count and be sure we are all here."

Table setting offers many chances for rational counting. "Put six place mats on each table." "How many more forks do we need?" "Count out four napkins." Play activities also offer times for rational counting. "Mary, please give Tommy two trucks." A child is looking at his hands, which are covered with finger paint: "How many red hands do you have, Juan?"

Present a more challenging problem by asking an open-ended question. For instance: "Get enough napkins for everyone at your table," or "Be sure everyone has the same number of carrot sticks." In these situations, children aren't given a clue to help them decide how many they need

or how many each person should get. They must figure out how to solve the problem on their own. Often children will forget to count themselves. This presents an excellent opportunity for group discussion to try to figure out what went wrong. The teacher could follow up such an incident by reading a book, such as *Six Foolish Fishermen* (Elkin, 1968/1971; see Appendix B), in which the fishermen make the same mistake.

Adult-Guided Activities. Although rote counting is learned mostly through naturalistic and informal activities, short, fun activities such as rhymes, songs, and finger plays can also be used to help children learn the number names in the right order. Classic songs include "This Old Man," "Johnny Works with One Hammer," and "Five Little Ducks."

A favorite old rhyme is as follows:

One, two, buckle your shoe.
Three, four, shut the door.
Five, six, pick up sticks.
Seven, eight, shut the gate.
Nine, ten, a big fat hen.

Or a finger play can be used, such as "Five Little Birdies." Hold up five fingers. As each bird leaves, "fly" your hand away and come back with one less finger standing up.

Five little birdies sitting by the door,
One flew away and then there were four.
Four little birdies sitting in a tree,
One flew away and then there were three.
Three little birdies sitting just like you,
One flew away and then there were two.
Two little birdies having fun,
One flew away and then there was one.
One little birdie sitting all alone,
He flew away and then there were none.

More direct ways of practicing rote counting are also effective. Clapping and counting at the same time teaches number order and gives practice in rhythm and coordination. With a group, everyone can count at the same time, "Let's count together. One, two, three …" Or ask individual children, "Count as far as you can."

Groups of zero to four items are special in the development of rational counting skills. Children perceive the number of items in groups in this range without counting, and so these groups are easy for children to understand. Children should have many experiences and activities with groups of size zero to four before they work with groups of five and more. With adult-guided activities, start with groups of two because so many groups of two occur naturally. For example, the child has two eyes, two hands, two arms, and two legs. Two pieces of bread are used to make a sandwich, and riding a bike with two wheels is a sign of being big. For this reason, activities using two are presented first in the following examples.

DAP naeyc

ACTIVITIES

NUMBER: GROUPS OF TWO

Objective: To learn the concept of two.

Materials: The children's bodies, the environment, a document camera, interactive whiteboard, flannelboard and/or a magnetic board, pairs of objects, pictures of pairs of objects.

Naturalistic and informal activities: As children play with materials in the classroom, note any occasions when they identify two objects. Ask questions such as "How many shoes do you need for your dress-up outfit?" or "Can two cups of sand fill the bowl?"

Adult-guided activities:

1. Put several pairs of felt pieces (e.g., hearts, triangles, or bunnies) on the flannelboard (or magnets on the magnet board), or use the document camera or interactive whiteboard. Point to each group in turn: "What are these? How many are there?"

2. Have the children check their bodies and the other children's bodies for groups of two.

3. Have the children, one at a time, find groups of two in the room.

4. Using rummy cards, other purchased picture cards, or cards you have made, make up sets of cards with identical pairs. Give each child a pack with several pairs mixed up. Have them sort the pack and find the groups of two.

5. Fill a container with many objects. Have the children sort out as many groups of two as they can find.

Follow-up: Have the materials available during center time.

Digital Download

ACTIVITIES

NUMBER: GROUPS OF THREE

Objective: To learn the concept of three.

Materials: Document camera, interactive whiteboard, flannelboard and/or magnet board, objects, picture cards.

Naturalistic and informal activities: As children play with materials in the classroom, note any occasions when they identify three objects. Ask leading questions, such as, if three children are playing house: "How many cups do you need for your party? Can three cups of sand fill the bowl?" Or to a 3-year-old: "How many candles were on your birthday cake?"

Activities: Do the same types of activities as before, now using groups of three instead of two. Emphasize that three is one more than two.

Follow-up: Have the materials available during center time.

Digital Download

ACTIVITIES

NUMBER: GROUPS OF ONE

Objective: To learn the concept that one is a group.

Materials: Document camera, interactive whiteboard, flannelboard and/or magnet board, objects, picture cards.

Naturalistic and informal activities: As children play with materials in the classroom, note any occasions when they identify a single object. Ask such questions as "How many cups does each person need for the party?" "How many glasses does each person get for milk at lunch?"

Adult-guided activities: Do the same types of activities using groups of one as were done for groups of two and three.

Follow-up: Have the materials available during center time.

Digital Download

ACTIVITIES

NUMBER: ZERO

Objective: To understand the idea that a group with nothing in it is called zero.

Naturalistic and informal activities: Note whether children use the terms none or zero during their play activities. Ask questions such as **"If all the sand falls on the floor, how much will be left in the sandbox?"** **"If you eat all of your beans, then how many will you have left?"**

Materials: Document camera, interactive whiteboard, flannelboard, magnet board, and objects.

Adult-guided activities:

1. Show the children groups of things on the flannelboard, magnet board, or use the document camera or interactive whiteboard and/or groups of objects. **"See all these things?"** Give them a chance to look and respond. **"Now I take them away. What do I have now?"** They should respond saying "nothing," "all gone," and/or "no more."

2. Put out a group (of flannel pieces, magnet shapes, or objects) of a size the children all know (such as one, two, three, or four). Keep taking one away. **"How many now?"** When none are left, say, **"This amount is called zero."** Repeat the activity until they can answer "zero" on their own.

3. Play a silly game. Ask, **"How many real live tigers do we have in our room?"** (Continue with other things that obviously are not in the room.)

Follow-up: Work on the concept informally. Ask questions: "How many children are here after everyone goes home?" After their snack, if all the food has been eaten: "How many cookies (crackers, pretzels, etc.) do you have now?" At NCTM's Illuminations website, children can use the online computer or iPad to do the activities *Let's Count to Five*. Ideas for helping children with understanding zero include nursery rhymes and songs and activities on the National Library of Virtual Manipulatives website.

Digital Download

After the children have grasped the ideas of groups of one, two, and three, go on to four, and finally to zero. Use the same kinds of activities. Once the students have these quantities in mind, go on to activities using groups of five. As you move to each larger group, emphasize the idea of *one more than*.

When the children have the idea of groups from zero to four, they can go on to larger groups. Some children are able to perceive five without counting, just as they perceive zero through four without actually counting. Having learned the groups of four and fewer, children can be taught five by adding one to groups of four. Once the children understand five as "four with one more" and six as "five with one more," then they can begin more advanced rational counting. The children can work with groups whose number they can find only by actually counting each object. An activity that provides a treat is counting Cheerios (see the *Cheerios Counting Book*, 2000, by Will and Barbara McGrath, Cartwheel/Scholastic, New York).

Before working with a child on counting groups of six or more, the adult must be sure the child can do the following activities:

- Recognize groups of zero to four without counting.

- Rote-count to six or more correctly and quickly.

- Recognize that a group of five is a group of four with one more added.

A number of activities can be used when children are learning about groups larger than four.

ACTIVITIES

NUMBER: USING GROUPS OF ZERO THROUGH FOUR

Objective: To understand groups of zero through four.

Materials: Document camera, interactive whiteboard, flannelboard, magnet board, and/or objects.

1. Show the children several groups of objects of different amounts. Ask them to point to groups of one, two, three, and four.

2. Give the children a container of many objects. Have them find groups of one, two, three, and four.

3. Show the children containers of objects (pennies, buttons, etc.). Ask them to find the containers with groups of zero, one, two, three, and four.

4. Give each child four objects. Ask each one to make as many different groups as she can.

5. Ask the children to find out, **"How many [name something] are in the room?"** (Suggest things for which there are fewer than five.)

ACTIVITIES

NUMBER/RATIONAL COUNTING: INTRODUCING FIVE

Objective: To understand that five is four with one more item added.

Materials: Document camera, interactive whiteboard, flannelboard, magnet board, and/or objects.

Naturalistic and informal activities: Have a variety of manipulatives in the math center. Note how children group the materials and whether they mention "how many." For example, "I have five red cubes" or "I need three green cubes." Ask questions such as, **"How many white cubes have you hooked together?"**

Adult-guided activities:

1. Show the children a group of four. **"How many in this group?"** Show the children a group of five. **"How many in this group?"** Note how many children already have the idea of five. Tell them, **"Yes, this is a group of five."** Have them make other groups with the same amount by using the first group as a model.

2. Give each child five objects. Ask them to identify how many objects they have.

3. Give each child seven or eight objects. Ask them to make a group of five.

Follow-up: Have containers of easily counted and perceived objects (such as buttons, poker chips, Unifix Cubes, and inch cubes) always available for the children to explore. Use books that focus on five, such as *Five Little Ducks* (Raffi, 1992) and *Five Little Monkeys Sitting in a Tree* (Christelow, 2007).

Children from ages 4 to 6 can play simple group games that require them to apply their counting skills. For example, a bowling game requires them to count the number of pins they knock down. A game in which they try to drop clothespins into a container requires them to count the number of clothespins that land in the container. They can compare the number of pins knocked down or the number of clothespins dropped into the containers by each child. By age 6 or 7, children can keep a cumulative score, using tally marks (see **Figure 3-13**). Not only can they count, they can compare amounts to find out who has the most and whether any of them have the same amount. Older children (see Chapter 7) will be interested in writing numerals and might realize that, instead of tally marks, they can write down the numeral that represents the amount to be recorded.

Students who are skilled at counting enjoy sorting small objects such as colored macaroni, beads, miniature animals, or buttons. At first they might be given a small amount, such

as 10 items, to work with. They can compare the amounts in the groups that they construct as well as comparing the amounts in their groups with a partner's. Two- to 3-year-olds enjoy counting Cheerios with the *Cheerios Counting Book* (McGrath & McGrath, 2000). Eventually they can move on to larger groups of objects and to more complex

Student	Score
Derrick	//////
Liu Pei	////////
Brent	////
Theresa	///////

FIGURE 3-13 By age 6 or 7, children can keep a cumulative score using tally marks.

ACTIVITIES

NUMBER/RATIONAL COUNTING: GROUPS LARGER THAN FIVE

Objective: To be able to count groups of amounts greater than five.

Materials: Document camera, interactive whiteboard, flannelboard and/or magnet board, objects for counting, pictures of groups on cards, items in the environment.

Naturalistic and informal activities: Have a variety of manipulatives in the math center. Note how children group the materials and whether they mention "how many," such as "I have seven red cubes" or "I need six green cubes." Ask questions such as, **"How many white cubes have you hooked together? If you hooked one more cube to your line, how many would you have?"**

Adult-guided activities:

1. One step at a time, present groups on the flannelboard, magnet board, document camera, interactive whiteboard or groups made up of objects such as buttons, chips, inch-cube blocks, and so on. Have the children take turns counting them, together and individually.

2. Present cards with groups of six or more, showing cats, dogs, houses, or similar figures. Ask the children as a group or individually to tell how many items are pictured on each card.

3. Give the children small containers with items to count.

4. Count things in the room. **"How many tables [or chairs, windows, doors, children, teachers]?"** Have the children count all at the same time and individually.

Follow-up: Have the materials available for use during center time. Watch for opportunities for informal activities.

Digital Download

ACTIVITIES

RATIONAL COUNTING: FOLLOW-UP WITH ONE-TO-ONE CORRESPONDENCE

Objective: To combine one-to-one correspondence and counting.

Materials: Document camera, interactive whiteboard, flannelboard and/or magnet board and counting objects.

Activities: As the children work with the counting activities, have them check their groups that they say are the same number by using one-to-one correspondence. See the activities for this chapter.

Follow-up: Have the materials available during center time.

Digital Download

activities, such as recording data with number symbols and constructing graphs (see Chapter 5).

Another activity that builds number concepts is the 100-days celebration. Starting on the first day of school, the class uses concrete materials to record how many days of school have gone by. Attach two large, clear plastic cups to the bulletin board. As a recording device, each day, place a drinking straw or tongue depressor into the cup on the right. Also, count in unison the number of days of school, and add another object to the cup. Ten is used as an informal benchmark. Whenever 10 items are collected, bundle them with a rubber band, and place them in the left-hand cup. Explain that when the left-hand cup has 10 bundles, it will be the 100th day.

On the 100th day, each child brings a plastic zip-top bag containing 100 items. It is exciting to see what they bring: pennies, short lengths of string, buttons, pieces of ribbon, raisins, beads, marbles, and so on. Working in pairs, they can check their collections by counting out groups of 10 and counting how many groups they have. To aid their organization, large mats with 10 circles on each or 10 clear plastic glasses can be supplied. Late 4-year-olds as well as kindergarten and primary-grade students enjoy this activity.

Kindergartners can work with simple problem-solving challenges. Schulman and Eston (1998) describe a type of problem that kindergartners find intriguing. The children in the example were in the second half of kindergarten and had previously worked in small groups. The basic situation was demonstrated as the "carrot and raisin" problem.

Jackie had carrots and raisins on her plate. She had seven items in all. What did Jackie have on her plate?

The children selected orange rods and small stones to represent carrots and raisins, respectively. They were given paper plates to use as work mats. When they had a solution that worked, they recorded it by drawing a picture. As they worked and shared ideas, they realized that many different groupings were surfacing. They recorded all the solutions. Of course, what they were discovering were the facts that compose seven. This same context then led to other problems of varying degrees of difficulty (sea stars and hermit crabs in a tide pool, pineapples and pears in a fruit basket, seeds that germinated and seeds that didn't). Some children continued with random strategies while others discovered organized strategies.

Other kinds of problem-solving activities can provide challenges for children learning to count. The activities in "Bears in the House and in the Park" provide simple word problems for pre-K–2 students (Greenes et al., 2003). Using teddy bear counters or chips, children model problems such as the following.

> *Story Problem 1*
> *There are two bears in the kitchen.*
> *There are three bears in the living room.*
> *How many bears are downstairs? (Five) (p. 11)*

Copley (2004) includes activities such as "Hanny Learns to Count from the Prairie Dogs," "Benny's Pennies," and "How Many Are Hiding?"

Quite a bit of computer software, website resources, and apps have been designed to reinforce counting skills and the number concept. Five-year-old George sits at the computer, deeply involved with the online game, *How Many Bugs in a Box?* He presses the keys that solve each problem. His friend Kate joins him and comments on the bug pictures. They both count the figures in each group and compare the results. The technology box includes a list of counting resources that the reader might wish to review.

Technology for Young Children

Try to obtain some of the software or explore online resources. Write a review of each of the items you view.

- *Reader Rabbit's Math Ages 4–6*
- *Math Blaster Ages 4–6*
- *Caillou Counting*
- *How Many Bugs in a Box*
- *The Counts Countdown CD*
- *Learning about Numbers, 123 Count with Me, Counting Carnival, Elmo's Magic Numbers, Counting with Elmo*
- *Math on the PBS Kids website has a large selection of online games*

Also check on the counting and number sense activities found at NCTM's Illuminations website.

3-2d Helping Children with Special Needs

Most young children learn to count and develop number sense through informal everyday experiences and through books and rhymes, but others need additional teacher-guided experiences. Some children need extra verbalization through finger plays and rhymes. Others need more multisensory experiences using their motor, tactual, auditory, and visual senses. Some examples are presented here:

- Jumping up and down on a trampoline, saying "One, one, one …" to get an understanding of the unit.
- Doing other exercises and counting the number of movements.
- Connecting with nursery rhymes, such as by seeing how many times children can jump over a candlestick after reciting "Jack Be Nimble."

Rational counting follows a prescribed sequence that should take on a rhythmical pattern. Children can be helped to achieve this goal through the following types of activities:

- Counting objects while putting them into containers provides an auditory-tactile-verbal experience. Various types of containers can be used. Cube blocks or large beads can be dropped and counted. Children who have difficulty with motor control may need to take a break between dropping each block, or an adult can hand the blocks over one at a time.
- Self-correcting form boards or pegboards as well as Montessori cylinder boards can be used to help in developing counting and number sense.

Some children have difficulty organizing their work. They may count a group in a random manner. They may need to be taught to methodically pick up each object for counting and put each into a new place. Start with straight lines, and then move to irregular patterns. Gradually move toward asking the child to count out a specific number of objects, and count each object with the child.

Most young children enjoy learning a new language. As ELL students learn to count in English, English-speaking students can learn to count in a second language.

3-2e Informal Post-Evaluation

Informal evaluation can be done by noting the children's answers given during adult-guided instruction sessions. The teacher should also observe the children during center time and notice whether they apply what they have learned. When children choose to explore materials used in the adult guided lessons during center time, the teacher can ask questions. For instance, Kaitlin is at the flannelboard, arranging the felt shapes in rows. As her teacher goes by, he stops and asks, "How many bunnies do you have in that row?" If four children are playing house, the teacher can ask, "How many children in this family?"

Formal evaluation can be done with one child by using tasks such as those in Appendix A or asking questions such as those below. Portfolios can provide material demonstrating children's progress. "Hundreds" collections and graphs can be placed in portfolios. Photos of children working with materials might also be included. Anecdotes and checklists can be used to record milestones in number concept growth and development.

Kathy Richardson (1999, p. 7) provides questions to guide evaluation of counting and number sense. Some key questions for counting are:

- To what amount can children work with (i.e., five, ten, twelve, etc.)?

- What kinds of errors do the children make? Are they consistent or random?

- Do they stick with the idea of one-to-one correspondence as they count?

- Are they accurate? Do they check their results?

- Do they remember the number they counted to and realize that is the amount in the group (cardinal number)?

Here are some key questions to consider when evaluating number sense:

- Can the children subitize perceptually, that is, recognize small groups of four or five without counting?

- Knowing the amount in one group, can they use that information to figure out how many are in another group?

- Can children make reasonable estimates of the amount in a group and revise their estimate after counting some items?

- When items are added to a group that they have already counted, do children count on or start over?

The answers to these questions help you evaluate whether the children understand the concepts of number and number sense.

3-3 LOGIC AND CLASSIFICATION STANDARDS FOR SCIENCE AND MATH

The Core Curriculum State Standards for Mathematics (CCSSM) for the end of kindergarten states that children will be able to classify objects and count the number of objects in categories (National Governors, 2010). NGSS science standard K-LS1-1 states, "Scientists look for patterns and order when making observations about the world"; the idea is for students to emulate what scientists do when they are doing science activities. The NCTM (2000) standards include more detailed expectations for logic and classifying focus on the ability of children:

- To sort, classify, and order objects by size, number, and other properties (see also the last section of this chapter and Chapter 5)

- To sort and classify objects according to their attributes

- To organize data about the objects (see also Chapter 5)

In science as well as mathematics, an understanding of **logical grouping** and classifying is essential. Constructing logical groups provides children with valuable logical thinking experiences. As children construct logical groups, they organize materials by classifying them according to some common criteria. A group may contain from zero (an empty group) to an endless number of things. The youngest children may group materials by criteria that are not apparent to adults, but that make sense to them. As children develop, they gradually begin constructing groups for which the criteria are apparent to adults. Children also note common groupings they observe in their environment: Dishes that have the same pattern go together, and cars have four tires plus a spare, making a total of five in the group. Logical thinking and classification skills are fundamental concepts that apply across the curriculum (**Figure 3-14**).

To **add** is to put together or to join groups. For example, the four tires on the wheels plus the spare in the trunk equals five tires. To **subtract** is to separate a group into smaller groups. One tire goes flat and is taken off. It is left for repairs, and the spare is put on. A group of one (the flat tire) has been taken away or subtracted from the group of five. There are now two groups: four good tires on the car and one flat tire being repaired.

Before doing any formal addition and subtraction, children need to learn about groups and how they can join and separate them (**Figure 3-15**). In other words, children must practice **sorting** (separating) and **grouping** (joining). This type of activity is called **classification**. The child performs tasks in which he separates and groups things because they belong together for some reason. The groups may belong together because they are the same color or the same shape, do the same work, are the same size, are always together, and so on. For example, a child may have a box of wooden blocks and a box of toy cars (wood, metal, and plastic). The child has two groups: blocks and cars. He then takes the blocks out of the box and separates them by grouping them into four piles: blue blocks, red blocks, yellow blocks, and green blocks. He now has four groups of blocks. He builds a garage with the red blocks. He puts some cars in the garage. He now has a new group of toys. If he has put only red cars in the garage, he now has a group of red toys. The blocks and toys could be grouped in many other ways by using shape (large, medium, and small) and material (wood, plastic, and metal) as the basis for the groups. **Figure 3-16** illustrates some possible groups using the blocks and cars.

Young children spend much of their playtime in just such classification activities. As children work busily at these sorting tasks, they simultaneously learn words that label the activities. This happens when another person tells them the names and makes comments: "You have made a big pile of red things." "You have a pile of blue blocks and a pile of green blocks." "Those are plastic, and those are wood." As children learn to speak, the adult questions them: "What color are these? Which ones are plastic?" "How many _____?" For the child to count, the adult must identify a specific group.

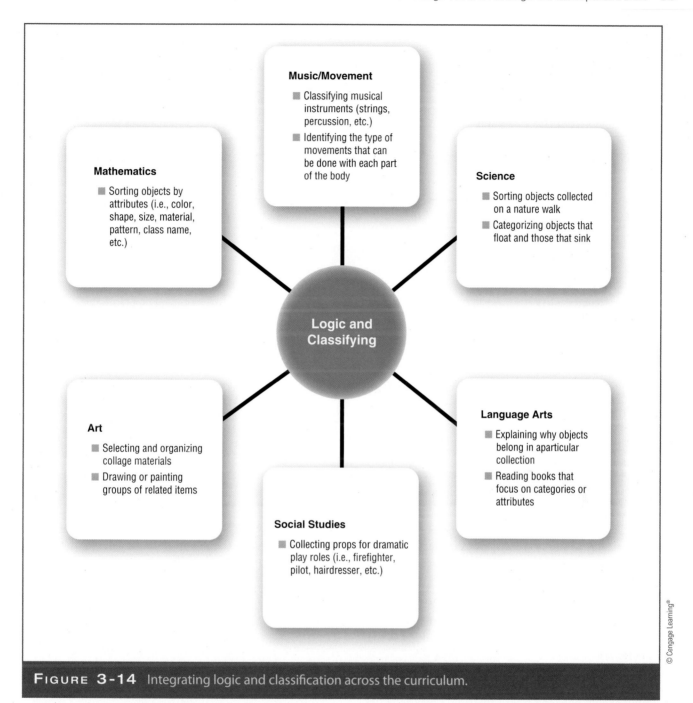

Figure 3-14 Integrating logic and classification across the curriculum.

The child learns that things may be grouped together using several kinds of common features.

- **Color:** Things can go together that are the same color.
- **Shape:** Things may all be round, square, triangular, and so on.
- **Size:** Some things are big and some are small; some are fat and some are thin; some are short and some are tall.
- **Material:** Things are made out of different materials, such as wood, plastic, glass, paper, cloth, or metal.
- **Pattern:** Things have different visual patterns—such as stripes, dots, or flowers—or they may be plain (no design).

- **Texture:** Things feel different from each other (smooth, rough, soft, hard, wet, dry).
- **Function:** Some items do the same thing or are used for the same thing (e.g., all in a group are for eating, writing, or playing music).
- **Association:** Some things do a job together (candle and match, milk and glass, shoe and foot), come from the same place (bought at the store or seen at the zoo), or belong to a special person (the hose, truck, and hat belong to the firefighter).
- **Class name:** Some names may belong to several things (people, animals, food, vehicles, weapons, clothing, homes).

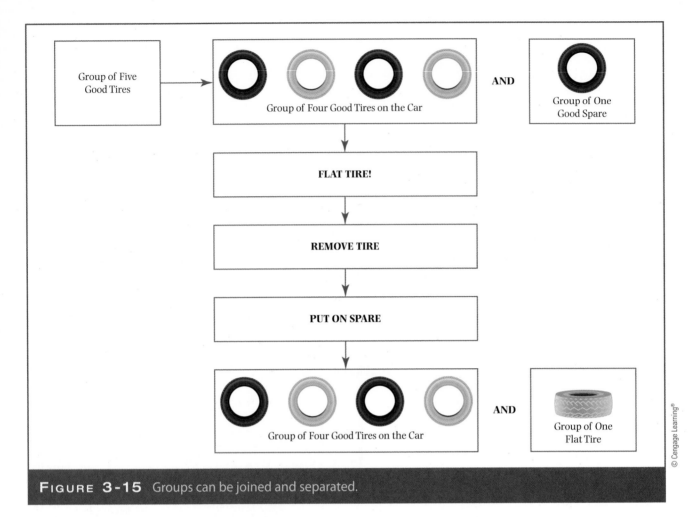

Figure 3-15 Groups can be joined and separated.

- **Common features:** All have handles or windows or doors or legs or wheels, for example.
- **Number:** All are groups of specific amounts (see section 3.2 in this chapter), such as pairs and groups of three, four, five, and so forth.

Which criteria children select or exactly how they group are not as important as their process of logical thinking as they sort and group.

3-3a Informal Pre-Assessment

The adult should note and record the child's play activities. Does she sort and group her play materials? For example, she might play with a pegboard and put each color peg in its own row, or she might build two garages with big cars in one and small cars in another. When offered several kinds of crackers for snack, she might pick out only triangular shapes. She might say, "Only boys can be daddies—girls are mothers." More formal assessment can be made using the tasks in Appendix A. Two examples are shown on p. 98.

3-3b Activities

Naturalistic Activities. Sorting and grouping are some of the most basic and natural activities for young children.

Much of their play involves organizing and reorganizing the things in their world. Infants learn the group of people who take care of them most of the time (child care provider, mother, father, relatives, or friends), while others are put into the group of "strangers." They learn that some objects, when pressed on their gums, reduce the pain of growing teeth. These fall into the group of teething things.

As soon as children are able to sit up, they find great fun in putting things into containers and dumping them out. They can never have too many boxes, plastic dishes, and coffee cans, along with such items as large plastic beads, table tennis balls, and teething toys. (Be sure the items are too large to swallow.) With this type of activity, children have their first experiences making groups.

By age 3, children sort and group items to help organize their play activities. They sort out from their things those that they need for what they want to do. They may pick out wild animal toys for their zoo, people dolls for family play, big blocks for a house, blue paper circles to paste on paper, girls or boys for friends, and so on (**Photo 3-4**).

Informal Activities. Adults can let children know that sorting and grouping activities are of value in informal ways by showing that they approve of what the children

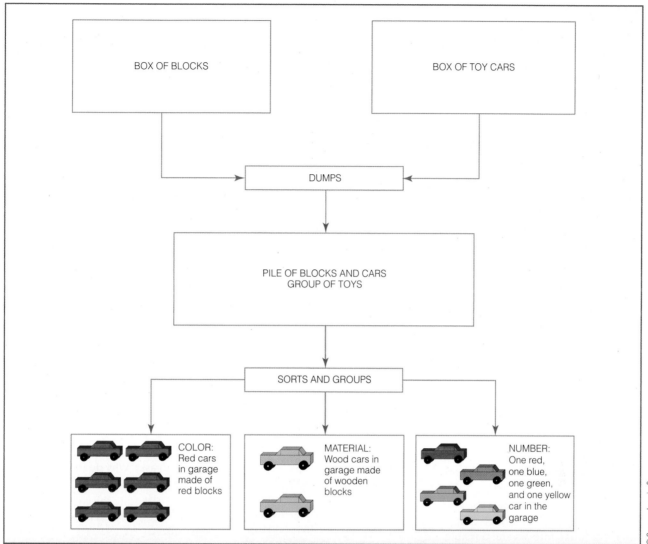

FIGURE 3-16 Classification (forming groups) may be evident in children's play—as with this child, who sorts blocks and cars into several logical groupings.

PHOTO 3-4 The child sorts out the Duplo blocks that fit her building plan.

are doing. This can be done with a look, smile, nod, or comment.

Adults can also build children's classification vocabulary in informal ways. They can label the child's product and ask questions about what the child has done:

- "You have used all blue confetti in your picture."

- "You've used all the square blocks."

- "You have the pigs in this barn and the cows in that barn."

- "You painted green and purple stripes today."

- "I see you put the wild animals here and the farm animals over there."

- "You separated the spoons from the forks."

- "You put the crayons in the can and the pencils in the box."

SAMPLE ASSESSMENT TASK

5J   PREOPERATIONAL AGES 4–6

LOGIC AND CLASSIFYING, CLUE SORT: CHAPTER 3

METHOD Interview.

SKILL The child is able to classify and form groups using verbal and/or object clues.

MATERIALS 20 to 25 objects (or pictures of objects or cutouts) that can be grouped into several possible groups according to criteria such as color, shape, size, or category (e.g., animals, plants, furniture, clothing, or toys).

PROCEDURE Set all the objects in front of the child in a random arrangement. Try the following types of clues.

1. **"Find some things that are [name a specific color, shape, size, material, pattern, function, or class]."**

2. Hold up one object, picture, or cutout; say, "Find some things that belong with this." After the choices are made, ask, **"Why do these things belong together?"**

EVALUATION Note whether the child makes a conventional logical group and provides a conventional logical reason such as "because they are cars," "they are all green," "you can eat with them." Or does he have a creative reason that is logical to the child if not to the adult; for example: "My mother would like them," "They all have points," or "I like these colors, but I don't like those."

INSTRUCTIONAL RESOURCE
R. Charlesworth, *Math and Science for Young Children*, 8th ed., San Francisco, CA: Cengage Learning, 2016.

SAMPLE ASSESSMENT TASK

5K   PREOPERATIONAL AGES 4–6

LOGIC AND CLASSIFYING, FREE SORT: CHAPTER 3

METHOD Interview.

SKILL Child is able to classify and form sets in a free sort.

MATERIALS 20 to 25 objects (or pictures of objects or cutouts) that can be grouped into several possible sets according to criteria such as color, shape, size, or category (e.g., animals, plants, furniture, clothing, or toys).

PROCEDURE Set all the objects in front of the child in a random arrangement. Say, **"Put the things together that belong together."** If the child looks puzzled, backtrack to the previous task, hold up one item, and say, **"Find some things that belong with this."** When a group is completed, say, **"Now find some other things that belong together."** Keep on until all the items are grouped. Then point to each group and ask, **"Why do these things belong together?"**

EVALUATION Note the criteria that the child uses, as listed in task 5J, Appendix A.

INSTRUCTIONAL RESOURCE
R. Charlesworth, *Math and Science for Young Children*, 8th ed., San Francisco, CA: Cengage Learning, 2016.

- "Show me which things will roll down the ramp."
- "Which seeds are from your apple? Which are from your orange?"
- "I see you put the hamsters in the silver cage and the mice in the brown cage."

As children's vocabularies increase, they become able to label and describe how and why they are sorting and grouping. In addition, words give them shortcuts for labeling groups.

Adult-Guided Activities. Sorting and grouping, which form the basis of classification, lend themselves to many activities with many materials **(Photo 3-5)**. As discussed in Chapter 1, real objects are used first, and then representations of objects (e.g., cutouts, pictures) can be used.

PHOTO 3-5   These cards can be sorted by shape and/or color.

Charlesworth

One-to-one correspondence skills go hand in hand with sorting and grouping. For example, given three houses and three pigs, children may give each pig a house (three groups) or place the pigs in one group and the houses in another (two groups).

The following activities help children develop the ability to construct groups.

NGSS Classification is one of the most important fundamental skills in science. Scientists look for patterns and order when making observations about the

---

ACTIVITIES

LOGIC AND CLASSIFICATION: COLOR

Naturalistic classifying and sorting take place during young children's daily play activities.

Objective: To sort and group by color.

Materials: Several different objects that are the same color and four objects each of a different color. For example, a red toy car, a red block, a red bead, a red ribbon, a red sock; and one yellow car, one green ribbon, one blue ball, and one orange piece of paper.

Naturalistic and informal activities: Provide students with many opportunities to experiment with color. Provide objects and art materials such as crayons, paint, colored paper, and the like. Label the colors: **"You have lots of green in your picture. You've used all red Lego blocks."** Note when the children label the colors: "Please pass me a piece of *yellow* paper." "I can't find my *orange* crayon." Ask questions: **"Which colors will you use for your penguins?"**

Adult-guided activities:

1. Hold up one red object and say, **"Find the things that are the same color as this."** After all the red things have been found: **"These things are all the same color. Tell me the name of the color."** If there is no correct answer: **"The things you picked out are all red things."** Ask, **"What color are the things that you picked out?"**

2. Put all the things together again: **"Find the things that are not red."**

Follow-up: Repeat this activity with different colors and different materials. During center time, place a container of brightly colored materials. Observe whether the children put them into groups by color. If they do, ask, **"Why did you put those together?"** Accept any answer they give, but note whether they give a color answer.

Digital Download

ACTIVITIES

LOGIC AND CLASSIFICATION: ASSOCIATION

Objective: To form groups of things that go together by association.

Materials: Buy or make picture card sets. Each set can have one of the following themes:

1. Pictures of people in various jobs and pictures of things that go with specific jobs:

Worker	Things That Go with the Worker's Job
letter carrier	letter, mailbox, stamps, hat, mailbag, mail truck
airplane pilot	airplane, hat, wings
doctor	stethoscope, thermometer, bandages
trash collector	trash can, trash truck
police officer	handcuffs, pistol, hat, badge, police car
firefighter	hat, hose, truck, boots and coat, hydrant, house on fire
grocer	various kinds of foods, bags, shopping cart, cash register

Start with about three groups, and keep adding more.

2. Things that go together for use:

Item	Goes with
glass tumbler	carton of milk, pitcher of juice, can of soda pop
cup and saucer	coffeepot, teapot, steaming teakettle
match	candle, campfire
paper	pencil, crayon, pen
money	purse, wallet, bank
table	four chairs

Start with three groups, and keep adding more.

3. Things that are related, such as animals and their babies.

Naturalistic and informal activities: During center time, provide groups of items that go together such as those just described. Provide both objects and picture sets. Note what the children do with the items. Do they group related items for play? Ask questions such as these: "Which things belong together?" "What do you need in order to eat your cereal?"

Adult-guided activities:

1. One at a time, show the children the pictures of people or things that are the main clue (e.g., the workers) and ask, "Who [what] is this?" When they have all been named, show the go-with pictures one at a time: "Whom [what] does this belong to?"

2. Give each child a clue picture. Hold each go-with picture up in turn: "Who has the person [thing] this belongs with?" "What do you call this?"

3. Give a group of pictures to one child and say: "Sort these out. Find all the workers, and put the things with them that they use." Or "Here is a glass, a cup and saucer, and some money. Look through these pictures, and find the ones that go with them."

Follow-up: Have groups of pictures available for children to use during center time. Note whether they use them individually or make up group games to play. Keep introducing more groups.

ACTIVITIES

LOGIC AND CLASSIFICATION: SIMPLE SORTING

Objective: To practice the act of sorting.

Materials: Small containers, such as plastic margarine dishes, filled with small objects: buttons of various sizes, colors, and shapes, for example, or dried beans, peas, corn; another container with smaller divisions in it (such as an egg carton).

Naturalistic and informal activities: Notice whether children sort as they play. Do they use pretend food when pretending to cook and eat a meal? Do the children playing adults select adult clothing to wear? When provided with animal figures, do children demonstrate preferences? During center time, place materials such as those just described on a table. Observe how the children sort.

Adult-guided activities:

1. Have the sections of the larger container marked with a model, such as each kind of button or dried bean. The children match each thing from their container with the model, until everything is sorted into new groups in the egg carton (or another large container with small sections).

2. Use the same materials, but do not mark the sections of the sorting container. See how the children sort on their own.

Follow-up: Have these materials available during center time. Make up more groups, using different kinds of things for sorting.

ACTIVITIES

LOGIC AND CLASSIFICATION: CLASS NAMES, DISCUSSION

Objectives: To discuss groups of things that can be put in the same class and to decide on the class name.

Materials: Things that can be put in the same group on the basis of class name, such as:

1. Animals: several toy animals

2. Vehicles: toy cars, trucks, motorcycles

3. Clothing: a shoe, a shirt, a belt

4. Things to write with: a pen, pencil, marker, crayon, chalk

Naturalistic and informal activities: During center time, note whether children use class names during their play. Give examples of labeling classes: **"You like to play with the horses when you select from the animal**

collection." Ask questions such as **"Which is your favorite vehicle?"**

Adult-guided activities: The same plan can be followed for any group of things.

1. Bring the things out one at a time until three have been discussed. Ask about each:

    a. **"What can you tell me about this?"**

    b. Then ask five specific questions such as these: **"What do you call this? [What is its name?]" "What color is it?" "What do you do with it?"**

Or **"What does it do?"** Or **"Who uses this? What is it made of?"**

c. Show the three things discussed: **"What do you call things like this? These are all [animals, vehicles, clothes, things to write with]."**

2. Put two or more groups of things together that have already been discussed. Ask the children to sort them into new groups and to give the class name for each group.

Follow-up: Put together groups (in the manner described here) that include things from science and social studies.

world (K-SLS1-1) (Strategic Partners Group, 2013, p. 168). Examples of how classification might be used during science investigations appear on p. 101.

3-3c Helping Children with Special Needs

Copley, Jones, and Dighe (2007) suggest several methods for meeting the needs of English language learners, advanced learners, and children with disabilities. Keep the language simple for ELL students, and repeat rhymes and chants. Classification activities provide many opportunities for building English vocabulary. Include culturally relevant materials, and use the children's primary language, if possible. Advanced learners may become bored unless they are offered more challenging experiences.

ACTIVITIES

LOGIC AND CLASSIFICATION: SORTING A NATURE WALK COLLECTION

Objective: To sort items collected during a nature walk.

Materials: The class has gone for a nature walk. Children have collected leaves, stones, bugs, and so on. They have various types of containers (e.g., plastic bags, glass jars, plastic margarine containers).

Safety Note: Caution children not to touch insects. You can show pictures of insects children are likely to encounter to reduce their temptation to pick them up. Also, describe or show pictures of poison ivy, poison oak, and other poisonous plants they might encounter, and instruct children not to touch them. (This means that the adult should scope out the trip's terrain ahead of time.)

Naturalistic and informal activities: Develop collections with items that children bring in from home, and place them in the science center. Encourage children to observe birds that may be in the area. If allowed by the school, have animals visit, such as children's pets, a person with a guide dog, or a person with a dog trained to do tricks. Have books on nature topics in the library center.

Adult-guided activities:

1. Have the children spread out pieces of newspaper on tables or on the floor.

2. Ask them to dump their plants and rocks on the table. (Live things should remain in their separate containers.)

3. **"Look at all the things you have collected. Put things that belong together in groups. Tell me why they belong together."** Let the children explore the materials and identify leaves, twigs, flowers, weeds, smooth rocks, rough rocks, light and dark rocks, and so on. After they have grouped the plant material and the rocks, have them sort their animals and insects into different containers. See whether they can label their collections (e.g., earthworms, ants, spiders, beetles, ladybugs).

4. Help them organize their materials on the science table. Encourage them to write labels or signs using their own spellings, or help them with spelling if needed. If they won't attempt to write themselves, let them dictate labels to you.

Follow-up: Encourage the children to examine all the collections and discuss their attributes. Have some plant, rock, insect, and animal reference books on the science table. Encourage the children to find pictures of items like theirs in the books. Read what the books tell about their discoveries.

ACTIVITIES

LOGIC AND CLASSIFICATION: SORTING THINGS THAT SINK AND FLOAT

Objective: To find out which objects in a collection sink and which float.

Materials: A collection of many objects made from different materials. You might ask each child to bring one thing from home, and then add some items from the classroom. Have a large container of water and two empty containers labeled "Sink" and "Float." Make a large chart, with a picture or name of each item, where the results of the explorations can be recorded (**Figure 3-17**).

Naturalistic and informal activities: Provide many opportunities for water play, and include items that float and sink. Note the children's comments as they play with the objects. Make comments such as, **"Those rocks seem to stay on the bottom while the boat stays on top of the water."** Ask questions: **"What do you think will happen if you put a rock in a boat?"**

Adult-guided activities:

1. Place the materials on the science table, and explain to everyone what the activity is for.

2. During center time, let individuals and/or groups of two or three experiment by placing the objects into the water and then into the appropriate container after they float or sink.

3. When the children are finished sorting, they can record the objects' names at the top of the next vacant column on the chart and check off which items sank and which floated.

4. After the children have sorted the items several times, have them compare their lists: **"Do the items always float [sink]? Why?"**

Follow-up: The activity can continue until everyone has had an opportunity to explore it. New items can be added. Some children might like to make a boat in the carpentry center.

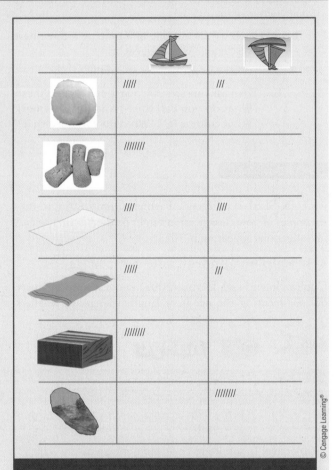

FIGURE 3-17 The students can record the results of their exploration of the floating and sinking properties of various objects.

© Cengage Learning®

LOGIC AND CLASSIFICATION: CLASSIFYING CHARACTERISTICS OF GARDEN PLANTS[1]

Objective: To learn that plants are organized in families that share related characteristics.

Materials: Obtain examples of a garden plant family such as squash (cucumbers, melons, gourds, pumpkins, winter and summer squash).

Naturalistic and informal activities: Place the squash examples in the science center where they can be examined by the students. Note the students' exploratory activities and comments. Ask the students what the items are. Do they know their names? What do they find are the characteristics of the squash examples, that is, color, shape, size, and so on. What is the same? What is different? What is inside?

Adult-guided activities: Ask the group to tell you the characteristics they have noted from examining the squash examples. List them on the smartboard or whiteboard. Explain that these plants are all related as they belong to the squash family. Ask the students what is inside each example. One by one, cut open the squash, and ask the students to tell what they observe. Wash and drain the seeds, and sort them into groups.

Follow-up: Ask the students whether these squash can be eaten. Which are good raw? Which would they prefer cooked? Investigate some other garden plant families such as these:

- Nightshade: bell pepper, tomato, potato, eggplant, chili pepper

- Lentils: beans, peas, peanuts, soy beans, clover, alfalfa

[1] Burpee Home Gardens, "*I Can Grow,*" Ball Horticultural Company and W. Adlee Burpee Company, 2011. Can be found online on the Burpee website, www.burpee.com.

Some prekindergartners may be ready to use number symbols, create charts and graphs, or use more advanced computer programs. Children with disabilities can benefit from accommodations that meet their needs and that support their strengths while working with their problem areas. As described in section 3.2, children with disabilities may need more multisensory experiences; they may need to have concepts broken down for them into smaller parts; and they may benefit from special technology or other accommodations. In Chapter 12 these factors will be discussed further.

3-3d Evaluation

As the children play, note whether each one sorts and groups as part of his or her play activities. Such behavior should increase as children grow and have more experiences with sorting and classification activities. Children should use more names of features when they speak during work and play. They should use color, shape, size, material, pattern, texture, function, association words, and class names. For example:

- Enrique has a handful of colored candies. "First, I'll eat the orange ones." He carefully picks out the orange candies and eats them one at a time. "Now, the reds." He goes on in the same way until all the candies are gone.

- Diana plays with some small wooden animals. "These farm animals go here in the barn. Aiden, you build a cage for the wild animals."

- Mr. Flores tells Evan to pick out, from a box of toys, some plastic ones to use in the water table.

- Yolanda asks the cook if she can help sort the clean tableware and put it away.

- George and Sam build with blocks. George tells Sam: "Put the big blocks here, the middle-sized ones here, and the small blocks here."

- Tito and Ako take turns reaching into a box that contains items that are smooth or rough. When they touch an item, they say whether it is smooth or rough, guess what it is, and then remove it and place it on the table in the smooth or the rough pile.

- Jin-sody is working with containers, each of which contains a substance with either a pleasant, an unpleasant, or a neutral odor. On the table are three pictures: a happy face, a sad face, and a neutral face. She puts each of the containers on one of the three faces, according to her feelings about each odor.

For more structured evaluation, the sample assessment tasks and the tasks in Appendix A may be used.

Technology for Young Children

TECHNOLOGY CONNECTION: SORTING AND CLASSIFYING ONLINE

Sorting online using virtual manipulatives can provide a challenge for young children. At the NCTM Illuminations website, the Amazing Attributes lessons serve this purpose. During the lesson properties, students find items everywhere in the environment that fall into categories by color, shape, or size. They sort pencils, crayons, and buttons, and explain the rationale for their groups. The Grandma's Button Box lesson centers on the story, *The Button Box* by Margarette Reid. The child in the story examines the different buttons in the box while the students who are listening to the story discuss the buttons' properties and similarities and differences. At the PBS Learning Media website, short videos can be viewed and down loaded. In the *Grocery Store Field Trip*, children select from the five different food groups and learn that they should eat a rainbow of colors every day to be healthy. On the PBS website SciGirls, the *Waste Audit* lesson focuses on sorting trash into different groups.

3-4 COMPARISON STANDARDS AND DESCRIPTION

According to CCSSM (2010), development of measurement relationships begins with simple comparisons of physical materials and pictures. The expectation is that students will be able to describe qualitative comparisons, such as

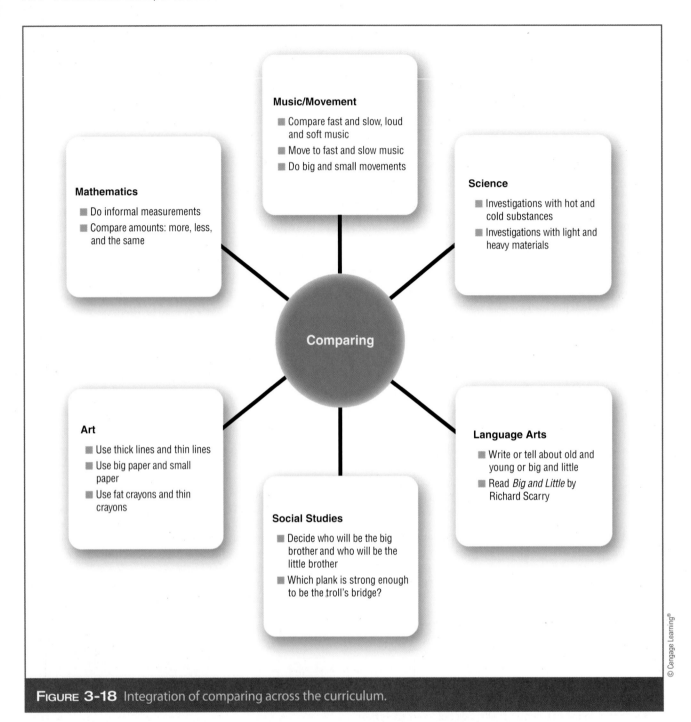

FIGURE 3-18 Integration of comparing across the curriculum.

© Cengage Learning®

"Mary is taller than Jenny" and quantitative comparisons such as "John has more marbles than Ben." **Figure 3-18** shows how comparing might be integrated across the content areas.

By the end of kindergarten, children should be able to identify whether the number of objects in one group is greater than, less than, or equal to the number of objects in another group by using strategies such as number sense, matching, and counting and by being able to compare two numbers between 1 and 10 presented as written numerals (CCSSM, 2010).

When **comparing**, children find a relationship between two things or groups of things on the basis of some specific characteristic or attribute. One type of attribute is an **informal measurement**, such as size, length, height, weight, or speed. A second type of attribute involves **quantity comparison**. To compare quantities, the child looks at two groups of objects and decides whether they have the same number of items or if one group has more. Comparing is the basis of ordering (see Chapter 5) and measurement (see Chapters 5 and 9).

Here are examples of measurement comparisons:

- "John is taller than Maria."
- "This snake is long; that worm is short."
- "Father bear is bigger than baby bear."

Here are examples of number comparisons:

- "Does everyone have two gloves?"
- "I have more cookies than you have."
- "We both have two dolls—that's the same."

3-4a The Basic Comparisons

To make comparisons and understand them, the child learns the following basic comparisons:

- Informal measurement:

large	small
big	little
long	short
tall	short
fat	skinny
heavy	light
fast	slow
cold	hot
thick	thin
wide	narrow
near	far
later	sooner (earlier)
older	younger (newer)
higher	lower
loud	soft (sound)

- Number

more	less/fewer

Children also sometimes find no difference when they make a comparison. For instance, the compared items might be the same size or the same age. With regard to quantity, they may discover that two compared groups contain the same amount (or number) of things. The concept of one-to-one correspondence and the skills of counting and classifying assist the child in comparing quantities.

3-4b Informal Pre-Assessment

Before beginning instruction, the children's current levels of understanding should be assessed. When children play, the teacher should note whether any of their activities show they are comparing. For example, when a bed is needed for a doll, and two shoeboxes are available, do children look the boxes over carefully and try different combinations to find the right size box for each doll? If there are two trucks, one large and one small, do the children build a bigger garage for the larger truck? The teacher should also note whether children use the words given in the preceding list of basic comparisons.

In individual interview tasks, the teacher should question children to see whether they understand and use basic comparison words. Present children with objects or pictures of things that differ or are the same regarding some attribute(s) or number, and then ask them to tell whether they are the same or different. Before giving the number comparison tasks, the teacher should be sure each child has begun to match, count, and classify. Two sample tasks are given on the pages 105 and 106; see also Appendix A.

3-4c Comparison Activities

Naturalistic, informal, and adult-guided activities can be used for instruction.

Naturalistic Activities. Young children have many contacts with comparisons in their daily lives. At home mother says, "Get up; it's *late*. Mia was up *early*. Eat *fast*. If you eat slowly, we will have to leave before you are finished. Use a *big* bowl for your cereal; that one is too *small*." At school, the teacher might say: "I'll pick up this *heavy* box; you pick up the *light* one." "Sit on the *small* chair; that one is too *big*." "Remember, the father bear's porridge was too *hot*, and the mother bear's porridge was too *cold*."

SAMPLE ASSESSMENT TASK

5D	PREOPERATIONAL AGES 4–5

COMPARING, INFORMAL MEASUREMENT: CHAPTER 3

SKILL The child will be able to point to big (large) and small objects.

MATERIALS A big block and a small block (a big truck and a small truck, a big shell and a small shell, etc.).

PROCEDURE Present two related objects at a time and say, "Find [point to] the big block." "Find [point to] the small block." Continue with the rest of the object pairs.

EVALUATION Note whether the child is able to identify big and small for each pair.

INSTRUCTIONAL RESOURCE
R. Charlesworth, *Math and Science for Young Children*, 8th ed., San Francisco, CA: Cengage Learning, 2016.

SAMPLE ASSESSMENT TASK

4D   PREOPERATIONAL AGES 3–4

COMPARING, NUMBER: CHAPTER 3

SKILL The child compares groups and identifies which group has more or less (fewer).

MATERIALS Two dolls (toy animals or cutout figures) and 10 cutout posterboard cookies.

PROCEDURE Place the two dolls (toy animals or cutout figures) in front of the child. Say, "Watch—I'm going to give each doll some cookies." Put two cookies in front of one doll and six in front of the other. Say, "Show me the doll that has more cookies." Now pick up the cookies, and put one cookie in front of one doll and three in front of the other. Say, "Show me the doll that has fewer cookies." Repeat with different amounts.

EVALUATION Note whether the child consistently picks the correct amounts.

Some children might understand *more*, but not *fewer*. Some might be able to perceive a large difference between groups, such as two versus six, but not small differences, such as four versus five.

INSTRUCTIONAL RESOURCE
R. Charlesworth, *Math and Science for Young Children*, 8th ed., San Francisco, CA: Cengage Learning, 2016.

Digital Download

TeachSource Video

COMPARING TOWERS TO FIGURE OUT HOW MANY CUBES: A KINDERGARTEN LESSON

The teacher presents her kindergarten class with Unifix towers of different heights. The children use group discussion and individual presentation to describe the comparisons and explain their reasoning.

1. What is the concept explored in this lesson?
2. How does the teacher get the children to explain their thinking? What vocabulary does she use?
3. What concepts do the children seem to understand? How do they apply their knowledge of comparing? How do they apply their knowledge of counting?

© 2016 Cengage Learning®

Informal Activities. Small children are very concerned about size and number, especially in relation to themselves. They want to be bigger, taller, faster, and older. They want to be sure they have more—not fewer—things than other children have. These needs of young children bring about many situations where the adult can help in an informal way to aid the child in learning the skills and ideas of comparing.

Informal measurements are made in a concrete way. The things to be compared are looked at, felt, lifted, listened to, and so on, and then they are labeled.

- Kato (18 months old) tries to lift a large box of toy cars. Mr. Brown squats down next to him, holding out a smaller box of cars. "Here, Kato, that box is too big for your short arms. Take this small box."

As children use materials, they notice that things are different. Infants find that some things can be grabbed and held because they are *small* and *light*, whereas others cannot be held because they are *big* and *heavy*. When an infant crawls around, he discovers he cannot go behind the couch because the space is too *narrow*. He can go behind the chair because there is a *wide* space between the chair and the wall. When building with blocks, young children may find they have *more small* blocks than *large* ones. They notice that some people in their environment are big and that others are small in relation to them. Children often ask, "Am I a big boy?" or "Am I a big girl?"

PHOTO 3-6 This girl learns about big as she stretches to hold the ball.

© 2016 Cengage Learning®

- Kate and Chris (3-year-olds) run up to Mrs. Raymond. "We can run fast. Watch us. We can run faster than you. Watch us." Off they go across the yard while Mrs. Raymond watches and smiles.

- Sam and Gomez (5-year-olds) stand back to back. "Check us, Mr. Flores. Who is taller?" Mr. Flores says, "Stand by the mirror, and check yourselves." The boys stand by the mirror, back to back. "We are the same," they shout. "You are taller than both of us," they tell their teacher.

- After a fresh spring rain, the children are on the playground, looking at worms. Various comments are heard: "This worm is longer than that one." "This worm is fatter." Miss Collins comes up. "Show me your worms. It sounds like they are different sizes." "I think this small, skinny one is the baby worm," says Badru.

Comparative numbers are also developed in a concrete way. When comparing groups of things:

- Just a look may be enough if the difference in number is large. "Teacher! Juanita has all the spoons and won't give me one!" cries Tanya.

- If the difference is small, then children have to use their matching skills (one-to-one correspondence). Depending on their level of development, children may physically match each time, or they may count. "Teacher! Juanita has more baby dolls than I do." "Let's check," says Mr. Brown. "I already checked," replies Tanya; "She has four, and I have three." Mr. Brown notes that each girl has four dolls. "Better check again," says Mr. Brown. "Here, let's see. Tanya, put each one of your dolls next to one of Juanita's." Tanya matches them up. "I was wrong. We have the same." (A child at a higher level of development could have been asked to count in this situation.)

To promote informal learning, teachers should put out materials that children can use to learn comparisons on their own. Teachers also must be ready to step in and support a child's discovery by using comparison words and by giving needed help with comparison problems that the children meet in their play and other activities.

Adult-Guided Activities. Most children learn the idea of comparison through naturalistic and informal activities. For those who do not, more formal experiences can be planned. Many commercial materials are available individually and in kits that are designed for teaching comparison skills and words. Also, the environment is full of things that can be used. The following are some examples of basic types of activities that can be repeated with different materials.

3-4d Helping Children with Special Needs

Comparing groups begins with concrete objects and one-to-one correspondence comparisons. The comparison of pictorial representations is a more advanced step that may require extra time and practice for some children. Begin with card sets that show groups in a variety of configurations (e.g., several groups of three or four). Make up matching lotto games such as those depicted in Chapter 7. Have the children compare all kinds of visual configurations such as stripes, shapes, animals, and so forth. Have them count out loud for the auditory stimulation. Have them experience tactile stimulation by providing sandpaper shapes or sand glued on card drawings. Use terms such as *the same as*, *less than*, and

PHOTO 3-7 Sending different cars down the spiral incline track provides experience with fast and slow and the effect of gravity on speed.

© 2016 Cengage Learning®

PHOTO 3-8 Swinging helps develop the concept of high and low.

© 2016 Cengage Learning®

DAP **naeyc**

ACTIVITIES

COMPARISONS: INFORMAL MEASUREMENTS

Objectives: To gain skill in observing differences in size, speed, temperature, age, and loudness; to learn the words associated with these differences.

Materials: Use real objects first. Once the child can do the tasks with real things, then introduce pictures and whiteboard or smartboard drawings.

Comparison	Things to use
large–small and big–little	buttons, dolls, cups, plates, chairs, books, records, spools, toy animals, trees, boats, cars, houses, jars, boxes, people, pots and pans
long–short	string, ribbon, pencils, ruler, snakes, worms, lines, paper strips
tall–short	people, ladders, brooms, blocks, trees, bookcases, flagpoles, buildings
fat–skinny	people, trees, crayons, animals, pencils, books
heavy–light	containers of the same size but different weight (e.g., shoe boxes or coffee cans filled with items of different weights and taped shut)
fast–slow	toy cars or other vehicles for demonstration, the children themselves and their own movements, cars on the street, music, talking
hot–cold	containers of water, food, ice cubes, boiling water, chocolate milk and hot chocolate, weather
thick–thin	paper, cardboard, books, pieces of wood, slices of food (bologna, cucumber, carrot), cookie dough
wide–narrow	streets, ribbons, paper strips, lines (chalk, crayon, paint), doorways, windows
near–far	children and fixed points in the room, places in the neighborhood, map
later–sooner/ earlier	arrival at school or home, two events
older– younger/ newer	babies, younger and older children, adults of different ages; any items brought in that were not in the environment before
higher–lower	swings, slides, jungle gyms, birds in trees, airplanes flying, windows, stairs, elevators, balconies, shelves
loud–soft	voices singing and talking, claps, piano, drums, records, doors slamming

Naturalistic and informal activities: Observe children as they use a variety of classroom materials. Take note of their vocabulary: Do they use any of the terms previously listed? Observe whether they make any informal measurements or comparisons as they interact with materials. Comment on their activities: **"You built a _tall_ building and a _short_ building." "You can pour the _small_ cup of water into the _big_ bowl."** Ask questions such as, **"Which clay snake is _fat_ and which is _skinny_?" "Who is _taller_, you or your sister?"**

Adult-guided activities: The basic activity involves the presentation of two items to be compared using opposite terms. The items can be real objects, cutouts, or pictures—whatever is most appropriate. Then ask the comparison question. For example: **The teacher places two pieces of paper in front of the children. Each piece is 1 inch wide. One is 6 inches long, and the other is 12 inches long.** "Look carefully at these strips of paper. Tell me what is different about them." **If there is no response:** "Are they the same length, or are they different lengths?" **If no one responds with longer or shorter:** "Show me which one is (longer) (shorter)." **From a variety of objects, ask the children to select two and tell which is longer and which is shorter.**

- The teacher places two identical containers on the table. One is filled with sand; the other is empty. They are both taped closed, so the children cannot see inside. **Pick up each container, saying, "Tell me what is different about them."** If there is no response or an incorrect one, hold each can out in turn to a child. **"Hold this container in one hand and this container in the other hand."** [Point.] **"This one is heavy; this one is light. Now, you show me the heavy container [light container]."** Children who have a problem with this should do more activities that involve the concept.

An almost endless variety of experience can be offered with many things that give the child practice exploring comparisons.

Follow-up: On a table, set up two empty containers (make one tall and one short, one fat and one thin, or one big and one little) and a third container filled with potentially comparable items such as tall and short dolls, large and small balls, fat and thin cats, long and short snakes, big and little pieces of wood, and so on. Have the children sort the objects into the correct empty containers.

ACTIVITIES

COMPARISONS: NUMBER

Objective:

- To enable the child to compare groups that are different in number.
- To enable the child to use the terms *more, less, fewer,* and *same number.*

Materials: Any of the objects and things used for matching, counting, and classifying.

Naturalistic and informal activities: Notice whether children use any of the comparison vocabulary during their daily activities: "He has *more* red Unifix Cubes than I do." "I have fewer jelly beans than Mark." Ask questions: **"Does everyone have the same number of cookies?"** Make comments such as, **"I think you need one more dress for your dolls."**

Adult-guided activities: The following basic activities can be done using many different kinds of materials.

1. Set up a flannelboard with many felt shapes or a magnet board with many magnet shapes. Put up two groups of shapes: **"Are there as many circles as squares [red circles as blue circles, bunnies as chickens]? How many circles are there? How many squares?"** The children can point, tell with words, and/or move the pieces around to show that they understand the idea.

2. Have cups, spoons, napkins, or food for snack or lunch. **"Let's find out if we have enough [name the item] for everyone."** Wait for the children to find out. If they have trouble, suggest they match or count.

3. Set up any kind of matching problems where one group has more things than the other group: cars and garages, firefighters and fire trucks, cups and saucers, fathers and sons, hats and heads, cats and kittens, animals and cages, and so on.

Follow-up: Put out groups of materials that the children can use on their own. Go on to cards with pictures of different numbers of things that the children can sort and match. Watch for chances to present informal experiences.

- **"Are there more boys or girls here today?"**
- **"Do you have more thin crayons or more fat crayons?"**
- **"Do we have the same number of cupcakes as we have people?"**

Digital Download

---

more. Auditory comparisons can also be made with sounds—for instance, one drumbeat compared with three drumbeats.

3-4e Informal Evaluation

Teachers should note whether children can use more comparing skills during their play and routine activities. Without disrupting their activity, teachers can ask questions as children play and work.

- The child is playing with farm toys: "Do you have more cows or more chickens in your barn?"

- The child has made two clay snakes: "Which snake is longer? Which is fatter?"

- The child is sorting blue chips and red chips into bowls: "Do you have more blue chips or more red chips?"

- The child is talking about her family: "Who is older, you or your brother? Who is taller?"

The assessment tasks in Appendix A may be used for formal evaluation interviews.

SUMMARY

3-1 One-to-One Correspondence

The most basic math skill is one-to-one correspondence. Starting in infancy, children learn about one-to-one relationships. Sensorimotor and early preoperational children spend much of their playtime in such activities.

Informal Pre-Assessment. Children's beginning knowledge of one-to-one correspondence can be assessed through observation of their play behavior.

Activities. Many opportunities for informal one-to-one correspondence activities are available during play and daily routines. Materials used for adult-guided activities with individuals and/or small groups should also be made available for free exploration. Materials and activities can be varied in many ways to make one-to-one correspondence fun and interesting. Once children have a basic understanding of the one-to-one concept, they can apply the concept to higher-level activities and materials as a means to increase the vocabulary of children with language difficulties.

Informal Post-Evaluation. This can be done through observation during play noting use of correspondence activity and vocabulary. "I gave each doll a bed." Individual assessment through administration of interview assessment tasks may be used to evaluate learning.

3-2 Number Sense and Counting Standards and Description

According to CCSSM, by the end of kindergarten, children are expected to count to 100 by 1s and 10s, write numbers from 0 to 20, count 20 objects, and compare groups of objects by using number sense, matching, or counting. Number sense or the number concept connects counting with quantity. Counting, one-to-one correspondence, arranging and rearranging groups, and comparing quantities help in developing number sense, which underlies all mathematical operations. The number concept involves an understanding of oneness, twoness, and so on. Rote counting is saying from memory the names of the numerals in order. Rational counting consists of using number sense to attach the number names in order to items in a group to find out how many items are in the group.

Informal Pre-Assessment. Children can be observed during their daily activities for their use of counting and indications of number sense development. For example, the child has a large pile of Unifix Cubes: "Look, I have a million cubes."

Activities. Teach counting using naturalistic, informal, and adult-guided activities appropriate to each child's age and level of maturity. This chapter includes examples of activities that support the development of number sense and counting. Some children with special needs may need additional multisensory experiences to reinforce their counting skills and understanding of number.

Informal Post-Evaluation. Evaluation can be done through observation during play activities in which any logical classification behaviors are noted and through administration of individual assessment tasks.

3-3 Logic and Classification Standards and Description

CCSSM standards for the end of kindergarten are that children will be able to classify objects and count the number of objects in categories. By sorting objects and pictures into groups based on one or more common criteria, children exercise and build on their logical thinking capabilities. The act of putting things into groups by sorting out those with one or more common features is called *classification* and is an essential process in all scientific inquiries. Classifying is a part of children's normal play.

Pre-Assessment. Pre-assessment can be done through observation and/or through administration of interview assessment tasks.

Activities. Naturalistic, informal, and adult-guided classification activities can be done following the sequence of materials described in Chapter 3. The sequence progresses from using just objects, to combining objects with pictures, then to using cutouts, and eventually to using picture cards. Books are another excellent pictorial mode for learning class names and members. Computer games that reinforce classification skills and concepts are also available. Logical grouping and classification are essential math and science components. Accommodations need to be made for children with special needs.

Informal Post-Evaluation. Observation and/or individually administered interview tasks can be used.

3-4 Comparison Standards and Description

The CCSSM standards include that preschool and kindergarten students should be able to do informal measurement using comparisons of opposites such as short and tall and light and heavy. Comparison of groups such as more and less is also important in early childhood.

Informal Pre-Assessment. Observation of children in action and/or individual interview tasks can be used.

Activities. Naturalistic, informal, and adult-guided experiences support the learning of these concepts. Children with special needs may need accommodations.

Informal Post-Evaluation. Observation and/or individual interview tasks may be used to assess the effectiveness of activities.

FURTHER READING AND RESOURCES

Brandone, A., Cimpian, A., Leslie, S., & Gelman, S. A. (2012). Do lions have manes? For children, generics are about kinds rather than quantities. *Child Development*, *83*(2), 423–433.

Copple, C., & Bredekamp, S. (Eds.). (2009). *Developmentally appropriate practice in early childhood programs serving children birth through age eight*, 3rd ed. Washington, DC: National Association for the Education of Young Children.

Eichinger, J. (2009). *Activities linking science with mathematics*. Arlington, VA: NSTA Press. (Activities 1 & 2).

Equity for diverse populations. (2009). *Teaching Children Mathematics* [focus issue], *16*(3).

Hildebrandt, M. E., Biglan, B., & Budd, L. (2013), Let's take a road trip. *Teaching Children Mathematics*, *19*(9), 548–553.

Manfra, L., Dinehart, L. H. B., & Sembiante, S. F. (2014). Associations between counting ability in preschool and mathematics performance in first grade among a sample of ethnically diverse, low-income children. *Journal of Research in Childhood Education*, *28*(1).

McGuire, P., Kinzie, M. B., & Berch, D. B. (2012). Developing number sense in pre-K with five-frames. *Early Childhood Education Journal*, *40*(4), 213–222.

Novakowski, J. (2009). Classifying classification. *Science and Children*, *46*(7), 25–29.

Schwerdtfeger, J. K., & Chan, A. (2007). Counting collections. *Teaching ChildrenMathematics*, *3*(7), 356–361.

REFERENCES

Burns, C. (2012, June 26). What does the way you count on your fingers say about your brain? *Science Blog*. www.theguardian.com.

Burpee Home Gardens, "*I can grow*," (2011). Ball Horticultural Company and W. Adlee Burpee Company. www.burpee.com.

Charlesworth, R. (2016). *Math and science for young children*, 8th ed. San Francisco, CA: Cengage Learning.

Clements, D. H. (1999). Subitizing: What is it? Why teach it? *Teaching Children Mathematics, 5*(7), 400–405.

Christelow, E. (2007). *Five little monkeys sitting in a tree*. New York: Clarion.

Common Core State Standards for Mathematics. (July 2010). www.corestandards.org.

Copley, J. V. (Ed.). (2004). *Showcasing mathematics for the young child*. Reston, VA: National Council of Teachers of Mathematics.

Copley, J. V., Jones, C., & Dighe, J. (2007). *Mathematics: The creative curriculum approach*. Washington, DC: Teaching Strategies.

Elkin, B. (1968/1971). *Six foolish fishermen*. New York: Scholastic Books.

Feigenson, L., Libertus, M. E., & Halberda, J. (2013). Links between the intuitive sense of number and formal mathematics ability. *Child Development Perspectives, 7*(2), 74–79,

Fosnot, C. T., & Cameron, A. (2007). *Games for early number sense*. Portsmouth, NH: Heinemann.

Greenes, C. E., Dacey, L., Cavanagh, M., Findell, C. R., Sheffield, L. J., & Small, M. (2003). *Navigating through problem solving and reasoning in prekindergarten–kindergarten*. Reston, VA: National Council of Teachers of Mathematics.

Kamii, C. (1982). *Number in preschool and kindergarten*. Washington, DC: National Association for the Education of Young Children.

Marshall, J. (2006). Math Wars 2: It's the teaching, stupid! *Phi Delta Kappan, 87*(5), 356–363.

McGrath, W., & McGrath, B. (2000). *Cheerios counting book*. New York: Cartwheel/Scholastic.

National Association for the Education of Young Children (NAYC) and National Council of Teachers of Mathematics (NCTM) (2010). *Early childhood mathematics: Promoting good beginnings*. Washington, DC: Authors.

National Council of Teachers of Mathematics (NCTM). (2000). *Principles and standards for school mathematics*. Reston, VA: Author.

National Council of Teachers of Mathematics. (2006, October). Curriculum focal points for prekindergarten through grade 8 mathematics: A quest for coherence, *Teaching Children Mathematics, 13*(3). http://www.nctm.org.

National Governors Association Center for Best Practices, Council of Chief State School Officers. (2010). Common Core State Standards for Mathematics. Washington, DC: Author.

Neergaard, L. (2013, March 26). *Early number sense plays role in later math skills*. Yahoo! News. http://news.yahoo.com.

Orozco, J., & Kleven, E. (1997). *Diez deditos and other playground rhymes and action songs from Latin America*. New York: Scholastic.

Petersen, L. A., & McNeil, N. M. (2013). Effects of perceptually rich manipulatives on preschoolers' counting performance: Established knowledge counts. *Child Development, 84*(3), 1020–1033.

Raffi. (1992). *Five little ducks (Raffi songs to read)*. New York: Crown.

Rasicot, J. (2012, November 9). Learning to count is important for school readiness, study says. *Education Week Early Years blog*. http://blogs.edweek.org.

Reys, R. E., Lindquist, M. M., Lambdin, D. V., Smith, N. L., & Suydam, M. N. (2004). *Helping children learn mathematics*, 7th ed. New York: Wiley.

Richardson, K. (1999). *Developing number concepts: Planning guide*. Parsippany, NJ: Seymour.

Schulman, L., & Eston, R. (1998). A problem worth revisiting. *Teaching Children Mathematics, 5*(2), 73–77.

Strategic Partners Group. (2013). *Next generation science standards*. Washington, D.C.: National Academies Press.

Van De Walle, J. A., Karp, K. S., & Bay-Williams, J. M. (2013). *Elementary and middle school mathematics: Teaching developmentally*, 8th ed. Boston: Pearson.

MORE PREKINDERGARTEN AND KINDERGARTEN

CONCEPTS AND SKILLS: EARLY GEOMETRY, PARTS AND WHOLES, AND APPLICATIONS OF FUNDAMENTAL CONCEPTS TO SCIENCE AND ENGINEERING

LEARNING OBJECTIVES

After reading this chapter, you should be able to:

4-1 Assess, plan, teach, and evaluate shape concept lesson activities following national standards.

4-2 Assess, plan, teach, and evaluate spatial concept lesson activities following national standards.

4-3 Assess, plan, teach, and evaluate parts and wholes concept lesson activities following national standards.

4-4 Assess, plan, teach, and evaluate science concept lesson activities following national standards.

STANDARDS ADDRESSED IN THIS CHAPTER

naeyc

NAEYC Professional Preparation Standards

5. Use content knowledge to build meaningful curriculum.

5a. Understand content knowledge and resources in mathematics and science.

5c. Design, implement, and evaluate developmentally meaningful and challenging curriculum for each child.

DAP Guidelines

2c. Know desired program goals.

3c. Use the curriculum framework in planning to ensure there is ample attention to important learning goals.

Common Core State Standards for Math

KGA2 Correctly name shapes regardless of their orientation or overall size.

MP1 Make sense of problems and persevere in solving them.

MP4 Model with mathematics.

Next Generation Science Standards

K-2-ETS1-1 Ask questions based on observations.

K-PS3-1 Make observations to collect data that can be used to make comparisons.

4-1 EXPECTATIONS AND CHARACTERISTICS OF SHAPE

According to the Common Core State Standard for Mathematics (National Governors Association Center, 2010), by the end of kindergarten, children should be able to describe and identify shapes as well as analyze, compare, create, and compose shapes. During the preprimary years, children should be able to reach the first expectation for geometry (NCTM, 2000): Recognize, name, build, draw, compare, and sort two- and three-dimensional shapes. This beginning knowledge of geometry can be integrated with other content areas, as illustrated in **Figure 4-1**. Geometry for young children is more than naming shapes; it is understanding the attributes of shape and applying them to problem solving. Geometry also includes spatial sense, which is discussed in the section on spatial sense and spatial relations later in this chapter. In the beginning of this chapter, we examine the identification of shapes.

Each object in the environment has its own shape. Much of the play and activity of infants during the sensorimotor

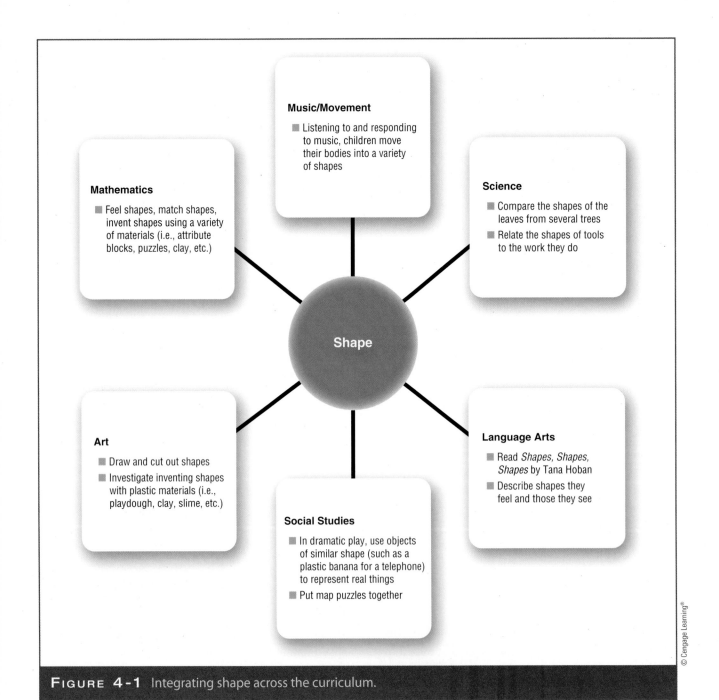

Music/Movement
- Listening to and responding to music, children move their bodies into a variety of shapes

Mathematics
- Feel shapes, match shapes, invent shapes using a variety of materials (i.e., attribute blocks, puzzles, clay, etc.)

Science
- Compare the shapes of the leaves from several trees
- Relate the shapes of tools to the work they do

Shape

Art
- Draw and cut out shapes
- Investigate inventing shapes with plastic materials (i.e., playdough, clay, slime, etc.)

Language Arts
- Read *Shapes, Shapes, Shapes* by Tana Hoban
- Describe shapes they feel and those they see

Social Studies
- In dramatic play, use objects of similar shape (such as a plastic banana for a telephone) to represent real things
- Put map puzzles together

FIGURE 4-1 Integrating shape across the curriculum.

stage centers on learning about shape. Infants learn about objects by looking and feeling with their hands and mouth. Babies learn that some shapes are easier to hold than others. They learn that things of one type of shape will roll. They learn that some things have the same shape as others. Young children see and feel shape differences long before they can describe these differences in words. In the late sensorimotor and early preoperational stages, the child spends a lot of time matching and classifying things. Shape is often used as the basis for these activities.

Children also enjoy experimenting with creating shapes. Three-dimensional shapes grow out of their exploration of malleable substances such as playdough and clay. When they draw and paint, children create many kinds of two-dimensional shapes, from the stage of controlled scribbles to representational drawing and painting. Their first representational drawings usually consist of circles and lines. Young children enjoy drawing blob shapes, cutting them out, and gluing them onto another piece of paper.

As children move into the middle of the preoperational period, they begin to learn that some shapes have specific names such as **circle**, **triangle**, **square**, **cylinder**, and **sphere**. Children first learn to describe the basic characteristics of each shape in their own words, such as "four straight sides," "a curved line," or "it has points." Gradually, the conventional geometry vocabulary is introduced. Children need opportunities to freely explore both two- and three-dimensional shapes. Examples of two-dimensional shapes (circle, triangle, square, rectangle, rhombus, and ellipse) and three-dimensional shapes (cylinder, sphere, **triangular prism**, and **rectangular prism**) are illustrated in **Figures** 4-2 and 4-3, respectively. Children need time to freely explore the properties of shapes.

Manipulatives such as unit blocks, attribute blocks, and Legos provide opportunities for exploration. The value of unit blocks is described in more detail in Chapter 12. Blocks and Legos provide experiences in organizing shapes into structures that can be used as the basis for dramatic play. Kindergartners fly their Lego airplanes around the classroom while

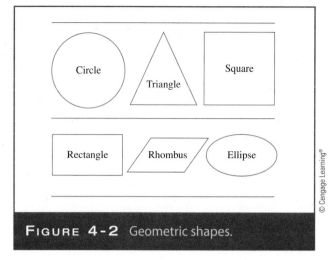

FIGURE 4-2 Geometric shapes.

© Cengage Learning®

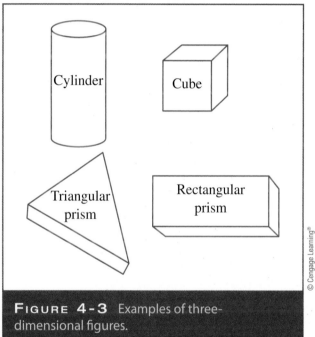

FIGURE 4-3 Examples of three-dimensional figures.

© Cengage Learning®

others build castles with unit blocks. Two children make designs with pattern blocks; three children are examining puzzle pieces, looking for places where shapes fit.

BRAIN CONNECTION

IS GEOMETRY HARDWIRED INTO OUR BRAINS?

Some controversy focuses on the results of research done with adult subjects who are members of the isolated Amazon Munduruku tribe. The tribe members have no verbal names for geometric concepts and yet have an excellent understanding of geometry. They have a working intuition for lines and shapes without the language labels. They can design and build houses and make tools applying their intuitive geometry. Some critics believe this is not "authentic" geometry. It may be that developmentally an applied knowledge of geometry precedes the knowledge of theoretical geometry taught in school. It may be that practical thinking should be taught before abstract thinking. From the early childhood constructivist point of view, it makes sense to have children explore shapes and build constructions naturalistically and informally before emphasizing shape labels and spatial terminology.

A. Wilkins, Geometry Is Hard-Wired into Our Brains, May 24, 2011, io9.com, *http://io9.com/5805127/geometry-is-hardwired-into-our-brains.*

Preschoolers are just beginning to develop definitions of shapes, which probably are not solidified until after age 6 (Hannibal, 1999). When working with shapes, use a variety of models of each category of shape so that children generalize and perceive that there is not just one definition. For example, triangles with three equal sides are the most common models, so children frequently do not perceive right triangles, isosceles triangles, and so forth as real triangles (**Figure 4-4**). Many preschoolers do not see that squares are a type of rectangle. After experience with many shape examples and much discussion of attributes, children begin to see beyond the obvious and can generalize to related shapes.

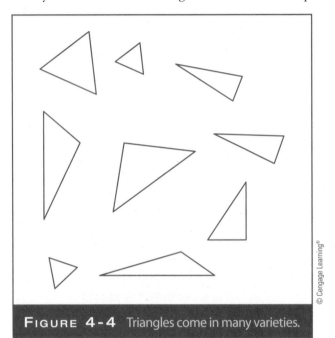

FIGURE 4-4 Triangles come in many varieties.

© Cengage Learning®

4-1a Pre-Assessment

As the child plays with materials, the adult should note whether he groups things together because the shape is the same or similar. For example, a child plays with a set of plastic shape blocks. The set contains triangles, squares, and circles that are red, blue, green, yellow, or orange. Sometimes the child groups them by color, sometimes by shape. Another child is playing with beads of different colors and shapes. Sometimes she makes strings of the same shape and sometimes of the same color. The child may use certain shape names in everyday conversation.

The individual interview tasks for shape center on discrimination, labeling, matching, and sorting.

- *Discrimination* tasks assess whether the child can see that one form has a different shape from another form.

- *Labeling* tasks assess whether the child can find a shape when the name is given and whether he can name a shape when a picture is shown to him. At a higher level, he finds shapes in pictures and in his environment.

- *Matching* requires the child to find a shape like one shown to her.

- A *sorting* task is one in which the child must separate a mixed group of shapes into groups having the same shape (see Chapter 3).

- *Description* involves being able to provide the characteristics of a shape, such as triangles have three sides, and rectangles have four sides.

Two sample tasks follow.

SAMPLE ASSESSMENT TASK

4E   PREOPERATIONAL AGES 3–4

SHAPE, IDENTIFICATION: CHAPTER 4

METHOD Interview.

SKILL When provided with shapes of varying types, size, and colors, the child labels and describes them using his or her current knowledge.

MATERIALS A variety of shapes, both two- and three-dimensional. Select items from small unit blocks, cube block sets, tangrams, and/or attribute blocks; you can also make cardboard cutouts or cover cylindrical containers and small boxes with contact paper. Have 15 to 20 different objects.

PROCEDURE Lay out the materials in front of the child. **"Tell me about these. What are they called? They are all different shapes. Do you have any names for any of these shapes? What makes the shape a [name of shape]? Are any of the shapes the same in any way? Have you seen anything else with this shape [either a shape the child selects or one you select] at school? Outside? At home? What kind of picture can you make with these shapes?"**

EVALUATION Note whether the child has labels for any of the shapes,

whether she makes any connections to familiar items in the environment; whether she can make a picture with them that is logical; and in general, whether she appears to have noticed the attributes of shape in the environment. Whether she uses conventional labels at this point is not important.

INSTRUCTIONAL RESOURCE
R. Charlesworth, *Math and Science for Young Children*, 8th ed., San Francisco, CA: Cengage Learning, 2016.

SAMPLE ASSESSMENT TASK

5E   PREOPERATIONAL AGES 5–6

SHAPE, GEOMETRIC SHAPE RECOGNITION: CHAPTER 4

METHOD Interview.

SKILL The child can identify shapes in the environment.

MATERIALS The natural environment.

PROCEDURE Once a child has had experience with a variety of two- and three-dimensional shapes, the following question can be used to assess his ability to recognize and generalize. **"Look around the room. Find as many shapes as you can. Can you find a [square, triangle, rectangle, cylinder, sphere, circle, rectangular prism]?"**

EVALUATION Note how observant the child is. Does he note the obvious shapes such as windows, doors, and tables? Does he look beyond the obvious? How many shapes and which shapes is the child able to find?

INSTRUCTIONAL RESOURCE
R. Charlesworth, *Math and Science for Young Children*, 8th ed., San Francisco, CA: Cengage Learning, 2016.

Digital Download

4-1b Shape Activities

Naturalistic Activities. Naturalistic activities are the most important in learning about shape. The child perceives the idea of shape through sight and touch. The infant needs objects to look at, to grasp, and to touch and taste. The toddler needs different things of many shapes to use as she sorts and matches. She needs many containers (e.g., bowls, boxes, coffee cans) and many objects (e.g., big beads, table tennis balls, poker chips, empty thread spools). She needs time to fill containers with these objects of different shapes and to dump the objects out and begin again. As she holds each object, she examines it with her eyes, hands, and mouth.

The older preoperational child enjoys a junk box filled with things such as buttons, checkers, bottle caps, pegs, small boxes, and plastic bottles that he can explore. The teacher can also set up a box of *attribute blocks* (wood or plastic blocks in geometric shapes). Geometric shapes and other shapes can also be cut from paper and/or cardboard and placed out for the child to use. **Figure 4-5** shows some blob shapes that can be put into a box of shapes to sort.

In dramatic play, the child can put to use his ideas about shape. The preoperational child's play is representational. He uses things to represent something else that he does not have at the time. He finds something that is "close to" and thus can represent the real thing. Shape is one of the main characteristics used when the child picks a representational object.

- A stick or a long piece of wood is used for a gun.
- A piece of rope or old garden hose is used to put out a pretend fire.
- The magnet board shapes are pretend candy.
- A square yellow block is a piece of cheese.
- A shoe box is a crib, a bed, or a house—as needed.
- Some rectangular pieces of green paper are dollars, and some round pieces of paper are coins.

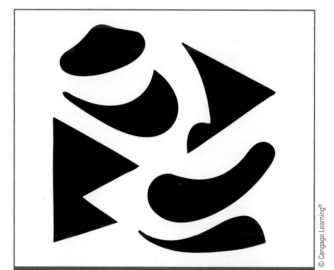

FIGURE 4-5 Blob shapes: You can make up your own.

© Cengage Learning®

- A paper towel roll is a telescope for looking at the moon.
- A blob of playdough is a hamburger or a cookie (**Photo 4-1**).

Informal Activities. The teacher can let the child know that he notices her use of shape ideas in activities through comments and attention. He can also supply her with ideas and objects that will fit her needs (**Photo 4-2**). He can suggest using objects at hand, or he can give the child a box to be used for a bed or a house, some blocks or other small objects for her pretend food, or green rectangles and gray and brown circles for play money.

Labels can be used during normal activities. The child's knowledge of shape can be used, too.

- "The forks have sharp points; the spoons are round and smooth."

PHOTO 4-1   Children learn about shape as they explore playdough during naturalistic play.

- "Put square place mats on the square tables and rectangular place mats on the rectangular tables."
- "Today we'll have some crackers that are shaped like triangles."
- As a child works on a hard puzzle, the teacher takes her hand and has her feel the empty space where the piece fits.
- As the children use clay or playdough, the teacher remarks, "You are making lots of shapes. Kate has made a ball, which is a sphere shape; Jose, a snake, which is a cylinder shape; and Kaho, a pancake, which is a circle shape."

PHOTO 4-2   A puzzle provides an informal shape experience.

- During cleanup time, the teacher says, "Put the square rectangular prism blocks here and the other rectangular prism blocks over there."

The teacher should respond when the child calls attention to shapes in the environment.

The following examples show that children can generalize and that they can use what they know about shape in new situations.

- "Ms. Moore, the door is shaped like a rectangle." Ms. Moore smiles and looks over at George. "Yes, it is. How many rectangles can you find on the door?" "There are big wide rectangles on the sides and thin rectangles on the ends and the top and bottom."
- "The plate and the hamburger look round like circles." "They do, don't they?" agrees Mr. Brown.
- "Where I put the on purple paint, it looks like a butterfly." Mr. Flores looks over and nods.
- "The roof is shaped like a witch's hat." Miss Conn smiles.
- Watching a variety show on TV, the child asks: "What are those things that are shaped like bananas?" (Some curtains over the stage are yellow and do look just like big bananas!) Dad comments laughingly, "That is funny. Those curtains look like bananas."

▶❙❙ **TeachSource Video**

WHAT IS A TRIANGLE?

A Third-Grade Lesson

Students in a third-grade class demonstrate their knowledge of triangle and its defining characteristics.

1. What are some misconceptions the students have about triangles and other shapes?
2. How do different groups sort their triangles?
3. How do the students discover the different properties of the triangles?
4. What do the students need to spend more time exploring?
5. How would you adapt this lesson for the preschool/kindergarten level?

Adult-Guided Activities. Adult-guided activities are designed to help children see the attributes that are critical to each type of shape. These activities should provide more than learning the names of a limited number of models. Models should vary. For example, not every figure should have a horizontal base. Some examples should be rotated, as in Figure 4-4. Some nonexamples should be provided for comparison. Preoperational children need to learn that orientation, color, and size are irrelevant to the identification of shape. Clements and Sarama (2000, p. 487) suggest that children can be helped to learn what is relevant and what is irrelevant through the following kinds of activities:

- Identifying shapes in the classroom, school, and community

- Sorting shapes and describing why they believe a shape belongs to a group

- Copying and building with shapes, using a wide range of materials

Technology for Young Children

Make Your Own Shape Designs Online

On the Illuminations website, there are two activities that can be used to develop shape designs online.

1. **Patch Tool** provides shapes for children to make a patch of their own design.

2. **Shape Tool** can be used to create even more complex designs and even tessellations.

These activities support STREAM experiences

Children need both **haptic** and visual experiences to learn discrimination and labeling. These experiences can be described as follows:

- *Haptic activities* use the sense of touch to match and identify shapes. In these activities, the child cannot see to solve a problem but must use only his sense of touch. The items to be touched are hidden from view. The things may be put in a bag or a box or wrapped in cloth or paper. Sometimes a clue is given. The child can feel one thing and then find another that is the same shape. Or the child can be shown a shape and then asked to find one that is the same. Finally, the child can be given just a name (or label) as a clue.

- *Visual activities* use the sense of sight. The child may be given a visual or a verbal clue and asked to choose, from several things, the one that has the same shape. Real objects or pictures may be used.

- *Visual-motor activities* use the sense of sight and motor coordination at the same time. This type of

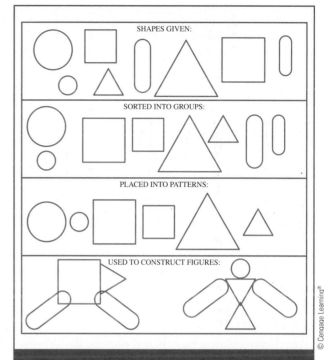

FIGURE 4-6 Shapes can be sorted into groups, placed into a pattern, or made into figures.

experience includes the use of puzzles, form boards, attribute blocks, flannelboards, magnet boards, Colorforms®, and paper cutouts, all of which the child can manipulate by herself. She may sort the things into sets or arrange them into a pattern or picture. Sorting was described in Chapter 3; examples of making patterns or pictures are shown in **Figure 4-6**.

The National Library of Virtual Manipulatives (2007) includes a variety of shape activities. For example, the selection includes activities with attribute blocks, triangles, geoboards, pattern blocks, and tangrams. As the child engages in haptic, visual, and visual-motor activities, the teacher can provide labels (words such as *round, circle, square, triangle, rectangle, shape, corners, points, cone, cylinder, rectangular prism*). Starting on page 120 are some examples of basic types of shape experiences for the young child.

4-1c Helping Children with Special Needs

Perceptual-Motor Challenges. Children who are challenged by perceptual-motor tasks can learn to identify shapes by practicing their perceptual-motor skills with shape templates. Large shape templates can be used on the chalkboard or smartboard. Students should start with a circle and then try reproducing the square, the triangle, the rectangle, and the diamond. After completing the large templates, they can work with desktop templates on paper. Once they have mastered drawing with the templates, they can move on to tracing and then to free drawing.

ACTIVITIES

SHAPE: FEELING BOX

Objective: To provide children with experiences that will enable them to use their sense of touch to label and discriminate shapes.

Materials: A medium-sized cardboard box with a hole cut in the top that is big enough for the child to put his hand in, but small enough that he cannot see inside; some familiar objects, such as a toy car, a small wooden block, a spoon, a small coin purse, a baby shoe, a pencil, and a rock.

Naturalistic and informal activities: During daily center time, the children should have opportunities to become acquainted with the objects just listed during their play activities. During their play, comment on the objects and supply the appropriate names: **"You have used the** *rectangular square prism blocks* **to build a garage for your** *car.***"**

Adult-guided activities:

1. Show children each of the objects. Be sure they know the name of each one. Have them pick up each object and name it.

2. Out of their sight, put the objects in the box.

3. Then do the following:

- Have another set of identical objects. Hold them up one at a time: **"Put your hand in the box. Find one like this."**

- Have yet another set of identical objects. Put each one in its own bag. **"Feel what is in here. Find one just like it in the big box."**

- Use just a verbal clue. **"Put your hand in the box. Find the rock [car, block]."**

- **"Put your hand in the box. Tell me the name of what you feel. Bring it out, and we'll see if you guessed it."**

Follow-up: Once the children understand the idea of the feeling box, introduce a mystery box. In this case, place familiar objects in the box, but do not tell the children what they are: They must feel them and guess. Children can take turns. Before a child takes the object out, encourage her to describe it (smooth, rough, round, straight, bumpy, having wheels, etc.). After the child learns about geometric shapes, fill the box with cardboard cutouts, attribute blocks, or three-dimensional models.

Digital Download

ACTIVITIES

SHAPE: DISCRIMINATION OF GEOMETRIC SHAPES

Objective: To see that geometric shapes may be the same or different from each other.

Materials: Any or all of the following may be used:

- Smartboard or tablet with shapes of various types, sizes, and colors

- Magnet board with magnet shapes of various types, sizes, and colors

- Flannelboard with felt shapes of various types, shapes, and colors

- Attribute blocks (blocks of various shapes, sizes, and colors)

- Cards with pictures of various geometric shapes in several sizes (all outlines or solids of the same or different colors)

- Three-dimensional models

Naturalistic and informal activities: During the daily center time, provide opportunities for the children to explore the materials. Observe whether they use any shape words, sort the shapes, match the shapes, make patterns, or make constructions. Ask them to describe what they have done. Comment, using shape words.

Adult-guided activities: The activities are matching, classifying, and labeling.

- *Matching:* Put out several different shapes. Show the child one shape: **"Find all the shapes like this one. Tell me why those belong together."**

- *Classifying:* Put out several different kinds of shapes. **"Put all the shapes that are the same kind together. Tell me how you know those shapes are all the same kind."**

- *Labeling:* Put out several kinds of shapes. **"Find all the triangles [squares, circles]."** Or **"Tell me the name of the shape."** [Point to one at random.]

Follow-up: Do individual and small group activities. Do the same basic activities with different materials.

Digital Download

ACTIVITIES

SHAPE: DISCRIMINATION AND MATCHING GAME

Objective: To practice matching and discrimination skills (for the child who has already had experience with the various shapes).

Materials: Cut out some shapes from cardboard. The game can be made harder by increasing the number of shapes used and/or by varying the size of the shapes and the number of colors. Make six bingo-type cards (each one should be different) as well as a spinner card that includes all the shapes used.

Activities:

1. Give each child a bingo card.

2. Have the children take turns spinning the spinner. Anyone whose card has the shape that the spinner

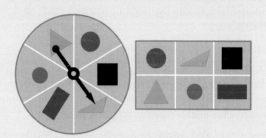

points to can cover the shape with a paper square or put a marker on it.

Follow-up: Once the rules of the game are learned, the children can play it on their own.

SHAPE: ENVIRONMENTAL GEOMETRY

Objective: To see that geometric shapes are all around in the environment.

Materials: The classroom, the school building, the playground, the home, and the neighborhood.

Activities:

1. Look for shapes on the floor, the ceiling, doors, windows, materials, clothing, trees, flowers, vehicles, walls, fences, sidewalks, and elsewhere.

2. Make a shape table. Cover the top, and divide it into sections. Mark each section with a sample shape. Have the children bring things from home and place them on the table on the shape that matches what they brought.

3. Make "Find the Shape" posters (**Figure 4-7**).

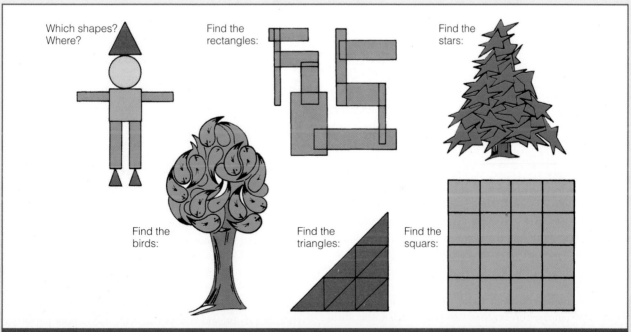

FIGURE 4-7 Find the shapes.

ELMER: AN INTEGRATED LESSON PLAN FOR AGES 4 TO 6

Objective: This plan integrates math, art, literacy, and social studies. Children can learn about squares, color, design, and self-concept.

Materials: Book: *Elmer* by David McKee (New York: Lothrop, Lee, & Shepard Books, 1964). Available from Scholastic.

Art materials: A variety of colored art paper (brown, pink, orange purple, blue, yellow, red, black, green, purple), scissors, glue sticks, crayons and/or markers

Naturalistic and informal activities: The children should have had many opportunities to cut paper and use glue sticks, crayons, and markers. The Elmer book should be in the library center for at least one week, where the children can look through it and request a reading.

Adult-guided activities: With the whole class or a small group read the story out loud.

1. Show the picture of the herd of elephants. Discuss the size differences. "What is the same about all but one elephant?" (color)

2. Show the picture of Elmer. Note that Elmer is a patchwork. Have the children identify the colors. Ask, "What shapes are Elmer's patchworks?" (squares)

3. Turn to the picture of Elmer upside down on a group of his friends. "How did Elmer make the other elephants happy?"

4. Show the picture of Elmer running away. "Why isn't Elmer happy?" "Why does Elmer change his color?" "What happens when he returns to the herd?" "What does he do?" "What did the other elephants do?" "Why did the elephants decide to have a colorful celebration parade every year?" "Was Elmer satisfied with his color after that?"

Follow-up: After the story reading, that day or the next, place the art materials out. Give each child an 8½-by-11-inch piece of white paper and smaller pieces of the other colors. Tell students they can design their own patchwork elephant.

Digital Download

Bilingual Geometry. Flores (1995) provides an approach to geometry for bilingual students in grades K–3. Geometry was taught in Spanish to develop higher-order thinking skills in the children's primary language. Kindergartners did five activities. The students used six templates: one square, one equilateral triangle, and four right triangles. They were given problems that required them to compare the template shapes with shapes on paper in different positions.

Multicultural Geometry. Zaslavsky (1996) presents a focus on comparing the shapes of homes in a variety of cultures. When asked to draw a floor plan, most children in Western culture start with a rectangle. They can then move on to study the shapes of homes in other cultures. Some Native Americans believed that the circle had great power and thus built their tepees on a circular base. The Kamba people in Africa also built on a circular base. The Yoruba of Nigeria build rectangular homes, as did the Egyptians. Students can learn how cultural beliefs and lifestyles influence the shapes of houses. Zaslavsky describes how art is a reflection of shape. Art is evident in items such as decorative pieces, household items, architecture, clothing, and religious artifacts. Art may have symbolic meaning, and art patterns are frequently based on geometric shapes. Later in this chapter, we see how art can reflect spatial concepts.

4-1d Informal Post-Evaluation

Through observing during center time and during adult-guided experiences, the teacher can see whether the child shows advances in ideas regarding shape. She observes whether the child uses the word *shape* and other shape words as he goes about his daily activities. When the child sorts and groups materials, the teacher notices whether he sometimes

uses shape as the basis for organizing. The adult gives the child informal tasks such as:

- "Put the box on the square table."
- "Fold the napkins so they are rectangle shapes."
- "Find two boxes that are the same shape."
- "Look carefully at the shapes of your puzzle pieces."
- "Make a design with these different-shaped tiles."

After a period of instruction, the teacher may use interview tasks such as those described in Appendix A.

4-2 SPATIAL SENSE AND SPATIAL CONCEPTS

Recall that spatial intelligence is one of the eight main intelligences identified by Howard Gardner in his *Theory of Multiple Intelligences*. Research supports that spatial talent and creativity are essential to successful STEM performance (Wai, 2013). Thus, spatial skills should be included in STEM curricula. The STEM subjects are highly creative in nature but also involve spatial talent. Children high in spatial talent are frequently neglected in school and may be labeled as dyslexic, such as Thomas Edison and Albert Einstein, due to poor performance in math and reading. The NCTM (2000) lists several expectations concerning young children's understanding and application of spatial relationships as one of the foundations of early geometry. According to CCSSM standards, K–2 geometry includes "shapes, their attributes and spatial reasoning" (p. 7). According to NCTM (2000), young children are expected to:

- Describe, name, and interpret relative positions in space and apply ideas about relative position.

- Describe, name, and interpret direction and distance in navigating space, and apply ideas about direction and distance.

- Find and name locations with simple relationships such as "near to" and "in."

A sense of spatial relationships, along with an understanding of shape, is fundamental to "interpreting, understanding, and appreciating our inherently geometric world" (NCTM, 1989, p. 48). Spatial sense experiences can integrate across content areas (**Figure 4-8**).

Math, science, and technology were originally integrated in the area of engineering known as **design technology** (Dunn & Larson, 1990). Young children apply their knowledge of spatial relations to building and construction projects. They are natural engineers who continuously engage in problem-solving activities. From the constructivist point of view, the environment just has to provide materials that inspire problem solving, such as the block center (Van Meeteren & Zan, 2010). Children's activities as engineers are primitive,

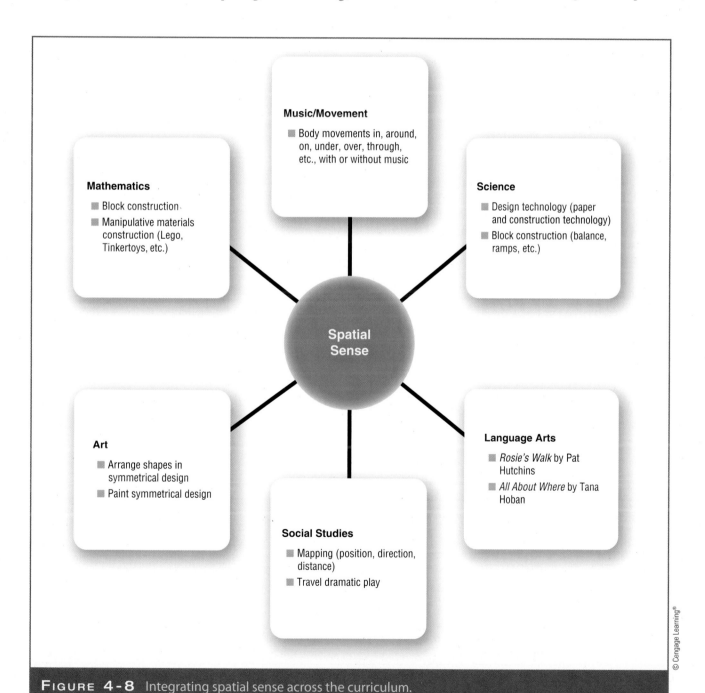

Music/Movement
- Body movements in, around, on, under, over, through, etc., with or without music

Mathematics
- Block construction
- Manipulative materials construction (Lego, Tinkertoys, etc.)

Science
- Design technology (paper and construction technology)
- Block construction (balance, ramps, etc.)

Spatial Sense

Art
- Arrange shapes in symmetrical design
- Paint symmetrical design

Language Arts
- *Rosie's Walk* by Pat Hutchins
- *All About Where* by Tana Hoban

Social Studies
- Mapping (position, direction, distance)
- Travel dramatic play

© Cengage Learning®

FIGURE 4-8 Integrating spatial sense across the curriculum.

BRAIN CONNECTION

SPATIAL INTELLIGENCE

Spatial intelligence is an important predictor of achievement in science, technology, engineering, and mathematics (Dewar, 2011–2012). It is the kind of thinking used by architects and engineers when they design a building or by a chemist thinking about a three-dimensional molecule. According to Dewar, research supports the theory that spatial skills can be improved through training. Using spatial language helps increase spatial intelligence. For example, rather than pointing at the basket and saying, "Put the toy over there," the teacher should say, " Put the ball in the basket." It is important to begin in toddlerhood, when children are initially developing oral language.

G. Dewar, Spatial Intelligence in Children: Why Training Matters, *Parenting Science, November 2012,* http://www.parenting.com.

but serve as the basis for what adult engineers do. An engineer can be playful and imaginative, just like a young child. According to Petroski (2003), the professional engineer's fundamental activity is design. "Design is rooted in imagination and choice—and play" (Petroski, 2003, pp. 4–5).

Children naturally assemble materials and construct things that fit their needs. They place a blanket over a card table to make a tent or a cave, and they transform an empty box covered with wallpaper scraps into a doll bed. Building on their own ideas and solving their own problems, children can create their own curriculum. At the preoperational level, children need construction materials to explore. At the elementary level, as they emerge into concrete operations, design engineering takes on a more formalized structure, which is discussed later in this text. Pollman (2010) describes the importance of spatial literacy to problem solving in situations involving the mental rotation of objects in space, perspective taking, the coordination of one or more spaces, the representation of space (such as maps), and reasoning regarding how one space may relate to another. Research indicates that spatial thinking is closely related to mathematical thinking in general. The STEM movement supports providing engineering instruction for young children. For example, the Museum of Science in Boston offers a program in engineering for elementary grades (Hu, 2010). Children in kindergarten are challenged with problems such as building

safer structures for the Three Little Pigs or a fence that will keep rabbits safe. Kindergarteners in Hampton, Virginia, designed and built communities out of recycled materials and rebuilt them as computer models (Deal, 2012). Design technology is discussed further in Chapter 7, and STEM is discussed in Chapter 9. **Table 4-1** outlines the five spatial concepts that are important during early childhood and can guide movement and construction.

4-2a Pre-Assessment

Teachers can learn a great deal about children's understanding of space by observing them. Note whether children use "space words," and how they respond to them. Do they respond with an appropriate act when told to:

- "Put the book *on* the table."
- "Please *take off* your hat."
- "You'll find the soap *under* the sink."
- "Stand *behind* the gate."
- "Sit *between* Kate and Chris."

Do they answer space questions using space words?

- "Where is the cat?" *On* the bed.
- "Where is the cake?" *In* the oven.
- "Which way did John go?" He went *up* the ladder.

TABLE 4-1 Five Early Childhood Spatial Concepts

Space Concept	Question	Answers
Position	Where (am I, are you, is he)?	on, off; on top of, over, under; in, out; into, out of; top, bottom; above, below; in front of, in back of, behind; beside, by, next to; between
Direction	Which way?	up, down; forward, backward; around, through; to, from; toward, away from; sideways; across
Distance	What is the relative distance?	near, far; close to, far from
Organization and pattern	How can things be arranged so that they fit in a space?	arranging things in the space until they fit or until they please the eye
Construction	How is space made? How do things fit into the space?	arranging things in the space until they fit; change the size and shape of the space so that things will fit

Teachers should note the use of organization and pattern arrangement during play activities.

- When children do artwork, such as a collage, do they take time to place the materials on the paper in a careful way? Do they seem to have a design in mind?

- Do drawings and paintings show balance? Do they seem to get everything into the space that they want to have in it, or do they run out of space?

- As they play with objects, do they place them in straight rows, circle shapes, square shapes, and so on?

Teachers should note children's use of construction materials, such as blocks and containers.

- Do the children use unit blocks to make structures into which toys (such as cars and animals) can be placed?

- Do children use large hollow blocks to make buildings into which large toys and children will fit?

- Can children usually find the right size container to hold things (e.g., a shoe box that makes an appropriately sized bed for her toy bear)?

Teachers should also note children's use of their body in space.

- When children need a cozy place to play, do they choose one that fits their size, or do they often get stuck in tight spots?

- Do children manage to move their bodies without too many bumps and falls?

The individual interview tasks for space center on relationships and the use of space. The following are examples of interview tasks.

SAMPLE ASSESSMENT TASK

3G   PREOPERATIONAL AGES 2–3

SPACE, POSITION: CHAPTER 4-2

METHOD Interview.

SKILL Given a spatial relationship word, the child is able to place objects relative to other objects on the basis of that word.

MATERIALS A small container such as a box, cup, or bowl; an object such as a coin, checker, or chip.

PROCEDURE "Put the coin [checker, chip] in the container." Repeat using other space words: *on, off of, out of, in front of, next to, under, over.*

EVALUATION Observe whether the child is able to follow the instructions and place the object correctly relative to the space word used.

INSTRUCTIONAL RESOURCE R. Charlesworth, *Math and Science for Young Children,* 8th ed., San Francisco, CA: Cengage Learning, 2016

Digital Download

SAMPLE ASSESSMENT TASK

4F   PREOPERATIONAL AGES 3–4

SPACE, POSITION: CHAPTER 4-2

METHOD Interview.

SKILL Child will be able to use appropriate spatial relationship words to describe positions in space.

MATERIALS Several small containers and several small objects, for example, four small plastic glasses and four small toy figures, such as a fish, dog, cat, and mouse.

PROCEDURE Ask the child to name each of the objects (so that you can use his name for them if it differs from yours). Line up the glasses in a row. Place the animals so that one is *in*, one *on*, one *under*, and one *between* the glasses. Then say, **"Tell me where the fish is."** Then, **"Tell me where the dog is."** Then, **"Tell me where the cat is."** Finally, **"Tell me where the mouse is."** Frequently, children will insist on pointing. Say, **"Do it without pointing. Tell me with words."**

EVALUATION Note whether the child responds with position words and whether the words used are correct.

INSTRUCTIONAL RESOURCE R. Charlesworth, *Math and Science for Young Children,* 8th ed., San Francisco, CA: Cengage Learning, 2016.

Digital Download

4-2b Activities

Naturalistic Activities. Children first learn about space through everyday motor activities. As they move their bodies in space, they learn **position**, **direction**, and **distance** relationships, and they also learn about the use of the space. Children in the sensorimotor and preoperational stages need equipment that lets them place their own bodies on, off, under, over, in, out, through, above, below, and so on.

They need places to go up and down, around and through, and sideways and across. They need things that they can put in, on, and under other things, as well as things that they can place near and far from other things. They need containers of many sizes to fill; blocks to build with; and paint, collage materials, wood, clay, cutouts, and such to be made into patterns and organized in space. Thus, when children are matching, classifying, and comparing, they are learning about space at the same time.

Children who crawl and creep often go under furniture. At first, they sometimes get stuck when they have not correctly judged the clearance under which they will fit. As they begin to pull themselves up, they try to climb on things. This activity is important not only for motor development but for spatial learning. However, many pieces of furniture are not safe or are too high. An empty cardboard beverage bottle case with the cardboard dividers still in it may be taped closed and covered with some colorful Contac paper. This makes a safe and inexpensive place to climb. Teachers can make several, and children will have a set of large construction blocks.

Each time children handle an object, they may learn more than one skill or idea (**Photo 4-3**). For instance, Juanita builds a house with some small blocks. The blocks are different colors and shapes. First, Juanita picks out all the blue rectangular prisms and piles them three high in a row. Next she picks all the red rectangular prisms and piles them in another direction in a row. Next she piles orange rectangular prisms to make a third side to her structure. Finally, she lines up some yellow cylinders to make a fourth side. She places two pigs, a cow, and a horse in the enclosure. Juanita has sorted the blocks by color and shape. She has made a structure with space for her farm animals (a class) and has put the animals *in* the enclosure.

With the availability of information on outer space flight in movies and on television, children might demonstrate the concept during their dramatic play activities. For example, they might build a space vehicle with large blocks and fly off to a distant planet or become astronauts on a trip to the moon.

Photo 4-3 Young children take pride in their construction projects.

Children begin to integrate position, direction, distance, organization, pattern, and construction through mapping activities. Early mapping activities involve developing more complex spaces, such as building houses and laying out roads in the sand or laying out roads and buildings with unit blocks. Another activity is playing with commercial toys that include a village printed on plastic along with houses, people, animals, and vehicles that can be placed on the village. When provided with such materials, children naturally make these types of constructions, which are the concrete beginnings of understanding maps.

Informal Activities. Spatial sense involves many words to be learned and attached to actions. Teachers should use spatial words (as listed earlier in the chapter) as they fit into the daily activities. They should give spatial directions, ask spatial questions, and make spatial comments. Examples of directions and questions are in the assessment section of this chapter. Examples of spatial comments are as follows:

- "Carlos is at the *top* of the ladder."
- "Cindy is *close* to the door."
- "You have the dog *behind* the mother in the car."
- "You children made a house big enough for all of you." (construction)
- "You pasted all the square shapes on your paper." (organization and pattern)

Jungle gyms, packing crates, ladders, ramps, and other equipment designed for large muscle activity give children experiences with space. They climb *up*, *down*, and *across*. They climb *up* a ladder and crawl or slide *down* a ramp. On the jungle gym they go *in* and *out*, *up* and *down*, *through*, *above*, *below*, and *around*. They get *in* and *out* of packing crates. On swings they go *up* and *down* and *backward* and *forward* and see the world *down below*.

With large blocks, boxes, and boards, children make structures that they can get *in* themselves (**Photo 4-4**). Chairs and tables may be added to make a house, train, airplane, bus, or ship. Props such as a steering wheel, firefighter or police hats, ropes, hoses, discarded radios, and the like inspire children to build structures on which to play. With small blocks, children make houses, airports, farms, grocery stores, castles, and trains (**Photo 4-5**). They then place their toy animals, people, and other objects in spatial arrangements, patterns, and positions. They learn to fit their structures into the space available, such as on the floor or on a large or small table. They might also build space vehicles and develop concrete mapping representations in the sand or with blocks. Teachers can ask questions about their space trip or their geographic construction: "How far is it to the moon?" "Show me the roads you would use to drive from Richard's house to Kate's house."

PHOTO 4-4 Block construction supports the development of spatial sense.

PHOTO 4-5 This toddler enjoys building with Legos.

As children work with art materials, they choose what to glue or paste on the paper. A large selection of collage materials such as scrap paper, cloth, feathers, plastic bits, yarn, wire, gummed paper, cotton balls, bottle caps, and ribbon offer children a choice of things to organize within the available space. As they get past the first stages of experimentation, children plan their painting. They may paint blobs, geometric shapes, stripes, or realistic figures. They may enjoy printing with sponges or potatoes. All these experiences add to their ideas about space and relate to STEAM.

Adult-Guided Activities. Adult-guided activities of many kinds can be done to help children with their ideas about space and her skills in the use of space. Beginning on p. 128, we describe basic activities for the three kinds of space relations (position, direction, and distance) and the two ways of using space (organization/pattern and construction through design technology).

4-2c Helping Children with Special Needs

Much of young children's knowledge and understanding of spatial relations comes through their outdoor experiences of running, jumping, and climbing. Children with physical disabilities often miss out on these experiences. There is a movement across the country to construct Boundless Playgrounds® (Boundless Playgrounds, 2008; Shane's Inspiration, 2007). These playgrounds are designed to enable physically challenged children to play alongside their more able-bodied peers. Children with perceptual-motor

disabilities can work at a chalkboard, whiteboard, or flannel board, putting chalk marks or markers above (below, on, etc.) lines or drawings of objects. A recent case study tells about a young autistic boy with verbal language delays who went to a nature-based, public, outdoor boundless playground space (Rosenow, 2013). He became involved in building with tree branches, tree cookies, and other natural items, much to the astonishment of his mother and his siblings. He was able to express himself through visual-spatial materials.

Children of all cultures need opportunities for play (de Melendez & Beck, 2013). Music and movement provide opportunities for learning about space and spatial relations. Movement can be inspired by playing instruments from a variety of cultures. Children of all cultures can construct spatial arrangements through their art projects (Zaslavsky, 1996).

4-2d Informal Post-Evaluation

Informal evaluation can be done through observation. Teachers should note the following as children proceed through the day:

- Do they respond to space words in a way that shows understanding?

- Do they answer space questions and use the correct space words?

DAP **naeyc**

ACTIVITIES

SPACE: RELATIONSHIPS, PHYSICAL SELF

Objective: To help the child relate his position in space to the positions of other people and things.

Materials: The child's own body, other people, and things in the environment.

Naturalistic and informal activities: Encourage children to use their bodies in gross motor activity such as running, climbing, jumping, lifting, pulling, and so on. Assist them in motor control behaviors such as defining their own space and keeping a safe distance from others.

Adult-guided activities:

1. Set up an obstacle course using boxes, boards, ladders, tables, chairs, and similar items. Set it up so that, by following the course, children can physically experience position, direction, and distance. This can be done indoors or outdoors. As the child goes through the course, use space words to label his movement: **Leroy is going *up* the ladder, *through* the tunnel, *across* the bridge, *down* the slide, and *under* the table. Now he is *close to* the end.**

2. Find Your Friend: Place children in different places: sitting or standing on chairs or on blocks or boxes, under tables, sitting three in a row on chairs facing different directions, and so on. Have each child take a turn to find a friend.

   "Find a friend who is on a chair [a box, a ladder]."

   "Find a friend who is under [on, next to] a table."

   "Find a friend who is between two friends [behind a friend, next to a friend]."

   "Find a friend who is sitting backward [forward, sideways]."

   "Find a friend who is above [below] another friend."

   Have the children think of different places they can place themselves. When they know the game, let the children take turns making the *find* statements.

3. *Put Yourself Where I Say:* One at a time, give the children instructions for placing themselves in a position.

   "Climb up the ladder."

   "Walk between the chairs."

   "Stand behind Tanya."

   "Get on top of the box."

   "Go close to [far from] the door."

   Once the children learn the game, they can give the instructions.

4. *Where Is Your Friend?* As in Activity 2, Find Your Friend, place the children in different places. This time ask *where* questions. The child must answer in words. For example, **"Where is your friend?"** The child answers, "Tim is under the table" or "Mary is on top of the playhouse."

Follow-up: Set up indoor and outdoor obstacle courses for the children to use during playtime.

SPACE, RELATIONSHIPS, OBJECTS

Objective: To be able to relate the position of objects in space to other objects.

Materials: Have several identical containers (cups, glasses, or boxes) and some small objects such as blocks, pegs, buttons, sticks, and toy animals.

Naturalistic and informal activities: Observe how children play with objects during center time. Do they stack their blocks? Do they put dolls in beds? Do they place vehicles in structures? Comment on their placements: **"The red block is *on* two green blocks." "The doll is *in* the bed."** Give instructions: **"Sit *next* to Mary." "Put the place mat *under* the dishes." "Put this brush *in* the red paint."** Note whether the children are able to comply.

Adult-guided activities:

1. *Point to:* Place objects in various spatial relationships such as shown in this diagram:

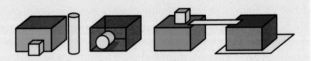

   "Point to the thing that is in [on, under, between, behind] a box."

2. *Put the:* Place some containers out, and set some objects to the side. Tell the child, **"Put the [object] in [on, through, across, under, near] the container."**

3. *Where is?* Place objects as in Activity 1 and/or around the room. Ask, **"Where is the [object]? Tell me where the [object] is."** The child should reply using a space word.

Follow-up: Repeat the activity, using different objects and containers. Leave the materials out for the children to use during center time.

SPACE, USE, CONSTRUCTION—DESIGN TECHNOLOGY/ENGINEERING

Objective: To organize materials in space in three dimensions through construction.

Materials: Wood chips, polythene, cardboard, wire, bottle caps, small empty boxes (e.g., tea, face cream, toothpaste, frozen foods) and other waste materials that can be recycled for construction projects, glue, tape, cardboard, and/or plywood scraps.

Naturalistic and informal activities: Provide children with the opportunity to build structures using construction toys (unit blocks, Legos, Unifix Cubes, etc.) during center time. Also provide them with opportunities to make a variety of collages, which provide the children with experience in organizing materials and using glue.

Adult-guided activity: Give the child a bottle of glue, a roll of masking tape, and a piece of cardboard or plywood for a base. Let her choose, from the scrap materials, things that can be used to build a structure on the base. Encourage her to take her time, to plan, and to choose carefully which items to use and where to put them.

Follow-up: Keep plenty of waste materials on hand so that children can make structures when they are in the mood.

SPACE, USE, CONSTRUCTION—DESIGN TECHNOLOGY/ENGINEERING

Objective: To organize materials in three-dimensional space through construction.

Materials: Many kinds of construction materials can be purchased that help the child to understand space and improve hand–eye coordination and small muscle skills. Some examples follow:

1. Legos (jumbo for the younger child, regular for the older child or for one with good motor skills)
2. Tinkertoy sets
3. Big Bolt Construction Set
4. Snap-N-Play Blocks
5. Rig-A-Jig
6. Octons, Giant Slot, and Build (and other things with parts that fit together)

Naturalistic and informal activities: Once the child understands how he can use the toys, leave him alone with the materials and his imagination.

Adult-guided activity: Add challenge by having the children think first about what they might like to construct. Older children can draw a sketch of their plan. Next, they can make their project. After they are finished, ask them to reflect on the result. Is it what they had planned? Is it different? If different, in what ways? Do they need to make any changes? When they are satisfied with their construction, they can draw a sketch or (if a camera is available) take a photo to place in their portfolio.

Follow-up: Encourage students to engage in further design technology projects.

SPACE: MAPPING

Objective: To integrate basic space concepts through simple mapping activities.

Materials: Make a simple treasure map on a large piece of poster board. Draw a floor plan of the classroom, indicating major landmarks (learning centers, doors, windows, etc.) with simple drawings. Draw in some paths going from place to place. Make a brightly colored treasure chest from a shoe box. Make a matching two-dimensional movable treasure chest that can be placed anywhere on the floor plan.

Naturalistic and informal activities: Children should have opportunities for sand play and unit block play with a variety of vehicles. Note whether they construct roads, bridges, tunnels, and so on. Ask, **"Where does your road go?"** They should have a miniature house with miniature furniture to arrange. Ask, **"How do you decide where to place the furniture?"** Include maps as a dramatic play prop. Observe whether children find a way to use the maps in their play. How do they use them? Does their activity reflect an understanding of what a map is for?

Adult-guided activity: Hide the treasure chest somewhere in the room. Place the small treasure chest on the floor plan. Have the children discuss the best route to get from where they are to the treasure, using only the paths on the floor plan. Have them try out their routes to see whether they can discover the treasure.

Digital Download

Technology for Young Children

Cassandra, a preschool teacher, was given four touch tablets to try out in her classroom. (Shifflet, Toledo, & Mattoon, 2012). She had concerns about the value of using the tablets. First she tried some apps herself and then had her 4-year-old nephew try one. Without any instruction, he maneuvered through the apps. Cassandra followed the NAEYC technology guidelines and introduced one tablet to her class. After the introduction to the group, during center time four children moved into the library center and worked together on the tablet. One by one she added the other three tablets in the library center. She received several surprises: (1) the tablets enhanced cooperative interactions; (2) the children collaborated on projects; (3) the children practiced digital citizenship, taking turns and eventually moving on to other areas of exploration; (4) the children still wanted real-life experiences. Doing both a real and a virtual cookie baking activity, the children recognized the advantages and disadvantages of both. Cassandra concluded that when used selectively and with intention, technology can enhance early childhood education. A recommended app for geometry for Android and Apple iPods is *shape builder preschool puzzle*.

R. Shifflet, C. Toledo, & C. Mattoon, C., Touch Tablet Surprises: A Preschool Teacher's Story, Young Children, 67(3), 2012, 36–41.

- Does their artwork and block building show an increase in organization and use of pattern?
- Dot they handle their body well in space?
- Does their use of geoboards, parquetry blocks, inch cubes, and/or pegboards show an increase in organization and patterning?

After children have completed several space activities, teachers can assess their progress, using the interview tasks described in Appendix A.

4-3 STANDARDS AND PART–WHOLE RELATIONSHIPS

Young children have a natural understanding and interest in **parts** and **wholes** that can be used later as a bridge to understanding **fractions**, which are included in the third-grade Common Core State Standards for Mathematics (2010) (see Chapter 9). NCTM (2000) expectations require that young children develop a sense of whole numbers and represent them in many ways by breaking groups down into smaller parts. They are also expected to understand and represent commonly used fractions such as one-quarter, one-third, and one-half. They should learn that objects and their own bodies are made up of special (unique) parts; which groups of things can be divided into parts; and that whole things can be divided into smaller parts.

Parts of Wholes

- A body has parts (arms, legs, head).
- A car has parts (engine, doors, steering wheel, seats).
- A house has parts (kitchen, bathroom, bedroom, living room).
- A chair has parts (seat, legs, back).

Division of Groups into Parts

- Children pass out cookies for snack.
- They deal cards for a game of picture rummy.
- They give each friend one of their toys to play with.
- They divide their blocks so that each child can build a house.

Division of Whole Things into Parts

- One cookie is broken in half.
- An orange is divided into several segments.
- A carrot or banana is sliced into parts.
- The contents of a bottle of soda pop are put into two or more cups.
- A large piece of paper is cut into smaller pieces.

Young children focus on the number of things they see. Two-year-old Pablo breaks up his graham cracker into small pieces. "I have more than you," he says to Mukki, who has one whole graham cracker also. Pablo does not see that, although he has more *pieces* of cracker, he does not have more crackers. Ms. Moore shows Chris a whole apple. "How many apples do I have?" "One," says Chris. "Now watch," says Ms. Moore as she cuts the apple into two pieces. "How many apples do I have now?" "Two!" answers Chris. As Chris enters concrete operations, he will see that a single apple is always a single apple, even though it may be cut into parts.

Gradually. children are able to see that a whole is made up of parts. They also begin to see that parts may be the same (equal) in size and amount or different (unequal) in size and amount. They compare number and size (see Chapter 3) and develop the concepts of *more, less,* and *the same*. These concepts are prerequisites to the understanding of fractions, which are introduced in the primary grades. An understanding of *more, less,* and *the same* underlies learning that objects and groups can be divided into two or more equal parts while maintaining the same amount. Part–whole concepts can be integrated into other content areas (**Figure 4-9**) here.

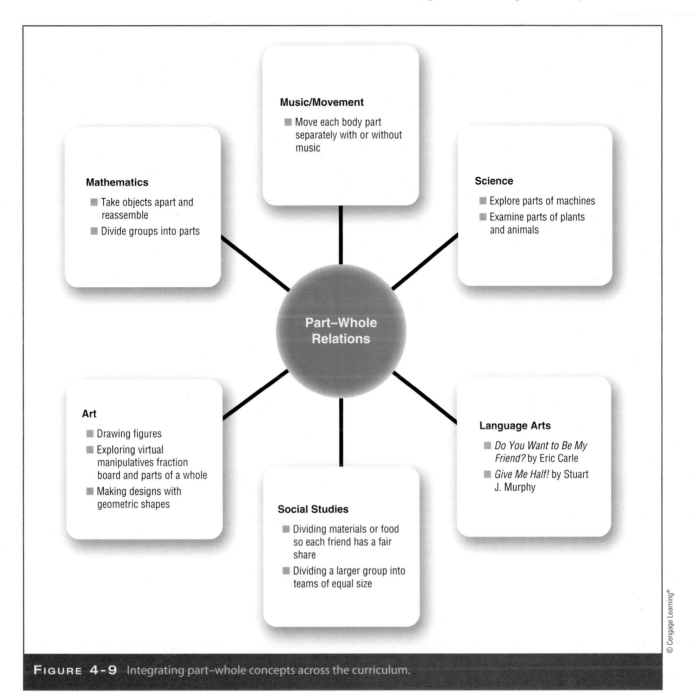

FIGURE 4-9 Integrating part–whole concepts across the curriculum.

BRAIN CONNECTION

NEURAL BASIS OF FRACTION KNOWLEDGE

At the nonsymbolic level, young children can understand fractions. That is, they can deal with concrete and pictorial representations. Fractions at the **symbolic level** (i.e., ½, ¾, etc.) are difficult to conceptualize (Siegler, Fazio, Bailey, & Zhou, 2013). Brain research shows that whole numbers and fractions are processed in the same regions of the brain (intraparietal sulcus, IPS). There seems to be an underlying commonality in the neural basis of whole number and fraction knowledge, and yet whole numbers are easier to work with and understand than fractions. The problems associated with understanding symbolic fractions is discussed in Chapter 8.

R. S. Siegler, L. K. Fazio, D. H. Bailey, & X. Zhou, Fractions: The New Frontier for Theories of Numerical Development, Trends in Cognitive Sciences, 17(1), 2013, 13–19.

4-3a Pre-Assessment

As children work and play, teachers should observe whether they use the words *part* and *whole* and whether they use them correctly. Teachers should note their actions.

- Do they try to divide items to be shared equally among their friends?

- Will they think of cutting or breaking something into smaller parts if there is not enough for everyone?

- Do they realize when a part of something is missing (such as the wheel of a toy truck, the arm of a doll, the handle of a cup)?

See the Sample Assessment Tasks for interview questions.

SAMPLE ASSESSMENT TASK

3H   PREOPERATIONAL AGES 2–3

PARTS AND WHOLES, MISSING PARTS: CHAPTER 4

METHOD Interview.

SKILL The child is able to tell which part(s) are missing from objects and/or from pictures of objects.

MATERIALS Several objects and/or pictures of objects and/or people with parts missing.

OBJECTS

A doll with a leg or an arm missing

A car with a wheel missing

A cup with a handle broken off

A chair with a leg gone

A face with only one eye

A house with no door

PICTURES Mount pictures of common things on poster board. Parts can be cut off before mounting.

PROCEDURE Show the child each object or picture. **"Look carefully. Which part is missing from this?"**

EVALUATION Observe whether the child is able to tell which parts are missing from both objects and pictures. Does she have the language label for each part? Can she perceive what is missing?

INSTRUCTIONAL RESOURCE
R. Charlesworth, *Math and Science for Young Children*, 8th ed., San Francisco, CA: Cengage Learning, 2016.

Digital Download

SAMPLE ASSESSMENT TASK

5F   PREOPERATIONAL AGES 4–5

PARTS AND WHOLES, PARTS OF A WHOLE: CHAPTER 4

METHOD Interview.

SKILL The child can recognize that a whole divided into parts is still the same amount.

MATERIALS Apple and knife.

PROCEDURE Show the child the apple. **"How many apples do I have?"** After you are certain the child understands

that you have one apple, cut the apple into two equal halves. **"How many apples do I have now?"** If the child says, "Two," press the halves together and ask, **"How many apples do I have now?"** Then cut the apple into fourths and eighths, following the same procedure.

EVALUATION If the child can tell you that there is still one apple when it is

cut into parts, he is able to mentally reverse the cutting process and may be leaving the preoperational period.

INSTRUCTIONAL RESOURCE
R. Charlesworth, *Math and Science for Young Children*, 8th ed., San Francisco, CA: Cengage Learning, 2016.

Digital Download

SAMPLE ASSESSMENT TASK

6D   PREOPERATIONAL AGES 5–6

PARTS AND WHOLES, PARTS OF GROUPS: CHAPTER 4

METHOD Interview.

SKILL The child can divide a group of objects into smaller groups.

MATERIALS Three small dolls (or paper cutouts) and a box of pennies or other small objects.

PROCEDURE Have the three dolls arranged in a row, **"I want to give**

each doll some pennies. Show me how to do it so that each doll will have the same amount."

EVALUATION Note how the child approaches the problem. Does she give each doll one penny at a time in sequence? Does she count out pennies until there are three groups with

the same amount? Does she divide the pennies in a random fashion? Does she have a method for finding out whether each has the same amount?

INSTRUCTIONAL RESOURCE
R. Charlesworth, *Math and Science for Young Children*, 8th ed., San Francisco, CA: Cengage Learning, 2016.

Digital Download

4-3b Part–Whole Activities

Naturalistic Activities. Newborn infants are not aware that all their body parts are part of them. Their early explorations lead them to find out that their hands are connected by arms to their shoulders, and that those toes are connected to legs. As they explore objects, they learn that they also have different parts. As they begin to sort and move objects around, they learn about parts and wholes of groups.

The following are some examples of young children's use of the part–whole concept (**Photo 4-6**).

- Two-year-old Pablo has a hotdog on his plate. The hotdog is cut into six pieces. He gives two pieces to his father, gives two to his mother, and keeps two for himself.

- Three-year-old Han is playing with some toy milk bottles. He says to Ms. Brown, "You take two like me."

- Three-year-old Kate is sitting on a stool in the kitchen. She sees three eggs boiling in a pan on the stove. She points as she looks at her mother. "One for you, one for me, and one for Dad."

- Tanya is slicing a carrot. "Look, I have a whole bunch of carrots now."

- Juanita is lying on her cot at the beginning of naptime. She holds up her leg. "Mrs. Raymond, is this part of a woman?"

- Ayi runs up to Mr. Brown and says, "Look I have a whole tangerine."

Informal Activities. Teachers can help children develop their understanding of parts and wholes many times during the day by using the words *part*, *whole*, **divide**, and **half**.

- "Today, everyone gets *half* of an apple and *half* of a sandwich."

- "Too bad; *part* of this game is missing."

- "Take this basket of crackers, and *divide* them up so everyone gets the same amount."

PHOTO 4-7   Touch your ear!

- "No, we won't cut up the carrots. Each child gets a *whole* carrot."

- "Give John *half* the blocks, so he can build, too."

- "We have only one apple left. Let's divide it up."

- "Point to the *part* of the body when I say the name" (**Photo 4-7**).

Children can be given tasks that require them to learn about parts and wholes (**Photo 4-8**). When children are asked to pass something, to cut up vegetables or fruit, or to share materials, they learn about parts and wholes.

PHOTO 4-6   Children point at body parts.

PHOTO 4-8   Magnet Builders are assembled into animal cages.

▶❚❚ TeachSource Video

© 2016 Cengage Learning®

THE HIDING ASSESSMENT 1

In this interview the boy is shown small groups of objects that he counts, and then part of the group is hidden. He is then asked how many are hidden.

1. What part–whole relationship is illustrated in this interview?

2. What part–whole relationships does the student know?

What size groups should she work on next?

Adult-Guided Activities. Children can be given adult-guided experiences in all of the three types of part–whole relationships.

- Activities can be done that help children become aware of special parts of people, animals, and things.

- Other groups of activities involve dividing groups into smaller groups.

- The third type of activity gives children experiences in dividing wholes into parts.

4-3c Helping Children with Special Needs

Preprimary grade children learn about parts and wholes while developing both their social skills and their mathematics concepts. Children with behavior problems may have difficulty sharing materials, but they should be provided with many opportunities to do so. For example, let them pass out materials to a group or have them give part of what they are using to another child.

Cultural factors are always important to consider when teaching math. Bonner (2009) provides an example of a culturally responsive math teacher whose African American students were very successful. This teacher's instructional practice was characterized by so-called *warm*

ACTIVITIES

PARTS AND WHOLES: PARTS OF THINGS

Objective: To learn the meaning of the term *part* as it refers to parts of objects, people, and animals.

Materials: Objects or pictures of objects with parts missing.

Naturalistic and informal activities: Give students time to play with a wide variety of toys and other objects. Label the parts—such as doll body parts or parts of vehicles or furniture—as they fit naturally occurring situations. For example: **"You put a shoe on each of the doll's feet." "There are four wheels on the truck." "You found all the pieces of the puzzle."** Ask questions such as, **"Which toys have wheels?" "Which toys have arms and legs?"** Comment on sharing: **"That is really nice that you gave your friend some of your blocks."** Note the examples given earlier in this unit.

Adult-guided activities:

1. *The Broken Toys:* Show the child some broken toys or pictures of broken toys. **"What's missing from these toys?"** After the child says what is missing

from each toy, bring out the missing parts (or pictures of missing parts). **"Find the missing part that goes with each toy."**

2. *Who or What is Hiding?* The basic game is to hide someone or something behind a screen so that only a part is showing. The children then guess who or what is hidden. Two children or objects could be hidden with part of only one showing, and the children could guess who or what is hidden and explain which clues told them the answer.

3. Try the activity described in the digital download lesson plan.

Follow-up: Explore shapes such as Tangrams, fraction circles, and fraction squares (Didax). Also, puzzles provide parts and wholes experiences. Read and discuss books such as *Tail Toes Eyes Ears Nose* by Marilee Robin Burton (1992) and the books listed in Figure 4-9.

GUESS WHAT?

Objective: To promote further understanding of parts and wholes.

Materials: A colorful magazine picture or a poster depicting a person or a common object (such as a car, house, box

of cereal) and five sheets of construction paper. Glue the picture onto one sheet of paper. Cut a 3-inch-diameter hole in the next piece of paper, and place it on top of the picture; cut a 2-inch hole in the next sheet of paper, and lay that on top of the other two; cut a 1-inch hole in the next sheet, and put it on the stack. Be sure the holes line up so that, when stacked, a part of the picture always shows through. Put a cover sheet of paper with no holes on top and write "GUESS WHAT?" on it. Staple the sheets together like a book. (As an alternative to making books, you could purchase books such as the Peephole Books published by HarperCollins.)

Naturalistic and informal: Students explore part–whole materials such as puzzles and replicas. They look through peephole books.

Adult-guided activities: Show the class the GUESS WHAT? book. Open to the first page with the small hole. Have students guess what is in the picture. As you turn each page, one by one, have students guess. Note how big the hole has to be before they identify what is in the picture. Discuss which visible part was the clue that told them what the picture contained. Compare with the list at the beginning of the unit.

Follow-up: Have students suggest other ways to play the game. Suggest they might want to make their own *Guess What?* books.

PARTS AND WHOLES: DIVIDING GROUPS

Objective: To give the child practice in dividing groups into parts (smaller groups).

Materials: Two or more small containers and some small objects, such as pennies, dry beans, or buttons.

Naturalistic and informal activities: Provide the children with opportunities to explore small objects and containers and to observe how they use the materials. Do they put the same or similar materials together? (see Chapter 3). Do they count items? Do they compare groups? Do they put some similar items in different containers? Refer to the examples given earlier in this unit.

Adult-guided activities: On the table, place small containers (start with two, and increase the number as the children are able to handle more). Put the pennies or other objects

in a bowl next to the containers. Say, **"Divide these up so that each container has some."** Note whether the children go about the task in an organized way and whether they try to put the same number in each container. Encourage them to talk about what they have done: **"Do they all have the same amount? Does one have more? How do you know? If you put all the pennies back into the same container, would you still have the same amount?" Let's do it and check the amount."** Note whether the children realize that the total amount does not change when the objects in the group are separated. In other words, can they conserve number?

Follow-up: Increase the number of smaller groups to be made. Use different types of containers and different objects.

PARTS AND WHOLES: DIVIDING WHOLES INTO PARTS

Objective: To divide whole things into two or more parts.

Materials: Real things or pictures of things that can be divided into parts by cutting, tearing, breaking, or pouring.

Naturalistic and informal activities: Provide children with plenty of opportunities to explore puzzles, construction toys, easily divisible fruits (such as oranges), and so on. Talk about the parts and wholes as in the examples given earlier in this unit.

Adult-guided activities:

1. Have the children cut up fruits and vegetables for their snack or lunch. Provide a sharp knife so that the job is not frustrating, but be sure to show them how to cut properly so as not to hurt themselves. Children with poor coordination can tear lettuce, break off orange slices, and cut the easier things such as string beans or bananas.

2. Give the child a piece of paper. Have him cut (or tear) it and then fit the pieces back together. Ask him to count how many parts he made.

3. Give the child a piece of playdough or clay. Have him cut it with a dull knife or tear it into pieces. How many parts did he make?

4. Use a set of plastic measuring cups and a larger container of water. Have the children guess how many quarter cupfuls of water will fill a cup measure. Let each child try the one-fourth, one-third, and one-half cups, and ask them to count how many of each of these cups will fill the one-cup measure.

Follow-up: Make or purchase some self-correcting part–whole materials. Examples:

1. Fraction pies—circular shapes available in rubber and magnetic versions (see Didax)

2. Materials that picture several parts or halves of a whole: chunky puzzles, inlay puzzles, fraction circles, Fundamental Fraction Kit (Constructive Playthings)

3. Fraction pizza (Hatch)

4. Fraction triangles, fraction circles, fraction squares, fraction pizzas, fraction cubes, fraction spheres (ETA/Cuisenaire)

demanding: "a combination of high expectations, firm and authoritative classroom management, and culturally familiar communication patterns" (p. 3). Major elements in this teacher's instructional approach included applying knowledge of her students' lives, cultures, and interests; being caring and demanding; using rituals common to the children's' everyday interactions; and constantly reflecting and revising.

Md-Yunus (2009) points out the importance of culturally appropriate food practice, using rice as an example. Rice is frequently used in the sensory table and along with beans, pasta, and other foods for math activities. Rice is a basic food in many cultures, as are other foods, such as the dried beans and pasta that are often used in classroom projects. Md-Yunus is concerned that we are teaching children that it is okay to play with and to waste food when they should be taught to respect food.

4-3d Informal Post-Evaluation

Teachers should observe and note whether children show increased use of part–whole words and more skills in his daily activities.

- Can they divide groups of things into smaller groups?

- Can they divide wholes into parts?

- Do they realize that objects, people, and animals have parts that are unique to each?

- Can they share things equally with others?

Individual evaluations can be done using the assessment tasks described earlier in the unit.

4-4 SCIENCE AND ENGINEERING STANDARDS AND CONNECTION TO MATHEMATICS

The Next Generation Science Standards (Strategic Partners Group, 2013) and the Framework (National Research Council, 2012) emphasize that, for children, the essence of learning lies not in memorizing facts, but in carrying out the processes of inquiry: asking questions; making observations; and gathering, organizing, and analyzing data and in design solutions. The fundamental concepts and skills that children construct during the preprimary period are essential to investigating science and engineering problems. Moomaw and Davis (2013) describe how STEM fits into preschool developmentally appropriate practice. As children explore and investigate, they develop an understanding of mathematical and science relationships.

The fundamental concepts and skills of one-to-one correspondence, number sense and counting, sets and classifying,

comparing, shape, space, and parts and wholes are basic to developing the abilities needed for scientific inquiry and design solutions. This section of Chapter 4 shows how the concepts presented in Chapters 3 and 4 appear naturally when children in the sensorimotor and preoperational periods of development explore science problems. Background material can be found in Chapter 1. Chapters 3 and 4 suggest methods of pre-assessment and post-evaluation using observation and individual interview tasks. Individual interview assessments are included with each concept and skill and are expanded in Appendix A.

NGSS standards begin at the kindergarten level. At this level, specific areas for study are described, but the method of instruction is left open ended. Kindergarten areas of study are motion and stability, energy structures and processes, Earth's systems, and Earth and human activity. The standards provide performance objectives for each area. These areas will be discussed further in Chapter 11. As with the math activities, each activity that follows includes naturalistic, informal, and adult-guided activities.

4-4a Informal Pre-Assessment

As with mathematics, observation and interview are the major science evaluation tools. Science educators refer to the interview questions as formative assessment probes (Ashbrook, 2013; Keeley, 2013). Probes are questions that are designed to discover what children already know about the topic area.

4-4b Science and Engineering Activities

Naturalistic Activities. Young children are naturally curious and identify problems as they explore their environment. Infants examine, taste, and feel objects. Toddlers are into everything, checking the contents of waste baskets, seeing how many objects will fit in a grocery bag, sorting out preferred toys from a large group, checking the contents of kitchen drawers and cabinets, and so on. Shaffer, Hall, and Lynch (2013) describe how a group of toddlers become fascinated with insects. The toddlers' study of insects began as a naturalistic child-guided project, moved on to an informal child-guided project with support from the teachers, and finally to adult- and child-guided projects as children and teachers collaborated. The children used their counting, comparing, and sorting skills in their study of rocks. Teachers encouraged children's explorations through conversations, reading, photographs and documentation, and child drawings. Shaffer, Hall, and Lynch follow the advice of Frances and David Hawkins (p. 16):

- Start with nature.

- Seize the moment.

- Become a researcher alongside the children.

- Become a researcher alongside adults.

- Think of your classroom as a laboratory.

Informal Activities. Informal activities grow out of naturalistic activities, as explained previously. Moomaw and Davis (2013) describe how they integrated STEM into a preschool class of 3- to 5-year-olds. The class investigated bird song patterns, pendulums, and inclines, based on their interests: life science and physics. Ogu and Schmidt (2013) relate how kindergartners developed an interest in rocks and moved on to do a long-term investigation with the support of their teachers.

Adult-Guided Activities. The following lesson plans center on some of young children's natural interests. The topics are Fall Leaves, Sense of Touch, Animals and Their Homes, Apples in the Fall, Process of Change, Seashells, and Construction and Sorting Seeds.

ACTIVITIES

COLLECTING AND COMPARING FALL LEAVES

Objective: Exploring the sizes and shapes of fall leaves.

Materials: Leaves of different sizes and shapes. Check to be sure that there are not any harmful plants such as poison ivy or poison oak. Small plastic lunch bags for collecting leaf samples.

Naturalistic and informal activities: Take children on a walk to collect leaves. As the children explore the leaves, encourage them to notice and talk about similarities and differences among the leaves.

Adult-guided activities: As the children inspect the leaves that they have collected, help them to observe closely by asking, **"What other leaves are like this one?"** Then ask, **"How are the leaves different?"** Give the children construction paper to arrange groups of similar leaves, and encourage discussion of the similarities and differences. Some children will enjoy creating a picture with the leaves, and others will wonder whether the leaves will grow into a tree.

Follow-up: Children will enjoy drying and pressing leaves between newspaper and cardboard. The children can write their names beside the leaves they collect. When the leaves are pressed and dry, they can be made into holiday cards, or the dry leaves can be pressed for display in the classroom or at home. Place the leaves between waxed paper squares, with the waxed side toward the leaves; then cover with a cloth and press with a warm iron.

FABRIC PICTURES: USING THE SENSE OF TOUCH

Objective: Identifying and exploring various materials with the sense of touch.

Materials: Cardboard cut into squares of any size, nontoxic glue, swatches of various fabrics, a variety of different textures such as sandpaper, wallpaper, cotton, silk, velvet, and so on.

Naturalistic and informal activities: Place all of the fabrics on the activity table for the children to touch, pick up, and examine. Provide time for the children to explore the textures. Then, encourage discussion about the fabrics the children are touching. **"Does anyone else have a piece of fabric that feels the same as yours? How does your fabric feel to your fingers?"**

Adult-guided activities: Give the children the cardboard squares and demonstrate how to use one or two drops of glue to affix each piece of fabric on their cardboard square. Ask the children to create a touching board by selecting fabric pieces and arranging them on their cardboard. Older children may want to create a picture using the fabrics. Display the touching pictures, and ask the children to find their fabric picture. **"How did you know that was your fabric picture?"**

Follow-up: You may want to stick to fabrics and paper initially. Once the children are comfortable with the activity, add three-dimensional objects such as sticks, string, yarn, and other objects to the fabric pictures.

ANIMALS AND THEIR HOMES

Objective: To apply one-to-one correspondence to the study of animals and their homes.

Materials: Illustrations such as **Figures 4-10, 4-11,** and **4-12.**

Naturalistic and informal activities: Young children usually include animals in their play activities. If they ask questions and show an interest in animal habitats, provide the games described below.

Adult-guided activities:

1. Create a bulletin-board background of trees (one tree should have a cavity), a cave, a plant containing a spiderweb, and a hole in the ground. Hang a beehive from a branch, and place a nest on another branch. Ask the children to tell you where each of the following animals might live: owl, bird, bee, mouse,

FIGURE 4-10 "Find a home for the bear."

spider, and bear. Place the animal by the appropriate home. Then, make backgrounds and animals for each child, and let the child paste the animal where it might live (see **Figure 4-10**). Ask, "Do you think a plant is a good place for a spider to spin a web?" "Why do you think so?" (Outdoor insects can land in the web.) Have the children describe the advantages of living in the different homes.

2. Another animal matching activity involves the preparation of six animals and six homes (see **Figure 4-11**).

FIGURE 4-11 Find the shapes.

These animals and homes may be used as a cut-and-paste activity or put in a poster-and-folder game format that can be used repeatedly in learning centers. In the matching activity, the children must cut out a home and paste it into the box next to the animal that lives there. For example, a bee lives in a beehive, a horse in a barn, an ant in an anthill, a bird in a nest, a fish in an aquarium, and a child in a human home. Ask, "Why would an ant live in the ground?" Emphasize that animals try to live in places that offer them the best protection or source of food. Discuss how each animal is suited to its home.

3. Counters are effective in reinforcing the fundamental concept of one-to-one correspondence. For example, when children study about bears, make and use bear counters that can be put into little bear caves. As the children match each bear to its cave, they understand that there are the same number of bears as there are caves. Lead the children in speculating why bears might take shelter in caves (convenient, will not be disturbed, hard to find, good place for baby bears to be born, etc.).

4. Children enjoy working with felt shapes. Cut out different-sized felt ducks, bears, ponds, and caves for children to match on a flannelboard. If children have the materials available, they will be likely to play animal matching games on their own, such as "match the baby and adult animals" or "line up all the ducks, and find a pond for each one." Have children compare the baby ducks with the adult ducks by asking: "In what ways do the babies look like their parents?" "How are they alike?" "Can you find any differences?" Emphasize camouflage as the primary reason that baby animals usually blend in with their surroundings. The number of animals and homes can be increased as the children progress in ability.

5. After telling or reading the story "Goldilocks and the Three Bears," draw three bears of different sizes, without noses. Cut out noses that will match the blank spaces, and have the children match the nose to the bear (see **Figure 4-12**). You might want to do this first as a group and then have the materials available for the children to work with individually. Point out that larger bears have bigger noses. Retell the story, using three sizes of unit block rectangular prisms for bears and a cylinder for Goldilocks. Have children volunteer to play each character.

Follow-up: Have the games available for the children to use during center time. One-to-one correspondence and the other skills presented in this chapter cannot be developed in isolation of content. Emphasize the science concepts and process skills when you utilize animals as a means of developing fundamental skills. Further animal matching and sorting activities can be created by putting pictures into categories of living and nonliving things, **invertebrates**, **reptiles**, **amphibians**, birds, and fish.

When comparing major groups of animals—reptiles, for example—try to include as many representatives of the group as possible. Children can study pictures of turtles (land turtles are called **tortoises**, and some freshwater turtles are called **terrapins**), snakes, lizards, alligators, and crocodiles and then match them to their respective homes. The characteristics of each reptile can be compared and contrasted. The possibilities for matching, counting, comparing, and classifying animals are limitless and make for a natural integration of math and science.

FIGURE 4-12 "Which nose belongs to Baby Bear?"

© Cengage Learning®

APPLES IN THE FALL

Objective: Identify varieties of apples; sort and count groups; and recognize that apples grow on trees.

Materials: A variety of apples, four to six of each variety.

Naturalistic and informal activities: In the fall, children may have visited an apple orchard or may have gone on a field trip to an apple orchard. Place the apples in a large basket or other container. Encourage the children to examine the apples and tell you what they notice.

Adult-guided activities: Emphasizing science content while learning number concepts enables children to relate these subjects to their everyday lives and to familiar, concrete instances. Sort the apples by different sizes and colors. Count each group. Ask, "Where do apples grow?" "What can we make with apples?"

Follow-up:

1. Before they cook the apples to make apple pies, the children can taste the different types of apples, tally their choices, and count to see which apple the class likes best.

2. Apple trees. Use a felt board or a smartboard for this game that requires the children to pick apples from trees. For this activity, create two rows of apple trees with four felt trees in each row. The trees are filled with one to nine apples, and the corresponding numerals are shown at the bottom of each row. Ask, "How many apples can you pick from each tree?" As a child picks apples off a tree, she counts aloud:

"One, two, three, four, five. I picked five apples from the apple tree." If she knows some numerals, she can point to and name the corresponding numeral name (**Figure 4-13**).

FIGURE 4-13 "How many apples can you pick?"

© Cengage Learning®

MAKING PLAYDOUGH: THE PROCESS OF CHANGE

Objective: To experience the process of change by mixing playdough ingredients, observing the process of change, changing the shape of the dough, and observing the change from wet to dry.

Materials: Flour, salt, water, bowl, measuring cups.

Naturalistic and informal activities: Place small paper cups of flour, salt, and water on a table. Ask the children what they think is in the cups. "How could you find out? Ask whether they could taste, smell, or feel. The children can explore the cups and make comments until they reach a conclusion about the contents.

Adult-guided activities: Have the children dispose of the small cups of flour, salt, and water. Get out one or more larger bowls, containers of flour and salt, a pitcher of warm water, and measuring cups (1 cup and 1/4 cup.)

Four children at a time do the following. Show the children a pictorial recipe: 4 cups flour, 1 cup iodized salt, and 1¾ cups warm water. Help the children measure the ingredients and pour them into the bowl. Have the children take turns mixing the ingredients (with a large spoon or by hand). Show the children how to knead the dough. Have them take turns kneading for a total of 10 minutes. Ask them to describe how their dough feels. Give them each a ball of dough, and explain they can make any shape they wish to (**Photo 4-9**). Repeat the process with another group. Tell students that they can save their dough

PHOTO 4-9   This girl explores her playdough.

shapes. "What will the dough be like after it sits out in the air or if it is baked in the oven?" If you bake the dough, set the oven temperature to 300 degrees and bake until the dough is hard, Air drying will take several days to harden. See MaryAnn F. Kohl, *Mudworks*, Mt. Rainier, MD: Gryphon House,1989.

Follow-up: When the dough is hard, it can be painted. Other type of dough recipes can also be tried.

EXPLORING SEASHELLS

Objective: Examine and identify the characteristics of seashells.

Materials: Even children who live near the ocean may no longer be able to collect seashells. However, seashells are fascinating to young children. They can be purchased in bulk online. A large tub or sand and water table is also needed.

Naturalistic and informal activities: Pour the bulk seashells into the tub or sand/water table. Tell the children they may explore the seashells and tell what they find out.

"What do you notice about the seashells?" "Where did they come from?" "Is there anything inside them?" "Was there anything inside them in the past?" Note whether the children sort and match shells by color, size, shape, or other criteria. "Why does your group belong together? " "How many are in this group?" "Which group has more?" Have some related books available in the library center. Read one during story time.

Follow-up: Make seashell collages or paint seashore pictures. Some related books are listed here:

M. Berkes, Seashells by the Seashore, *Nevada City, CA: Dawn Publications, 2002;* W. M. Hutchinson, A Child's Book of Seashells. *Rivergrove, IL: Maxton, 1954;* P. M. Ryan, Hello Ocean, *Watertown, MA: Talewinds, 2001;* C. K. Tibbits, Seashells, Crabs and Sea Stars: Take-Along Guide, *New York: Cooper Square, 1999;* and K. W. Zoefeld, What Lives in a Shell? *New York: HarperCollins, 1994.*

CONSTRUCTION

Objective: To follow-up on children's interests in building.

Materials: Unit blocks, hollow blocks, and other construction materials as needed.

Naturalistic and informal activities: From the playground, children observe the nearby construction. Probe their construction knowledge. Find out what they observe. What more would they like to know? Make a list of their comments. Note whether there is an increase in construction activity in the classroom dramatic play.

Adult-guided activity: Encourage construction (**Photo 4-10**). Have children describe their structures and explain how they build them and what activities happen in them. Provide materials as needed, such as for signs, furniture, trucks for hauling materials, and so on. Take photos and/or videos of the constructions. Have children explain their structures to the class.

Follow-up: Children can draw pictures of structures they are familiar with, that they have built, or that they would like to build. Teachers can read relevant stories such as these:

M. Dahl, One Big Building: A Counting Book About Construction. *Mankato, MN: Picture Window Books, 2004; and A. Roeder,* 13 Buildings Children Should Know, *New York: Prestel, 2009.*

© 2016 Cengage Learning®

Photo 4-10   Building with unit blocks can be a group project.

SORTING SEEDS (PRE-K–K)

Objective: To practice sorting seeds in different ways and identifying the positions of certain seeds relative to the whole assemblage.

Materials: Two or three each of several different kinds of seeds, such as peas, lima beans, sunflower seeds, corn, radish seeds, marigold seeds, and large seeds for other flowers and vegetables; small cardboard box with cover; white typing paper.

Activities:

1. Put the seeds in the box, put the cover on, and shake it to mix the seeds. Pour out the seeds onto a sheet of white paper. Ask the children (or child) to group the seeds by putting those that are alike together in separate piles. Ask them to give a descriptive name for each group of seeds.

2. Ask the children to point to the pile of seeds that is closest to them; furthest away from them. Then ask them to select one seed from each pile and put them on the white paper in a straight line. Which seeds are at the ends of the line? Which is in the middle? (If there are more than three seeds, ask them to identify all the seeds that are not at the ends.)

3. Using one of each kind of seed, ask children to line them up, putting the radish seed (or some other seed) in the middle. Tell them to put the pea seed at one end and the lima bean seed at the other end.

Follow-up: Plant some of the seeds, and keep a record of which ones grow.

Digital Download

4-4c Informal Post-Evaluation

As with mathematics, observation and interview are the major science evaluation tools. Science educators refer to the interview questions as assessment probes (Ashbrook, 2013; Keeley, 2013). Following a learning experience, probes are designed to discover what children have learned about the topic area.

Technology for Young Children

Teachers can use several software programs available on CDs or online as an additional tool for teaching fundamental concepts in science. Although not a substitute for manipulating materials, using the technology can reinforce concepts that have already been introduced, especially as children become familiar with the use of a computer or a tablet as a tool. Using technology tools teachers can create all sorts of activities to reinforce fundamental concepts and skills in science.

Sammy's Science House is a software and online program that features a section called "The Workshop," where children can be engineers and choose the pieces that will make whatever object is displayed. Another section of *Sammy's Science House* is called "The Sorting Station," where children sort items (plants vs. animals) into the correct category. *Recycle It!* has children sort trash into collection bins. This activity is available online, from Amazon, and from YouTube. *ThemeWeavers: Animals* (pre-K–2) is another software package that uses beginning math concepts and skills to explore science.

SUMMARY

4-1 Shape

Each thing the child meets in the environment has shape. The child explores his world and learns in a naturalistic way about the shape of each object in it. Adults help by giving the child things to view, hold, and feel. Adults also teach the child words that describe shapes and the names of geometric shapes: square, circle, triangle, cylinder, triangular prism, and so on. Through the exploration of shapes and spatial relations, the child builds the foundation of geometry.

Pre-Assessment. Observations and interviews can be used for pre-assessment.

Activities. The concept of shape can be taught through naturalistic, informal, and adult-guided, intentionally planned experiences. Concepts of shape can be applied to developing perceptual-motor integration, bilingual lessons, and comparisons of the meaning of shape across cultures.

Evaluation. Evaluation of children's learning can be done through observations and interviews.

4-2 Spatial Sense and Spatial Concepts

Spatial sense is an important part of geometry and mathematics in general. The child needs to understand the spatial relationship between his body and other things. He must also understand the spatial relationship among things around him. Things are related through position, direction, and distance. Children must also be able to use space in a logical way. They learn to fit things into the space available and to make constructions in space. Playground and art experiences help them build spatial concepts.

Pre-Assessment. Observations and interviews can be used for pre-assessment.

Activities. Naturalistic experiences involve exploration through movement and exploring construction materials. Informal activities occur when children move their bodies in space or construct with blocks or art materials and the adult labels the spatial relationship. Adult-guided activities might include directions games, object games, map activities, and construction.

Evaluation. Evaluation of children's learning can be done through observations and interviews.

4-3 Standards and Part–Whole Relationships

Young children have a natural interest in parts and wholes. This interest and the ideas learned are the foundations of learning about fractions. The children learn that things, people, and animals have parts. They learn that groups can be divided into parts (groups with smaller numbers of things). They learn that whole things can be divided into smaller parts or pieces.

Pre-Assessment. Observations and interviews can be used for pre-assessment.

Part–Whole Activities. Experiences in working with parts and wholes help the young child move from the preoperational level to the concrete perspective and on to understanding that the whole is no more than the sum of all its parts. Such experiences can also teach some essential social skills.

Evaluation. Evaluation of children's learning can be done through observations and interviews.

4-4 Science and Engineering Standards and Connection to Mathematics

The process of inquiry is the critical standard for children. The fundamental concepts from mathematics emerge during children's investigations of their world.

Pre-Assessment. This is done through observation and questioning probes designed to ascertain students' prior knowledge.

Activities. Science experiences for young children are planned around their natural interests. Adult support of their interests may lead into adult-guided experiences.

The example lessons in the science section of Chapter 4 center on collecting and comparing fall leaves, applying the sense of touch, construction, and other topics of interest to young children.

Post-Assessment. Through observation and questioning we can determine what students have learned.

FURTHER READING AND RESOURCES

Ashbrook, P. (2011). Sense of place. *Science and Children, 49*(1), 30–31.

Ashbrook, P. (2014). Shape exploration: Another dimension. *Science and Children, 5*(5), 30–31.

Children's Engineering Journal, 1(1). Online journal, http://www.vtea.org.

Gavin, M. K., & Moylan, K. G. (2012). 7 steps to high-end learning. *Teaching Children Mathematics, 19*(3), 184–192.

Piccolo, D. L., & Test, J. (2010/2011). Preschoolers thinking during block play. *Teaching Children Mathematics, 17*(5), 310–315.

Taylor-Cox, J. (2009). Teaching with blocks. *Teaching Children Mathematics, 15*(8), 460–463.

REFERENCES

Ashbrook, P. (2013). Are they getting it? *Science and Children, 51*(3), 24–25.

Berkes, M. (2002). *Seashells by the seashore*, Nevada City, CA: Dawn Publications.

Bonner, E. P. (2009). Achieving success with African American learners: A framework of culturally responsive mathematics teaching. *Childhood Education, 86*(1), 2–6.

Boundless Playgrounds. Home page. July 2, 2008. http://www.boundlessplaygrounds.org. (This site has links to 100 boundless playground sites.)

Burton, M. R. (1992). *Tail, toes, eyes, ears, nose*. New York: Harper Trophy. (This children's book teaches parts of eight animals.)

Charlesworth, R. (2016). *Math and science for young children*, 8th ed. San Francisco, CA: Cengage Learning.

Clements, D. H., & Sarama, J. (2000). Young children's ideas about geometric shapes. *Teaching Children Mathematics, 6*(8), 482–488.

Dahl, M. (2004). *One big building: A counting book about construction*. Mankato, MN: Picture Window Books.

Deal, T. (2012, Fall), Kindergarten civil engineers. *The Children's Engineering Journal, 10*, p. 2.

de Melendez, W. A., & Beck, V. (2013). Teaching young children in multicultural classroom (4th ed.). Belmont, CA: WadsworthCengage Learning.

Dewar, G. (2011–2012). *Spatial intelligence in children: Why training matters*. Last updated November 2012. http://www.parenting.com.

Dunn, S., & Larson, R. (1990). *Design technology: Children's engineering*. Bristol, PA: Falmer, Taylor & Francis.

Flores, A. (1995). Bilingual lessons in early grades geometry. *Teaching Children Mathematics, 1*, 420–424.

Hannibal, M. A. (1999). Young children's developing understanding of geometric shapes. *Teaching Children Mathematics, 5*(6), 353–357.

Hu, W. (2010). Studying engineering before they can spell it. *New York Times*, June 13 2010, http://www.nytimes.com/2010/06/14/education/14engineering.html?pagewanted=all&_r=0.

Hutchinson, W. M. (1954). *A child's book of seashells*. Rivergrove, IL: Maxton Publishers.

Keeley, P. (2013). Is it melting? Formative assessment for teacher learning. *Science and Children, 51*(3), 26–28.

Md-Yunus, S. (2009). Rice, rice, rice in the bin: Addressing culturally appropriate practice in early childhood classrooms. *Childhood Education, 86*(1), 27–31.

Moomaw, S., & Davis, J. A. (2013). STEM comes to preschool. In A. Shillady (Ed.), *Exploring Science* (pp. 17–22). Washington, DC: National Association for the Education of Young Children.

National Governors Association Center for Best Practices, Council of Chief State School Officers. Common Core State Standards for Mathematics (2010). Washington, DC: Author. wwwcorrstndards.org.

National Council of Teachers of Mathematics (NCTM). (1989). *Curriculum and evaluation standards for school mathematics*. Reston, VA: Author.

National Council of Teachers of Mathematics (NCTM). (2000). *Principles and standards for school mathematics*. Reston, VA: Author.

Rosenow, N. (2013). Communicating through construction. *ExchangeEveryDay*, August 29, 2013. http://childcareexchange.com

National Library of Virtual Manipulatives. (2010). *Geometry (grades pre-K–2)*. http://nlvm.usu.edu.

National Research Council. (2012). *A framework for K-12 science education practices*. Washington, DC: National Academies Press.

Ogu, U., & Schmidt, S. R. (2013). Kindergartners investigate rocks and sand: Addressing multiple learning styles through an inquiry-based approach. In A. Shillady (Ed.), *Exploring Science* (pp. 61–67). Washington, DC: National Association for the Education of Young Children.

Petroski, H. (2003, January 24). *Early education*. Presentation at the Children's Engineering Convention (Williamsburg, VA). http://www.vtea.org.

Pollman, M. J. (2010). *Blocks and beyond: Strengthening early math and science skills through spatial learning*. Baltimore, MD: Brookes.

Roeder, A. *13 buildings children should know*. New York: Prestel, 2009.

Ryan, P. M. (2001). *Hello Ocean*. Watertown MA: Talewinds.

Shaffer, L., Hall, E., & Lynch, M. (2013). Toddlers scientific explorations: Encounters with insects. In A. Shillady (Ed.), *Exploring Science* (pp. 11–16). Washington, DC: National Association for the Education of Young Children.

Shane's Inspiration. (2007). Retrieved August 1, 2007, from www.shanesinspiration.org.

Shifflet, R., Toledo, C., & Mattoon, C. (2012). Touch tablet surprises: A preschool teacher's story. *Young Children, 67*(3), 36–41.

Siegler, R. S., Fazio, L. K., Bailey, D. H., & Zhou, X. (2013). Fractions: the new frontier for theories of numerical development. *Trends in Cognitive Sciences, 17*(1), 13–19.

Strategic Partners Group. (2013). *Next Generation Science Standards*. Washington, DC: National Academies Press.

Tibbits, C. K. (1999) *Seashells, crabs and sea stars: Take-along guide*. New York: Cooper Square.

Van Meeteren, B., & Zan, B. (2010, Fall). *Revealing the work of young engineers in early childhood education. Early Childhood Research & Practice, 12*(2). http://ecrp.uiuc.edu.

Wai, J. (2013, July 31). Why we need to values students' spatial creativity. Mind/Shift. http://kqed.org/mindshift/2013/07/why-we-need-to-value-spatial-creativity/.

Wilkins, A. Geometry is hard-wired into our brains, io9.com, May 24, 2011, http://io9.com/5805127/geometry-is-hardwired-into-our-brains.

Zaslavsky, C. (1996). *The multicultural math classroom*. Portsmouth, NH: Heinemann.

Zoefeld, K. W. (1994). *What lives in a shell?* New York: HarperCollins.

CHAPTER 5

PRE-K–K: ORDERING, MEASUREMENT, AND DATA COLLECTION AND ANALYSIS

LEARNING OBJECTIVES

After reading this chapter, you should be able to:

5-1 Plan, teach, and evaluate ordering, seriation, and patterning concept lesson activities, following national standards.

5-2 Plan, teach, and evaluate measurement (volume, weight, length, and temperature) concept lesson activities, following national standards.

5-3 Plan, teach, and evaluate time concept lesson activities, following national standards.

5-4 Plan and teach data and graph concept lesson activities, following national standards.

5-5 Plan and teach science concept application lesson activities, following national standards.

STANDARDS ADDRESSED IN THIS CHAPTER

naeyc

NAEYC Professional Preparation Standards

5. Use content knowledge to build meaningful curriculum.

5a. Understand content knowledge and resources in mathematics and science.

5c. Design, implement, and evaluate developmentally meaningful and challenging curriculum for each child.

DAP Guidelines

2c. Know desired program goals.

3c. Use the curriculum framework to ensure there is attention to important learning goals.

Common Core State Standards for Math

MP1	Make sense of problems and persevere in solving them.
MP4	Model with mathematics.
K.MD.A.1	Describe measureable attributes of objects, such as length or weight.
K.MD.A.2	Directly compare two objects with a measureable attribute in common, to see which object has "more" or "less" of the attribute, and describe the difference.

Next Generation Science Standards

K-LS1-1	Scientists look for patterns and order when making observations about the world.
K-PS3-1	Make observations (firsthand or from media) to collect data that can be used to make comparisons.

5-1 STANDARDS AND EXPECTATIONS

The Common Core State Standards for Mathematics (CCSSM) (National Governors Association Center for Best Practices, 2010) do not address ordering, seriation, and patterning directly. However, as described in Chapter 3, the standards do include describing and comparing measureable attributes. The applications described in this first section of this chapter extend comparisons to more than two items.

Ordering is a higher level of comparing (Chapter 4) that is another step toward measurement (Cross, Woods, & Schweingruber, 2009). Ordering involves comparing more than two things or more than two groups. It also involves placing things in a sequence from first to last. In Piaget's terms, ordering is called **seriation**. **Patterning** is related to ordering in that children need a basic understanding of ordering before they can do patterning. It involves making or discovering auditory, visual, and motor regularities. Patterning includes (1) simple patterns such as placing Unifix Cubes in a sequence by color and/or number, (2) number patterns such as days of the week and patterns on the 100s chart, (3) patterns in nature such as spiderwebs and designs on shells, (4) quilt patterns, and (5) graphs. Movement can also be used

to develop pattern and sequence through clapping, marching, standing, sitting, jumping, and the like. Patterns are the basis of algebraic thinking (Taylor-Cox, 2003). Patterns are also important understandings in more advanced elementary mathematics such as times tables, addition, and skip counting (Geiser, 2006–2012).

Children start to develop ordering and seriation in the sensorimotor stage. Before the age of 2, the child likes to work with nesting toys. *Nesting toys* are items of the same shape but of varying sizes so that each one fits into the larger ones. If they are put into each other in order by size, they will all fit in one stack. Ordering and seriation involve seeing a pattern that follows continuously in equal increments. Other types of patterns involve repeated sequences that follow a preset rule. Daily routine is an example of a pattern that is learned early; that is, infants become cued into night and day and to the daily sequence of diaper changing, eating, playing, and sleeping. As they experiment with rattles, they might use a regular pattern of movement that involves motor, auditory, and visual sequences repeated over and over. As the sensorimotor period progresses, toddlers line up blocks, placing a large one, then a small one; then again large, small—or perhaps red, green, yellow, red, green, yellow.

An early way of ordering is to place a pattern in one-to-one correspondence with a model, as in **Figure 5-1**. This gives

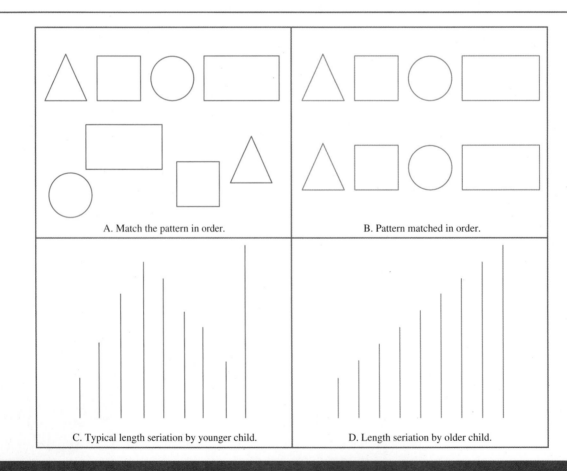

A. Match the pattern in order.

B. Pattern matched in order.

C. Typical length seriation by younger child.

D. Length seriation by older child.

FIGURE 5-1   Ordering by pattern and seriating by size.

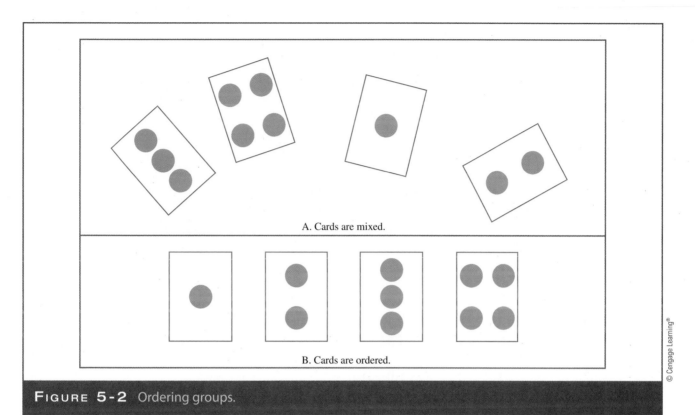

© Cengage Learning®

FIGURE 5-2 Ordering groups.

the child the idea of ordering. Next, he learns to place things in ordered rows on the basis of length, width, height, and size. At first the child can think of only two things at one time. When ordering by length, he places sticks in a sequence as shown in Figure 5-1(C). As he develops and practices, he will be able to use the whole sequence at once and place the sticks as in Figure 5-1(D). As the child develops further, he can order things by other characteristics, such as color shades (dark to light), texture (rough to smooth), and sound (loud to soft).

Once the child can place one set of things in order, he can go on to double seriation. For double seriation, he must put two groups of things in order. This is a use of matching, or one-to-one correspondence (Chapter 3).

Groups of things can also be put in order by the number of things in each group. By ordering groups, each having one more thing than the others, the child learns the concept of **one more than**. In **Figure 5-2**, some cards with different numbers of dots are shown. In Figure 5-2(A), the cards are mixed; in Figure 5-2(B), the cards have been put in order so that each group of dots has one more dot than the card before.

More complex patterns involve the repetition of a sequence. For example, the teacher might present children with a pile of shapes such as those depicted in Figure 5-1, show the pattern, and then ask them to select the correct shapes to repeat the pattern in a line (rather than matching underneath, one to one). The teacher can develop patterns with Unifix Cubes, cube blocks, beads, alphabet letters, numerals, sticks, coins, and many other items. He can develop auditory patterns with sounds such as hand clapping and drumbeats, or he can pattern motor activities such as by

giving the command to jump, jump, and then sit. To solve a pattern problem, children must be able to figure out what comes next in a sequence.

Ordering and patterning words include such words as *next*, *last*, *biggest*, *smallest*, *thinnest*, *fattest*, *shortest*, *tallest*, *before*, and *after*. Also included are the ordinal numbers: first, second, third, fourth, and so on, to the last thing. Ordinal terms are matched with counting in **Figure 5-3**. Ordering, seriation, and patterning can be integrated into the content areas (see **Figure 5-4**).

5-1a Pre-Assessment

While the child plays, the teacher should note activities that might show that the child is learning to order things. Notice how she uses nesting toys. Does she place them in each other so she has only one stack? Does she line them up in rows from largest to smallest? Does she use words such as *first* ("I'm first") and *last* ("He's last") on her own? In her dramatic play, does she go on train or plane rides where chairs are lined up for seats and each child has a place (first, second, last)? Seriation may be reflected in children's drawings. For example, in **Figure 5-5**, a child has drawn a picture of his family members in order of their height. The teacher can seriate paint chips from light to dark, such as from light pink to dark burgundy. He can put sequence stories (such as a child blowing up a balloon) on cards for the child to put in order.

Also, during play the teacher should watch for evidence of patterning behavior. Patterns might appear:

■ In artwork such as paintings or collages; in motor activity such as movement and dance; in musical activity such as chants and rhymes.

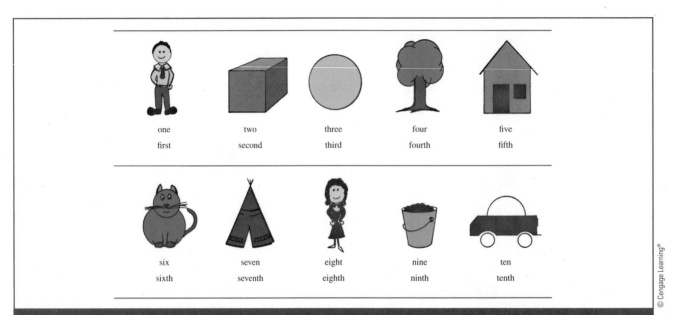

FIGURE 5-3 Counting numbers and ordinal numbers.

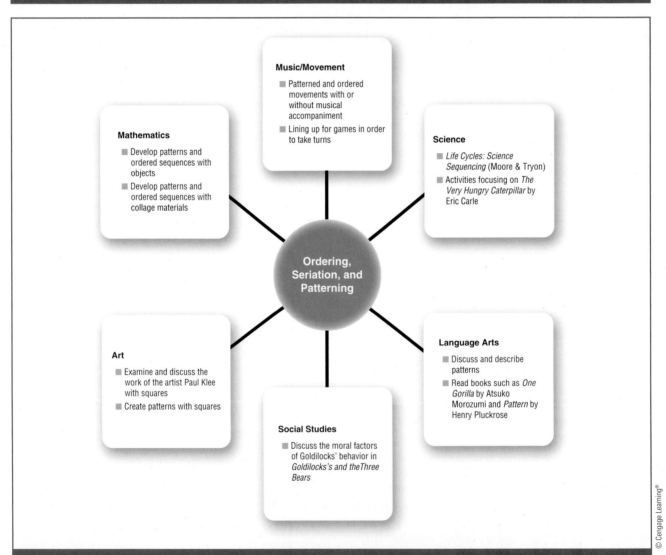

FIGURE 5-4 Integrating ordering, seriation, and patterning across the curriculum.

FIGURE 5-5 A young child draws his family in order by size.

- In language activities such as acting out patterned stories (e.g., "The Three Billy Goats Gruff" or "Goldilocks and the Three Bears").
- With manipulative materials such as Unifix Cubes, Teddy Bear Counters, Legos, building blocks, attribute blocks, beads for stringing, geoboards, and so on.

Ask the child to order different numbers and kinds of items during individual interview tasks, as in the examples that follow and in Appendix A. Here are examples of three assessment tasks.

SAMPLE ASSESSMENT TASK

5G   PREOPERATIONAL AGES 4–5

ORDERING, SEQUENTIAL/ORDINAL NUMBER: CHAPTER 5

METHOD Interview.

SKILL Child can order up to five objects relative to physical dimensions, and identify the ordinal position of each.

MATERIALS Five objects or cutouts that vary in equal increments of height, width, length, or overall size dimensions.

PROCEDURE Start with five objects or cutouts. If this proves to be difficult, remove the objects or cutouts; then put out three and ask the same questions. **"Find the [tallest, biggest, fattest or shortest, smallest, thinnest]. Put them all in a row from tallest to shortest [biggest to smallest, fattest to thinnest]."** If the child accomplishes the task, ask, **"Which is first? Which is last? Which is second? Which is third? Which is fourth?"**

EVALUATION Note whether the children find the extremes but mix up the three objects or cutouts that belong in the middle. This is a common approach for preoperational children. Note whether children approach the problem in an organized way or in a disorganized, unplanned way.

INSTRUCTIONAL RESOURCE
R. Charlesworth, *Math and Science for Young Children*, 8th ed., San Francisco, CA: Cengage Learning, 2016.

Digital Download

SAMPLE ASSESSMENT TASK

6H   TRANSITIONAL AGES 5–7

ORDERING, DOUBLE SERIATION: CHAPTER 5

METHOD Interview.

SKILL Child will place two sets of 10 items in double seriation.

MATERIALS Two sets of 10 objects, cutouts, or pictures of objects that vary in one or more dimensions in equal increments such that one item in each set is the correct size to go with an item in the other set. The sets could be children and baseball bats, children and pets, chairs and tables, bowls and spoons, cars and garages, hats and heads, and so on.

PROCEDURE Suppose you have decided to use hats and heads. First, place the heads in front of the child in random order. Instruct the child to line the heads up in order from smallest to largest. Help them if needed, asking, for example, **"Find the smallest. Good—now which one comes next? And next?"** If the child is able to line up the heads correctly, then put out the hats in a random arrangement. Tell the child, **"Find the hat that fits each head, and put it on the head."**

EVALUATION Note how the children approach the problem—in an organized way or a haphazard fashion. Note whether their solution is entirely or only partially correct. If they get a close approximation, repeat the procedure again with seven or five items to see whether they grasp the concept when fewer items are used. A child going into concrete operations should be able to accomplish the task with two groups of 10 objects. Transitional children may be able to perform the task correctly with fewer items in each group.

INSTRUCTIONAL RESOURCE
R. Charlesworth, *Math and Science for Young Children*, 8th ed., San Francisco, CA: Cengage Learning, 2016.

Digital Download

SAMPLE ASSESSMENT TASK

6I   TRANSITIONAL PERIOD AGES 5–7

ORDERING, PATTERNING: CHAPTER 5

METHOD Interview.

SKILL Child can copy, extend, and describe patterns made with concrete objects.

MATERIALS Color cubes, Unifix Cubes, Teddy Bear Counters, attribute blocks, small toys, or other objects that can be placed in a sequence to develop a pattern.

PROCEDURE

1. *Copy patterns.* One at a time, make patterns of various levels of complexity (each letter stands for one type of item such as one color of a color cube, one shape of an attribute block, or one type of toy). For example, A-B-A-B could be red block–green block–red block–green block or big triangle–small triangle–big triangle–small triangle. Show the following series of patterns, and tell the child, **"Make a pattern just like this one."** (If the child hesitates, point to the first item and say, **"Start with one like this."**)

   a. A-B-A-B

   b. A-A-B-A-A-B

   c. A-B-C-A-B-C

   d. A-A-B-B-C-C-A-A-B-B-C-C

2. *Extend patterns.* Make patterns as in activity 1, but this time say, **"This pattern isn't finished. Make it longer. Show me what comes next."**

3. *Describe patterns.* Make patterns as in activities 1 and 2. Say, **"Tell me about this pattern. (What comes first? Next? Next?) If you wanted to continue the pattern, what would come next? Next?"**

4. If the child easily accomplishes the foregoing tasks, then try some more difficult patterns, such as the following:

   a. A-B-A-C-A-D-A-B-A-C-A-D

   b. A-B-B-C-D-A-B-B-C-D

   c. A-A-B-A-A-C-A-A-D

EVALUATION Note which types of patterns are easiest for the children. Are they more successful with the easier patterns? With copying? With extending? With describing?

INSTRUCTIONAL RESOURCE
R. Charlesworth, *Math and Science for Young Children*, 8th ed., San Francisco, CA: Cengage Learning, 2016.

Digital Download

5-1b Activities

The three types of activities as applied to ordering, seriation, and patterning are described, followed by sample lesson plans.

Naturalistic Activities. Just as children's natural development guides them to sort things, so does it guide them to put things in order and to arrange them in patterns (see **Photo 5-1**). As children sort, they often put the items in rows or arrange them in patterns. For example, Kate picks out blocks that are all of one size, shape, and color, and she lines them up in a row. She then adds to the row by lining up another group of blocks of the same size, shape, and color. She picks out blue blocks and yellow blocks and lines them up, alternating colors. Pete is observed examining his mother's measuring cups and spoons. He lines them up from largest to smallest (see **Photo 5-2**). Then he makes a pattern: cup-spoon-cup-spoon-cup-spoon-cup-spoon (see **Photo 5-3**).

As the child's speech ability increases, he uses order words. "I want to be *first*." "This is the *last* one." "Daddy Bear

PHOTO 5-1 Children construct concepts of ordering, seriation, and patterning as they explore materials during play.

PHOTO 5-2 The child matches shapes ordered by size.

PHOTO 5-3   This child is making a shape pattern.

© Cengage Learning®

has the *biggest* bowl." "I'll sit in the *middle*." As he starts to draw pictures, he often draws mothers, fathers, and children, and places them in a row from smallest to largest.

Informal Activities. Informal teaching can go on quite often during the child's daily play and routine activities. Some examples follow:

- Eighteen-month-old Brad has a set of mixing bowls and measuring cups to play with on the kitchen floor. He puts the biggest bowl on his head. His mother smiles and says, "The *biggest* bowl fits on your head." He tries the smaller bowls, but they do not fit. Mom says, "The *middle-sized* bowl and the *smallest* bowl don't fit, do they?" She sits down with him and picks up a measuring cup. "Look, here is the cup that is the *biggest*. These are *smaller*." She lines them up by size. "Can you find the *smallest* cup?" Brad proceeds to put the cups one in the other until they are in a single stack. His mother smiles, "You have them all in *order*."

- Five-year-old Enrique, 4-year-old Chin, and 3-year-old Jim come running across the yard to Mr. Brown. "You are all fast runners." "I was *first*," shouts Enrique. "I was *second*," says Chin. "I was *third*," says Jim. Enrique shouts, "You were *last*, Jim, 'cause you are the *littlest*." Jim looks mad. Mr. Brown says, "Jim was both *third* and *last*. It is true Jim is the *littlest* and the *youngest*. Enrique is the *oldest*. Is he the *biggest*?" "No!" says Jim, "He's *middle size*."

- Mary is sharing some small candies with some friends and her teacher. "Mr. Brown, you and I get five because we are the *biggest*. Diana gets four because she's the *next* size. Pete gets three. Leroy gets two, and Brad gets one. Michael doesn't get any 'cause he's a baby." "I see," says Mr. Brown, "you are dividing them so the *smallest* people get the least, and the *biggest* get the most."

- Mrs. Red Fox tells her first graders that she would like them to line up boy-boy-girl-girl.

- Second grader Liu Pei decides to draw a picture each day of her bean sprout, showing how high it is on that day. Soon she has a long row of bean sprout pictures, each a little taller than the one before. Mr. Wang comments on how nice it is to have a record of the bean sprout's growth from the day it sprouted.

- Miss Collins tells the children, "You have to take turns on the swing. Tanya is *first* today."

These examples show how the adult can make comments that help the child see her own ordering of words and activities. Many times in the course of the day, opportunities come up where children must take turns. These times can be used to the fullest for teaching order and ordinal number. The teacher can place many kinds of materials out for children that help them practice ordering. Some of these materials are self-correcting, such as the Montessori cylinders: each cylinder fits in only one place.

Adult-Guided Activities. Adult-guided experiences with ordering and patterning can be done with many kinds of materials. The teacher can purchase or make these materials. Things of different sizes are easy to find at home or school. Measuring cups and spoons, mixing bowls, pots and pans, shoes, gloves, and other items of clothing are easily available in several different sizes. Paper and cardboard can be cut into different sizes and shapes. Paper-towel rolls can be made into cylinders of graduated sizes. The artistic teacher can draw pictures of the same item in graduated sizes. Already drawn materials, such as Richardson's (1999) Unifix Cube train patterns, counting boards, or working-space papers, can be used for patterning. The following basic activities can be done with many different kinds of objects, cutouts, and pictures.

Jorge, a kindergartner, enjoys exploring patterns with Virtual Manipulatives online: *color pattern* challenges Jorge to arrange colors to complete a pattern; *pattern blocks* provide opportunities to build patterns with virtual pattern blocks.

5-1c Helping Children with Special Needs

An understanding of patterns and ordering provides children with a foundation for understanding algebraic relationships. A multisensory approach to instruction can be used to meet the needs of all children. The art of many cultures includes special patterns (Zaslavsky, 1996). Children can make stamped repeated patterns with sponges and other materials. They can also use stencils for creating patterns. Pattern blocks can be explored. Children can be introduced to the patterns common to a variety of cultures. They might bring materials from home, including patterns.

Children with perceptual-motor challenges may benefit from extra time using large colored beads. Beads are usually available in six colors and three shapes. For the first step, the children can select five or six beads of any color or shape to practice stringing. Once the children feel comfortable with stringing, they can begin to string patterns. They can start with the simplest patterns such as all cubes or all spheres or all cylinders in one color and gradually move to A-B and more complex patterns in small steps. Sequence terms can be applied to instructions—for example, "First blue, second yellow."

ACTIVITIES

ORDERING AND PATTERNING: THE BASIC CONCEPT

Objective: To help the child understand the idea of order and sequence.

Materials: Large colored beads with a string, for the teacher and each child.

Naturalistic and informal activities: Have the container of beads available during center time. As the children explore the beads, note whether they develop patterns based on color. Comment: "First you lined up the blue beads and then the red beads." "You lined up two yellow, two red, and two blue beads."

Adult-guided activities: The beads are put in a box or bowl within reach. Say, **"Watch me. I'm going to make a string of beads."** Start with three beads. Add more as each child learns to do each amount. Lay the string of three beads down where each child can see it: **"Now you make one like mine. Which kind of bead should you take first?"** When the first bead is on, **"Which one is next?"** When two are on, **"Which one is next?"**

Use patterns of varying degrees of complexity.

1. A-B-A-B
2. A-B-C-A-B-C
3. A-A-B-A-A-C-A-A-D
4. Make up your own patterns.

Follow-up: Make a string of beads. Pull it through a paper-towel roll so that none of the beads can be seen. Say, **"I'm going to hide the beads in the tunnel. Now I'm going to pull them out. Which one will come out first? Next? Next?"** and so on. Then pull the beads through and have the children check as each bead comes out.

ORDERING/SERIATION: DIFFERENT SIZES, SAME SHAPE

Objective: To make comparisons of three or more items of the same shape and different sizes.

Materials: Four to 10 squares cut with sides 1 inch, 1¼ inch, 1½ inch, and so on.

Naturalistic and informal activities: During center time, have available a container of the squares and other shapes in a sequence of sizes. Note how the children use the shapes. Do they sequence them by size? Comment: "You put the biggest square first." "You put all the same sizes in their own piles."

Adult-guided activity: Lay out the shapes. **"Here are some squares. Stack them up so the biggest is on the bottom."** Mix the squares up again. **"Now, put them in a row, starting with the smallest."**

Follow-up: Do the same thing with other shapes and materials.

ORDERING/SERIATION: LENGTH

Objective: To make comparisons of three or more things of the same width but different lengths.

Materials: Sticks, strips of paper, yarn, string, Cuisenaire Rods, drinking straws, or anything similar cut in different lengths and such that each item is the same difference in length from the next one.

Naturalistic and informal activities: Have containers of each type of material available during center time. Place some of the items in the art center to be used for collages. Note how the children explore the materials. Do they line them up in sequence? Comment: "You put the largest (smallest) first." "Tell me about what you made."

Adult-guided activity: Place the sticks in a mixed order. **"Line these up from shortest to longest (longest to shortest)."** Help if needed. **"Which one comes next?" "Which one of these is longest?" "Is this the next one?"**

Follow-up: Do this activity with many different kinds of materials.

ORDERING/SERIATION: DOUBLE SERIATION

Objective: To match, one to one, two or more ordered sets of the same number of items.

Materials: Three Bears flannelboard figures or cutouts made by hand: Mama Bear, Papa Bear, Baby Bear, Goldilocks, three bowls, three spoons, three chairs, and three beds.

Naturalistic and informal activities: Have the flannelboard and story pieces available during center time. Note how the children use the material. Do they tell the story? Do they line up the pieces in sequence? Comment if they hesitate: "What comes next in the story?" Note whether they sequence and/ or match the materials by size; "You matched up each bear with its chair (bowl, bed)."

Adult-guided activity: Tell the story. Use all the order words: *biggest, middle-sized, smallest, next.* Follow up with questions: **"Which is the biggest bear? Find the biggest bear's bowl (chair, bed, spoon)."** Use the same sequence with each character.

Follow-up: Let the children act out the story with the felt pieces or cutouts. Note whether they use the order words, whether they change their voices, and whether they match each bear to the correct bowl, spoon, chair, and bed.

ORDERING: SETS

Objective: To order groups of one to five objects.

Materials: Glue buttons or draw dots on five cards.

Naturalistic and informal activities: Have the cards available during center time. Note whether the children sequence them from one to five items. Comment: "Tell me how many buttons (dots) there are on each card." "Which cards have more than one?"

Adult-guided activity: Lay out the cards. Put the card with one button in front of the child. **"How many buttons on this card?"** Child answers. Say, **"Yes, there is one button.**

Find the card with one more button." If the child picks out the card with two, say, **"You found one more. Now find the card with one more button."** Keep on until all five are in line. Mix the cards up. Give the stack to the child. **"Line them all up by yourself. Start with the smallest group."**

Follow-up: Repeat with other materials. Increase the number of groups as each child learns to recognize and count larger groups. Use loose buttons (chips, sticks, or coins), and have the child count out her own groups. Put each group in a small container or on a small piece of paper.

ORDERING: ORDINAL NUMBERS

Objective: To learn the ordinal numbers first, second, third, and fourth. (The child should be able to count easily to four before doing this activity.)

Materials: Four balls or beanbags, four common objects, four chairs.

Naturalistic and informal activities: Have the materials available during center time or gym time, as appropriate. Note how the children use them. Note whether they figure out that they must take turns. Comment: "You are doing a good job taking turns. Mary is first, José is second, Larry is third, and Jai Li is fourth."

Adult-guided activities:

1. Use games that require children to take turns. Just keep in mind that young children cannot wait very long. Limit the group to four children, and keep the game moving fast. For example, give each of the four children one beanbag or one ball. Say, **"How many bags are there? Let's count. One, two, three, four. Can I catch them all at the same time? No, I can't. You will have to take turns: you are first, you are**

second, you are third, and you are fourth." Have each child say his number: "I am [first, second, third, and fourth]." **"Okay, first, throw yours."** [Throw it back.] **"Second, throw yours."** [Throw it back.] After each has had his turn, have all of them do it again. This time have them tell you their ordinal number name.

2. Line up four objects. Say, **"This one is first, this one is second, this one is third, and this one is fourth."** Ask the children: **"Point to the [fourth, first, third, second]."**

3. Line up four chairs. **"We are going to play bus [plane, train]."** Name a child: **"_____, you get in the third seat."** Fill the seats. Go on a pretend trip. **"Now we will get off. Second seat, get off. First seat, get off. Fourth seat, get off. Third seat, get off."**

Follow-up: Make up some games that use the same basic ideas. As each child knows first through fourth, add fifth, then sixth, and so on.

PATTERNING: AUDITORY

Objective: To copy and extend auditory patterns.

Materials: None needed.

Naturalistic and informal activities: Note whether the children engage in spontaneous chants and rhymes. Encourage them by joining in their rhythmic activities.

Adult-guided activities: Start a hand-clapping pattern. Ask the children to join you. **"Listen to me clap."** [Clap, clap, (pause), clap (repeat several times).] **"You clap along with me."** Keep on clapping for 60–90 seconds so that everyone has a chance to join in. Say, **"Listen. When I stop, you finish the pattern."** Do three repetitions, then stop. Say, **"You do the next one."** Try some other patterns such as, **clap, clap, slap the elbow** or **clap, stamp the foot, slap the leg.**

Follow-up: Help the children develop their own patterns. Have them use rhythm instruments (e.g., drums, jingle bells, or sound cans) to develop patterns.

PATTERNING: OBJECTS

Objective: To copy and extend object patterns.

Materials: Several small plastic toys such as vehicles, animals, or peg people; manipulatives such as Unifix Cubes, inch cubes, or attribute blocks—or any other small objects such as coins, bottle caps, eating utensils, or cups.

Naturalistic and informal activities: Provide opportunities to explore many kinds of materials, such as those listed above. After the children have had some adult-guided pattern activities, note whether they develop patterns during their independent activity periods. Do they call your attention to their pattern constructions? Can they describe their constructions when you ask them to?

Adult-guided activities: Have the children explore ways to make patterns with the objects. Have them see how many different kinds of patterns they can make.

Follow-up: Find additional ideas for pattern activities in this chapter's Further Reading and Resources listing.

PATTERNING: EXPLORING PATTERNS IN SPACE

Objective: To organize materials in space in a pattern.

Materials: Many kinds of materials are available that will give the child experiences with making patterns in space.

1. *Geoboards* are square boards with attached pegs. Rubber bands of different colors can be stretched between the pegs to form patterns and shapes.

2. *Parquetry and pattern blocks* are blocks of various shapes and colors that can be organized into patterns.

3. *Pegboards* are boards with holes evenly spaced. Individual pegs can be placed in the holes to form patterns.

4. *Color inch cubes* are cubes with 1-inch sides. They are available in sets with red, yellow, blue, green, orange, and purple cubes.

Naturalistic and informal activities: Provide children time for exploring materials during center time. Note the patterns the children construct. Do they call your attention to their pattern constructions? Can they describe their constructions when you ask them to?

Adult-guided activities:

1. Have the children experiment freely with the materials and create their own patterns.

2. Purchase or make patterns for the children to copy.

Follow-up: After showing the children how to use the materials, leave them out during center time.

PATTERNING: ORGANIZING PATTERNS IN SPACE

Objective: To organize materials in space in a pattern.

Materials: Construction paper, scissors, and glue.

Naturalistic and informal activities: Children should already have been involved with many activities (naturalistic as well as informal and adult guided) and have had many opportunities to work in small groups before being assigned the following activity.

Adult-guided activities: Provide a poster-sized piece of construction paper and an assortment of precut construction-paper shapes (e.g., squares, triangles, circles). Suggest that the children, working in small groups, create as many different patterns as they can and glue them on the big piece of paper.

Follow-up: Offer the activity several times. Use different colors for the shapes, use different sizes, and change the choice of shapes.

For auditory learners, more opportunities for auditory patterns can support their understanding of pattern and ordering. Rhymes with repeated patterns work well with these children. Kinesthetic learners do well with patterned movement activities such as two steps, two jumps, and so on. Children can also use movement to work with sequence; for example, they can line up "first, second, third," and so forth to do patterned movement or take turns doing patterns.

5-1d Post-Evaluation

Note whether children's use of ordering and patterning words and their involvement in ordering and patterning activities have increased during play and routine activities. Without disrupting the children's activities, ask questions or make comments and suggestions.

- "Who is the biggest? [The smallest?]"
- (As the children put their shoes on after their nap) "Who has the longest shoes? [The shortest shoes?]"
- "Who came in the door first today?"
- "Run fast. See who can get to the other side of the gym first."
- (The children are playing train) "Well, who is in the last seat? She must be the caboose. Who is in the first seat? She must be the engineer."
- "Everyone can't get a drink at the same time. Line up with the shortest person first."
- "Great, you found a new pattern to make with the Unifix Cubes!"
- "Sam made some patterns with the inkpad and stamps."

Richardson (1999, pp. 78–79) suggests noting whether children can:

- Copy patterns.
- Extend patterns.
- Create patterns.
- Analyze a given pattern.

5-2 MEASUREMENT STANDARDS AND EXPECTATIONS

The Common Core State Standards (National Governors Association Center for Best Practices, 2010) for kindergarten provide expectations for children in the beginning stages of **measurement**, including describing the measureable attributes of objects, such as **length** or **weight**. Children should be able to describe several measureable attributes of a single object, as well as compare and order objects according to these attributes. This chapter addresses these attributes plus the attributes of **temperature** and **volume**. By the time they reach kindergarten, young children are expected to understand measurement with nonstandard units such as multiple copies of objects of the same size (e.g., paper clips). Measurement connects geometry and number, building on children's experiences with comparisons (Chapter 3). Length is the major focus for younger children, but experiences with weight, volume, and temperature are also important. Estimation is an important measurement tool in the early stages.

Measurement is one of the most useful skills in math and science. *Measurement* involves assigning a number to things so that they can be compared on the basis of the same attributes. Numbers can be assigned to attributes such as volume, weight, length, and temperature. For example, the child drinks *one cup* of milk. Numbers can also be given to time measurement. However, time is not an attribute of things and so is presented separately. **Standard units**, such as pints, quarts, liters, yards, meters, pounds, grams, and degrees, tell us exactly how much (*volume*); how heavy (*weight*); how long, wide, or deep (*length*); and how hot or cold (*temperature*). A number is assigned to a standard unit to let us make a comparison. Two quarts contain more than 1 quart, 2 pounds weigh less than 3 pounds, 1 meter is shorter than 4 meters, and 30° is colder than 80°.

5-2a Stages of Development

The concept of measurement develops through five stages, as outlined in **Figure 5-6**. The first stage is a **play stage**.

Piagetian Stage	Age	Measurement Stage
Sensorimotor and Preoperational	0–7	1. Plays and imitates
		2. Makes comparisons
Transitional: Preoperational to Concrete Operations	5–7	3. Uses arbitrary units
Concrete Operations	6+	4. Sees need for standard units
		5. Uses standard units

FIGURE 5-6 Stages in the development of the concept of measurement.

© Cengage Learning®

The child imitates older children and adults. She plays at measuring with rulers, measuring cups, measuring spoons, and scales, as she sees others do. She pours sand, water, rice, beans, and peas from one container to another as she explores the properties of volume. She lifts and moves things as she learns about weight. She notes that those who are bigger than she is can do many more activities, and she has her first concept of length (height). She finds that her short arms cannot always reach what she wants them to reach (length). She finds that she has a preference for cold or hot food and cold or hot bathwater, and she begins to learn about temperature. This first stage begins at birth and continues through the sensorimotor period into the preoperational period.

The second stage in the development of the concept of measurement is the one of making **comparisons** (Chapter 3). The concept of measurement is well underway by the preoperational stage. The child is always comparing: bigger–smaller, heavier–lighter, longer–shorter, and hotter–colder.

The third stage, which comes at the end of the preoperational period and at the beginning of concrete operations, is one in which the child learns to use what are called **arbitrary units**; that is, anything the child has can be used as a unit of measure. She will try to find out how many coffee cups of sand will fill a quart milk carton; the volume of the coffee cup is the arbitrary unit. She finds out how many toothpicks long her foot is; the length of the toothpick is the arbitrary unit. As she goes through the stage of using arbitrary units, she learns concepts needed to understand standard units.

When the child enters the period of concrete operations, she begins to see the need for standard units. She can see that, to communicate with someone else in a way that the other person will understand, she must use the same units the other person uses. For example, the child says that her paper is 9 thumbs wide. Another person cannot find another piece of paper of the same width unless the child and her thumb are there to measure it. But if she says her paper is 8½ inches wide, another person will know the exact width of the paper. In this case, the thumb is an arbitrary unit, and the inch is a *standard unit.*

The same is true for other units. When cooking, standard measuring cups and spoons must be used for the recipe to turn out correctly. If any coffee cup or teacup and just any spoon are used when following a recipe, the measurement will be arbitrary and inexact, and the chances of a successful outcome are poor. The same can also be said of building a house. If nonstandard measuring tools are used, the house will not come out as it appears in the plans, and one carpenter will not be communicating clearly with another.

The last stage in the development of the concept of measurement begins in the concrete operations period. In this last stage, the child begins to use and understand the standard units of measurement, such as inches, meters, pints, liters, grams, degrees, and the like.

Obviously, prekindergartners and most kindergartners are still exploring the concept of measurement.

Prekindergartners are usually in stages 1 (play and imitation) and 2 (making comparisons). The kindergartners begin in stage 2 and move into stage 3 (arbitrary units). During the primary grades, students begin to see the need for standard units (stage 4) and move into using standard units (stage 5).

Measurement can be integrated into the other content areas (see **Figure 5-7**).

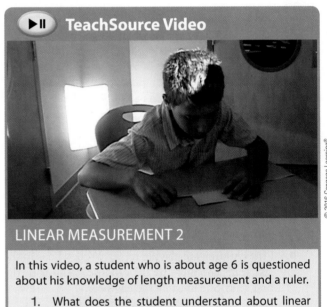

TeachSource Video

LINEAR MEASUREMENT 2

In this video, a student who is about age 6 is questioned about his knowledge of length measurement and a ruler.

1. What does the student understand about linear measurement?
2. What are the student's misconceptions?
3. Where is he in the stages of development of measurement understanding?

5-2b How the Young Child Thinks About Measurement

A review of Piaget will help explain why young children do not understand standard units in the sensorimotor and preoperational stages. Recall from Chapter 1 that the young child is fooled by appearances. He believes what he sees before him. He does not keep old pictures in mind, as he will do later. He is not yet able to conserve (or save) the first way something looks when its appearance is changed. When the ball of clay is made into a snake, he thinks the volume (the amount of clay) has changed because it looks smaller to him. When the water is poured into a differently shaped container, he thinks there is more or less water depending on the height of the glass. Because he can focus on only one attribute at a time, the most obvious dimension determines his response.

Two more examples are shown in **Figure 5-8**. In the first task, the child is fooled when a crooked road is compared with a straight road. The straight road looks longer

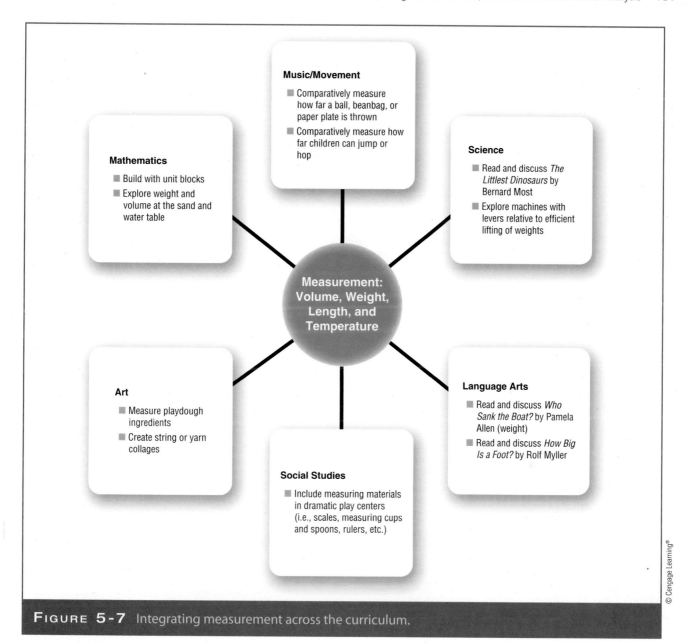

FIGURE 5-7 Integrating measurement across the curriculum.

(*conservation of length*). In the second task, size is dominant over material, and the child guesses that the Ping-Pong ball weighs more than the hard rubber ball. He thinks that because the table tennis ball is larger than the hard rubber ball, it must be heavier.

The young child becomes familiar with the words of measurement and learns which attributes can be measured during the preprimary period. He learns mainly through observing older children and adults as they measure. He does not need to be taught the standard units of measurement in a formal way. Martin (2012) suggests that children use invented units of measurement throughout elementary school; as children develop intellectually, they will begin to use standard units such as yard, foot, meter, pound, and the like. At this early stage, the young child needs to gain a feeling that things differ on the basis of

"more" and "less" of some attributes. He gains this feeling mostly through his own observations and firsthand experimental experiences.

5-2c Pre-Assessment

To assess measurement skills in the young child, the teacher observes. The teacher notes whether the child uses the term *measure* in the adult way. He notes whether she uses adult measuring tools in her play as she sees adults use them. He looks for the following kinds of incidents.

■ Mary is playing in the sandbox. She pours sand from an old bent measuring cup into a bucket and stirs it with a sand shovel. "I'm measuring the flour for my cake. I need three cups of flour and two cups of sugar."

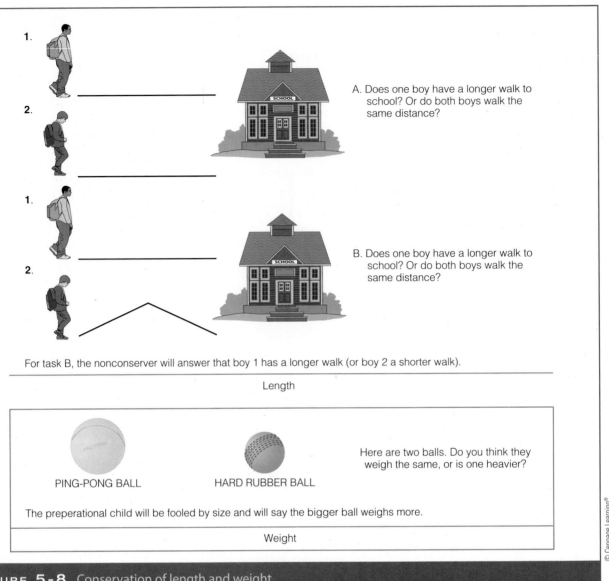

A. Does one boy have a longer walk to school? Or do both boys walk the same distance?

B. Does one boy have a longer walk to school? Or do both boys walk the same distance?

For task B, the nonconserver will answer that boy 1 has a longer walk (or boy 2 a shorter walk).

Length

PING-PONG BALL

HARD RUBBER BALL

Here are two balls. Do you think they weigh the same, or is one heavier?

The preoperational child will be fooled by size and will say the bigger ball weighs more.

Weight

FIGURE 5-8 Conservation of length and weight.

- Juanita is seated on a small chair. Kate kneels in front of her. Juanita has her right shoe off. Kate puts Juanita's foot on a ruler. "I am measuring your foot for your new shoes."

- The children have a play grocery store. Jorge puts some plastic fruit on the toy scale. "Ten pounds here."

- Azam is the doctor, and Bob is his patient. Azam takes an imaginary thermometer from Bob's mouth. "You have a hot fever."

Peggy Ashbrook (2011) provides some techniques for assessment of children's prior knowledge about measurement. For example she shows four-year-old students a rain gauge and asks them how they could describe the amount of water to other people. They come up with several nonstandard units that could be used.

Individual interviews for the preoperational child can be found in this chapter. For the child who is near concrete operations (past age 5), the conservation tasks in Chapter 1 and in Appendix A may be used to determine whether children are conservers and thus probably ready to use standard units of measurement.

5-2d Activities

Naturalistic Activities. Young children's concepts of measurement develop, for the most part, from their natural everyday experiences exploring the environment, discovering its properties, and so constructing their own knowledge. The examples in the assessment section of this unit demonstrate how children's play activities reflect their concepts of measurement (Photo 5-4). Mary has seen someone make a cake and may have helped. Kate has been to the shoe store and knows the clerk must measure the customer's feet before bringing

Photo 5-4 Children explore the fundamentals of measurement as they explore at the sensory table.

Photo 5-5 This girl engages in informal volume measurement.

out a pair of shoes to try on. Jorge has seen the grocer weigh fruit. Azam knows that a thermometer tells how "hot" a fever is. Observant young children pick up these ideas on their own without being told specifically that they are important.

The child uses his play activities to practice what he has seen adults do. He also uses play materials to learn ideas through experimentation and trial and error. Water, sand, dirt, mud, and other such materials teach the child about volume (Harpring, 2006–2012). As he pours these substances from one container to another, he learns about *how much* (amount). The child can use containers of many sizes and shapes: buckets, cups, plastic bottles, dishes, bowls, and coffee cans. Shovels, spoons, strainers, and funnels can also be used with these materials. When playing with water, the child can also learn about weight if he has some small objects—such as sponges, rocks, corks, small pieces of wood, and marbles—that may float or sink. Any time a child tries to put something in a box, envelope, glass, or any other container, he learns something about volume.

The child can begin to learn the idea of linear measure (length, width, and height) and area in his play. The unit blocks that are usually found in the early childhood classroom help the child learn the idea of units. He will soon learn that each block is a unit of another block. Two, four, or eight of the small blocks, when placed end to end, are the same length as one of the longer blocks. As he builds enclosures (houses, garages, farmyards, etc.), he is forced to pick his blocks so that each side is the same length as the one across from it.

The child learns about weight and balance on the teeter-totter. He soon learns that it takes two people for it to go up and down. He also learns that it works best when the two are near the same weight and are the same distance from the middle.

The child has many contacts with temperature. He learns that his soup is hot, warm, and then, as it sits out, cold. He likes cold milk and hot cocoa. He learns that the air may be hot or cold. If the air is hot, he may wear shorts or just a bathing suit. If the air is cold, he will need a coat, hat, and mittens.

Informal Activities. Through these kinds of experiences, the young child learns about measurement (**Photo 5-5**). The activities provide children with many opportunities for informal teaching. As the child plays, one job for the adult is to help by pointing out properties of materials that the child may not be able to find on her own. For instance, if a child says she must have all the long blocks to make her house large enough, the teacher can show her how several small blocks can do the job. She can show the child how to measure how much string will fit around a box before she cuts off a piece to use.

The teacher can also take these opportunities to use measurement words such as the names of units of measurement and the words listed in Chapter 6. She can also pose problems for the child. Some examples are:

- "How can we find out if we have enough apple juice for everyone?"
- "How can we find out how many paper cups of milk can be poured from a gallon container?"
- "How can we find out if someone has a high fever?"
- "Without going outside, how can we find out if we need to wear a sweater or coat?"
- "How can we find out who is the tallest boy in the class? The child who weighs the most?"
- "How many of these place mats will fit around the table?"
- "Who lives the longest distance from school?"

The teacher's responsibility is to provide environmental opportunities for exploring and discovering measurement concepts (**Photo 5-6**).

© 2016 Cengage Learning®

PHOTO 5-6 Outdoors, the sandbox provides opportunities for informal measurement.

Adult-Guided Activities. The young child learns most of his basic measurement ideas through his play and home activities that come through the natural routines of the day. He gains a feeling for the need for measurement and learns the language of measurement. Adult-guided activities must be chosen with care. The activities should make use of the child's senses. They should be related to what is familiar to the child and expand what he already knows. They should pose problems that will show him the need for measurement. They should give the child a chance to use measurement words to explain his solution to the problem. The following activities are examples of these kinds of experiences, along with the naturalistic and informal experiences that serve as their foundation.

5-2e Helping Children with Special Needs

Measurement lends itself very well to the first cooperative learning activities. Two children can form a buddy group. They can work together with the younger children comparing

ACTIVITIES

MEASUREMENT: VOLUME

Objectives:

- To learn the characteristics of volume.
- To see that volume can be measured.
- To learn measurement words used to tell about volume (*more, less, too big, too little, the same*).

Materials:

- Sandbox (indoors and/or out), water table (or sink or plastic dishpans).
- Many containers of different sizes: bottles, cups, bowls, milk cartons, cans (with smooth edges), boxes (for dry materials).
- Spoons, scoops, funnels, strainers, beaters.
- Water, sand, pebbles, marbles, seeds, or anything else that can be poured.

Note: Some educators feel it is inappropriate to use food for play. Be cautious. Also be sure to watch for allergies: some children are allergic to peanuts, other tree nuts, chocolate, and the like.

Naturalistic and informal activities: Allow plenty of time for experimenting with the materials during center time. Observe whether children are into the pretend play measurement stage, are making comparisons, or mention that any amount of sand will fill up the container. "Which bottle will hold more water?" "You filled that milk carton up to the top."

Adult-guided activities:

1. Have several containers of different kinds and sizes. Fill one with water (or sand or pebbles). Pick out another container. Ask the children: **"If I pour this water from this bottle into this other bottle, will the second bottle hold all the water?"** After each child has made her prediction, pour the water into the second container. Ask a child to tell what she saw happen. Continue with several containers. Have the children line up the containers from the one that holds the most to the one that holds the least.

2. Pick out one standard container (coffee cup, paper cup, measuring cup, or tin can). Have one or more larger containers. Say, **"If I want to fill the big bowl with sand and use this paper cup, how many times will I have to fill the paper cup and pour sand into the bowl?"** Write down the children's predictions. Let each child have a turn filling the cup and pouring sand into the bowl. Using slash marks, record how many cups of sand are poured. Have the children count the number of marks when the bowl is full. Compare this amount with what the children thought the amount would be.

Follow-up: Do the same types of activities using different sizes of containers and common objects. For example, have a doll and three different-sized boxes. Have the children decide which box the doll will fit into.

ACTIVITIES

MEASUREMENT: WEIGHT

Objectives:

- To learn firsthand the characteristics of weight.
- To learn that weight and size are different attributes (big things may have less weight than small things).
- To learn that *light* and *heavy* are relative terms.

Materials:

- Things in the classroom or brought from home, for example, manipulatives, paper clips, buttons, crayons, pencils, small toys.
- A teeter-totter, a board and a block, a simple pan balance.
- Sand, seeds, sawdust, pebbles, dirt.
- A ball collection with balls of different sizes and materials: ball bearings, table tennis, golf, solid rubber, foam rubber, Styrofoam, balsa wood, cotton, balloons.

Naturalistic and informal activities: During center time, provide opportunities for the children to experiment with a simple pan balance using a variety of materials. Note whether they use any weight vocabulary (such as *heavy* or *light*). Ask them to explain their actions. Outdoors or in the gym, provide a teeter-totter. Note how they find ways to balance. Ask them what happens when children of different weights or different numbers of children sit on each end.

Adult-guided activities:

1. Have the child name things in the room that he can lift and things he cannot lift. Which things can he not lift because of size and which because of weight? Compare things such as a stapler (small and heavy) and a large paper bag (large and light). Have the children line up things from heaviest to lightest.

2. Have the children experiment with the teeter-totter. How many children does it take to balance the teacher? Make a balance with a block and a board. Have the child experiment with different things to see which makes the board balance.

3. Use a fixed-position pan balance for firsthand experiences with all types of things.

   a. Have the child try balancing small objects, such as paper clips, hair clips, bobby pins, coins, toothpicks, cotton balls, and so on, by placing them in the pans.

   b. From the collection of balls, pick out a pair. Have the child predict which of the two is heavier (lighter). Let him put one in each pan to check his prediction.

   c. Put a substance such as sand in one pan. Have the child fill the other pan with seeds until the pans balance. **"Are the amounts [volume] of sand and seeds the same?"**

   d. Have equal amounts of two different substances, such as sand and sawdust, in the balance pans. **"Do the pans balance?"**

Follow-up:

- Make some playdough with the children. Have them measure out one part flour and one part salt. Mix in some powder tempera. Add water until the mixture is pliable, but not too sticky.
- Have the students measure cooking and baking ingredients. See Chapter 6 for cooking ideas.
- Read *Who Sank the Boat?* by Pamela Allen.

Digital Download

ACTIVITIES

MEASUREMENT: LENGTH AND HEIGHT

Objectives:

- To learn firsthand the concepts of length and height.
- To help the child learn the use of arbitrary units.

Materials:

- The children's bodies.

- Things in the room that can be measured, for example, tables, chairs, doors, windows, shelves, books.
- Balls of string and yarn, scissors, construction paper, markers, chips, pennies, other small counters, pencils, toothpicks, ice-cream-bar sticks, unit blocks.

Naturalistic and informal activities: During center time, note whether the children engage in any comparison or length measurement activities. Unit blocks are especially good for naturalistic and informal measurement explorations. For example, when the children are using unit blocks, observe whether they appear to use trial and error to make their blocks fit as they wish. Comment, **"You matched the blocks so that your house has all the sides the same length."**

Adult-guided activities:

1. Present the child with problems where she must pick out something of a certain length. For example, string is tied between two sticks to mark off the side of the garden. Have a picture of the garden with the string along the side. Have several lengths of string, and tell the child to find out which string is the right length. Say, **"Which string will reach from one stick to the other stick?"**

2. Look around the room. Ask the children, **"Which things are close? Which things are far away?"**

3. Have several children line up. Have a child point out the tallest child and the shortest. Have the children line up from tallest to shortest. Ask the child to draw pictures of friends and family in a row from shortest to tallest.

4. Draw lines on construction paper. **"How many [chips, toothpicks, or other small objects] will fit on each line? Which line has more? Which line is longest?"** Gradually use paper with more than two lines.

5. Put a piece of construction paper on the wall from the floor up to about 5 feet. Have the children stand next to the paper, one at a time. Mark their heights, and label the marks with their names. Check the children's height each month. Note how much each child grows over the year.

6. Create an arbitrary unit such as a pencil, a toothpick, a stick, a long block, or a piece of yarn or string. Have children measure things in the room to see how many units long, wide, or tall the things are.

Follow-up:

- Keep the height chart out so that the children can look at it and talk about their heights. They should measure their height once a month and record it on their height chart. Depending on where they are in their math program, they can prepare a height graph and add to it every month.

- Read *The Littlest Dinosaurs* by Bernard Most (1989) and *How Big Is a Foot?* by Rolf Myller (1972).

Digital Download

ACTIVITIES

MEASUREMENT: TEMPERATURE

Objectives:

- To give the child firsthand experiences that will help him learn that temperature is the relative measure of heat.

- To learn that the thermometer is used to measure temperature.

- To experience hot, warm, and cold as related to things, weather, and the seasons of the year.

Materials: Ice cubes, hot plate, teakettle or pan, pictures of the four seasons, posterboard, markers, scissors, glue, construction paper, old magazines with pictures, real thermometers (body, indoors, and outdoors).

Naturalistic and informal activities: Note the children's talk regarding temperature. Make comments, such as, **"Be careful, the soup is very hot."** And **"It's cold today, so you must button up your coat."** Ask questions such as, **Do we need to wear mittens or gloves today?"** Also, keep children away from the hot plate, especially when it is on.

Adult-guided activities:

1. Have the children decide whether selected things in the environment are hot, cold, or warm. Examples are ice and boiling water, the hot and cold water taps, the radiators, the glass in the windows, their skin, and so on.

2. Show pictures of summer, fall, winter, and spring. Discuss the usual temperatures in each season. "What is the usual weather? What kinds of clothes are worn?" Make a cardboard thermometer. At the bottom, put a child in heavy winter clothes; above that, at various points on the thermometer, put a child in a light coat or jacket, then a child in a sweater, then one in short sleeves, then one in a bathing suit.

3. Each day discuss the outside temperature relative to what was worn to school.

4. Give the children scissors and old magazines. Have them find and cut out pictures of hot things and cold things. Have them glue the hot things on one piece of posterboard and the cold things on another.

5. Show the children three thermometers: one for body temperature, one for room temperature, and one for outdoor use. Discuss when and where each is used.

Follow-up: Discuss and record the outside temperature each day in some way (as on a graph, as discussed later in this chapter).

Digital Download

BRAIN CONNECTION

CAN BRAIN SCIENCE IMPROVE SPECIAL EDUCATION?

There is increasing interest in connecting neuroscience research to education. There is hope that brain-based research could someday provide clues to the best classroom practices for children with disabilities. Brain imaging shows some promise that biomarkers may be discovered that will indicate impairments even before the impairments show up in behavior. Learning disabilities such as dyscalculia may be identified. Currently caution must be taken when adopting "brain-based" curriculum as the research support is not yet present (Shah, 2011).

N. Shah, "Report Reveals Ways Brain Science Could Improve Special Ed," Education Week's blogs, July 14, 2011, blogs.edweek.org.

attributes (such as grouping objects into long and short) and with the kindergartners measuring with nonstandard units. The teacher can put children of different cultures and children of different abilities into buddy pairs. He can assign each child a responsibility: for example, one could handle the measuring tool, and the other could record the measurements.

Technology for Young Children

All young children can benefit from technology experiences—some are interactive, some are offline lesson plans. Evaluate any of these resources:

- Illuminations Lessons: Get the Turtle to the Pond; As People Get Older, They Get Taller; Block Pounds; Learning to Measure with Ladybug; Going Places: Measuring with Teacher's Feet; Facing Up; Ladybug Lengths; The Length of My Feet; What Should I Measure Next? How About Me!: Measuring Me; What Should I Measure Next? How About Me!: Mapping All of Me; pan balance and shapes activities (applet) lessons.

5-2f Evaluation

The teacher should note the children's responses to the activities given them. She should observe them as they try out the materials, and note their comments. She must also observe whether they are able to solve everyday problems that come up, by using informal measurements such as comparisons or nonstandard units. Use the individual interviews in Chapter 3 (comparisons) and in Appendix A.

COMMON CORE
STATE STANDARDS

5-3 TIME MEASUREMENT STANDARDS AND EXPECTATIONS

The Common Core State Standards (National Governors Association Center for Best Practices, 2010) for measurement includes expectations for the measurement of objects. However, time is also a measurable attribute but children are not expected to learn the concept of time measured by the clock until first grade, when they are capable of concrete operational thinking. Preschool and kindergarten children are learning the attributes of time that pertain to **sequence** and **duration**.

- *Sequence* of time is the order of events and is related to the ideas about ordering presented in earlier in this chapter. While learning to sequence things in patterns, the child also learns to sequence events. He learns that small, middle-sized, and large beads go in order for a pattern sequence. He gets up, washes his face, brushes his teeth, dresses, and eats breakfast for a time sequence.

- *Duration* of time is how long an event takes (seconds, minutes, hours, days, a short time, a long time).

5-3a Kinds of Time

A child has to learn three kinds of time. Unlike weight, volume, length, and temperature, time is a hard measure to learn because the child cannot see and feel it. There are fewer clues to help the child. The young child relates time to three things: personal experience, social activity, and culture.

In her **personal experience**, the child has her own past, present, and future. The past is often referred to as, "when I was a baby." "Last night" may mean any time before right now. The future may be "after my night nap" or "when I am big." The young child has difficulty with the idea that at one time her mother and dad were little and she was not yet born.

Time in terms of **social activity** is a little easier to learn and makes more sense to the young child. The young child tends to be a slave to order and routine. A change of schedule can be very upsetting because time for her is a sequence of predictable events. She can count on her morning activities being the same each day when she wakes up. Once she gets to school, she learns that there is order there too: First she takes off her coat and hangs it up, next she is greeted by her teacher, then she goes to the big playroom to play, and so on through the day.

A third kind of time relates to **culture**, and this type of time is fixed by clocks and calendars. Everyone learns this kind of time. It is a kind of time that the child probably does not really understand until she is in the concrete operations period. She can, however, learn the language (seconds, minutes, days, months, etc.) and the names of the timekeepers (clock, watch, calendar). She can also learn to recognize a timekeeper when she sees one.

5-3b Language of Time

Learning time depends on language no less than learning any part of math. Time and sequence words are listed in Chapter 6 and are listed again here for easy reference.

- **General words:** time, age

- **Specific words:** morning, afternoon, evening, night, day, noon

- **Relational words:** soon, tomorrow, yesterday, early, late, a long time ago, once upon a time, new, old, now, when, sometimes, then, before, present, while, never, once, next, always, fast, slow, speed, first, second, third, and so on

- **Duration words:** clock and watch (minutes, seconds, hours); calendar (date, names of days of the week names, names of the month, names of seasons, year)

- **Special days:** birthday, Passover, Juneteenth, Cinco de Mayo, Kwanza, Ramadan, Easter, Christmas, Thanksgiving, vacation, holiday, school day, weekend

Time concept experiences can be integrated into the other content areas (see **Figure 5-9**).

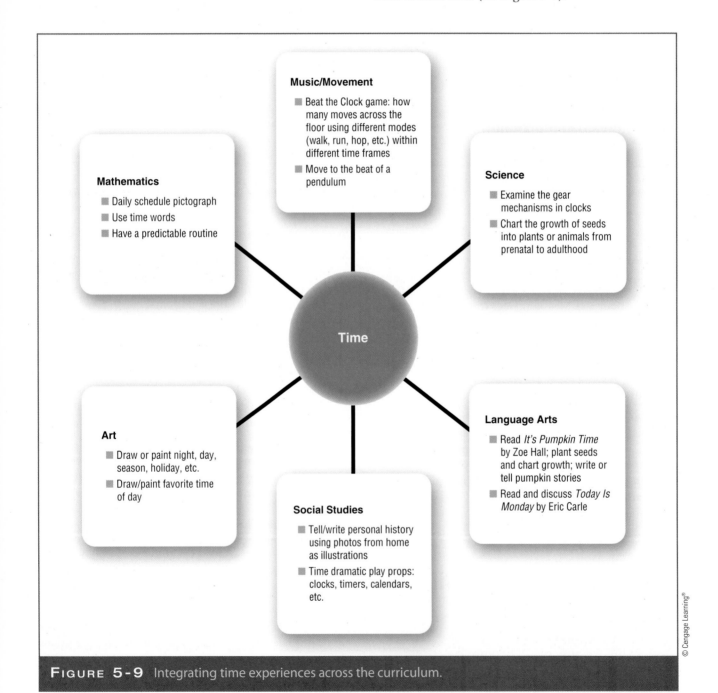

Music/Movement
- Beat the Clock game: how many moves across the floor using different modes (walk, run, hop, etc.) within different time frames
- Move to the beat of a pendulum

Mathematics
- Daily schedule pictograph
- Use time words
- Have a predictable routine

Science
- Examine the gear mechanisms in clocks
- Chart the growth of seeds into plants or animals from prenatal to adulthood

Time

Art
- Draw or paint night, day, season, holiday, etc.
- Draw/paint favorite time of day

Language Arts
- Read *It's Pumpkin Time* by Zoe Hall; plant seeds and chart growth; write or tell pumpkin stories
- Read and discuss *Today Is Monday* by Eric Carle

Social Studies
- Tell/write personal history using photos from home as illustrations
- Time dramatic play props: clocks, timers, calendars, etc.

© Cengage Learning®

FIGURE 5-9 Integrating time experiences across the curriculum.

5-3c Pre-Assessment

The teacher should observe the child's use of time language. She should note whether he makes an attempt to place himself and events in time. Does he remember the sequence of activities at school and at home? Is he able to wait for one thing to finish before going on to the next? Is he able to order things in a sequence?

The following are examples of the kinds of interview tasks that are included in Appendix A.

5-3d Activities

Time activities should proceed from naturalistic to informal, to adult guided.

Naturalistic Activities. From birth onward, children are capable of learning time and sequence. In an organized, nurturing environment, infants learn quickly that when they wake up from sleep, they are held and comforted, their diapers are changed, and then they are fed. The first sense of time duration comes from how long it takes for each of these events. Infants soon have a sense of how long they will be held and comforted, how long it takes for a diaper change, and how long it takes to eat. Time for the infant is a sense of sequence and duration of events.

The toddler shows her understanding of time words through her actions. When she is told that it's lunchtime, she runs to her high chair. When she is told it is time for a nap, she may run the other way. She will notice cues that mean it is time to do something new: toys are being picked up, the table is set, or Dad appears at the door. She begins to look for the events that tell her that one section of time ends and a new section is about to start.

As the child develops spoken language, she uses time words. She makes an effort to place events and herself in

---

SAMPLE ASSESSMENT TASK

5H   PREOPERATIONAL AGES 4–5

TIME, LABELING, AND SEQUENCE: CHAPTER 5

METHOD Interview.

SKILL Shown pictures of daily events, the child can use time words to describe the action in each picture and place the pictures in a logical time sequence.

MATERIALS Pictures of daily activities such as meals, nap, bath, playtime, bedtime.

PROCEDURE Show the child each picture. Say, **"Tell me about this picture. What's happening?"** After the child has described each picture, place all the pictures in front of her, and tell the child, **"Pick out [show me] the picture of what happens first each day."** After the child selects a picture, ask, **"What happens next?"** Continue until all the pictures are lined up.

EVALUATION When describing the pictures, note whether the child uses time words such as *breakfast time, lunchtime, playtime, morning, night,* and so on. Note whether she uses a logical sequence in placing the pictures in order.

INSTRUCTIONAL RESOURCE R. Charlesworth, *Math and Science for Young Children,* 8th ed., San Francisco, CA: Cengage Learning, 2016.

Digital Download

SAMPLE ASSESSMENT TASK

4I   PREOPERATIONAL AGES 3–6

TIME, IDENTIFY CLOCK OR WATCH: CHAPTER 5

METHOD Interview.

SKILL The child can identify a clock and/or watch and describe its function.

MATERIALS One or more of the following timepieces: conventional clock and watch, digital clock and watch. Preferably, include at least one conventional and one digital. If real timepieces are not available, use pictures.

PROCEDURE Show the child the timepieces or pictures of timepieces. Ask, **"What is this? What does it tell us? What is it for? What are the parts, and what are they for?"**

EVALUATION Note whether the child can label watches and clocks, and how much he is able to describe about the functions of the parts (long and short hands, second hands, alarm set, time changer, numerals). Note also whether the child tries to tell time. Compare his knowledge of conventional and digital timepieces.

INSTRUCTIONAL RESOURCE R. Charlesworth, *Math and Science for Young Children,* 8th ed., San Francisco, CA: Cengage Learning, 2016.

Digital Download

time. Adults need to listen and respond to what she has to say. The following are some examples.

- Carlos (18 months old) tugs at Mr. Flores's pants leg. "Cookie, cookie." "Not yet Carlos. We'll have lunch first. Cookies are after lunch."

- Kai (age 20 months) finishes her lunch and gets up. "No nap today. Play with dollies." Ms. Moore picks her up. "Nap first. You can play with the dolls later."

- "Time to put the toys away, Kate." Kate (age 30 months) answers, "Not now. I'll do it a big later on."

- Chris (3 years old) sits with Mrs. Raymond. Chris says, "Last night we stayed at the beach house." "Oh yes," answers Mrs. Raymond, "You were at the beach last summer, weren't you?" (For Chris, anything in the past happened "last night.")

- Mr. Flores is showing the group a book with pictures of the zoo. Richard (4 years old) comments, "I want to go there yesterday." Mr. Flores says, "We'll be going to the zoo on Friday."

- Rosa (6 years old) says, "One time, when I was real small, like 3 or something …" Her teacher listens as Rosa relates her experience.

The young child needs to have a predictable and regular routine because through this routine the child gains his sense of time duration and time sequence (see **Photo 5-7**). The child must also hear time words and be listened to when he tries to use his time ideas. Especially important is that his own time words be accepted. For instance Kate's "a big later on" and Chris's "last night" should be accepted. Kate

PHOTO 5-7　A consistent routine is the basis of the young child's understanding of time.

© Cengage Learning®

shows an understanding of the future and Chris of the past even though they are not as precise as an adult would be.

Informal Activities. The adult needs to capitalize on the child's efforts to gain a sense of time and time sequence. Reread the situations described in the previous section. In each, the adults do some informal instruction. Mr. Flores reminds Brad of the coming sequence. So do Ms. Moore and the adult with Kate. Mrs. Raymond accepts what Chris says but also uses the correct time words "last summer." Adults must listen to and expand on what children say.

The adult serves as a model for time-related behavior. She checks the clock and the calendar for times and dates. The teacher uses the time words listed in the Language of Time section. She makes statements and asks questions.

- "*Good morning*, Tom."

- "*Goodnight*, Mary. See you *tomorrow*."

- "What did you do over the *weekend*?"

- "Who will be our guest for lunch *tomorrow*?"

- "*Next week* on *Tuesday*, we will go to the park for a picnic."

- "Let me check the *time*. No wonder you are hungry. It's almost *noon*."

- "You are the *first* one here *today*."

Children will observe and imitate what the teacher says and does even before they understand the ideas completely.

An excellent tool for informal classroom time instruction is a daily picture/word schedule placed in a prominent place. **Figure 5-10** is an example of such a schedule. Children frequently ask, "When do we …?" "What happens after this?" and so on. Teachers can take them to the pictorial schedule and help them find the answer for themselves. "What are we doing now?" "Find [the activity] on the schedule." "What comes next?" Eventually, children will just have to be reminded to "Look at the schedule," and they will answer their own questions.

Adult-Guided Activities. Adult-guided time and sequence activities include sequence patterns with beads, blocks, and other objects; sequence stories; work centering on the calendar; and work centering on clocks. Experiences with pattern sequence and story sequence can begin at an early age. The infant enjoys looking at picture books. The toddler can listen to short stories and begin to use beads and clocks to make her own sequences. The adult-guided pattern, story, calendar, clock, and other time activities described next are for children older than 4½ years old.

5-3e Helping Children with Special Needs

Working with diverse families, time is an important factor to keep in mind, because different cultures vary in their view of time. Respect these views and try to work with families that view time in different ways. Westerners, particularly

Americans and Europeans, view scheduling and organization of time as critical in managing any organization—including schools and classrooms. Clocks, watches, and calendars run Western culture. Time is viewed as a commodity not to be wasted, and being late is considered rude. Yet other cultures have different views. For example, Latin Americans, Middle Easterners, and Native Americans view time as being more indefinite. The Chinese are also less concerned with time and schedules. When these two views meet, conflict and confusion can result. If we are socialized to depend on clock time, then promptness is valued. If we are geared to natural events, such as the rising and setting of the sun or the time it takes to finish the job, then promptness is not so important. As it applies to schooling, some families may not (at least initially) value being "on time." The importance of not missing essential instructional events can be explained, but children and parents should not be punished. Instead, they should be helped to see the importance of Western beliefs and the use of time to being successful in Western culture.

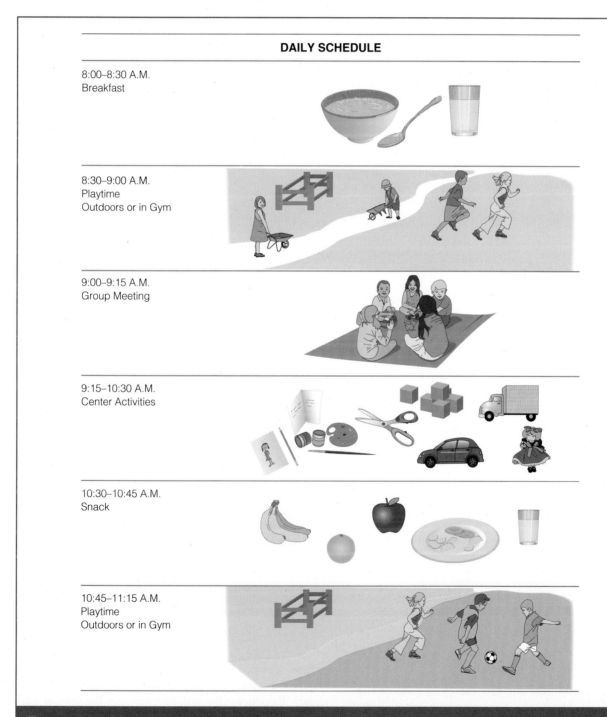

DAILY SCHEDULE

8:00–8:30 A.M.
Breakfast

8:30–9:00 A.M.
Playtime
Outdoors or in Gym

9:00–9:15 A.M.
Group Meeting

9:15–10:30 A.M.
Center Activities

10:30–10:45 A.M.
Snack

10:45–11:15 A.M.
Playtime
Outdoors or in Gym

FIGURE 5-10 A picture/word daily schedule supports the development of the concept of time sequence.

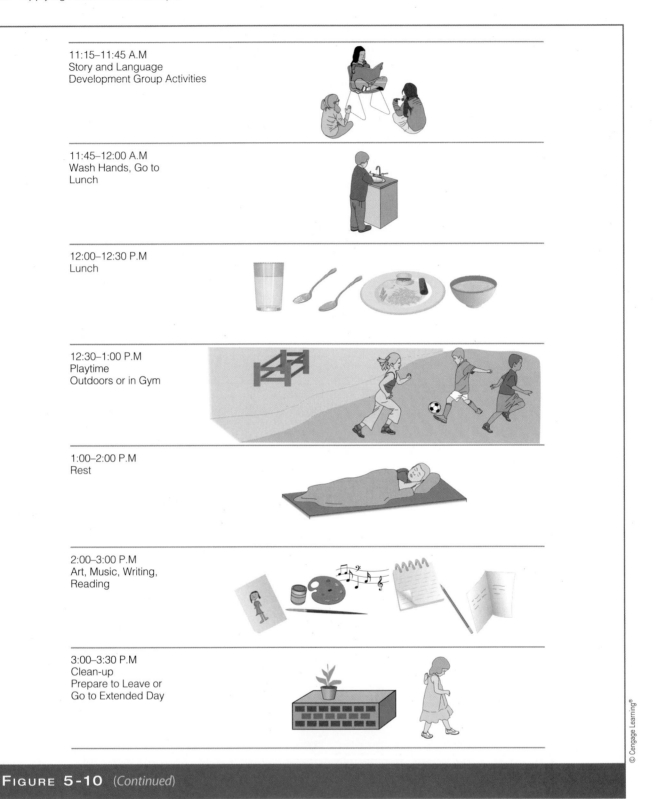

11:15–11:45 A.M
Story and Language
Development Group Activities

11:45–12:00 A.M
Wash Hands, Go to
Lunch

12:00–12:30 P.M
Lunch

12:30–1:00 P.M
Playtime
Outdoors or in Gym

1:00–2:00 P.M
Rest

2:00–3:00 P.M
Art, Music, Writing,
Reading

3:00–3:30 P.M
Clean-up
Prepare to Leave or
Go to Extended Day

© Cengage Learning®

Figure 5-10 (Continued)

5-3f Informal Post-Evaluation

The teacher should note whether the child's use of time words increases. He should also note whether her sense of time and sequence develops to a more mature level: Does she remember the order of events? Can she wait until one thing is finished before she starts another? Does she talk about future and past events? How does she use the calendar? The clock? The sequence stories? The teacher may use the individual interview tasks in this chapter and in Appendix A.

ACTIVITIES

TIME: SEQUENCE PATTERNS: WHAT IS NEXT?

Objective: To be able to understand and use the sequence idea of *next*.

Materials: Any real things that can be easily sequenced by category, color, shape, size, or other criterion. For example:

- Wooden beads and strings
- Plastic eating utensils
- Poker chips or buttons or coins
- Shapes cut from cardboard
- Small toy animals or people

Naturalistic and informal activities: If they have had opportunities to explore the materials, the children should be familiar with the names of all the items and be able to identify their colors. For example, a child selects all the horses from a container of animals: **"You have all the horses: brown ones [teacher points], black [teacher points], and white [teacher points]."**

Adult-guided activities: Use plastic eating utensils for this activity. Use knives (K), forks (F), and spoons (S) in three colors (C1, C2, and C3). Set up a pattern to present to the child. Present many kinds of patterns, including any of the following.

- Color: C1-C2-C1-C2 . . .

    C2-C3-C3-C2-C3-C3 . . .
- Identity: K-F-S-K-F-S . . .

    K-S-S-K-S-S . . .

Say to the child, **"This pattern is knife-fork-spoon [or whatever pattern is set up]. What comes next?"** Once the child has the idea of pattern, set up the pattern and say, **"This is a pattern. Look it over. What comes next?"**

Follow-up: Do the same activity with some of the other materials suggested. Also try it with the magnet board, flannelboard, chalkboard, and smartboard.

Digital Download

ACTIVITIES

TIME: SEQUENCE STORIES

Objective: To learn sequences of events through stories.

Materials: Picture storybooks that have clear and repetitive sequences of events, such as:

- *The Gingerbread Man*
- *The Three Little Pigs*
- *The Three Billy Goats Gruff (Rounds)*
- *Henny Penny*
- *Caps for Sale*
- *Brown Bear, Brown Bear*
- *Polar Bear, Polar Bear*

The classics are available in many versions from Amazon, Barnes and Noble and other booksellers.

Naturalistic and informal activities: Place the books in the library center where children can make selections during center time, rest time, or book time. Note which children appear to be familiar with the stories as they turn the pages, pretending to read to themselves, a friend, or a doll or stuffed animal.

Adult-guided activities: Read the stories several times until the children are familiar with them. Before going on to the next event, ask, **"What happens next?"** Have the children say some of the repeated phrases such as "Little pigs, little pigs, let me come in," "Not by the hair on my chinny-chin-chin," "Then I'll huff and I'll puff and I'll blow your house in." Have the children try to repeat the list of those who chase the gingerbread man. Have them recall the whole story sequence.

Follow-up: Obtain Insect Lore Life Cycle kits and figurines (ladybugs, butterflies, ants, mealworms, silkworms, earth worms). Obtain some sequencing cards from Lakeshore. Encourage children to reenact and retell the stories and events that are read to them. Encourage them to pretend to read familiar storybooks. This kind of activity helps with comprehending the stories and the sequences of events in them.

Digital Download

ACTIVITIES

TIME: GROWING SEEDS

Objective: To experience the growth of a plant.

Materials: Radish or lima bean seeds, clear plastic cups, a sharp pencil, a 6-inch paper plate, some rich soil, a tablespoon.

Naturalistic and informal activities: During center time, provide dirt and small shovels, rakes, pots, and similar objects in the sand and water table. Talk with the children about what else they might need to grow something. Note whether they talk about planting seeds.

Adult-guided activities:

1. Give the child a clear plastic cup. Have her make a drainage hole in the bottom with the sharp pencil.

2. Set the cup on the paper plate.

3. Have the child put dirt in the cup up to about an inch from the top. Do not pack the soil.

4. Have the child poke three holes in the dirt with her pointer finger.

5. Have her put one seed in each hole and cover the seeds with dirt.

6. Have the child add 1 tablespoon of water.

7. Place the pots in a sunny place, and watch the seeds grow. If they children plant the seeds close to the side of the cup, they can watch what happens to the seed as it germinates and thus observe the sequence of development.

8. Have the children water the plants each day. Ask them to record how many days go by before the first plant pops through the soil.

Follow-up: Plant other types of seeds. Discuss which steps take place before the plant breaks through the ground. In the fall, use the book It's Pumpkin Time by Zoe Hall (1999) to introduce a seed project and explain how we get the pumpkins we carve for Halloween.

Digital Download

ACTIVITIES

TIME: THE FIRST CALENDAR

Objective: To learn what a calendar is and how it can be used to keep track of time.

Materials: Cut a one-week calendar from posterboard with sections for each of the seven days, identified by name. In each section, cut tabs with a razor blade; you can slip signs under the tabs to indicate special times and events or the daily weather. These signs could have pictures of birthday cakes, items seen on field trips, umbrellas to show rainy days, the sun to show fair days, and so on.

Naturalistic and informal activities: In the writing center or in the dramatic play center, place a number of different types of calendars. Note whether the children know what they are and whether they use them in their pretend play activities. Ask them to explain how they are using the calendars. Where else have they seen them? Who uses them?

Adult-guided activities: Each day, discuss the calendar. Use the following key questions:

- "Who knows today's name?"
- "Who remembers yesterday's name?"

- "Who knows tomorrow's name?"
- "What special day comes this week [birthday, holiday, field trip]?"
- "What did we do yesterday?"
- "Do we go to school on Saturday and Sunday?"
- "How many days until …?"
- "How many days of the week do we go to school?"
- "What day of the week is the first day of school?"
- "What day of the week is the last day of school?"

Caution: You do not have to ask every question every day or spend more than 2–3 minutes on the activity. The calendar is still an abstract item for young children (see Beneky, Ostrosky, & Katz, 2008; and Schwartz, 1994).

Follow-up: Read Today Is Monday by Eric Carle (1993). Discuss which foods the students like to eat on each day of the week. They could draw, dictate, or write their own weekly menus.

Digital Download

ACTIVITIES

TIME: THE USE OF THE CLOCK

Objective: To find out how the clock is used to tell us when it is time to change the activity.

Materials: A school wall clock and a handmade or purchased large clock face such as that made by the Judy Company.

Naturalistic and informal activities: Place a large wooden toy clock in the dramatic play center. Note whether the children use it as a dramatic play prop. Do they use time words? Do they make a connection to the clock on the classroom wall or to the daily schedule picture?

Adult-guided activity: Point out the wall clock to the children. Show them the clock face. Let them move the hands around. Explain how the clock face is made just like the real clock face. Show them how you can set the hands on the clock face so that they are the same as the ones on the real clock. Each day, set the clock face for important times (e.g., cleanup, lunch, time to get up from the nap). Explain that when the real clock and the clock face have their hands in the same place, it will be time to do the next activity.

Follow-up: Do this every day. Soon each child will begin to catch on and check the clocks. Instead of asking, "When do we get up from our nap?" they will be able to check for themselves.

Digital Download

ACTIVITIES

TIME: BEAT THE CLOCK GAME

Objective: To learn how time limits the amount of activity that can be done.

Materials: Minute Minder or a similar timer.

Naturalistic and informal activities: Note how children react to time limit warnings (e.g., **"Five minutes until cleanup"**). Use a signal (bell, buzzer, dim the lights, etc.) as a cue. Note whether the children react with an understanding of time limits (**"Five minutes until we go outside"**).

Adult-guided activities: Have the child see how much of some activity he can do in a set number of minutes—for example, in three, four, or five minutes.

1. How many pennies can be put in a penny bank one at a time?

2. How many times can he bounce a ball?

3. How many paper clips can he pick up one at a time with a magnet?

4. How many times can he move across the room: walking, crawling, running, going backward, sideways, and so on? Set the timer between three and five minutes. When the bell rings, have the child stop. Then count to find out how much the child accomplished.

Follow-up: Try many different kinds of activities and different lengths of time. Have several children do the tasks at the same time. Who does the most in the time given?

Digital Download

ACTIVITIES

TIME: DISCUSSION TOPICS FOR LANGUAGE

Objective: To develop use of time words through discussion.

Materials: Pictures collected or purchased. The pictures could show the following:

- Day and night
- Activities that take a long time and a short time
- Picture sequences that illustrate times of day, yesterday, today, and tomorrow
- Pictures that illustrate seasons of the year
- Pictures that show early and late

Naturalistic and informal activities: During center time, place the time pictures on a table. Observe as the children examine the pictures. Note whether they use any time words. Ask them to describe the pictures.

Adult-guided activities: Discuss the pictures using the key time words.

Follow-up: Put pictures on the bulletin board that the children can look at and talk about during their center time.

Digital Download

5-4 DATA AND GRAPHING STANDARDS AND EXPECTATIONS

The Common Core State Standards (National Governors Association Center for Best Practices, 2010) expectation for the end of kindergarten is that children can classify objects and count the number of objects in each category. "The main purpose of collecting data is to answer questions when the answers are not immediately obvious" (NCTM, 2000, p. 109). Children's questions should be the major source of data. The beginnings of data collection are included in the fundamental concepts learned and applied in classifying in a logical fashion (see Chapter 3).

Data collection activities can begin even before kindergarten, as students collect groups of data from their real-life experiences and depict the results of their data collection in simple graphs. Consider the following example from Ms. Moore's classroom:

Ms. Moore hears George and Sam talking in loud voices. She goes near them and hears the following conversation.

GEORGE: "More kids like green than blue."
SAM: "No! No! More like blue!"
GEORGE: "You are all wrong."
SAM: "I am not. You are wrong."

Ms. Moore goes over to the boys and asks, "What's the trouble, boys?" George replies, "We have to get paint to paint the house Mr. Brown helped us build. I say it should be green. Sam says it should be blue."

Sam insists, "More kids like blue than green."

Ms. Moore asks, "How can we find out? How do we decide on questions like who will be our next president?" George and Sam look puzzled. Then George says, "I remember when Mom and Dad voted. We could have the class vote." Sam agrees that voting is a good idea. Ms. Moore then asks them how they might have all the students vote. George and Sam are afraid that if they ask for a show of hands, their classmates might just copy whoever votes first. Ms. Moore then suggests that they put out a green box and a blue box and a bowl of green and blue cube blocks. George's eyes light up. "I see! Then each person could vote by putting either a blue block in the blue box or a green block in the green box." Sam agrees.

After setting up the boxes and blocks, Sam and George go around the room. They explain the problem to each child. Each child comes over to the table, chooses one block, and places the block in the matching box. When the voting is completed, George and Sam empty the boxes and stack the blocks as shown in **Figure 5-11**.

Ms. Moore asks the boys what the vote shows. Sam says, "The green stack is higher. More children like the idea of painting the house green." "Good," answers Ms. Moore,

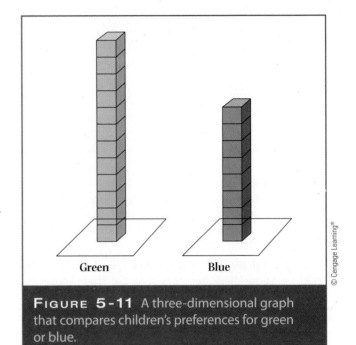

FIGURE 5-11 A three-dimensional graph that compares children's preferences for green or blue.

© Cengage Learning®

"Would you like me to write that down for you?" Sam and George chorus, "Yes!"

"I have an idea," says George, "Let's make a picture of this for the bulletin board so that everyone will know. Will you help us, Ms. Moore?"

Ms. Moore shows them how to cut out squares of green and blue paper to match each of the blocks used. The boys write "Green" and "Blue" on a piece of white paper and then paste the green squares next to the word "Green" and the blue squares next to the word "Blue." Ms. Moore shows them how to write the title: "Choose the Color for the Playhouse." Then they glue the description of the results at the bottom. The results can be seen in **Figure 5-12**. Like Sam and George, children can answer their own questions by collecting data and making a graph (Reed, 2013).

In the preceding example, the teacher helped the children solve their problem by helping them make two kinds of graphs. **Graphs** are used to show visually two or more comparisons in a clear way. When making a graph, a child uses basic skills such as classification, counting, comparing quantities, one-to-one matching, and communicating through describing data. By making a concrete structure or a picture that shows some type of information, the child visualizes a variety of different quantities. Graphing provides an opportunity to apply several fundamental concepts and skills, as illustrated in **Figure 5-13**.

5-4a Stages of Development for Making and Understanding Graphs

The types of graphs that young children can construct progress through five stages of development. The first three

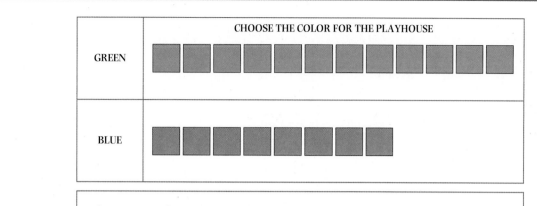

CHOOSE THE COLOR FOR THE PLAYHOUSE

| GREEN | |
| BLUE | |

The green row is longer than the blue row. More children like green than blue. We will buy green paint for our playhouse. 12 like green. 8 like blue.

by George and Sam

FIGURE 5-12 The color preference graph is copied using squares of green and blue paper, and the children dictate their interpretation.

Classifying
■ Green and blue

Communicating
■ Describing the data orally
■ Describing the data in written language
■ Describing the data pictorially

Counting
■ Number of blocks of each color selected

Graphing

Comparing
■ Height of the stacks of blocks
■ Lengths of the rows in the square paper graphs

Matching One-to-One
■ Blocks
■ Paper squares

FIGURE 5-13 Graphing can be used to describe data in any of the content areas and provides an opportunity to apply fundamental concepts and skills.

April has the most birthdays. There are four.
March and October have no birthdays.
Three months have three.
One month has two.
Five months have one.

FIGURE 5-14 "When is your birthday?"

stages are described in this chapter; the fourth is included in Chapter 7, and the fifth is in Chapter 9.

- In **stage one, object graphs**, the child uses real objects to make her graph. Sam and George used cube blocks. At this stage, only two things are compared. The main basis for comparison is one-to-one correspondence and the visualization of length and height.

- In **stage two, picture graphs**, more than two items are compared. In addition, a more permanent record is made, such as when Sam and George glued squares of colored paper on a chart for the bulletin board. An example of this type of graph is shown in **Figure 5-14**. The teacher has lined off 12 columns on posterboard (or large construction paper). Each column stands for one month of the year. The teacher gives each child a paper circle. Crayons, water markers, glue, and yarn scraps are available so that each child can draw her own head and place it on the month for her birthday. When each child has put her "head" on the graph, the children can compare the months to see which month has the most birthdays.

- In **stage three, square paper graphs**, the children progress through the use of more pictures to block charts. They no longer need to use real objects, but can start right off with cutout squares of paper. **Figure 5-15** shows this type of graph. In this stage, the children work more independently.

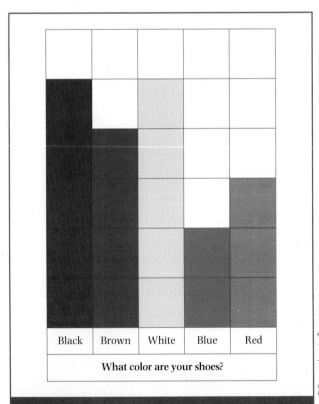

What color are your shoes?

Black	Brown	White	Blue	Red

FIGURE 5-15 A block graph made with paper squares.

5-4b Discussion of a Graph

As the children talk about their graphs and dictate descriptions for them, they use the following concept words:

less than	the same as
more than	none
fewer than	all
longer, longest	some
shorter, shortest	a lot of
the most	higher
the least	taller

5-4c Materials for Making Graphs

Many kinds of materials can be used for first-stage graphs. An example has been shown in which cube blocks were used, but other materials can also be used.

At first, it is best to use materials that can be kept in position without being knocked down or pushed apart by young children. Stands can be made from dowel rods. A washer or curtain ring is then placed on the dowel to represent each thing or person (**Figure 5-16[A]**). Strings and beads can be used. The strings can be hung from hooks or a rod; the lengths are then compared (Figure 5-16[B]). Unifix Cubes (Figure 5-16[C]) or pop beads (Figure 5-16[D]) can also be used.

Once the children have worked with the more stable materials, they can use the cube blocks and any other things that can be lined up. Poker chips, bottle caps, coins, spools, and corks are good for this type of graph work (**Figure 5-17**).

At the second stage, graphs can be made with these same materials, but with more comparisons made. Then the children can go on to more permanent recording by gluing down cutout pictures or markers of some kind (**Figure 5-18**).

At the third stage, the children can use paper squares. This prepares the way for the use of squared paper (see Chapter 7).

Many interesting graphing materials are available on the Internet and in the form of software.

5-4d Topics for Graphs

Students can research any question of interest and put the information into graphical form. For example, a group of kindergartners collected information about their school bus (Colburn & Tate, 1998), and another group of young children studied a tree that grows on their campus (El Harim, 1998).

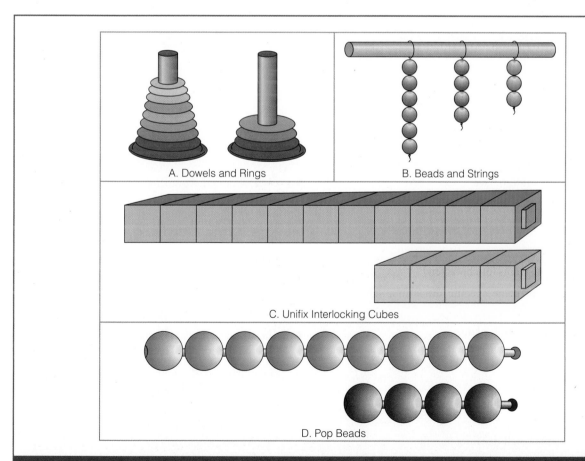

A. Dowels and Rings

B. Beads and Strings

C. Unifix Interlocking Cubes

D. Pop Beads

FIGURE 5-16 Four examples of three-dimensional graph materials.

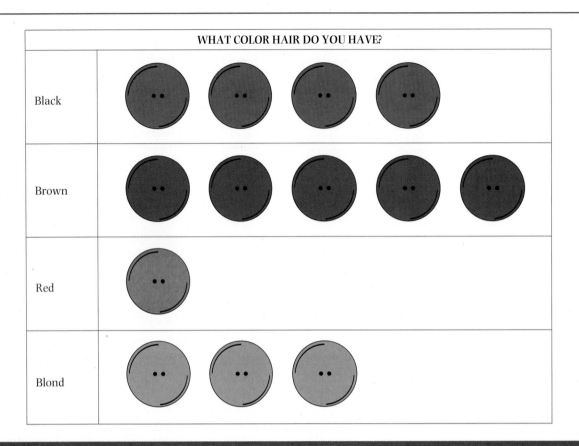

FIGURE 5-17 Graphs made with buttons glued to cardboard.

Once children start making graphs, they often think of problems to solve on their own. The following are some comparisons that might be of interest:

- The number of brothers and sisters
- Hair color, eye color, clothing colors
- Kinds of pets children have
- Heights of children in the class
- The number of children in class each day
- Sizes of shoes
- Favorite TV programs (or characters)
- Relative sizes of some specific dinosaurs, school buses, and people
- Rates of growth of bean plants
- Number of days it rains versus outdoor temperature
- Favorite foods
- Favorite colors
- Favorite storybooks
- Type of weather each day for a month
- The number of cups of water or sand that will fill different containers

- Time, in seconds, to run across the playground
- The number of baby hamsters class members predict that their female hamster will bear
- The number of days class members predict that it will take for their bean seeds to sprout
- Data obtained regarding sinking and floating objects (Chapter 3)
- A comparison of the number of seeds found in an apple, an orange, a lemon, and a grapefruit
- Students' predictions regarding which items will be attracted by magnets
- The frequency with which different types of insects are found on the playground
- The distance that rollers will roll when ramps of different degrees of steepness are used
- A comparison of the number of different items that are placed in a balance pan to weigh the same as a standard weight
- The frequency count of each color in a bag of M&M's, Skittles, or Trix
- The frequency with which the various combinations of yellow and orange show up when the counters

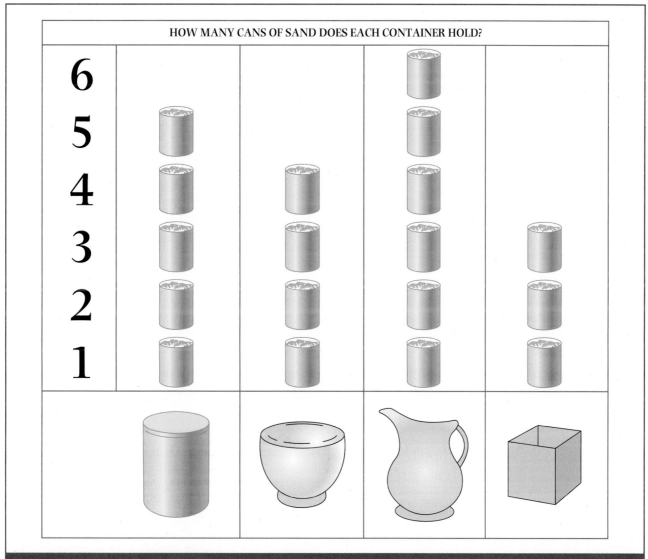

FIGURE 5-18 Graph made with paper cutouts.

(orange on one side and yellow on the other) are shaken and then tossed out on the table

- Voting on real-life questions such as how to arrange tables, what to have to eat for the class party, who they prefer in the current presidential election, whether they want to study mice or fish, or electing a class president (Classroom elections, 2012)

5-5 SCIENCE STANDARDS AND EXPECTATIONS

The Next Generation Science Standards (NGSS Lead States, 2013) and the Framework (National Research Council, 2012) emphasize that, for children, the essence of learning lies not in memorizing facts, but in carrying out the processes of inquiry—asking questions; making observations; and gathering, organizing, and analyzing data— and in design solutions. The fundamental concepts and skills that children construct during the preprimary period are essential to investigating science and engineering problems. Moomaw and Davis (2013) describe how STEM fits into preschool developmentally appropriate practice. As children explore and investigate, they develop an understanding of mathematical and science relationships. This part of Chapter 5 provides examples of how concepts of ordering and patterning, measurement, and graphing can be applied to preprimary science and engineering investigations.

5-5a Ordering and Patterning

Underlying the concept of patterning are the concepts of comparing and ordering. Ordering is a higher level of comparing because ordering involves comparing more than two things or more than two groups. It also involves placing things in a sequence from first to last. As indicated earlier, in Piaget's terms, this ordering is called *seriation*. Children must have some understanding of seriation before they develop the more advanced skill of patterning.

Ordering and patterning build on the skills of comparing. If children have not had prior experience in comparing, they will not be ready to order and find patterns. The following activities involve using a science emphasis in shape, animals, color, and sound while making or discovering visual, auditory, and motor regularities.

1. ***Sun, moon, and stars.*** Use your flannelboard or smartboard to help children recognize patterns in flannel or smartboard figures of the moon, sun, and star shapes. Start the activity by discussing the shapes in the night sky. Then, place the moon, sun, and star shapes in a pattern on the flannelboard. Make a game of placing a figure in the pattern and

having the children decide which figure comes next. As the children go through the process of making a pattern with the flannel figures, they are also reinforcing the concept of shapes existing in the night sky.

The natural patterns found in the night sky are an ideal observational activity for young children. When the sun goes down and the child can see the moon and stars, it is time to observe the night sky. Observing the changes in the sky from day to night reinforces the patterns that children learn at a very young age. Children may also be aware of the changes in the shape of the moon and may want to draw those shapes.

2. ***Animal patterns.*** Make patterns for shapes that go together in some way, such as zebra, tiger, and leopard (wild animals) or pig, duck, and cow (farm animals). After introducing children to the pattern game described in activity 1, have them manipulate tagboard animal shapes in the same way.

DAP **naeyc**

ACTIVITIES

FABRIC CARDS: ORDERING AND COMPARING

Objective: Ordering and comparing fabrics by touch.

Materials: Cardboard cut into small squares (2–3 inches works well), nontoxic glue, swatches of various fabrics with different textures (rough, smooth, ridged, soft, etc.).

Naturalistic and informal activities: Give the children a variety of different cardboard squares, each covered with a different fabric on one side, and observe them as they explore and talk about the textures of these fabric cards. Ask, **"Does anyone have a fabric card that feels very soft? Are there any rough-feeling fabric cards?"**

Adult-guided activities: Ask the children to order their fabric cards from the smoothest to the roughest. The cards can be shuffled to play matching games or placed on a classroom board that displays what the children know about ordering and comparing with their sense of touch.

Follow-up: You may want to have a large classroom fabric card display that shows the students' skills in ordering and comparing fabrics. Smaller individual sets can be used by the children on their own or in pairs. Try using as many types of fabrics as possible.

Digital Download

3. ***Sound Patterns.*** In the following scenario, Mrs. Jones introduces sound patterns to her kindergarten children.

Mrs. Jones brings out plastic bells. She selects three widely varied tones, rings them for the children, and asks: "Can you tell me what you hear?" Janie responds, "Bells, I hear bells!" The teacher asks, "Do any of the bells sound different?" "Yes," the children say. "In what way do they sound different?" Mrs. Jones asks. "Some sound like Tinkerbell, and some do not," Andrew responds. After giving the children a chance to ring the bells, Mrs. Jones puts a red, a yellow, and a blue construction-paper square on a table. She asks, "Will someone put the bell with the highest sound on the

red card?" After Lai completes the task, Mrs. Jones asks the children to find the bell with the lowest sound and finally the one whose sound is between the highest and lowest. Each bell has its own color square.

Patterns can be found in the sounds that rubber bands make. Construct a rubber band banjo by placing three different widths of rubber bands around a cigar box, the open end of a coffee can, a milk carton, or a margarine tub. Have children experiment with the rubber band "strings" of varying length, and see if they notice differences in sound. Playing around with strings and homemade instruments helps prepare children for future concept development in sound (**Photos 5-8** and **5-9**).

PHOTO 5-8   Rhythm sticks provide for investigation of sound and rhythm.

PHOTO 5-9   These cylinders can be decorated and made into maracas.

Rhythmic patterns can be found in classic poems and songs such as "There Was a Little Turtle." Have children add actions as they sing the song.

There was a little turtle.
He lived in a box.
He swam in a puddle.
He climbed on the rocks.
He snapped at a mosquito.
He snapped at a flea.
He snapped at a minnow.
And he snapped at me.
He caught the mosquito.
He caught the flea.
He caught the minnow.
But he didn't catch me.

4. *Making Patterns with Technology.* Websites such as Illuminations include applets and activities for creating or completing patterns. Some of these activities include Multiple Square Repeating Patterns, Magical Magic Squares, Eating Patterns, Growing Patterns, and others. The applet Pattern Blocks provides for students to make any desired pattern. Children might want to design a quilt pattern and could experiment online.

5. *Engineering.* A performance expectation in kindergarten is K-Ps2-1: Plan and conduct an investigation to compare the effects of different strengths or different direction of pushes and pulls on the motion of an object. Moomaw and Davis (2013) describe children's exploration of a pendulum. The pendulum was placed on a table with some small blocks. The children investigated different ways to knock over stacks of blocks. They varied the placement of the blocks, the direction of the pendulum, and/or the force used to push the pendulum. By recording the variations in the length of the string holding the pendulum, placement of the blocks, and the force used to push the pendulum, the children could observe any patterns.

5-5b Measurement: Volume, Weight, Length, and Temperature

The National Science Education Framework (National Research Council, 2012) and Next Generation Science Standards (NGSS Lead States, 2013) emphasize that the meaning of measurement and how to use measurement tools are a part of any investigation. These ideas are introduced frequently throughout the early years.

Measurement is basically a spatial activity that must include the manipulation of objects in order to be understood. If children are not actively involved with materials as they measure, they simply will not understand measurement. Water and sand are highly sensory science resources for young children. Both substances elicit a variety of responses to their physical properties, and they can be used in measurement activities. Keep in mind that, for sand and water to be effective as learning tools, long periods of "messing around" with the substances should be provided. For further information on the logistics of handling water and sand and a discussion of basic equipment needs, see Chapter 12 of this book. The following activities and lessons use sand and water as a means of introducing measurement.

1. *Fill it up.* Put out containers and funnels of different sizes and shapes in the sand and water table, and invite children to pour liquid from one to the other. Aspects of pouring can be investigated. Ask, "Is it easier to pour from a wide- or narrow-mouthed container?" "Do you see anything that could help you pour liquid into a container?" "Does the funnel take longer? Why?" Add plastic tubing to the water center. Ask, "Can a tube be used to fill up a container?" "Which takes longer?" (**Figure 5-19**).

FIGURE 5-19 "Can a tube be used to fill a container?"

FIGURE 5-20 Children explore volume by weighing sand.

2. *Squeeze and blow.* Plastic squeeze bottles or turkey basters will encourage children to find another way to fill the containers. After the children have manipulated the baster and observed air bubbling out of it, set up the water table for a race. You will need table tennis balls, tape, and basters. First, ask the children how they think the basters can be used to move the tennis balls across the water table. The objective is to move the ball across the water by squeezing the turkey baster. After allowing the children some practice time, place a piece of tape lengthwise down the center of the table and begin. Use a piece of string to measure how far the ball is moved. Compare the distances with the length of string. Ask, "How many squeezes does it take to cover the distance?"

3. *A cup is a cup.* *Volume* is how much space a solid, liquid, or gas takes up or occupies. For example, when a one-cup measure is full of water, the volume of water is one cup. Volume can be compared by having children fill small boxes or jars with sand. Use sand in similar containers, and compare the way the sand feels. Compare the heft of a full container with that of an empty container. Use a balance scale to dramatize the difference. If you do not have a commercial balance, provide a homemade balance and hanging cups. Children will begin to weigh different levels of sand in the cups. Statements such as, "I wonder if sand weighs more if I fill the container even higher?" can be overheard. Let children check predictions and discuss what they have found (**Figure 5-20**).

4. *Sink or float.* Comparisons such as big–little and heavy–light are made when children discover that objects of different sizes sink and float. Make a chart to record observations. After discussing what the terms *sink* and *float* mean, give the children a variety of floating and nonfloating objects to

manipulate. Ask, "What do you think will float? Big corks? Small marbles?" As children sort objects by size and shape and then test whether they sink or float, they are discovering science concepts and learning about measurement.

Ms. Moore has her class predict, "Will it sink or float?" Her materials include a leaf, nail, balloon, cork, wooden spoon, and metal spoon. She makes a chart with columns labeled *sink* and *float* and has the children place the leaf and so on where they think they will go. Elisabeth excitedly floats the leaf. "It floats, it floats!" she says. Because Elisabeth correctly predicted that the leaf would float, the leaf stays in the *float* column on the chart. Diana predicts that the metal spoon will float. "Oh, it's not floating. The metal spoon is sinking." Diana moves the metal spoon from the *float* column to the *sink* column on the chart. In this way, children can predict and compare objects as they measure weight and buoyancy (**Figure 5-21**).

5. *Little snakes.* Many children in preschool and kindergarten are not yet conserving length. For example, they still think that a flexible stick may vary in length if its shape is changed in some way. Therefore, use care in assessing your students' developmental stages. The child must be able to conserve in order for measurement activities to make sense. In the following scenario, a teacher of young children assesses the conservation of length while relating length to animals.

Mrs. Raymond reinforces the length concept by giving each child in her class two pipe cleaners. She instructs them to place the pipe cleaners side by side and asks, "Which pipe cleaner is longer?" Then she tells the children to bend one of the pipe

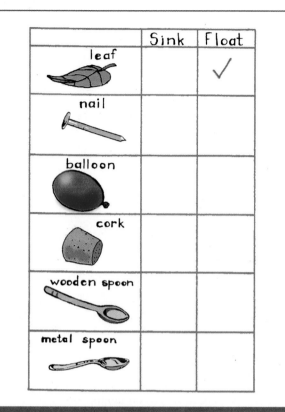

	Sink	Float
leaf		✓
nail		
balloon		
cork		
wooden spoon		
metal spoon		

FIGURE 5-21 *"Do you think the leaf will sink or float?"*

cleaners and asks, "Which is longer now?" She repeats this several times, having the children create different shapes.

Then the children make the pipe cleaners into little snakes by gluing small construction-paper heads on one end of each pipe cleaner. Mrs. Raymond shows the children pictures of a snake that is coiled and one that is moving on the ground (try to find pictures of the same kind of snake). She asks, "Is the coiled snake shorter?" "Yes," the children say. "Let's see if we can make our pipe cleaners into coiled snakes," instructs Mrs. Raymond. "Oh," says Jimmie, "this really looks like a coiled snake."

The teacher asks the students to lay out the other pipe cleaners to resemble a moving snake and asks, "Which is longer?" There are a variety of responses as the children manipulate the pipe cleaner snakes to help them understand that the coiled and moving snakes are the same lengths. Let them practice coiling and uncoiling the "snakes" and discuss how snakes move. Ask, "Can you tell how long a snake is when it is coiled up?" "Was your coiled-up snake longer than you thought?"

6. **Outdoors:** *A big and little hunt.* Height, size, and length can be compared in many ways. For example, Mrs. Jones takes her children on a big and little hunt.

After taking the children outside, Mrs. Jones has them sit in a circle and discuss the biggest and smallest things that they can see. Then she asks them, "Of all the things we have talked about, which is the smallest?" Jacob and Olivia are certain that the leaves are the smallest, but Sam and Lai do not agree. "The blades of grass are smaller," Sam observes. "Are they?" Mrs. Jones asks. "How can we tell which is smaller?" "Let's put them beside each other," Olivia suggests. The children compare the length of each item and discuss which is longer and wider.

7. **Body part measures.** Children enjoy measuring with body parts, such as a hand or foot length. Ask, "How many feet is it to the door?" Let the children count the number of foot lengths they must take. Or ask, "How many hands high are you?"

Give children pieces of string and have them measure head sizes. Then take the string, and measure other parts of their bodies. Compare their findings.

8. **How long will it take to sink?** Let children play for five minutes with dishpans of water, a kitchen scale, a bucket of water, and an assortment of objects. Then, give the children plastic tubes to explore and measure. As one child drops a piece of charcoal into a plastic tube filled with water, count in measured beats the amount of time that the charcoal takes to sink. Ask, "Will it sink faster in cold water or hot water?"

9. **Hot or not.** The following activities and questions correlate with science and, in many cases, integrate into the curriculum of a preschool or kindergarten.

    ■ Take an outdoor walk to feel the effects of temperature (**Photo 5-10**). "Is it warmer or colder outside?"

PHOTO 5-10   A sunny day provides a weather setting for outdoor play.

- Visit a greenhouse. Predict what the temperature will be inside the greenhouse; discuss the reasons for these predictions.

- Notice differences in temperature in different areas of the supermarket. Ask, "Are some areas colder?" "Which is the warmest area of the supermarket?"

- Melt crayons for dripping on bottles and painting pictures. Notice the effect of heat on the crayons. Ask, "Have you ever felt like a melted crayon?" "Act out the changes in a melting crayon with your bodies."

- Put some finger paints in the refrigerator. Have children compare how the refrigerated paints and room-temperature paints feel on their hands.

- Ask, "What happens to an ice cream cone as you eat it? Why do you think this happens?"

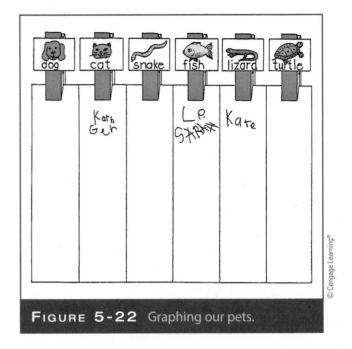

FIGURE 5-22   Graphing our pets.

5-5c Communicating with Graphs

When children make graphs, they use the basic process skills of observing, classifying, comparing, and measuring visually communicated information. In fact, making a graph is in itself an act of communication. A *graph* is a way of displaying information so that predictions, inferences, and conclusions can be made. See earlier in this chapter for directions on introducing graphs to children and for problem-solving topics that result in graph making.

When using graphs, it is essential that the meaning of the completed graph be clear to the children. With questions and discussion, it is possible for a graph to answer a question, solve a problem, or show data so that something can be understood

Practice Graphs. In the following scenario, Mrs. Jones uses Unifix Cubes to provide children with an opportunity to manipulate and construct two types of graphs.

Mrs. Jones distributes cubes of different colors to her kindergarten class. After the children have time to examine the cubes, she suggests that they stack the cubes by color. As the cubes are stacked, a bar graph is naturally created. Mrs. Jones lines up each stack of cubes and asks, "Which color cube do we have the most of?" Marissa says, "The blue stack is the tallest. There are more blue cubes." "How do you know?" Marissa says she counted the cubes in each stack. "Good," answers Mrs. Jones. "Can anyone tell me which stack of cubes is the smallest?" "The yellow ones," says Katie. The children count the number of cubes in each stack and duplicate the three-dimensional cube graph by making a graph of colored posterboard squares. The children place red, blue, yellow, and green squares in columns of color that Mrs. Jones has prepared on a tagboard background. In this way, children learn in a concrete way the one-to-one correspondence that a bar graph represents.

Pets Graph. Once children understand the concept of graphs, they can graph data from their investigations. Graphs can be used to compare the type and number of children's pets and give early literacy experiences. Make a list of the pets that your children have. Divide a bristol board into columns to represent every pet named. Cover the board with clear laminate film. Make labels with pet categories such as dogs, cats, snakes, fish, lizards, turtles, and so on. Glue the labels to clothespins. Then, place a labeled clothespin at the top of each column. Have the children write their names in the appropriate column (**Figure 5-22**).

Favorite Foods. Divide a posterboard into columns and paste or draw a picture of each food group at the top of each column. Allow each child to draw a picture of his or her favorite food and paste it under the appropriate column. Velcro can also be used to attach the pictures, and the children can write their names under their choice.

Graphing Attractions: Magnets. Simple magnets can be fun to explore. A real object graph can be made with ruled bristol board. Rule the board into columns to equal the number of magnets. Trace the shape of a magnet at the top of each column. Attach a drapery hook below each picture, and proceed as Mrs. Carter does in the following description.

After letting the children explore metal objects such as paper clips, Mrs. Carter places a pile of paper clips on the table along with different types of magnets. She invites Kara to choose a magnet and see how many paper clips it will attract. Kara selects a horseshoe-shaped magnet and hangs paper clips from the end, one at a time, until the magnet no longer attracts any clips. "Good," says Mrs. Carter. "Now, make a chain of the paperclips that your magnet attracts." After Kara makes the paperclip chain, Mrs. Carter directs her to hang it on the drapery hook under the drawing of the horseshoe-shaped magnet.

"I bet the magnet that looks like a bar will attract more paper clips," predicts Ethan. He selects the rod magnet and begins to attract as many paper clips as he can. Then, he makes a chain and hangs it on the drapery hook under the rod magnet. The process is repeated until each child in the group has worked with a magnet. Mrs. Carter makes no attempt to teach the higher-level concepts involved in magnetic force; rather, her purpose is to increase the children's awareness and give them some idea of what magnets do.

In this scenario, children observe that magnets can be different shapes and sizes (horseshoe, rod, disk, the letter U, ring, etc.) and attract a different amount of paper clips. They also have a visual graphic reminder of what they have accomplished.

ACTIVITIES

WHICH IS THE STRONGEST?

Objective: Observing, sequencing, and ordering; communicating with graphs.

Materials: Ideally, a magnet of the same size for each child to begin magnet exploration, a variety of magnet sizes and strengths to be introduced later, and a variety of metallic and nonmetallic items available for testing—the larger, the better. If using metal magnets, be sure that they are clean and free of rust and/or sharp edges.

Naturalistic and informal activities: Give students a lot of time to explore the magnets and the effect they have on different objects. Have both metallic and nonmetallic objects available for the children to explore with magnets. Listen to the children's discussion about the magnets. Ask, **"What happens when you touch an object with a magnet? What do you think will be attracted to your magnets?"**

Digital Download

SUMMARY

5-1 Comparison Standards and Expectations

The process of comparing more than two things is called *ordering* or *seriation*. There are four basic types of ordering activities. Patterning is related to ordering and includes auditory, visual, and physical motor sequences that are repeated. Patterns may be copied, extended, or verbally described. Children can learn about patterns common to a variety of cultures.

Assessment. Observation and individual interviews.

Activities. Naturalistic, informal, and adult guided. Concrete materials are easy to find. Virtual manipulatives are available online.

Informal Post-Evaluation. Observation and individual interviews.

5-2 Measurement Standards and Expectations

The concept of measurement develops through five stages. Preoperational children are in the early stages: play, imitation, and comparing. They learn about measurement mainly through naturalistic and informal experiences that encourage them to explore and discover. Transitional children move into the stage of experimenting with arbitrary units. During the concrete operations period, children learn to use standard units of measurement.

Pre-Assessment. Observation, questioning, and individual assessment interviews can document what the students already know and understand.

Activities. Naturalistic, informal, and adult-guided activities support children's understanding of measurement.

Measurement activities lend themselves to cooperative learning groups with two members.

Informal Post-Evaluation. Observation, questioning, and individual assessment interviews can document what the students have learned.

5-3 Time Standards and Expectations

The young child can begin to learn that time has duration and that time is related to sequences of events. The child first relates time to his personal experience and to his daily sequence of activities. Not until the child enters the concrete operations period can he use units of time as adults use them.

Pre-Assessment. Observation and informal interview tasks are used.

Activities. For the most part, the young child learns her concept of time through naturalistic and informal experiences. When she is about the age of 4½ or 5, she can do adult-guided activities as well. It is important to understand that some families from non-Western cultures may not view time as Westerners do.

Informal Post-Evaluation. Observation and informal interview tasks are used.

Stages of Development for Making and Understanding Graphs. The first graphs are three-dimensional and made with real objects. The next are made with pictures and the next with paper squares. Children can discuss the results of their graph projects and dictate a description of the graph's meaning to be displayed alongside the graph.

Materials for Making Graphs. Concrete objects such as unit blocks and cube blocks, buttons, spools, and paper and pencil for recording data.

Topics for Graphs. Any of the many questions that curious children may ask.

5-4 Science Standards and Expectations

Science standards and expectations are guided by the NGSS Standards and the Framework of K–12 Science Education. Fundamental math concepts are used in science investigations.

Ordering and Patterning. When more than two things are ordered and placed in sequence, the process is called seriation. If children understand seriation, they will be able to develop the more advanced skills of patterning. Patterning involves repeating auditory, visual, or physical motor sequences.

Measurement: Volume, Weight, Length, and Temperature. Children begin to understand measurement by actively manipulating measurement materials. Water and sand are highly sensory and are effective resources for young children to use to develop concepts of volume, temperature, length, and weight. Time measurement is related to sequencing events. The use of measurement activities will formalize and develop further when children enter the concrete operations period.

Communicating with Graphs. Graph making gives children an opportunity to classify, compare, count, measure, and visually communicate information. A graph is a way of displaying information so that predictions, inferences, and conclusions can be made in learning science concepts.

FURTHER READING AND RESOURCES

Ashbrook, P. (2011). Recording data with young children. *Science and Children, 48*(5), 22–23.

Cadzow-Wardell, L. (2009/2010). White trillium. *Teaching Children Mathematics, 16*(5), 264–267.

Cox, D., & Lo, J. (2009). Math by the month: Comparing sizes. *Teaching Children Mathematics, 16*(4), 204–205.

Dacey, L., Cavanagh, M., Findell, C. R., Greenes, C. E., Sheffield, L. J., & Small, M. (2003). *Navigating through measurement in prekindergarten–grade 2.* Reston, VA: National Council of Teachers of Mathematics.

Dubon, L. P., & Shafer, K. G. (2010). Storyboards for meaningful patterns. *Teaching Children Mathematics, 16*(6), 325–329.

Lacefield, W. O., III. (2009). The power of representation: Graphs and glyphs in data analysis lessons for young children. *Teaching Children Mathematics, 15*(6), 324–326.

Measurement [Focus Issue]. (2006). *Science and Children, 44*(2).

Sheffield, L. J., Cavanagh, M., Dacey, L., Findell, C. R., Greenes, C. E., & Small, M. (2002). *Navigating through data analysis and probability in prekindergarten–grade 2.* Reston, VA: National Council of Teachers of Mathematics.

REFERENCES

Allen, P. (1982). *Who sank the boat?* New York: Sandcastle Books.

Ashbrook, P. (2011). Measuring learning. *Science and Children, 48*(9), 20–21.

Beneke, S. J., Ostrosky, M. M., & Katz, L. G. (2008). Calender time for young children: Good intentions gone awry. *Young Children, 63*(3), 12–16.

Carle, E. (1993). *Today is Monday.* New York: Scholastic Books.

Classroom elections. (2012). *Teaching Children Mathematics, 219*(1), 216–218.

Colburn, K., & Tate, P. (1998). The big, yellow laboratory. *Science and Children, 36*(1), 22–25.

Cross, C. T., Woods, T. A., & Schweingruber, H. (2009). *Mathematics learning in early childhood.* Washington, DC: National Academies Press.

El Harim, J. L. (1998). A treemendous learning experience. *Science and Children, 35*(8), 26–29.

Geiser, T. (2006–2012). Preschool math: Exploring patterns. *Education.com.* Updated August 6, 2013. www.education.com.

Hall, Z. (1999). *It's pumpkin time.* New York: Scholastic Books.

Harpring, S. (2006–2012). Summertime science for preschoolers. *Education.com.*

Martin, J. M. (2012). *Elementary science methods*, 6th ed. Belmont, CA: Wadsworth Cengage Learning.

Moomaw, S., & Davis, J. A. (2013). STEM comes to preschool. In A. Shillady (Ed.). Exploring Science. Washington, DC: National Association for the Education of Young Children.

Most, B. (1989). *The littlest dinosaurs.* San Diego, CA: Harcourt Brace.

Myller, R. (1972). *How big is a foot?* New York: Atheneum.

National Council of Teachers of Mathematics (NCTM). (2000). *Principles and standards for school mathematics.* Reston, VA: Author.

National Governors Association Center for Best Practices, Council of Chief State School Officers. (2010). Common Core State Standards for Mathematics. Washington, DC: Author. www.corestandards.org.

National Research Council. (2012). *A framework for K–12 science education*. Washington, DC: National Academies Press.

NGSS Lead States. (2013). *Next Generation Science Standards: For states, by states*. Washington, DC: National Academies Press.

Reed, M. K. (2013). Early childhood building blocks: Children using data to find answers. *Resources for Early Childhood*. rec.ohiorc.org.

Richardson, K. (1999). *Developing number concepts: Counting, comparing, and pattern (Book 1)*. Parsippany, NJ: Seymour.

Schwartz, S. (1994). Calendar reading: A tradition that begs remodeling. *Teaching Children Mathematics, 1*(2), 104–109.

Shah, N. (2011, July 14). Report reveals ways brain science could improve special ed. *Education Week's blogs*. blogs.edweek.org/edweek/speced/2011/07/while_neuroscience_research_co.hhtml?print=1.

Taylor-Cox, J. (2003). Algebra in the early years? Yes. *Young Children, 58*(1), 14–21.

Zaslavsky, C. (1996). *The multicultural math classroom*. Portsmouth, NH: Heinemann.

INTEGRATING THE CURRICULUM

LEARNING OBJECTIVES

After reading this chapter, you should be able to:

6-1 Explain how the national standards, play, and thematic units and projects relate to STEM and STEAM.

6-2 Explain the importance of language and literacy to math, science, and engineering concept formation.

STANDARDS ADDRESSED IN THIS CHAPTER

naeyc

NAEYC Professional Preparation Standards

2a. Understand diverse family and community characteristics.

4b. Understand effective strategies and tools for early education, including appropriate use of technology.

5a. Understand content knowledge and resources in mathematics and science.

DAP Guidelines

3.D.1. Teachers plan curriculum experiences that integrate children's learning.

Common Core State Standards Math

MP1　Make sense of problems and persevere in solving them.

MP4　Model with mathematics.

Next Generation Science Standards

K-ESS3-1　Use a model.

K-ESS3-2　Read grade-appropriate texts and/or use media to obtain information.

K-ESS3-3　Communicate solutions with others in oral and/or written forms, using models and/or drawings.

6-1 STANDARDS AND STEM AND STEAM

The Common Core Standards for Mathematics (National Governors Association Center for Best Practices, 2010), New Generation Science Standards (NGSS Lead States, 2013), and the Framework for K–12 Science Education (National Research Council, 2012) focus on content areas skills, understandings, and processes that can be applied across the curriculum and particularly when combined with engineering, technology, and the arts as STEM and STEAM (see Chapter 1). Children can apply and experience problem solving, reasoning, communication, connections, and hands-on learning through *dramatic play, thematic and project approaches*, and an integrated curriculum (Owens, 2008). STEM integrates science, technology, engineering, and mathematics and fits well with the project approach to be discussed later in this chapter (Katz, 2010). STEAM integrates the arts into STEM. The idea of integrating the arts into STEM is controversial (Jolly, 2013). There are differences of opinion regarding whether and how the arts should be incorporated into STEM. Jolly (2013) suggests two approaches to take when adopting STEAM:

1. The STEM subjects could serve the arts. For example, children could design beautiful musical instruments or structures.

2. Arts and artists could serve STEM. Children could enhance their engineering projects by making them appealing to look at and thus more marketable.

A scientific process can also be viewed as a creative process, which compares a carefully done science investigation to a carefully done creation of a musical composition or a novel (Williams, 2013). The Rhode Island School of Design is a leader in promoting the addition of art to STEM (STEM to STEAM, n.d.). There are many examples of art, math, and science in collaboration. Computer science Professor Erik Demaine and artist Martin Demaine use computational origami applied to industrial problems, such as folding airbags. Artists Salvador Dali and M. C. Escher were influenced by the geometry in nature.

Teachers are seeing that the Common Core can be taught through interdisciplinary thematic units and projects (Heitin, 2013). The Common Core State Standards for English/Language Arts/Literacy (National Governors Association, 2010) sets standards for nonfiction reading. Standards are also set for literacy requirements for history/social studies, science, and technical subjects.

6-1a Play and Learning

Play is the major medium through which children learn (see Chapter 1). They experiment with grown-up roles, explore materials, and develop rules for their actions (Eisenhauer &

Feikes, 2009). Curriculum that meets national standards can be implemented through the use of **thematic units and projects** that integrate mathematics; science, engineering, and technology; social studies; language arts; music; and movement. Themes may be selected by the teacher (Isbell, 1995) and/or the children (Helm & Katz, 2011; Katz & Chard, 2000).

Integrated curriculum naturally includes mathematics. Remember that mathematics is composed of fundamental concepts that are used for thinking and investigating the world in all the content areas. Authentic, real-world learning experiences can be provided to children through an environment that promotes science (Bosse, Jacobs, & Anderson-Topete, 2013) (**Photo 6-1**). A discovery area set up in the classroom promotes exploration. Magnifiers, plants, animals, rocks, fossils, shells, pine cones, pan balances, science- and math-themed books, and so on, can capture students' interests. Take advantage of the outdoors by encouraging bird watching, leaf collecting, and worm and bug hunting. As described in earlier chapters, toddlers have explored insects (Shaffer, Hall, & Lynch, 2013); preschoolers have studied birds (Moomaw & Davis, 2013) and investigated physics questions (Stoll, Hamilton, Oxley, Eastman, & Brent, 2013); and kindergartners have examined rocks and sand (Ogu & Schmidt, 2013). STEM and STEAM come naturally to preschoolers and kindergarteners.

In this chapter, we demonstrate how dramatic play and thematic units and projects can enrich children's acquisition of concepts, language, and knowledge, not only in science and mathematics but also in the other content areas. Furthermore, all the content areas offer rich settings for social learning, science investigations, and mathematical problem solving. Chapter 1 described the commonalities between math and science. Chapter 2 provided a basic lesson plan and examples of science projects that incorporate math, social studies, language arts, fine arts, motor development, and dramatic play. Chapters 10 and 11 include integrated projects and activities for the primary level. This chapter emphasizes the natural

PHOTO 6-1 Authentic experiences—like the one this boy is getting as he investigates the goat's reaction to being brushed—help to promote a scientific environment.

© 2016 Cengage Learning®

play of young children as the basis for developing thematic projects that highlight the potentials for an interdisciplinary curriculum for young children. Ashbrook (2009) describes how children can engage in a science investigation exploring safe odors. They can integrate math by making a chart of the smells investigated and placing a tally mark by their favorite. They can count up the tally marks for each food and graph the result. Geist and Geist (2008) integrate music and math, and Whitin and Piwko (2008) integrate poetry and math.

Concepts and skills are valuable to children only if they can be used in everyday life. Young children spend most of their waking hours involved in play, which can be used as a vehicle for applying concepts. Young children like to feel big and do "big person" things. They like to pretend they are grown up and want to do as many grown-up things as they can. Role-playing can be used as a means for children to apply what they know as they take on a multitude of grown-up roles.

6-1b Dramatic Role Playing

Dramatic role-playing is an essential part of thematic projects. For example, using food as the theme for a project could afford opportunities for children to apply concepts and carry out science investigations and mathematics problem solving as well as for them to try out adult roles and do adult activities. Children can grow food and shop for groceries; plan and prepare meals, snacks, and parties; serve food; and enjoy sharing and eating the results of their efforts. Teachers can offer children opportunities that provide experiences for social education as they learn more about adult tasks, have experiences in the community, and learn about their own and other cultures. Teachers can use these experiences to assess and evaluate through observation.

Butterworth and Lo Cicero (2001) described a project that grew from the interests of 4- and 5-year-old Latino children in a transitional kindergarten class. The teachers used the Reggio Emilia approach (Edwards, Gandini, & Forman, 1998) in developing the project; that is, they began with the children's culture. In this case, they had the children tell stories about their trips to the supermarket and transformed these stories into math problems. The market provided a setting that led the children naturally to talk about quantity and money. After presenting their stories, the children reenacted them through dramatic play. They pretended to buy fruit and take it home to eat. Setting the table naturally posed problems in rational counting and one-to-one correspondence. The project continued on into more complex problems and other types of child-selected dramatic play (**Photos 6-2** and **6-3**).

When children are engaged in dramatic role-playing, they practice what it is like to be an adult (**Photo 6-4**). They begin with a simple imitation of what they have observed. Their first roles reflect what they have seen at home. They bathe, feed, and rock babies. They cook meals, set the table, and eat. One of their first outside experiences is to go shopping, which is soon reflected in dramatic play. They begin by carrying things in bags, purses, and other large containers. At first, they carry around anything that they can stuff in

PHOTO 6-2   These boys shop in the preschool grocery store.

their containers. Gradually, they move into using more realistic props such as play money and empty food containers. Next, they might build a store with big blocks and planks. Eventually, they learn to play cooperatively with other children. One child might be the mother, another the father, another the child, and another the store clerk. As the children move toward this stage, teachers can provide more props and background experiences that will expand the raw material children have for developing their role-playing. Problem-solving skills are refined as children figure out who will take which role, provide a location for the store and home, and develop the rules for the activity.

PHOTO 6-3   Grocery store shelves are stocked and ready for shopping.

© 2016 Cengage Learning®

PHOTO 6-4   A pizza store is set up for dramatic play.

Children can learn about adult roles through field trips to businesses such as restaurants, banks, the post office, and stores, both in the local neighborhood and in the extended community. Museums, construction sites, hospitals, fire stations, and other places offer experiences that can enrich children's knowledge of adult roles. Books, audio recordings, videos, DVDs, online investigations, and classroom visitors can also provide valuable experiences for children. Following such experiences, teachers can provide props to support children's dramatic role-playing. They can also set up each type of business or service center in the classroom with appropriate props.

Some examples of dramatic play centers and props are listed here.

- Set up a toy store by having the children bring old toys from home, which they could pretend to buy and sell.

- Set up a grocery store using items that might otherwise be discarded, such as empty food containers, which the children could bring from home. The children could make food from playdough, clay, or papier-mâché. Plastic food replicas can be purchased.

- Organize a clothing store into departments for children, ladies, and men; children can bring discarded clothing and shoes from home.

- Stock a jewelry store with old and pretend jewelry (such as macaroni necklaces and cardboard watches).

- Stock service centers such as the post office, fire station, police station, automobile repair shop, hospital, beauty shop, and the like with appropriate props.

- Build transportation vehicles such as space vehicles, automobiles, trucks, and buses using large blocks, lined-up chairs, or with commercially made or teacher-made steering wheels and other controls.

- Set up a zoo, veterinarian's office, circus, farm, or pet shop. Have children bring stuffed animals from home to live in the zoo, visit the vet, act in the circus, live on the farm, or be sold in the pet shop. Classify the animals as to which belong in each setting. Children can predict which animals eat the most, are dangerous to humans, are the smartest, and so on. Provide play money to pay for goods and services.

- Organize health and medical service centers. Provide props for medical play. Tie these in with discussions of good nutrition and other health practices. The children can "pay the bill" for the services, and the medical staff can tell the patients their temperatures and count their heartbeats.

- Create space science vehicles. Provide props for space travel (e.g., a big refrigerator carton that can be made into a spaceship, paper-bag space helmets, etc.). Provide materials for making mission control and designing other planetary settings. Students can count down to lift off, decide how many passengers and crew can make the trip and estimate the miles to their destination and the time for the trip.

- Create water environments. Provide toy boats, people, rocks for islands, and the like. Discuss floating and sinking. Outdoors, use water for firefighter play and for watering the garden. Have a container (bucket or large dishpan) that can be a fishing hole, and use waterproof fish with a safety pin or other metal object attached so they can be caught with magnet fish bait. Investigate why the magnet/metal combination makes a good combination for pretend fishing. Count how many fish each child catches. Provide clear plastic tubing, beakers, measuring cups, and plastic containers.

- Set up simple machines. Vehicles, a packing box elevator, a milk carton elevator on a pulley, a plank on rollers, and so on, make interesting dramatic play props, and their construction and functioning provide challenging problems for investigation. Physics can be explored with ramps and pathways (DeVries & Sales, 2011).

- As described earlier, a science center provides a place for scientist play.

Concepts are applied in a multitude of play activities, such as those just described. The following are some examples:

- Exchanging play money for goods or services provides practice for one-to-one correspondence.

- Groups and classifying are involved in organizing each dramatic play center in an orderly manner (e.g., placing all the items in the drugstore in the proper place).

- Counting can be applied to figuring out how many items have been purchased and how much money must be exchanged.

- Comparing and measuring can be used to decide whether clothing fits, to determine the weight of fruits and vegetables purchased, to check a sick person's temperature, and to decide on which size box of cereal or carton of milk to purchase.

- Spatial relations and volume concepts are applied as items purchased are placed in bags, boxes, and/or baskets and as children discover how many passengers will fit in the space shuttle or can ride on the bus.

- Number symbols can be found throughout dramatic play props—for example, on price tags, play money, telephones, cash registers, scales, measuring cups and spoons, thermometers, rulers, and calculators.

Pollman (2010) connects spatial concepts across the curriculum to math, science, art, literature, social studies, and technology. Pocket calculators are excellent props for dramatic play. Children can pretend to add up their expenses, costs, and earnings. As they explore calculators, they will learn how to use them for basic mathematical operations. Methods for introducing calculators are described in section 6-4. (See resources in **Figure 6-1**.)

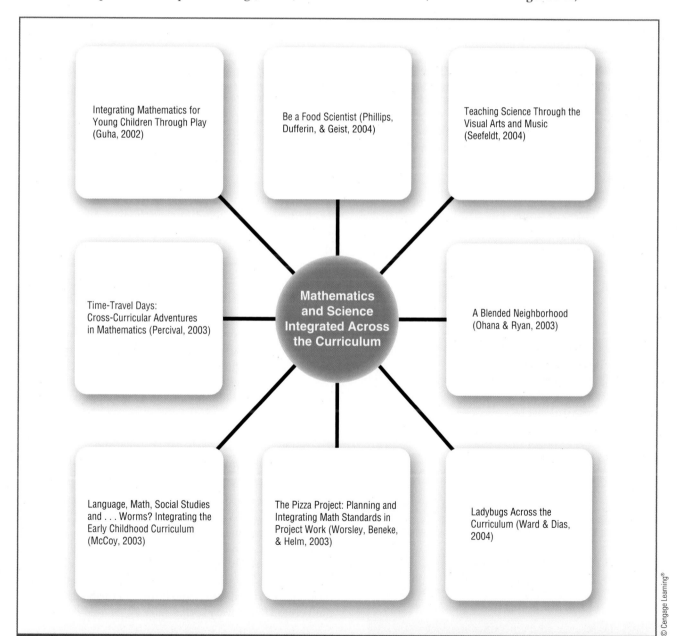

Integrating Mathematics for Young Children Through Play (Guha, 2002)

Be a Food Scientist (Phillips, Dufferin, & Geist, 2004)

Teaching Science Through the Visual Arts and Music (Seefeldt, 2004)

Time-Travel Days: Cross-Curricular Adventures in Mathematics (Percival, 2003)

Mathematics and Science Integrated Across the Curriculum

A Blended Neighborhood (Ohana & Ryan, 2003)

Language, Math, Social Studies and . . . Worms? Integrating the Early Childhood Curriculum (McCoy, 2003)

The Pizza Project: Planning and Integrating Math Standards in Project Work (Worsley, Beneke, & Helm, 2003)

Ladybugs Across the Curriculum (Ward & Dias, 2004)

© Cengage Learning®

Figure 6-1 Examples of resources for integrating mathematics and science across the curriculum.

6-1c A Thematic Project Example: Food

A project that focuses on food can involve a variety of curriculum areas and experiences. First, the teacher can list what the students say as they tell what they know about food and list some questions they may have about food that can serve as the basis for investigations. As scientists, children may observe the growth of food, the physical changes that take place when food is prepared, and the effects of food on the growth of humans and animals. They may also compare the tastes and smells of different foods and categorize them into those they like and those they dislike; sweet and sour; liquid and solid; "junk" and healthful; and groups such as meat and dairy products, breads and cereals, and fruits and vegetables.

One topic that should be introduced during initial discussions about food is the **Food Plate**. Developed by the United States Government, Department of Agriculture, the Food Plate shows the five main food groups and the relative amounts present in a well-balanced diet. Note that the categories of fruits and vegetables occupy half the plate. The Food Plate replaces the former Food Pyramid and is easier to read and interpret (see **Figure 6-2**). It can be used by people of all ages, including children of preschool age.

As mathematicians, children pour, measure, count, cut wholes into parts, and divide full pans or full bowls into equal servings. They count the strokes when mixing a cake, make sure the oven is on the correct temperature setting, and set the clock for the required baking time. At the store, they exchange money for food and weigh fruits and vegetables. They count the days until their beans sprout or the fruit

ripens. As engineers they use a variety of cooking tools such as mixers, spoons, measuring spoons and cups, and blenders.

Through food experiences, children learn much about society and culture. They can make foods from different cultures. They learn where food is grown, how it is marketed, and how it must be purchased with money at the grocery store (Photo 6-3). They cooperate with one another and take turns when preparing food. Then they share what they make with others.

Children can sing about food and draw pictures of their food-related experiences. They can move like an eggbeater, like a stalk of wheat blowing in the wind, or like a farmer planting seeds. The following are some examples of dramatic play, mathematics, and science food experiences.

Food and Dramatic Play. In the home living center at school, children purchase, cook, serve, and eat food as part of their role-playing. It was suggested in Chapter 5 that a simple measuring activity could be to make dough from flour and salt. Children can make the dough into pretend food to use as dramatic play props.

Food and Math. Cooking activities are a rich source of mathematics experiences. Following a recipe provides a sequencing activity. Each ingredient must be measured exactly using a standard measuring tool. The correct number of cups, tablespoons, eggs, and so on, must be counted out. Baked foods must be cooked at the correct temperature for the prescribed amount of time. Some foods are heated, whereas others are placed in the refrigerator or freezer. When the food is ready to eat, it must be divided into equal portions so that each person gets a fair share. A simple pictograph recipe can help children to be independent as they assemble ingredients (**Figure 6-3**).

Children who live in the country or who have a garden in the city have additional opportunities to apply math concepts to real-life experiences. They can count the number of days from planting until the food is ready to be picked. They can measure the growth of the plants at regular intervals. They can count the number of cucumbers harvested and the weight of the potatoes. If the child lives where livestock can be kept, the daily number of eggs gathered can be counted; the young calf can be weighed each week; and the amount of money collected for products sold can be counted. Children's natural curiosity about the world pulls them into nature.

A garden can be planted if space is available (Owings & Merino, 2010; Winters, Ring, & Burriss, 2010). Creating gardens is becoming a widespread school project (Starbuck, 2012). In fact, First Lady Michelle Obama, together with children invited from neighboring schools, has planted an "eating garden" (a garden of plants for food we eat like lettuce, squash, strawberries, and beans) on the South Lawn of the White House every spring since 2009.

It is generally believed that today's increased interest in planting vegetable gardens stems from Mrs. Obama's enthusiasm, models, and publicity (Cohen, 2014). The garden

ChooseMyPlate.gov

Source: USDA Center for Nutrition Policy and Promotion

FIGURE 6-2 MyPlate, USDA food guidance system.

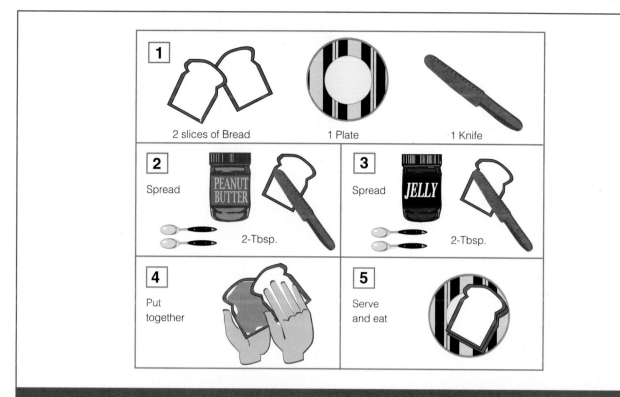

FIGURE 6-3 A pictograph for making a peanut butter and jelly sandwich.

© Cengage Learning®

provides a focus for project work (Helm, 2013). At Jefferson Elementary School in Wausau, Wisconsin, the school garden provides a setting for learning about healthy eating and plant growth, as well as opportunities for measurement experiences, such as weighing produce (Uhlig, 2013). In Columbia Heights, Minnesota, the school district planted an "edible schoolyard" supervised by a full-time science and garden specialist (Prather, 2013). The garden is incorporated into the curriculum at all levels, K–12. A rural Kansas School was saved from closure by taking on an agricultural focus (Attoun, 2013). The K–4 students learn math, reading, science, and responsibility as they do all the farm chores. They calculate how much feed each cow needs; count money from the sale of eggs and vegetables; and read books about the care and feeding of pigs, cows, sheep and chickens. Burpee Home Gardens provides lesson plans for helping children learn about growing vegetables (Burpee Home Gardens, 2011).

Setting the table at the home living center or for a real meal provides an opportunity for children to apply math skills. They can calculate the number of people to be seated and served, and match the number with the amount of tableware and the number of chairs, napkins, and place mats needed. Putting utensils and dishes away is an experience in sorting things into groups. Pictographs can be used to provide clues about where each type of item should be placed.

Food and Science. Each of the activities described under the previous section also involves science. The adult can ask the children to predict what will happen when the wet ingredient (water) is mixed with the dry ingredients (flour and salt) when making the playdough biscuits. Children can then make the mixture; observe and describe its texture, color, and density; and compare their results with their predictions. Next, they can predict what will happen when the dough is baked in the oven. When it is taken out, they can observe and describe the differences that take place during the baking process. The adult can also ask the children what would happen if the oven is too hot or if the biscuits are left in too long.

The opportunity to see eggs produced can lead to a discussion of where the eggs come from and what would happen if the eggs were fertilized. They could observe the growth from seed to edible food as vegetables are planted, cultivated, watered, and picked. Applesauce exemplifies several physical changes: from whole to parts, from solid chunks to soft lumps, and then to smooth and thick as cutting, heating, and grinding each have an effect. Children can also note the change in taste before and after the sugar is added. Stone soup offers an opportunity for discussing the significance of the stone. What does the stone add to the soup? Does a stone have nutrients? What really makes the soup taste good and makes it nutritious?

Food and Engineering. Working with food involves the use of many tools. Gardeners use shovels, spades, rakes, wheelbarrows, and clippers. Farmers use tractors and trucks and milking machines. Cooks use mixers, can openers, spoons, knives, and graters. All these tools were created by engineers.

Food and Social Studies. Each of the activities described involves social studies as well. City children might take a trip to the farm. For example, a trip to an orchard to get apples for applesauce is an enriching and enjoyable experience. Children might also take a trip to the grocery store to purchase the ingredients needed in their recipes. Then they can take turns measuring, cutting, adding ingredients, and doing whatever else is required as the cooking process proceeds. Stone soup is an excellent group activity because everyone in the class can add an ingredient. Invite people from different cultures to bring foods to class and/or help the children make their special foods. Children can note similarities and differences across cultures.

Food and the Arts. Food is the subject of many paintings (Chayka, 2012). Chayka selected what he believes are the greatest food still lifes in art history. Fruit, ham, quince, cabbage and melons, apples, cakes, lemons, drinking glasses, sea urchins, fruit and vegetable portraits, a jello map, and a skinned rabbit were included in the 10 selected paintings. When studying food, young artists also enjoy painting and drawing food. Clay and dough can also be used to fashion food items.

6-1d Working with Children with Special Needs

The multicultural curriculum can include learning about the favorite foods of different cultures. Children can make a variety of ethnic dishes. They can construct graphs of their favorite foods and write their favorite recipes. Young children can come up with delightful recipes for a class cookbook. Projects can center on the study of ethnic groups, geographical area, and customs of different cultures. Parents can contribute to these projects. Costumes, dolls, musical instruments, and other diverse cultural artifacts can be included in the dramatic play center. Projects can provide the hands-on experiences that are so essential for children with special needs.

NGSS

6-1e Focus on Nature

Drumlin Farm Community Preschool is a nature- and farm-based preschool located in Lincoln, Massachusetts (Plenda, 2013). The children are learning math, science, language, and curiosity. The school is located on a working farm and wildlife sanctuary operated by the Massachusetts Audubon Society. The back-to-nature school movement began in Scandinavia in the late 1960s and early 1970s and spread to other countries including, more recently, the United States. Children benefit by having time to explore nature, and they learn to regulate their own behavior. Nature can be explored through mathematics. Sibley and Kurz (2013) developed a set of math problems based on patterns in nature such as markings on monarch caterpillars, the commonalities between turtles and tortoises, natural symmetry, and the number of petals on flowers. Community Playthings, in collaboration with Exchange Press, has produced a booklet titled *The Wisdom of Nature*, which can be downloaded from the Community Playthings website.

Technology for Young Children

Peg + Cat: Math for 3- to 5-Year-Olds

Peg + Cat is a TV program designed by the Fred Rogers Center and is shown on PBS stations. Peg and Cat find themselves in the middle of math word problems that young children can help them solve. Peg represents a female model who can solve math problems, including counting, number recognition, patterns, measurement, addition, and shape labeling and recognition. Peg + Cat have a website at PBS Kids. On the website are games, adventures and videos. The following are some of the games:

- **Pizza Count.** Pizzas are ordered with a number of items to be placed on them. The child counts out and places the items ordered.

- **Chicken Dance.** A shape pattern gives a clue for completing the chicken dance.

- **Magical Shape Hunt.** Children save the mermaid's jewels, which are shaped like geometric solids such as spheres, cubes, and rectangular solids.

- **Paint Along.** Children can paint their own designs or copy according to directions given.

- **Rock Art.** Children can design their own rock gardens or add to pictures provided.

Music is included, as Peg often sings and plays her guitar, and the chickens dance and sing.

6-2 LANGUAGE, LITERACY, AND CONCEPT FORMATION

The NCTM five process areas are closely connected to the CCSSM standards (Koestler, Felton, Bieda, & Otten, 2013). The standards include expectations in five process areas: **problem solving, reasoning and proof, communications, connections,** and **representation.** In Chapter 1, *problem solving* was discussed as the major process focus in mathematics. For the youngest mathematicians, problem solving is the most important means of building mathematical knowledge. Problems usually arise from daily routines, play activities and materials, and stories. As children work with the materials and engage in activities already described, they figure things out, using the processes of reasoning, communications, connections, and representation. Logical *reasoning* develops in the early years and is especially important in working with classification and patterns. Reasoning enables students to draw logical conclusions, apply logical classification skills, explain their thinking, justify their problem solutions and processes, apply patterns and relationships to arrive at solutions, and make sense out of mathematics and science. *Communication* through oral, written, and pictorial language provides the means for explaining problem-solving and reasoning processes. Children need to provide a description of what they do, why they do it, and what they have accomplished. They need to use the language of mathematics in their explanations.

The important *connections* for young mathematicians are the ones between the naturalistic and informal mathematics they learn first and the formal mathematics they learn later in school. Concrete objects can serve as the bridge between informal and formal mathematics. Young children can "*represent* their thoughts about, and understanding of, mathematical ideas through oral and written language, physical gestures, drawings, and invented and conventional symbols" (NCTM, 2000, p. 136). In addition, the CCSSM and NGSS teams worked together to align and ensure consistency with each discipline's standards. Key topics in mathematics are aligned with science topics at the level where they will be needed. (NGSS Lead States, 2013).

Literacy skills are also necessary for learning and understanding science. Key literacy connections between science (NGSS) content and literacy (CCSS, for literacy) were identified by a team comprised of members from both groups. Reading requires an understanding of the norms and conventions of science as well as the ability to synthesize information and follow procedures. Students must also be able to interpret diagrams and data. Students need to present information both orally and in writing as well as in drawings and models. The inquiry and design models in science and engineering require students to ask questions, describe observations, and make simple sketches, drawings, and/or models (Ashcroft, 2013).

What the child does—and says—tells the teacher what the child knows about math and science. The older the child gets, the more important concepts become. The language the child uses and how she uses it provide clues to the teacher regarding the child's conceptual development. However, children may imitate adult use of words before the concept is highly developed. The child's language system is usually well developed by age 4; by this age children's sentences are much the same as an adult's, and their vocabulary is growing rapidly.

The adult observes what the child does from infancy through age 2 and looks for the child's first understanding and the use of words. Between the ages of 2 and 4, the child starts to put more words together into longer sentences. She also learns more words and what they mean.

Questions are used to assess the young child's concept development. "Which is the big ball? Which is the circle?" Having her respond with an appropriate action checks the child's understanding of words.

© 2016 Cengage Learning®

▶Ⅱ TeachSource Video

AN ENVIRONMENT WHERE WE LEARN FROM EACH OTHER: A KINDERGARTEN CLASS

Students in the kindergarten class share and discuss problem solutions.

1. How is oral language significant in supporting the children learning from each other?

2. What is the first way students share problem solutions?

3. What procedure is used to share with the whole class? How do the students' language skills support their explanations?

4. What is the teacher's role?

■ "Point to the big ball."

■ "Find two chips."

■ "Show me the picture in which the boy is on the chair."

These tasks do not require the child to say any words. She needs only to point, touch, or pick up something. Once the child demonstrates her understanding of math words by using gestures or other nonverbal answers, she can move on to questions she must answer with one or more words. The adult can ask the child the same questions as before, but in a way that requires a verbal response.

■ The child is shown two balls, one big and one small. "Tell me, what is different about these balls?"

■ The child is shown a group of objects. "Tell me, how many are there in this group?"

■ The child is shown a picture of a boy sitting on a chair. "Tell me, where is the boy?"

The child learns many concept words as he goes about his daily activities. By the time a child starts kindergarten, he uses many concept words that he has learned in a naturalistic way. (Examples have been included in Chapters 3 and 4.) The child uses both comments and questions, as exemplified here:

■ "Mom, I want two *pieces* of cheese."

■ "Mr. Brown, this chair is *small*."

- "*Yesterday* we went to the zoo."
- "The string is *long*."
- "The foot fits *in* the shoe."
- "This cracker is a *square* shape."
- "Look, some of the worms are *long* and some are *short*; some are *fat* and some are *thin*."
- "The *first* bean seed I planted is *taller* than the *second* one."
- "Outer space is *far* away."

Questions could be like these examples:

- "How *old* is he?"
- "*When* will I grow as *big* as you?"
- "Who has *more*?"
- "What *time* is my TV program?"
- "Is this a school *day*, or is it *Saturday*?"
- "What makes the bubbles when the water gets *hot*?"
- "Why does this roller always go *down* its ramp *faster* than that roller goes *down* its ramp?"
- "Why are the leaves turning *brown* and *red* and *gold* and falling *down on* the ground?"

The answers the child gets to these questions can help increase the number of concept words she knows and can use.

The teacher should use concept words during center time, lunch, and other times when an adult-guided concept lesson is not being done. She should also note which words the child uses during free times.

The teacher should encourage the child to use concept words even if he may not use them in an accurate, adult way. Some examples follow:

- "I can count—one, two, three, five, ten."
- "Aunt Helen is coming after my last nap." (Indicates future time.)
- "I will measure my paper." (Holds a ruler against the edge of the paper.)
- "Last night Grandpa was here." (It was actually several days ago.)
- "I'm six years old." (Really two years old.)
- "I have a million dollars." (Has a handful of play money.)

Adults should accept the child's use of the words, but they should use the words correctly themselves. Soon the child will develop a higher-level use of words as she is able to grasp higher-level ideas. For a 2- or 3-year-old, any group of more than two or three things may be called a *bunch*. Instead of using *big* and *little*, the child may use family words: "This is the mommy block" and "This is the baby block." Time (Chapter 5) is one concept that a child takes a long time to grasp. A young

child may use the same word to mean different time periods. The following examples were said by a 3-year-old.

- "*Last night* we went to the beach." (Last summer.)
- "*Last night* I played with Chris." (Yesterday.)
- "*Last night* I went to Kenny's house." (Three weeks ago.)

For this child, *last night* means any time in the past. One by one, he will learn that there are words that refer to times past such as *last summer*, *yesterday*, and *three weeks ago*.

Technology activities can also add to the child's vocabulary. The teacher uses concept words when explaining how to use the programs. Children enjoy working at the computer or with a tablet with friends and will use the concept words to communicate with each other as they work cooperatively to solve the problems presented on the computer screen or tablet.

We have already introduced many concept words, and more will appear in the chapters to come. The prekindergarten child continually learns words. (See **Photo 6-5**.) The next section presents the concept words that most children can use and understand by the time they complete kindergarten. However, the teacher must be cautious in assessing children's actual understanding of these concept words. The use of a concept word does not in itself indicate an understanding of the concept. Children imitate behavior they hear and see. Real understanding can be determined through an assessment interview.

6-2a Concept Words

The words that follow have been discussed in Chapters 3, 4, and 5.

- *One-to-one correspondence:* One, pair, more, each, some, group, bunch, amount
- *Number and counting:* Zero, one, two, three, four, five, six, seven, eight, nine, ten; how many, count, group, one more than, next, number
- *Logic and classifying:* Groups; descriptive words for color, shape, size, materials, pattern, texture, function,

PHOTO 6-5   Children enjoy exploring books.

association, class names, and common features; belong with; goes with; is used with; put with; the same

- *Comparing:* More, less, big, small, large, little, long, short, fat, skinny, heavy, light, fast, slow, cold, hot, thick, thin, wide, narrow, near, far, later, sooner, earlier, older, younger, newer, higher, lower, loud, soft

- *Geometry (shape):* Circle, square, triangle, rectangle, ellipse, rhombus, shape, round, point, square prism (cube), rectangular prism, triangular prism, cylinder, pyramid

- *Geometry (spatial sense):* Where (on, off, on top of, over, under, in, out, into, out of, top, bottom, above, below, in front of, in back of, behind, beside, by, next to, between); *which way* (up, down, forward, backward, around, through, to, from, toward, away from, sideways, across); *distance* (near, far, close to, far from); map, floor plan

- *Parts and wholes:* Part, whole, divide, share, pieces, some, half, one-quarter, one-third

- *Ordering:* First, second, third; big, bigger, biggest; few, fewer, fewest; large, larger, largest; little, littler, littlest; many, more, most; thick, thicker, thickest; thin, thinner, thinnest; last, next, then

- *Measurement of volume, length, weight, and temperature:* Little, big, medium, tiny, large, tall, short, long, far, farther, closer, near, high, higher, thin, wide, deep, cup, pint, quart, gallon, ounces, foot, inch, mile, narrow, measure, hot, cold, warm, cool, thermometer, temperature, pounds

- *Measurement of time and sequence:* Morning, afternoon, evening, night, day, soon, week, tomorrow, yesterday, early, late, a long time ago, once upon a time, minute, second, hour, new, old, already, Easter, Kwanza, Christmas, Passover, Hanukkah, Juneteenth (celebration of the ending of slavery in the United States) Pioneer Days, Cinco de Mayo, birthday, now, year, weekend, clock, calendar, watch, when, time, date, sometimes, then, before, present, soon, while, never, once, sometime, next, always, fast, slow, speed, Monday (and other days of the week), January (and other months of the year), winter, spring, summer, fall

- *Practical:* Money, cash register, penny, dollar, buy, pay, change, cost, check, free, store, map, recipe, measure, cup, tablespoon, teaspoon, boil, simmer, bake, degrees, time, hours, minutes, freeze, chill, refrigerate, pour, mix, separate, add, combine, ingredients

The child can use words before he is presented with them in an adult-guided activity. The child who speaks can become familiar with words and even say them before he understands the concepts they stand for. As children between ages 5 and 7 shift into concrete operations, they gain a conceptual understanding of more concept vocabulary, some of which they have already used and applied in their preoperational way.

- *Primary-level words:* Addition, subtraction, number facts, plus, add, minus, take away, total, sum, equal, difference, amount, altogether, in all, are left, number line, place value, rename, patterns, 1s, 10s, 100s, digit, multiplication, division, equation, times, divide, product, even, odd, fractions, halves, fourths, thirds, wholes, numerator, denominator, hours, minutes, seconds, measure, inches, feet, yards, miles, centimeter, meter, kilometer

6-2b Mathematics, Science, Engineering, and Literacy

Written language learning is also critical during the preschool, kindergarten, and primary years. Children's literature is an important element in the curriculum. (See **Photo 6-6**.) Preschoolers need to engage in prereading and prewriting experiences through exploring quality children's literature, story dictation, and story retelling (Morrow & Gambrell, 2004). By the end of kindergarten, children are expected to be in the beginning stages of becoming readers. The concept of how they should be taught has been a subject of controversy. Wren (2003) summarized the situation as follows: Some educators believe reading should begin with instruction in the rules of printed text (letters, sounds, etc.), whereas others believe reading should develop naturally through experiences with good literature. These two views are referred to as **phonics** versus **whole language**. The **balanced reading** approach, whereby phonics and whole language are used in a balanced fashion, is an attempt to settle the question. However, according to Wren (2003), there is no agreement on what constitutes a balanced reading program. Wren suggests that a truly balanced program should include both phonics and whole language approaches but should be refocused on the needs of children.

© 2016 Cengage Learning®

PHOTO 6-6 Literature experiences can provide a basis for problem solving and concept development.

LESSON PLAN FOR PRESCHOOL AND KINDERGARTEN

PICTURE BOOK MATH: GROWING COLORS

Objective: After reading the book *Growing Colors* and examining a selection of fruits and vegetables, students will be able to identify and categorize the fruits and vegetables and their categories and the colors illustrated.

Materials: The book *Growing Colors*; whichever of the fruits and vegetables illustrated in the book are available; a selection of drawing implements (crayons, markers, etc.) in colors from the book (red, orange, yellow, green, blue, purple, tan, brown, white, black); drawing paper.

Setting: Set the fruits and vegetables on trays on a table in the science or math center.

Activities:

1. Encourage the children to explore the fruits and vegetables and the book and to tell you what they observe.

2. Go through the book with the children, matching the colors in the illustrations to the fruits and vegetable.

3. Ask the children which vegetables and fruits are (orange, red, blue, etc.).

4. Have the children sort the fruits and vegetables into their categories.

5. Give each child a sheet of drawing paper and have him or her select one or more of the fruits and vegetables to draw. Have children dictate information about their picture.

Evaluation: Note which fruits and vegetables the children can identify and which colors they can name.

Follow-up: Cut up the fruits and vegetables into small pieces. (Be sure to check with your school administration before bringing a knife to school!) Have a smelling and tasting party. Make a chart with headings: smell and taste and like or dislike, and list the fruits and vegetables down the left side. Have the children select pieces of food one at a time and place an "X" under their choices of like and dislike. Have them give at least one reason for their choices. Count the like and dislike "Xs" for each fruit and vegetable. Tally the choices. If desired, ask children to display these data in the form of a graph; leave it up to the children to decide what kind of graph to use and how they are going to represent their data.

B. McMillan, Growing Colors. New York: Mulberry Books, 1988.

Digital Download

Literacy instruction has turned away from a strictly whole language philosophy, yet that approach may still be valuable for placing mathematics, science, and engineering concepts and skills in meaningful contexts given the emphasis in those disciplines on communication, reasoning, and making connections. Children can listen to good literature that is relevant to mathematics, science, and engineering and then experiment with writing. They can explain and discuss, record data, and write about their mathematics, science, and engineering explorations. They can keep science, engineering, and mathematics notebooks (Klentschy, 2010). Through these activities, children develop their spoken and written language vocabulary in a meaningful context. Refer to Chapter 1 for applications to problem solving.

6-2c Literature, Reading and Writing, Mathematics, and Science and Engineering

A tremendous growth has been seen in the use of children's literature as a springboard to curriculum integration in mathematics and science instruction. There have long been many books that include mathematics and science concepts (see Appendix B), but there has recently been an increasing number of major journal articles that describe literature-centered activities, books that present thematic activities centered on pieces of literature, and books featuring annotated lists of children's books related to mathematics and science. Examples of such literature have been included in previous chapters, and more can be found in subsequent chapters. The "Further Reading and Resources" section of this chapter includes some references to articles describing mathematics and science studies that focus on children's literature.

An example of an experience that focuses on mathematics, science, and writing is seen in Claudia Wangsgaard's first-grade classroom in Kaysville, Utah, where the students kept math journals in which they wrote about their solutions to math problems. For example, one day's math activities centered on the book *One Gorilla* by Atsuko Morozumi (1993). The narrative starts with one gorilla who wanders through each page; the book includes scenes in the jungle as well as in other locations. Jungle and non-jungle inhabitants are introduced in groups in numerical order up to 10: two butterflies and one gorilla among the flowers, three budgies and one gorilla in the house, four squirrels and one gorilla in the woods, and so on. The students discussed each illustration, locating the gorilla and counting the other creatures.

The class then divided up into groups of four to work cooperatively on the following problem: *How many creatures were there altogether in this story?* The students used a variety of materials: large sheets of blank paper, tubs of Unifix Cubes, pencils, and crayons. Mrs. Wangsgaard circulated from group to group, providing help as needed. When everyone was finished, the class members reassembled. A reporter from each small group explained the group results, summarizing what

was recorded on the group's poster. The groups used several communication procedures, such as drawing the number of Unifix Cubes or making marks to tally the number of creatures. Each group also wrote its procedure. For example:

We did unafick cubes and then we did tally Marcks and there were 56. Jason, Caitlin, Malorie, and Kady

This activity provided for cooperative learning and communication of thinking through concrete representations, drawings, and written and oral language. **Figure 6-4** illustrates how this activity might be included in a planning web for an extended study of jungle inhabitants using the book *One Gorilla* as the focus.

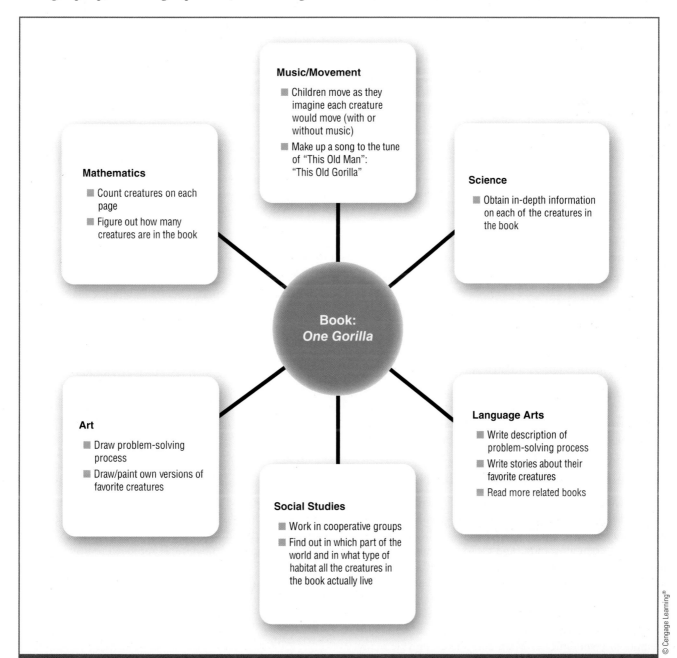

Music/Movement
- Children move as they imagine each creature would move (with or without music)
- Make up a song to the tune of "This Old Man": "This Old Gorilla"

Mathematics
- Count creatures on each page
- Figure out how many creatures are in the book

Science
- Obtain in-depth information on each of the creatures in the book

Book: One Gorilla

Art
- Draw problem-solving process
- Draw/paint own versions of favorite creatures

Language Arts
- Write description of problem-solving process
- Write stories about their favorite creatures
- Read more related books

Social Studies
- Work in cooperative groups
- Find out in which part of the world and in what type of habitat all the creatures in the book actually live

© Cengage Learning®

FIGURE 6-4 An integration across the curriculum, with literature as the focus.

STEM and STEAM inspire integrated projects with science, technology, engineering, mathematics, and reading and writing. In two kindergarten classes, students are investigating various science topics (Patrick, Mantzicopoulos, & Samarapungavan, 2013). Children are reading, writing, and talking science. They read books, which provide information on their topics, and record the results of their science inquiries with drawings and writing in their science notebooks. The children have recorded observations from a nature walk, a comparison of white flowers in plain and in colored water, and salt and beans emerged in water. They express the knowledge they have gained through observation in drawings and some written words.

A study on the effects of a mathematics program on preschoolers resulted in the students making significant gains in oral language skills (Sarama, Lange, Clements, & Wolfe, 2012). Improvement was documented on four oral language subtests: ability to recall key words, use of complex sentences, willingness to reproduce narratives independently, and inferential reasoning. Picture books also provide vehicles for problem solving (Marston, Muir, & Livy, 2013). Marston and colleagues provide examples of the types of math picture books, with illustrations of children's problem-solving work.

Language is critical for both math and science discussions and reports on the results of problem solving and inquiry projects (Cirillo, 2013; Sparks, 2013). Children need opportunities to explain, discuss, and provide arguments for their point of view.

6-2d Helping Children with Special Needs

Speech, Language, and Communication. Allen and Cowdery (2015) describe the importance of speech, language, and communication in child development. The purpose of language is communication, and clearly articulated speech makes for the best verbal communication. Other language systems consist of facial expressions, signs, and gestures. For children with hearing disabilities, American Sign Language can be a helpful augmentation for communicating. In an inclusive classroom, the teacher must attend to all children's attempts to communicate. Math and science provide many opportunities for communication, as indicated in this chapter. Teachers should be alert for children who may need extra help in the areas of speech and language. Allen and Cowdery

point out that, for young ELLs, drill and practice is not as effective as naturally occurring language experience. Books can be an important language mediator. Through hands-on, inquiry-based methods children are learning English. For example, in Sonoma Valley, California, ELL students are learning English through science (Fleming, 2013). Their natural curiosity motivates them to learn the science vocabulary.

Maintaining a Multicultural Approach to Language with Books. Whiteford (2009/2010) responds to the question: "Is mathematics a universal language?" Each culture has its own way of teaching mathematics. Children who move to the United States from another country, especially from Asia or Africa, may have learned a different numeric and counting system. Problem solving may not have been emphasized, and procedures may be different. Teachers need to be culturally responsive to their students.

Zaslavsky (1996) points out that literature is a means for participating in lives and cultures, both past and present, of people all over the world. Many picture books are available in translations from English to other languages and vice versa. A simple counting book is *¿Cuantos animals hay?* by Brian Wildsmith (1997). For Spanish speakers, this book supports their first language; for English speakers, there is the joy of learning another language. *Eight Animales on the Town (Ocho Animales)* by Susan M. Elya (2000) presents number names, animal names, and animal foods in English and Spanish. *We All Went on a Safari*, by Laurie Krebs and Julia Cairns (2003), takes the reader on a counting journey through Tanzania. Children of African heritage see the respect given to their culture, and all children learn some Tanzanian vocabulary, customs, and geography. Like the resources listed at the end of this chapter, many math and science literacy resources support a multicultural approach to instruction.

SUMMARY

6-1 National Standards Support Stem and Steam

The Common Core Standards for Mathematics (National Governors Association, 2010) and New Generation science standards (NGSS Lead States, 2013) focus on content areas skills, understandings, and processes that can be applied across the curriculum, particularly when combined with engineering, technology, and the arts as STEM and STEAM (see Chapter 1).

Play and Learning. Dramatic play and thematic units and projects provide math, science, and social studies experiences that afford children an opportunity to apply concepts and skills. They can predict, observe, and investigate as they explore these areas. As children play home, store, and service roles, they match, count, classify, compare, measure, and use spatial relations concepts and number symbols. They also practice the exchange of money for goods and services. Through dramatic play, they try out grown-up roles and activities.

Thematic Projects. Through thematic units and projects, mathematics and science can be integrated with other content areas. The thematic experiences provide real-life connections for abstract concepts. For teachers, these activities offer valuable opportunities for naturalistic and informal instruction as well as time to observe children and assess their ability to use concepts in everyday situations.

Focus on Nature. Children need time to explore the outdoors. This focus on nature is increasing.

6-2 Language, Literacy, and Concept Formation

As children learn math and science and engineering concepts and skills, they also add many words to their vocabularies. Math, science, and engineering have a language that is basic to their content and activities. Language is learned through naturalistic, informal, and adult-guided activities. Technology activities are excellent for promoting communication among children.

Mathematics, Science, Engineering, and Literacy. The whole language philosophy of literacy learning fits well with the emphasis in mathematics, science, and engineering on processes of problem solving, representation, communication, reasoning and proof, and making connections. The current focus of reading instruction is a balanced whole language–phonics approach. Books are a rich source of conceptual language that matches a child's growing understanding. They can also support a multicultural approach to instruction. For young children, books open the door to reading.

FURTHER READING AND RESOURCES

Ashbrook, P. (2014). Becoming attuned to sound. *Science and Children*, *51*(6), 26–27.

Community Playthings. (2010). *The wisdom of nature*. Ulster Park, NY: Author.

Integration

Krogh, S., & Morehouse, P. J. (2007). *The early childhood curriculum: Inquiry learning through integration.* New York: McGraw-Hill.

Markham, T. (2014). *How to reinvent project-based learning to be more meaningful.* www.thommarkham.com.

Miller, A. (2014, April 23). PBL and STEAM education: A natural fit. *Edutopia.* www.edutopia.org.

Yagi, S., & Olson, M. (2007). Supermarket math: K–2. *Teaching Children Mathematics*, *13*(7), 376.

Cooking and Food

Cook, D. (2006). *Family fun cooking with kids.* Burbank /Glendale, CA: Disney.

Cooking with Kids. A parent helper. www.pbs.org/parents /parenthelpers/cooking.html.

Wilburne, J. (2010). Grocery shopping math. *Teaching Children Mathematics*, *17*(1), 20–21.

Literacy

Ansberry, K., & Morgan, E., (2010). *Picture-perfect science lessons using children's books to guide inquiry, 3–6.* and (2012). More picture perfect science lessons, and (2013) Even more picture perfect science lessons. Arlington, VA: NSTA Press.

Bay-Williams, J. M., & Livers, S. (2009). Supporting math vocabulary acquisition. *Teaching Children Mathematics*, *16*(4), 238–245.

Fulwiler, B. R. (2011). *Writing in science in action.* Portsmouth, NH: Heinemann.

Royce, C. A., Morgan, E., & Ansberry, K. (2012). *Teaching science through trade books.* Arlington, VA: NSTA Press.

Tyminski, A. M., Richardson, S. L., & Winarski, E. (2010). Enhancing think-pair-share. *Teaching Children Mathematics*, *16*(8), 451–455.

Wheeler-Toppen, J. (Ed). (2011). *Science the "write" way.* Arlington, VA: NSTA Press.

Wilburne, J. M., Keat, J. B., & Napoli, M. (2011). *Cowboys count, monkeys measure, and princesses problem solve: Building early math skills through storybooks.* Baltimore, MD: Brookes.

REFERENCES

Allen, K. E., & Cowdery, G. E. (2015). *The exceptional child: Inclusion in early childhood education*, 8th ed. Cengage Learning.

Ashbrook, P. (2009). Safe smelling. *Science and Children*, *47*(2), 19–20.

Ashcroft, P. (2013). The STEM of inquiry. *Science & Children*, *51*(2), 30–31.

Attoun, M. (2013, September 1–7). Reading, writing & farming. *American Profile*, 4, 6.

Bosse, S., Jacobs, G., & Anderson-Topete, T. L. (2013). Science in the air. In A. Shillady (Ed.), *Exploring Science* (pp. 5–10). Washington, DC: National Association for the Education of Young Children.

Burpee Home Gardens. (2011). "I can grow": Bean beginnings. Ball Horticultural Co. and W. Atlee Burpee Company. www.burpeehomegardens.com.

Butterworth, S., & Lo Cicero, A. M. (2001). Storytelling: Building a mathematics curriculum from the culture of the child. *Teaching Children Mathematics, 7*(7), 396–399.

Chayka, K. (2012, September 21). *The greatest food still lifes in art history.* http://flavorwire.com.

Cirillo, M. (2013). *What does research say the benefits of discussion in mathematics class are? Brief.* NCTM (pdf). www.nctm.org.

Cohen, E. (2014). Spring has sprung: The sixth-annual White House garden planting. www.whitehouse.gov/blog/2014/04/03/spring-has-sprung-sixth-annual-white-house-garden-planting.

DeVries, R., & Sales, C. (2011). *Ramps & pathways.* Washington, DC: National Association for the Education of Young Children.

Edwards, C., Gandini, L., & Forman, G. (Eds.). (1998). *The hundred languages of children: The Reggio Emilia approach—Advanced reflections.* Greenwich, CT: Ablex.

Eisenhauer, M. J., & Feikes, D. (2009). Dolls, blocks, and puzzles: Playing with mathematical understandings. *Young Children, 64*(3), 18–24.

Elya, S. M. (2000). *Eight animals on the town.* New York: Penguin.

Fleming, N. (2013, March 27). Partnership blends science and English proficiency. *Education Week.* www.edweek.org.

Geist, K., & Geist, E. A. (2008). Do re mi, 1-2-3: That's how easy math can be. *Young Children, 63*(2), 20–25.

Heitin, L. (2013, March 13). In common core, teachers see interdisciplinary opportunities. *Education Week Teacher.* www.edweek.org.

Helm, J. H. (2013). *Project work and nature.* www.communityplaythings.com.

Helm, J. H., & Katz, L. G. (2011). *Young investigators: The project approach in the early years,* 2nd ed. New York: Teachers College Press & Washington, DC: National Association for the Education of Young Children.

Isbell, R. (1995). *The complete learning center book.* Beltsville, MD: Gryphon House.

Jolly, A. (November 3, 2013). Rethinking arts and STEM, *Middle Web Blog.* www.middleweb.com.

Katz, L. G. (Fall, 2010). STEM in the early years. *SEED papers.* http://ecrp.uiuc.edu.

Katz, L. G., & Chard, S. C. (2000). *Engaging children's minds: The project approach.* Westport, CT: Greenwood Publishing.

Klentschy, M. (2010). Making meaning with notebooks. *Science and Children, 48*(3), 8–9.

Koestler, C., Felton, M. D., Bieda, K. N., & Otten, S. (2013). *Connecting the NCTM process standards & the CCM practices.* Reston, VA: National Council of Teachers of Mathematics.

Krebs, L., & Cairns, J. (2003). *We all went on a safari: A counting journey through Tanzania.* Cambridge, MA: Barefoot Books.

Marston, J. L., Muir, T., & Livy, S. (2013). Can we really count on Frank? *Teaching Children Mathematics, 19*(7), 440–448.

Moomaw, S., & Davis, J. A. (2013). STEM comes to preschool. Science in the air. In A. Shillady (Ed.), *Exploring Science* (pp. 17–22). Washington, DC: National Association for the Education of Young Children.

Morozumi, A. (1993). *One Gorilla.* New York: Farrar, Straus & Giroux.

Morrow, L. M., & Gambrell, L. B. (2004). *Using children's literature in preschool.* Newark, DE: International Reading Association.

NGSS Lead States. (2013). *Next Generation Science Standards: For states, by states.* Washington DC: National Academies Press.

National Council of Teachers of Mathematics (NCTM). (2000). *Principles and standards for school mathematics.* Reston, VA: Author.

National Governors Association Center for Best Practices, Council of Chief State School Officers. (2010). *Common Core State Standards for Mathematics.* Washington, DC: Author. www.corestandards.org.

National Research Council (NRC). (2012) *Framework for K–12 science education.* Washington, DC: National Academies Press.

Ogu, U., & Schmidt, S. R. (2013). Kindergartners investigate rocks and sand: Addressing multiple learning styles through an inquiry-based approach. Science in the air. In A. Shillady (Ed.), *Exploring Science* (pp. 61–67). Washington, DC: National Association for the Education of Young Children.

Owens, K. (2008). *An integrated approach for young students.* www.nctm.org/resources.

Owings, S., & Merino, B. (2010). Dig deeply. *Science and Children, 48*(1), 32–37.

Patrick, H., Mantzicopoulos, P., & Samarapungaven, A. (2013). Integrating science inquiry with reading and writing in kindergarten. In A. Shillady (Ed.), *Exploring*

Science, Washington, DC: National Association for the Education of Young Children, pp. 48–54.

Plenda, M. (2013, October 6). Into the woods. *Boston Globe* Magazine. www.bostonglobe.com/magazine/2013/10/05/nature-preschools-…etting-kids-moving-and-learning/VmyOnPeCOeVhxV4xzncPAO/story.html.

Pollman, M. J. (2010). *Blocks and beyond.* Baltimore, MD: Brookes.

Prather, S. (2013, July 30). *Columbia Heights adds gardening teacher to help with science, math.* Minneapolis StarTribune. www.startribune.com.

Sarama, J., Lange, A. A., Clements, D. H., & Wolfe, C .B. (2012). The impacts of an early mathematics curriculum on oral language and literacy. *Early Childhood Research Quarterly, 27,* 489–502.

Shaffer, L. F., Hall, E., &Lynch, M. (2013). Toddlers scientific explorations: Encounters with insects. Science in the air. In A. Shillady (Ed.), *Exploring Science* (pp. 11–16). Washington, DC: National Association for the Education of Young Children.

Sibley, A., & Kurz, T. L. (2013). Exploring nature through mathematics. *Teaching Children Mathematics, 20*(1), 16–17.

Sparks, S. D. (2013, May 21). Students can learn by explaining, studies say. *Education Week.* www.edweek.org.

Starbuck, S. (2012). *Why garden?* www.communityplaythings.com/resources/articles/2012/why-garden.

STEM to STEAM. (n.d.). Retrieved September 11, 2013, from www.risd.edu/about/stem_to_steam/.

Stoll, J., Hamilton, A. Y., Oxley, E., Eastman, A. M., & Brent, R. (2013). Young thinkers in motion: Problem solving and physics in preschool. Science in the air. In A. Shillady (Ed.), *Exploring Science* (pp. 29–35). Washington, DC: National Association for the Education of Young Children.

Uhlig, K. (2013, September 11). Jefferson Elementary garden grows vegetables—and students' minds (with video). *Wausau Daily Herald.* www.wausaudailyherald.com.

Whiteford, T. (2009/2010). Is mathematics a universal language? *Teaching Children Mathematics, 16*(5), 276–283.

Whitin, D. J., & Piwko, M. (2008). Mathematics and poetry. The right connectiion. *Young Children. 63*(2), 34–39.

Wildsmith, B. (1997). ¿*Cuantos animales hay?* New York: Star Bright Books.

Williams, L. (2013, January 14). Should STEM become STEAM? *District Administration Magazine.* www.districtadministration.com.

Winters, J., Ring, T., & Burriss, K. (2010). Cultivating math and science in a school garden. *Childhood Education, 86*(4), 248-G.

Wren, S. (2003). *What does a "balanced approach" to reading instruction mean?* www.balancedreading.com.

Zaslavsky, C. (1996). *The multicultural math classroom.* Portsmouth, NH: Heinemann.

CHAPTER 7

TRANSITIONING FROM PRESCHOOL
TO KINDERGARTEN, TO PRIMARY

OBJECTIVES

After reading this chapter, you should be able to:

7-1 Assess, plan, teach, and evaluate number symbol concepts in line with national standards.

7-2 Assess, plan, teach, and evaluate groups and number symbols in line with national standards.

7-3 Assess, plan, and teach 13 higher-level concepts included in this chapter, in line with national standards.

7-4 Plan and teach science investigations in line with national standards.

STANDARDS ADDRESSED IN THIS CHAPTER

NAEYC Professional Preparation Standards

5. Use content knowledge to build meaningful curriculum.

5a. Understand content knowledge and resources in language, math, and science.

5c. Design, implement, and evaluate developmentally meaningful and challenging curriculum for each child.

DAP Guidelines

2C. Know desired program goals.

3C. Use the curriculum framework to ensure there is attention to important learning goals.

Common Core State Standards for Math

K.CC   Know number names and count sequence.

K.CC.1   Count to 100 by 1s and by 10s.

K.CC.2   Count forward beginning from a given number within the known sequence.

K.CC.3   Write numbers from 0 to 20.

K.OA   Understand addition and subtraction.

K.NBT   Work with numbers 11–19 to gain foundation for place value.

Next Generation Science Standards

K-LS1-1   Scientists look for patterns and order when making observations about the world.

K-PS2-1   Scientists use different ways to study the world.

K-SS3-1   Use a model to represent relationships.

7-1 NUMBER SYMBOLS AND CONCEPTS: STANDARDS AND EXPLANATIONS

According to the Common Core State Standards for Mathematics (2010), by the end of kindergarten children should know the number names and count sequence and be able to compare two numbers between 1 and 20 presented as written numerals. Number symbols are called **numerals**. Each numeral represents an amount and acts as a shorthand for recording *how many*. The young child sees numerals all around (**Figure 7-1**). He has some idea of what they are before he can understand and use them. He sees that there are numerals on his house, the phone, the clock, and the car license plate. He may have one or more counting books. He may watch a children's TV program where numeral recognition is taught. Sometime between the ages of 2 and 5, a child learns to name the numerals from 0 to 10. However, the child is usually 4 years old or older when he begins to understand that each numeral stands for a group of things of a certain amount that is always the same. He may be able to tell the name of the symbol *3* and count three objects, but he may not realize that the *3* can stand for the three objects or understand the **cardinal meaning** of three. This is illustrated in **Figure 7-2**. Dougherty (2010) describes the essential understandings that adults should have regarding number and numeration in order to teach prekindergarten through second grade.

Spending time on drills with numerals can be confusing for a child before she has had many concrete experiences with basic math concepts. During the pre-primary period, most experiences with numerals should be naturalistic and informal.

7-1a The Number Symbol Skills

Young children acquire six number symbol skills during the preoperational period.

- They learn to recognize and say the name of each numeral.

FIGURE 7-1 Numerals are everywhere in the environment.

© Cengage Learning®

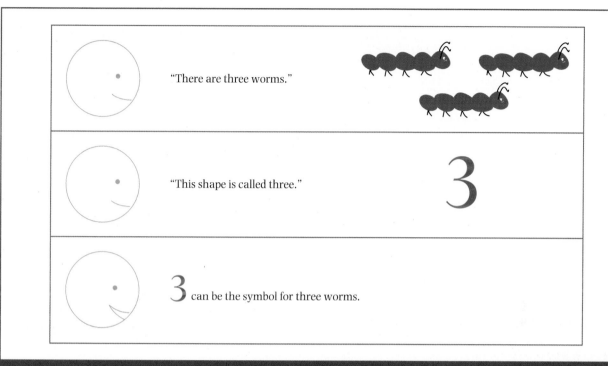

FIGURE 7-2 The child counts the objects, learns the symbol, and realizes that the symbol can represent the group.

- They learn to place the numerals in order: 0-1-2-3-4-5-6-7-8-9-10.

- They learn to associate numerals with groups: *1* goes with one thing.

- They learn that each numeral in order stands for one more than the numeral that comes before it (i.e., 2 is one more than 1, 3 is one more than 2, etc.).

- They learn to match each numeral to any group of the size that the numeral stands for and to make groups that match numerals.

- They learn to reproduce (write) numerals.

The first four skills are included early in this chapter. The last two are topics covered in the second half of this chapter.

Technology for Young Children

Math and Media in Preschool

In 2012, researchers at EDC and SRI developed a math and media curriculum for preschool that integrated media with hands-on activities such as digital videos and interactive games (Vidiksis, Jo, Hubert, & Llorente, 2013). Previous research suggested that technology could have positive effects on young children's learning if it was developmentally appropriate, provided professional development and support for the teachers, and was integrated into the classroom and the curriculum. The curriculum focused on counting, recognizing numbers and subitizing, recognizing and composing shapes, and patterning. The teacher's guide explained how to introduce the skills and concepts, model play, and engage the students. To begin a lesson, the teachers and students co-viewed a video that explained the current skill. Children would then move on to hands-on activities and then media activities. The classroom was supplied with an interactive whiteboard, a mini PC computer, three laptops with wireless mikes and headphones to be used in the laptop center, wireless routers, and Bluetooth adaptors for each laptop. Hands-on materials were also supplied. Teachers received professional development and coaching support.

R. Vidiksis, Y. Jo, N. Hubert, & C. Llorente, All hands on tech: Math and media in the preschool Classroom, 2013.

7-1b Pre-Assessment

The teacher should observe whether the child shows an interest in numerals. Does she repeat the names she hears on television? Does she point out and name numerals in the environment? Does she use self-correcting materials? (These materials are described in the Informal Activities sections of this chapter.) What does she do when she uses these materials? Individual interviews would include the types of tasks that follow.

SAMPLE ASSESSMENT TASK

4J   PREOPERATIONAL AGES 3–6

SYMBOLS, RECOGNITION: CHAPTER 7

METHOD Interview.

SKILL Child is able to recognize numerals 0 to 10 presented in sequence.

MATERIALS 5 × 8-inch cards with one numeral from 0 to 10 written on each.

PROCEDURE Starting with 0, show the child each card in numerical order

from 0 to 10. **"What is this? Tell me the name of this."**

EVALUATION Note whether the child uses numeral names correctly, indicating he knows the kinds of words associated with the symbols. Note which numerals he can label correctly.

INSTRUCTIONAL RESOURCE
R. Charlesworth, *Math and Science for Young Children*, 8th ed., San Francisco, CA: Cengage Learning, 2016.

Digital Download

SAMPLE ASSESSMENT TASK

6J   PREOPERATIONAL AGES 5 AND OLDER

SYMBOLS, ONE MORE THAN: CHAPTER 7

METHOD Interview.

SKILL Child is able to identify numerals that are "one more than."

MATERIALS 5 × 8-inch cards with one numeral from 0 to 10 written on each.

PROCEDURE Place the numeral cards in front of the child in order from 0 to 10.

Say, "Tell me which numeral means one more than two. Which numeral means one more than seven? Which numeral means one more than four?" (If the child answers these, then try *less than*.)

EVALUATION Note whether the child is able to answer correctly.

INSTRUCTIONAL RESOURCE
R. Charlesworth, *Math and Science for Young Children*, 8th ed., San Francisco, CA: Cengage Learning, 2016.

Digital Download

SAMPLE ASSESSMENT TASK

5L   PREOPERATIONAL AGES 4–6

SYMBOLS, SEQUENCING: CHAPTER 7

METHOD Interview.

SKILL Child is able to sequence numerals from 0 to 10.

MATERIALS 5 × 8-inch cards with one numeral from 0 to 10 written on each.

PROCEDURE Place all the cards, in random order, in front of the child,

and tell the child to put them in order. Ask, "Which comes first? Next? Next?"

EVALUATION Note whether the child seems to understand that numerals belong in a fixed sequence. Note how many are placed in the

correct order and which, if any, are labeled.

INSTRUCTIONAL RESOURCE
R. Charlesworth, *Math and Science for Young Children*, 8th ed., San Francisco, CA: Cengage Learning, 2016.

Digital Download

7-1c Activities

Number-symbol activities include naturalistic, informal and adult-guided instruction.

Naturalistic Activities. As the young child observes her environment, she sees numerals around her (**Photo 7-1**). She sees them on clocks, phones, houses, books, food containers, TV programs, money, calendars, thermometers, rulers, measuring cups, license plates, and on many other objects in

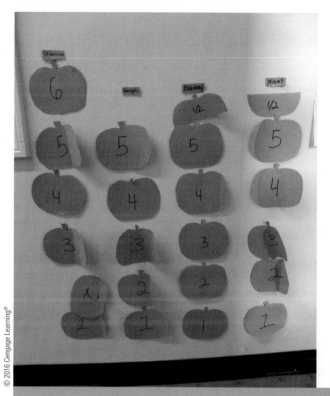 

PHOTO 7-1 Numerals in the environment provide opportunities for naturalistic and informal experiences.

many places. She hears people say number names, as in the following examples:

- "My phone number is 622-7732."
- "My house number is 1423."
- "My age is 6."
- "I have a five-dollar bill."
- "The temperature is 78 degrees."
- "Get a 5-pound bag of rabbit food."
- "We had 3 inches of rain today."
- "This pitcher holds 8 cups of juice."

Usually children start using the names of the number symbols before they actually match them with the symbols.

- Tanya and Juanita are ready to take off in their spaceship. Juanita does the countdown: "Ten, nine, eight, three, one, blast off!"
- Tim asks Ms. Moore to write the number 7 on a sign for his racecar.
- Ako notices that the thermometer has numbers written on it.
- Becca is playing house. She takes the toy cell phone and enters numerals: "One-six-two. Hello, dear, will you please stop at the store and buy a loaf of bread?"
- "How old are you, Pete?" "I'm 6," answers 2-year-old Pete.
- "One, two, three. I have three dolls."

- Tanya is playing house. She looks up at the clock. "Eight o'clock and time for bed," she tells her doll. (The clock actually says 9:30 a.m.)

Children begin to learn number symbols as they look and listen and then, in their play, imitate what they have seen and heard.

Informal Activities. During the preoperational period, most school activities with numerals should be informal. Experimentation and practice in perception with sight and touch are most important. Children's activities with self-correcting manipulative materials provide these experiences. **Self-correcting materials** are those the child can use by trial and error to solve a problem without adult's assistance. The material is made in such a way that it can be used successfully with very little help. **Manipulative materials** are things that have parts and pieces that the child can pick up and move in order to solve the problems that the materials present. The teacher observes the child as she works. He notes whether the child works in an organized way and whether she sticks with the material until she has finished the task.

Four basic types of self-correcting manipulative math materials can be used for informal activities. The teacher can make or buy these materials. The four basic groups of materials include (1) those that teach discrimination and matching, (2) those that teach sequence (or order), (3) those that give practice in association of symbols with groups, and (4) those that combine association of symbols and groups with sequence. Examples of each type are illustrated in **Figure 7-3** through Figure 7-6.

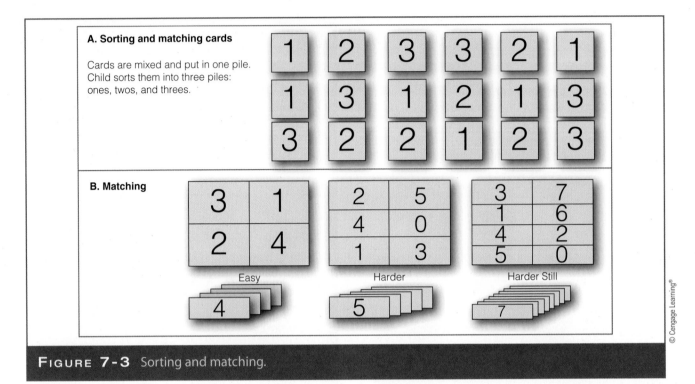

FIGURE 7-3 Sorting and matching.

The child can learn to discriminate one numeral from the other by sorting packs of numeral cards. He can also learn which numerals are the same as those he matches. Another type of material that serves this purpose is a lotto-type game. The child has a large card divided equally into four or more parts. He must match individual numeral cards to each numeral on the big card. These materials are shown in Figure 7-3 (A and B). He can also experiment with felt, plastic, magnetic, wooden, rubber, and cardboard numerals.

Many materials teach sequence or order. These may be set up so that parts can only be put together in such a way that, when the child is done, she sees that the numerals are in order in front of her, such as with Number Sequencing Puzzles from Lakeshore Learning Materials. The teacher can also teach sequence using a number line or number stepping-stones. Examples are the Step-by-Step Number Line from Hatch and the Didax Giant Walk-on Number Line, which let the child walk from one numeral to the next in order (**Figure 7-4A**). The teacher could set out numerals on the

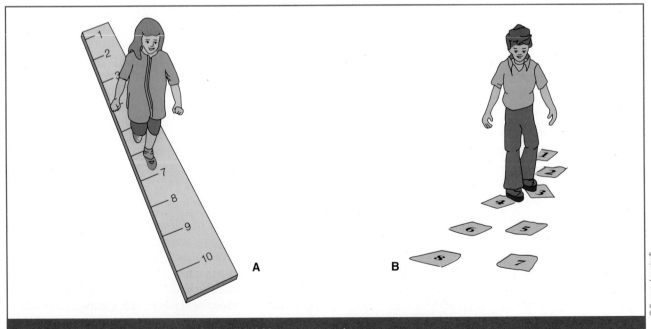

FIGURE 7-4 Materials that help a child learn numeral sequence.

floor that the child must step on in order (Figure 7-4B). There are also number sequence wooden inset puzzles (such as Hatch Number Puzzle and Animal Number Puzzles).

The hand calculator lends itself to informal exploration of numerals. First, show the students how to turn the calculator on and off. Tell them to watch the display window and then turn on the calculator. A 0 will appear first. Explain to the children that when they first turn on their calculators, a 0 will always appear. Then ask them to turn on their calculators and tell you what they see in the window. Have them practice turning their calculators on and off until you are sure they all understand this operation. Next, tell the children to press 1. Ask them what they see in the window. Note whether they tell you they see the same number. Next, have them press 2. A 2 will appear in the window next to the 1. Show them that they just need to press the C key to erase. Then let them explore and discover on their own. Help them by answering their questions and posing questions to them, such as, "What will happen if …?"

The teacher can purchase many materials that help the child associate each numeral with the group that goes with it. He could place large posters on the bulletin board (such as those found on the abcteach website), which give a visual association (**Figure 7-5A**). Children can see and touch numerals on textured cards, for example, Constructive Playthings Tactile Number Cards. The teacher could make numeral cards using sandpaper for the sets of dots and for the numerals (Figure 7-5B). Other materials require the child to use visual and motor coordination. She may have to match puzzle-like pieces (such as Caterpillar Number Match from Constructive Playthings) or match numeral pieces with groups (Figure 7-5C). She may put pegs in holes (using, e.g., Peg-It Number Boards from Constructive Playthings, Figure 7-5D). Unifix 1–10 Stair requires the same type of activity. The teacher could make cards that have numerals and dots the size of buttons or other counters. The child then places a counter on each dot (Figure 7-5E).

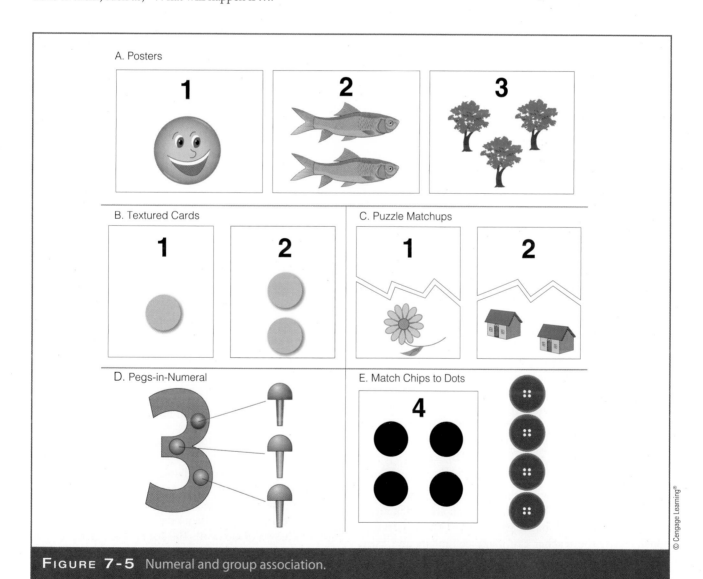

FIGURE 7-5 Numeral and group association.

© Cengage Learning®

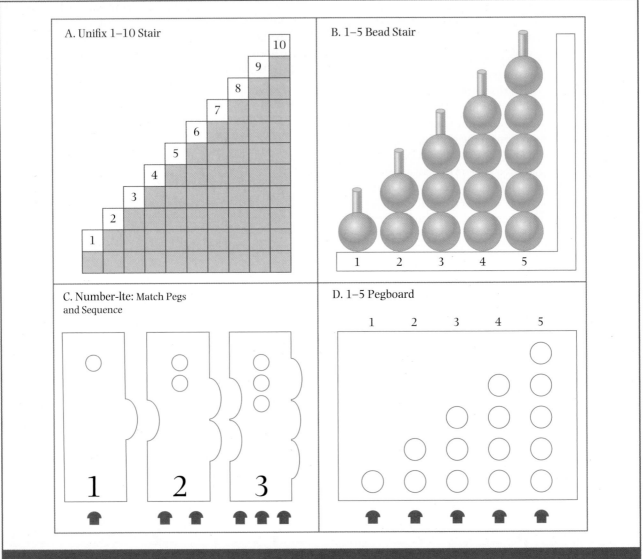

FIGURE 7-6 Sequence and association.

Materials that give the child experience with sequence and association at the same time are also available. Examples of these materials are shown in **Figure 7-6**. The basis of these materials is that the numerals are in a fixed order, and the child adds some sort of counter that can be placed only in the right amount. Unifix stairs are stuck together and can only be filled by the right amount (Figure 7-6A). Other materials illustrated are counters on rods (Figure 7-6B), sequence pegs in holes (Figure 7-6C), and a 1–5 pegboard (Figure 7-6D).

The teacher's role with these materials is to show the child how they can be used, and then step back and watch. After the child has learned to use the materials independently, the teacher can make comments and ask questions.

- "How many pegs are on this one?"

- "Can you tell me the name of each numeral?"

- "You put in the four pegs that go with that numeral 4."

- "How many beads are there here (pointing to stack of one)?" "How many here (pointing to stack of two, and so on)?"

- "Good, you separated all the numerals into piles. Here are all the 1s, and here are all the 2s."

The teacher could also introduce numerals informally as part of daily counting activities. For example, the class could keep track of the first 100 days of school (see Chapter 3). Children could make a 100-number line around the room. They add the appropriate numeral each day to the number line and add one straw to a collection. They keep adding a straw each day until they have a group of 10. The 10s are then grouped until there are 100. Each day the students agree on the current total. The strip should be wide enough so that large numerals (ones the students can easily see) can be glued or written on it.

The children could draw special symbols representing special days, such as birthdays, Halloween, Thanksgiving,

© 2016 Cengage Learning®

PHOTO 7-2 This calendar shows number sequence and is organized with an A-B pattern.

DAP naeyc

and so on, below the appropriate numeral on the line. The number line then serves as a timeline recording the class history. A weekly or monthly calendar may also be placed on the bulletin board next to the 100-days display. Calendars were introduced in Chapter 5. (See **Photo 7-2**)

1	2	3	4	5	6	7	8	9	10

Through this informal use of materials, most children will learn to recognize and say the name of each numeral, place the numerals in order, see that each numeral stands for one more than the one before it, and associate numerals with amounts. However, some children will need the adult-guided activities described next.

Numeral	Amount in Group
1	X
2	XX
3	XXX
4	XXXX
5	XXXXX
6	XXXXXX
7	XXXXXXX
8	XXXXXXXX
9	XXXXXXXXX
10	XXXXXXXXXX

ACTIVITIES

NUMERALS: RECOGNITION

Objective: To learn the names of the number symbols.

Materials: Write the numerals from 0 to 10 on cards.

Naturalistic and informal activities: Place the cards in the math center for the children to explore. Note whether children label and/or sequence the numerals or in any way demonstrate knowledge of the symbols and what they mean. Ask questions such as **"What are those? Do they have names?"**

Adult-guided activity: This is an activity that a child who can name all the numbers could do with a child who needs help. Show the numerals one at a time, in order, and say, "This numeral is called [number name]. Let's say it together: [number name]." Do this for each numeral. After number 10, say, **"I'll hold the cards up one at a time. You name the numeral."** Go through once. Five minutes at a time should be enough.

Follow-up: Give the child a set of cards to review on her own.

Digital Download

ACTIVITIES

NUMERALS: SEQUENCE AND ONE MORE THAN

Objective: To learn the sequence of numerals from 0 to 10.

Materials: Flannelboard or magnet board, felt or magnet numerals, felt or magnet shapes (such as felt primary cutouts or magnetic geometric shapes).

Naturalistic and informal activities: Place the numerals and shapes in the math center for the children to explore.

Note whether the children make groups and place numerals next to the groups. Ask questions such as, **"How many does this numeral mean?" "Why does this numeral go next to this group?" "Tell me about your groups."**

Adult-guided activity: Put the *0* up first, at the upper left-hand corner of the board. **"What is this numeral called?"**

If the child cannot tell you, say, "**This is called** *zero*." Put the *1* numeral up next, to the right of the *0*. "**What is this numeral called?**" If the child cannot tell you, say, "**This is 1. Say it with me: one.**" Continue to go across until the child does not know two numerals in a row. Then, go back to the beginning of the row. "**Tell me the name of this numeral. Yes, zero. What is the name of the next one? Yes, it is one. So I will put one rabbit here.**" Put one rabbit under the 1. "**The next numeral is one more than one. What is it called?**" After the child says "two" on his own or with your help, let him pick out two shapes to put on the board under the *2*. Keep going across until you have done the same with each numeral he knows, plus two that he does not know.

Follow-up: Have the child set up the sequence. If he has trouble, ask, "**What comes next? What is one more than _____?**" Leave the board and the numerals and shapes out during playtime. Encourage the children who know how to do this activity to work with a child who does not.

ACTIVITIES

NUMERALS: RECOGNITION, SEQUENCE, ASSOCIATION WITH GROUPS, ONE MORE THAN

Objective: To help the child to integrate the concepts of association with groups and *one more than* while learning the numeral names and sequence.

Materials: Cards with numerals from 0 to 10 and cards with numerals and groups from 0 to 10.

Naturalistic and informal activities: Place the cards in the math center for the children to explore. Note whether the children make matches and/or sequences. Ask, "**Can you tell me about what you are doing with the cards?**"

Adult-guided activities:

1. "I'm going to put down some cards. Each one has a numeral on it. They go up to number 10. Say the names with me if you know them."

2. "Here is another set of cards with numerals." Give the cards with numerals and groups to the child. "Match these up with the other cards. Let's say the names as you match."

Follow-up: Let the child do this activity on her own. Encourage her to use the self-correcting materials also.

Adult-Guided Activities. By the time young children finish kindergarten, they should be able to do the following activities:

- Recognize the numerals from 0 to 10 or more.

- Place the numerals from 0 to 10 or more in order.

- Know that each numeral represents a group one larger than the numeral before (and one less than the one that comes next).

- Know that each numeral represents a group of things.

Children may not always match the right numeral to the correct amount, but they will know that there is such a relationship. The 5-year-old child who cannot do one or more of the tasks listed needs some adult-guided scaffolding.

Most of the resources described in Chapter 3 include numeral recognition. Number symbols can also be incorporated in other content areas (**Figure 7-7**).

7-1d Helping Children with Special Needs

Cristina Gillanders (2007) examined the factors that enabled an English-speaking prekindergarten teacher to successfully teach Latino English language learners (ELLs).

First and foremost were the teacher's efforts to develop a positive relationship with the students. The teacher took the time to learn some Spanish. Her use of Spanish, however meager, in the classroom gave the Latino children social status, and they were then accepted by the English-speaking students as play partners. The teacher's experience as a second-language learner gave her empathy for the Latino students' struggles with learning English. Providing one-to-one attention and a consistent routine helped the Latino children feel comfortable. The teacher spoke some Spanish in the classroom and included Spanish materials in her program. Some of the English-speaking children became enthralled with the bilingual songs and videotapes included in the program, and the teacher enlisted the help of the Latino children in translations. Spanish became valued in the classroom and supported cross-language cooperative play. How does this example relate to mathematics and science? In any classroom, the quality of the social/emotional climate is important. In math and science, presenting some concepts using Spanish or other primary language vocabulary can make ELL children feel more comfortable because their primary language and culture become a valued part of the classroom culture.

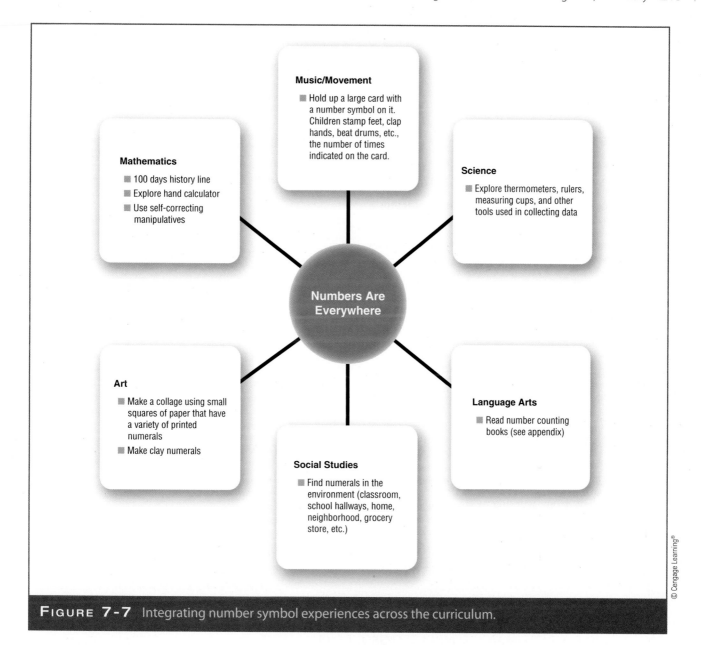

Mathematics
- 100 days history line
- Explore hand calculator
- Use self-correcting manipulatives

Music/Movement
- Hold up a large card with a number symbol on it. Children stamp feet, clap hands, beat drums, etc., the number of times indicated on the card.

Science
- Explore thermometers, rulers, measuring cups, and other tools used in collecting data

Numbers Are Everywhere

Art
- Make a collage using small squares of paper that have a variety of printed numerals
- Make clay numerals

Social Studies
- Find numerals in the environment (classroom, school hallways, home, neighborhood, grocery store, etc.)

Language Arts
- Read number counting books (see appendix)

© Cengage Learning®

FIGURE 7-7 Integrating number symbol experiences across the curriculum.

7-1e Post-Evaluation

The teacher may question the children as they work with the self-correcting materials. The teacher should note which numerals each child can name and whether the child names them in sequence. He may interview the child individually, using the assessment questions in this chapter and in Appendix A.

COMMON CORE STATE STANDARDS

7-2 GROUPS AND SYMBOLS: STANDARDS AND EXPLANATIONS

The activities in this part of Chapter 7 build on many of the ideas and skills presented in earlier chapters: matching, numbers and counting, groups and classifying, comparing,

ordering, and symbols. The Common Core State Standards for Math (2010) expectations for the end of kindergarten focus on several number skills and understandings in the area of counting and cardinality that relate to symbols and groups:

- Write numbers from 0 to 20 and represent corresponding groups of objects.

- Understand that each number name refers to a quantity that is one larger than the previous number.

- Compare numbers between 1 and 10 presented as written numerals.

The experiences in this part of the chapter are most meaningful to the child who can already do the following activities:

- Match things in one-to-one correspondence and match groups of things one to one.

- Recognize groups of one to four without counting, and count groups of up to at least 10 things accurately.

- Divide large groups into smaller groups, and compare groups of different amounts.

- Place groups containing different amounts in order from least to most.

- Name each of the numerals from 0 to 10.

- Recognize each of the numerals from 0 to 10.

- Be able to place each of the numerals in order from 0 to 10.

- Understand that each numeral stands for a certain number of things.

- Understand that each numeral stands for a group of things containing one more than the numeral before it and one less than the numeral after it

When the child has reached the objectives in the preceding list, she can then learn to do the following activities:

- *Match a symbol to a group.* If she is given a set of four items, she can pick out or write the numeral 4 as the one that goes with that group.

- *Match a group to a symbol.* If she is given the numeral 4, she can make or pick out a group of four things to go with it.

- *Reproduce symbols.* She can learn to write the numerals.

The movement from working with groups alone to working with groups and symbols, and finally to symbols alone, must be done carefully and sequentially. In *Workjobs II*, Mary Baratta-Lorton (1979) describes three levels of increasing abstraction and increasing use of symbols: the concept level, the connecting level, and the symbolic level. These three levels can be pictured as follows:

Concept level	ΔΔΔΔ	Number sense—the child has the concept of amounts.
Connecting level	ΔΔΔΔ 4	The child connects the group amount with the numeral.
Symbolic level	4	The child understands that the numeral is the symbol for an amount.

In Chapter 3, children worked at the concept level. The connecting level, which was introduced informally, is the major focus of this chapter. The symbolic level will be introduced in Chapters 8 and 9.

7-2a Informal Pre-Assessment

If the children can do the assessment tasks in Chapters 3, 4, and 5 and the first section of this chapter, then they have the basic skills and knowledge necessary to connect groups and symbols. In fact, they may be observed doing some symbol and grouping activities on their own if materials are made available for them to explore in the math center. Following are some individual interview tasks.

SAMPLE ASSESSMENT TASK

6M   PREOPERATIONAL/CONCRETE AGES 5–7

GROUPS AND SYMBOLS, MATCH SYMBOLS TO GROUPS: CHAPTER 7

METHOD Interview.

SKILL Child will be able to match symbols to groups, using numerals from 0 to 10 and groups of amounts 0 to 10.

MATERIALS 5 × 8-inch cards with numerals 0 to 10, ten objects (e.g., chips, cube blocks, buttons).

PROCEDURE Lay out the cards in numerical order in front of the child. One at a time, show the child groups of each amount in this order: 2, 5, 3, 1, 4.

Say, "Pick out the numeral that tells how many things are in this group." If the child does these correctly, go on to 7, 9, 6, 10, 8, and 0, using the same procedure.

EVALUATION Note which groups and symbols the child can match. The responses indicate where instruction can begin.

INSTRUCTIONAL RESOURCE R. Charlesworth, *Math and Science for Young Children*, 8th ed., San Francisco, CA: Cengage Learning, 2016.

Digital Download

SAMPLE ASSESSMENT TASK

6L   PREOPERATIONAL/CONCRETE AGES 5–7

GROUPS AND SYMBOLS, MATCH GROUPS TO SYMBOLS: CHAPTER 7

METHOD Interview.

SKILL Child will be able to match groups to symbols, using groups of amounts from 0 to 10 and numerals from 0 to 10.

MATERIALS 5 × 8-inch cards with numerals from 0 to 10, 60 objects (e.g., chips, cube blocks, coins, buttons).

PROCEDURE Lay out the numeral cards in front of the child in a random arrangement. Place the container of objects within easy reach. Make a group for each numeral. Let the child decide how to organize the materials.

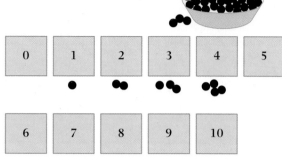

EVALUATION Note for which numerals the child is able to make groups and how the child goes about the task. For example, does he sequence the numerals from 0 to 10? Does he place the objects in an organized pattern by each numeral? Can he recognize some amounts without counting? When he counts, does he do so carefully? His responses indicate where instruction should begin.

INSTRUCTIONAL RESOURCE
R. Charlesworth, *Math and Science for Young Children*, 8th ed., San Francisco, CA: Cengage Learning, 2016.

Digital Download

SAMPLE ASSESSMENT TASK

6K   PREOPERATIONAL/CONCRETE AGES 5–7

GROUPS AND SYMBOLS, WRITE/REPRODUCE NUMERALS: CHAPTER 7

METHOD Interview.

SKILL Child can reproduce (write) numerals from 0 to 10.

MATERIALS Pencil, pen, black marker, black crayon, white paper, numeral cards from 0 to 10.

PROCEDURE Here is a piece of paper. Pick out one of these [teacher points to writing tools] that you would like to use. Now, write as many numbers as you can. If the child is unable to write from memory, show him the numeral cards. Copy any of these that you can.

EVALUATION Note how many numerals the child can write and whether they are in sequence. If the child is not able to write the numerals with ease, then at this time writing is probably not an appropriate mode of response to problems. Instead, have him do activities in which he can place movable numerals or markers on the correct answers.

INSTRUCTIONAL RESOURCE
R. Charlesworth, *Math and Science for Young Children*, 8th ed., San Francisco, CA: Cengage Learning, 2016.

Digital Download

7-2b Activities

Groups and symbols are learned through naturalistic, informal, and adult-guided instructional experiences.

Naturalistic Activities. As the children learn that groups and symbols go together, their understanding will be reflected in their daily play activities.

- Mary and Dean have set up a grocery store. Dean has made price tags, and Mary has made play money from construction paper. They have written numerals on each price tag and piece of money. Sam comes up and picks out a box of breakfast cereal and a carton of milk. Dean takes the tags. "That will be four dollars." Sam counts out four play dollar bills. Dean takes a piece of paper from a note pad and writes "Receipt." "Here, Sam."

- Brent has drawn a picture of a birthday cake with six candles and a big numeral 6. "This is for my next birthday. I will be 6."

■ The flannelboard and a group of primary cutouts have been left out in a quiet corner. George sits deep in thought as he places the numerals in order and counts out a group of cutouts to go with each numeral.

Each child uses the skills and concepts he or she has already learned from watching adults use them.

Informal Activities. The child can work with groups and numerals best through informal experiences. Each child needs a different amount of practice. By making available many materials that the child can work with on her own, the teacher can help each child have the amount of practice she needs. The child can choose to use the group of materials that she finds the most interesting.

Workjobs (Baratta-Lorton, 1972) and *Workjobs II* (Baratta-Lorton, 1979) are excellent resources for groups and symbols activities and materials. The basic activities for matching symbols to groups and groups to symbols require the following kinds of materials:

1. Materials in which the numerals are "fixed" and counters are available for making the groups. These are called *counting trays* and may be made or purchased. They may be set up with the numerals all in one row or in two or more rows (**Figure 7-8**).

2. Materials for which there are movable containers on which the numerals are written and counters of some kind. These might be pennies and banks, cups and buttons, cans and sticks, or similar container-counter combinations.

3. Individual numeral cards, each with a space for the child to make a group to match.

4. Groups of real things or pictures of things that must be matched to numerals written on cards.

The teacher could show each child a new set of materials and give him a turn at working with them. If the teacher finds that a child is having a hard time, she could give him some help and make sure he takes part in some adult-guided activities.

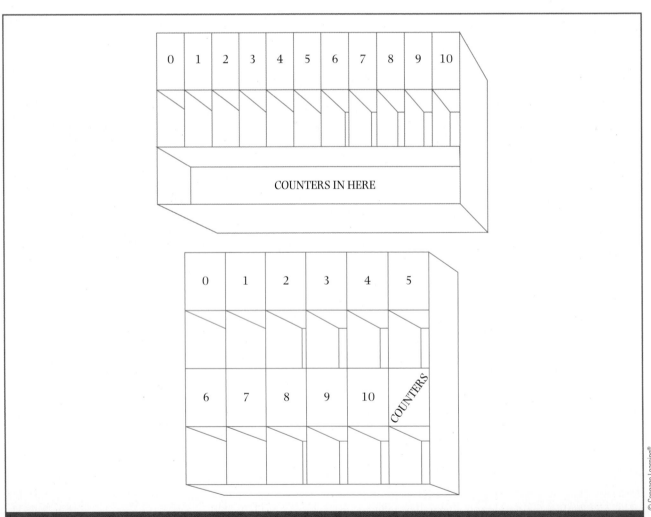

FIGURE 7-8 Counting trays can be set up with numerals all in one row or in two or more rows.

© Cengage Learning®

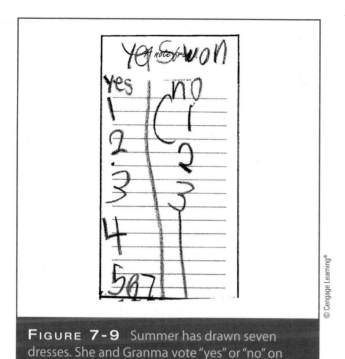

FIGURE 7-9 Summer has drawn seven dresses. She and Granma vote "yes" or "no" on each dress as to whether it is "good."

PHOTO 7-3 The sets and symbol matching puzzles are self-correcting.

Informal experiences in which the child writes numerals come up when the child asks how to write his age, phone number, or address. Some children who are interested in writing may copy numerals that they see in the environment—on the clock and calendar or on the numeral cards used in matching and group-making activities. The teacher should encourage these children and help them, if necessary. The teacher could make or buy a group of sandpaper numerals. The child can trace these with his finger to get the feel of the shape and the movement needed to make the numeral. Although formal writing lessons should not take place until the child's fine muscle coordination is well developed, some preschool children pick up writing on their own (**Figure 7-9**). For some children, formal writing lessons might not be appropriate until they are 7 or 8 years of age.

Adult-Guided Activities. Adult-guided activities with symbols and groups for the young child are done in the form of games. In one type of game, the child matches groups and numerals using a theme such as Letters to the Post Office or Fish in the Fishbowl (**Photo 7-3**). A second is the basic board game. A third type of game is the lotto or bingo type. In each case, the teacher explains and demonstrates the game. Once the children know the rules, two or more can play on their own. One example of each game is described. With a little imagination, the teacher can think of variations.

The last three activities are for the child who can write numerals. Fosnot and Cameron (2007) provide a variety of games that support number sense and groups and symbols.

Counting books are another resource for connecting groups and symbols. In most counting books, the numerals are included with each group to be counted. The teacher must be cautious in selecting counting books. Ballenger, Benham, and Hosticka (1984) suggest the following criteria for selecting counting books:

- The numerals should always refer to *how many*, not to ordinal position or sequence.
- The numeral names should also always refer to *how many*.
- The narrative on the page should clearly identify the group of objects the numeral is associated with.
- The illustrations of objects to be counted and connected to the numeral on each page should be clear and distinct.
- When ordinals are being used, the starting position (e.g., *first*) should be clearly identified.
- When identifying ordinal positions, the correct terms should be used (e.g., *first, second, third*, etc.).
- When numerals are used to indicate ordinal position, they should be written as *1st, 2nd, 3rd*, and so on.
- The numerals should be uniform in size (not small numerals for small groups and larger numerals for larger groups).
- The book should emphasize the concept of one-to-one correspondence.
- When amounts above 10 and their associated numerals are illustrated, the amounts should be depicted as a group of 10 plus the additional items.

ACTIVITIES

GROUPS AND SYMBOLS: FISH IN THE FISHBOWL

Objective: To match groups and symbols for the numerals 0 to 10.

Materials: Sketch 11 fishbowls about 7 × 10 inches on separate pieces of cardboard or poster board. On each bowl, write one of the numerals from 0 to 10. Cut out 11 fish, one for each bowl. On each fish, put dots, from 0 on the first fish to 10 on the last.

Naturalistic and informal activities: Place the fish and fishbowls in the math center for the children to explore. Note whether they make any matches as they play with them. Do they notice the dots and numerals and attempt to make matches? If they make matches, ask them to tell you about them.

Adult-guided activity: Play with two or more children. Line up the fishbowls (a chalk tray is a good place). One at a time, have each child choose a fish, sight unseen. Have her match her fish to its own bowl.

Follow-up:

1. Make fish with other kinds of sets, such as stripes or stars.

2. Line up the fish, and have the children match the fishbowls to the right fish.

ACTIVITIES

GROUPS AND SYMBOLS: BASIC BOARD GAMES

Objective: To match groups and symbols.

Materials: The teacher could purchase or make the basic materials, which include these:

- A piece of poster board (18 × 36 inches) for the game board
- Clear Contact or laminating material
- Marking pens
- Spinner cards, plain 3 × 5-inch file cards, or a die
- Place markers (chips, buttons, or other counters)

Figure 7-10 shows materials for three basic games. Set up the game boards with a theme of interest, such as a race car game. Themes might be Going to School, The Road to Happy Land, or whatever the teacher or children can imagine.

Naturalistic and informal activities: Put the games out, one at a time, during center time. Note whether any of the children are familiar with these types of games. Observe what they do. Do they know about taking turns? Do they know how to use the spinners and count the jumps? Do they make up rules?

Adult-guided activity: The basic activity is the same for each game. Each child picks a marker and puts it on Start. Then, each in turn spins the spinner (or chooses a card or rolls the die) and moves to the square that matches.

Follow-up:

1. Have the children learn to play the games on their own.

2. Make new games with new themes. Make games with more moves and using more numerals and with larger groups to match.

3. Let the children make up their own rules.

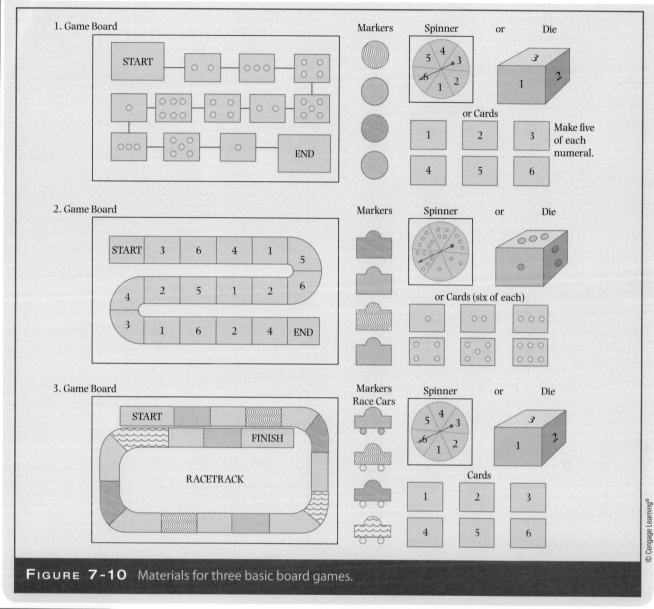

FIGURE 7-10 Materials for three basic board games.

ACTIVITIES

GROUPS AND SYMBOLS: LOTTO AND BINGO GAMES

Objective: To match groups and symbols.

Materials: Both games should have six basic game cards, each with six or more squares (the more squares, the longer and harder the game will be). For lotto, there is one card to match each square. For bingo, there must also be markers to put on the squares. For bingo, squares on the basic game cards are repeated; for lotto, they are not.

Naturalistic and informal activities: Put the games out, one at a time, during center time. Note whether any of the children are familiar with these types of games. Observe what they do. Do they know about taking turns? Do they know how to use the materials and make matches? Do they recognize the numerals on the bingo cards? Do they make up rules?

Adult-guided activities:

1. *Lotto game.* Each child receives a basic game card. The matching cards are shuffled and held up one at a time. The child must call out if the card has her mark on it (a dot, circle, triangle) and then match the numeral to the right group. The game can be played until one person fills her card or until everyone does.

2. *Bingo game.* Each child receives a basic game card together with nine chips. The matching set cards are

shuffled and then held up, one at a time. The child puts a chip on the numeral that goes with the group on the card. When someone gets a row full in any direction, the game starts again.

Follow-up: Make more games, using different picture groups and adding more squares to the basic game cards. Bingo cards must always have the same (odd) number of squares in both directions (e.g., grids that are three by three, five by five, or seven by seven). Select games from Fosnot and Cameron (2007).

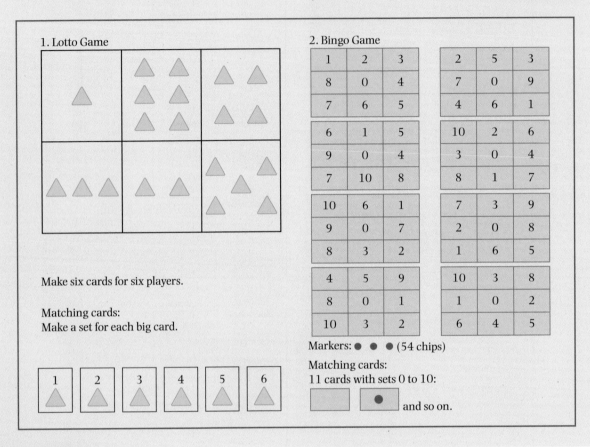

1. Lotto Game

Make six cards for six players.

Matching cards:
Make a set for each big card.

2. Bingo Game

Markers: ● ● ● (54 chips)

Matching cards:
11 cards with sets 0 to 10:

and so on.

ACTIVITIES

GROUPS AND SYMBOLS: MY OWN NUMBER BOOK

Objective: To match groups and symbols.

Materials: Booklets made with construction paper covers and several pages made from newsprint or other plain paper, hole puncher, yarn or brads to hold book together, crayons, glue, scissors, and more paper or stickers.

Naturalistic and informal activities:

- Provide the children with opportunities to make their own books in the writing center.

- Read number books with the children, and have them explore the books independently.

Adult-guided activity: The child writes (or asks the teacher to write) a numeral on each page of the book. The child then puts a group on each page. Groups can be made using:

- Stickers.
- Cutouts made by the child.
- Drawings done by the child.

Follow-up:

- Have the children show their books to one another and then take the books home.

- Read to the children some of the number books listed in Appendix B.

ACTIVITIES

GROUPS AND SYMBOLS: WRITING NUMERALS TO MATCH GROUPS

Objective: To write the numeral that goes with a group.

Materials: Objects and pictures of objects, whiteboard or Smart Board, crayons, pencils, and paper.

Naturalistic and informal activities: Have the children explore many numerals and groups and numeral materials. Make numeral models available in the writing center for the children to observe and copy.

Adult-guided activity: Show the child objects or pictures of objects. **"Write the numeral that tells how many [name**

of object] there are." The child then writes the numeral on the whiteboard or on a piece of paper.

Follow-up: Get some clear acetate. Make some set pictures that can be placed in acetate folders for the child to use on her own. Make acetate folders by taping acetate to a piece of cardboard of the same size, using plastic tape. The child can write on the acetate with a nonpermanent marker and then erase her mark with a tissue or a soft cloth.

Digital Download

McDonald (2007) provides several criteria for selecting counting books to provide a variety of experiences for the children:

a. Note whether quantities above 10 are in the book.

b. Note whether there are opportunities to conserve number.

c. Note whether a variety of different items are included for counting.

d. Note whether there are skip counting opportunities (e.g., count by 2s, 5s. 10s, and so on).

e. Note whether number and quantity are explored in a diversity of cultures and languages.

f. Note whether there is a grouping model of 10-plus with numbers larger than 10.

g. Note whether the illustrations encourage counting on.

h. Note whether math language (see Chapter 6) can be applied.

i. Note whether *zero* is used appropriately.

Computers and calculators can also be used for helping children acquire the groups and symbols connection (**Photo 7-4**). Most of the technology resources listed in other

chapters support counting, and symbol recognition also connects groups and symbols. These resources should also be evaluated using the same criteria suggested for books. Using their calculators, students could play games, such as closing their eyes, pressing a key, identifying the numeral, and then selecting or constructing a group that goes with the numeral. Many self-correcting computer/calculator-type toys are also available for children to enjoy.

Groups and symbol activities may be included in other content areas. See **Figure 7-11** for examples.

7-2c Working with Children with Special Needs

Purchase or make a variety of materials providing experiences for children that support making the connection between the symbols and the groups they represent. Verbal counting comes before the written symbol is introduced. Some children take longer than others to learn the written number sequence before connecting them with groups. Here are examples of materials and activities that can be used to support number recognition and sequence:

- Make or buy cards with numbers (be sure that there are several cards for each number). Have the children divide the cards and then turn them over one at a time, identifying matches.

- In kindergarten, learning one's street address and phone number provides a meaningful context for number identification. Provide each child with two sentence strips: one with the child's address and one with his or her phone number.

- Numbers above nine may be difficult for children with poor concepts of spatial awareness. Use color cueing to indicate the concepts of left and right. Numbers in the teens can be especially difficult: whereas 2 in the number is a clue in the twenties, the numeral 1 does not say "teen."

- Number sequencing can be done individually, in small groups, or by the whole class. During a class meet-

PHOTO 7-4 Technology provides a means for making symbol/group connections.

© Cengage Learning®

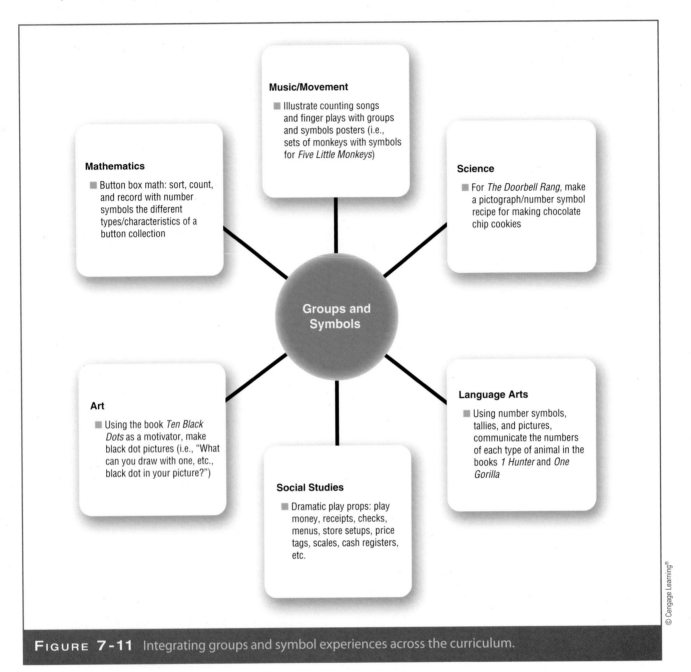

Music/Movement
- Illustrate counting songs and finger plays with groups and symbols posters (i.e., sets of monkeys with symbols for *Five Little Monkeys*)

Mathematics
- Button box math: sort, count, and record with number symbols the different types/characteristics of a button collection

Science
- For *The Doorbell Rang*, make a pictograph/number symbol recipe for making chocolate chip cookies

Groups and Symbols

Art
- Using the book *Ten Black Dots* as a motivator, make black dot pictures (i.e., "What can you draw with one, etc., black dot in your picture?")

Social Studies
- Dramatic play props: play money, receipts, checks, menus, store setups, price tags, scales, cash registers, etc.

Language Arts
- Using number symbols, tallies, and pictures, communicate the numbers of each type of animal in the books *1 Hunter* and *One Gorilla*

FIGURE 7-11 Integrating groups and symbol experiences across the curriculum.

© Cengage Learning®

ing, give several children large number cards, and ask them to line them up in sequence. Individuals or pairs of children can work at a table with numbers on 3 × 5-inch cards. Use flannelboards and Smart Boards as well. Calendars could also be used for matching. Use two calendars of the same month. Keep one intact and mounted and cut up the other for matching. Children can name each numeral as matched.

Once children can identify and name numerals in sequence, they can begin to associate the written number symbols with number concepts. A variety of activities have been described in this chapter, and some additional ideas follow:

- Make a hopscotch pattern on the ground. Write a number in each square. The child jumps or hops from square to square in order, stopping to clap the number in each square.

- The child traces around his hand and then numbers each finger.

- Provide the child with random written number symbols and some counting objects. Have her count out the amount that goes with each symbol.

- Provide the child with a sheet of paper with numbers written along the left side. Next to each number, have the child:

  a. draw the correct number of objects,
  b. place the correct number of stickers; or
  c. place the correct number of objects.

BRAIN CONNECTION

THE BRAIN AND NUMBERS

Scientists at Stanford University identified a brain "hot spot" that is activated when people view ordinary numerals like *6* or *38* (Goldman, 2013). Activity drops off when subjects are shown number words spelled out like *one* instead of *1*. The scientists believe this finding will lead to further research on how math-related information flows through the brain. There might be some ramifications for people with dyslexia. The area identified consists of about 1 to 2 million nerve cells in the inferior temporal gyrus, a region in the outer cortex of the brain.

B. Goldman, "Scientists Pinpoint Brain's Area for Numeral Recognition," Stanford School of Medicine News, *April 16, 2013, http://med.stanford.edu.*

7-2d Informal Post-Evaluation

With young children, observing their use of the materials for informal activities can be the most effective kind of evaluation. The adult can also notice what the children do when they play games with rules.

For children about to enter first grade, an individual interview should be done, using the assessment interviews in this chapter and in Appendix A.

7-3 STANDARDS AND EXPLANATIONS OF HIGHER-LEVEL CONCEPTS

The experiences in this part of the chapter include further applications of skills that children learned through the activities described in the previous chapters. These experiences support more complex applications of problem solving, reasoning, communication, connections, and representation (CCSSM, 2010). They are appropriate for preschool/kindergarten students who are developing at a fast rate and who can do the higher-level assessment tasks with ease or for older students who still need concrete experiences. The 11 areas presented all are included at lower levels in previous chapters and are included in CCSSM: **algebra, classification, shape, spatial relations, concrete whole number operations, graphs, symbolic level activities, quantities above 10, estimation, problem solving,** and **design technology/engineering.**

The Common Core State Standards for Mathematics (2010) for the end of kindergarten, which are relevant to the topics in this chapter are listed here. Children should:

- Understand addition as putting together and adding to, and understand subtraction as taking apart and taking from. Children should be able to represent addition and subtraction with concrete objects, drawing, and words; present solutions to word problems for amounts within 10; decompose numbers under 10 into pairs; identify, for any number from 1 to 9, which number can be added to make 10; and fluently add and subtract within 5.

- Work with numbers 11 to 19 as a foundation for place value; understand that these numbers are composed of 10 ones plus one, and ten ones plus 1, 2, 3, 4, 5, 6, 7, 8, and 9 ones, respectively.

- Classify objects and count the number of objects in each category.

- Identify and describe shapes.

- Analyze, compare, create, and compose shapes.

7-3a Informal Pre-Assessment

Assessment can determine where the children are in their *zones of proximal development* (ZPD; see Chapter 1), that is, where they can work independently and where they can complete tasks with support from scaffolding by an adult or a more advanced peer. Children can be individually interviewed using the interview tasks in the previous chapters, this chapter, and Appendix A.

COUNTING OBJECTS 2

The teacher does a developmental assessment task with a young child. The child is asked to estimate amounts, count objects, and add to and subtract from given quantities.

1. What can you say about the child's ability to count out a pile of objects? To estimate before counting?

2. What can you say about the child's ability to count on and count back by one?

3. With what number range is the child working? What number range should he be working with when solving problems?

© 2016 Cengage Learning®

The teacher looks at the child's level in each area and then makes a decision as to when to introduce these activities. When the teacher introduces any one activity to a child, it could capture the interest of another child who might be at a lower developmental level. Therefore, it is not necessary to wait for all the children to be at the highest level to begin. Children at lower levels can participate in these activities as observers and contributors. The higher-level child can serve as a model for the lower-level child. The lower-level child might be able to do part of the task, following the leadership of the higher-level child. For example, if a floor plan of the classroom is being made, the more advanced child might design it while other children draw pictures of the furniture to put on the floor plan. The more advanced child might get help from the less advanced child when she makes a graph. The less advanced child can count and measure; the more advanced child records the results. Children can work in pairs to solve concrete addition, subtraction, multiplication, and division problems. They can move into higher levels of symbol use and work with numerals and quantities greater than 10. They can also work together exploring calculators and computer software.

By the end of kindergarten, children should have an understanding of number (Marshall, 2006); that is, number sense should be well established. Number sense in first grade predicts later math ability (Sparks, 2013). Children should:

- Understand the idea of "twoness," "threeness," and so forth.

- Understand that the concept of number is independent of size, shape, and color.

- Be able to find groups everywhere that are two, three, four, five, and so on.

- Understand that arrangement in space (conservation of number) is independent of amount.

- Be able to examine and construct groups using different objects.

The book *What Comes in 2's, 3's, & 4's?* by Aker (1990) demonstrates the concept of number in pictures and provides the child with number sense experiences.

With number understood, students are ready to move on to more abstract ideas that are based on an understanding of number. *One Hundred Hungry Ants*, by Pinczes (1993), demonstrates how 100 is still 100 when broken down into smaller groups. *Miss Bindergarten Celebrates the 100th Day of Kindergarten* (1998), by Slate, shows how 100 is still 100 no matter how it is composed. *One is a Snail, Ten is a Crab: A Counting by Feet Book* (Sayre & Sayre, 2006) is a book where children count and add amounts in groups up to 100 according to the number of feet on a variety of living creatures in each group.

7-3b Activities, Skills, and Concepts

The following section of the chapter examines activities, skills, and concepts that cross-cut the fundamental skills and concepts. These areas include algebraic thinking, advanced classification, advanced shape concepts, advanced spatial relations concepts, advanced graphs, concrete and symbolic whole number problems, quantities above 10, estimation, and robotics.

Algebraic Thinking. Many people view algebra as a blockade to their progress in understanding mathematics and as a mindless abstract manipulation of symbols. The NCTM has promoted a vision of **algebra** as "a way of thinking, a method of seeing and expressing relationships" (Moses, 1997) that goes beyond numerical reasoning and that can begin in the elementary grades.

For preprimary-level children, algebraic thinking is reflected in their discovery of patterns as they sort and group objects, combine groups and count totals, build with blocks, and use objects as symbolic representations (**Photo 7-5**). As young children explore these materials, they construct generalizations that reflect an increasing understanding of patterns and relationships (Curcio & Schwartz, 1997).

Kindergartners solve "equations" with manipulatives and solve story problems based on groups of animals, people, or other things (Creno, 2013). The teacher explains to the students that they are going to do algebraic thinking and tells them that algebra is a way to create a group of something or take a group apart. Children then do a problem such as the following: They each take five beads, which represent kittens. Say, "Two kittens hid under the bed. How many kittens are left?" For more advanced students the teacher could read the book *Mystery Math: A First Book of Algebra* by David

PHOTO 7-5 Tablets have apps for sets and symbol activities.

© 2016 Cengage Learning®

A. Adler (2011). This book introduces simple equations in a delightful way as mysteries to be solved.

Children figure out how to balance their block buildings. They discover that 10 groups of 10 equal 100. Exploring with a pan balance, they find that if they put the same number of certain objects on each side, the pans will balance. They find that large groups break down into smaller groups, and each group is still the same number. They solve simple word problems. These discoveries are the outcome of the beginnings of algebraic thinking. As children move into higher-level activities, the teacher must continue to provide them with opportunities to explore and discover. Algebraic reasoning is also used extensively in science inquiry activities.

Classification. The higher levels of classification are called multiple classification, **class inclusion**, and hierarchical classification. **Multiple classification** requires the child to classify things in more than one way and to solve matrix problems. Figures 7-12 and 7-13 illustrate these two types of multiple classification. In **Figure 7-12**, the child is shown three shapes, each in three sizes and in three colors. He is asked to put the ones together that belong together. She is then asked to find another way to organize the shapes. The preoperational child will not be able to do this. She centers on her first sort. Some games are suggested in the activities that will help the child move to concrete operations.

Figure 7-13 illustrates matrix problems. Figure 7-13A shows a simple 2 × 2 matrix. In this case, both size and number must be considered to complete the matrix. The problem can be made more difficult by making the matrix larger. (Each row and column always has the same number of squares.) Figure 7-13B shows a 4 × 4 matrix. The easiest problem is to fill in part of a matrix. The hardest problem is to fill in a whole blank matrix, as illustrated in Figure 7-13C.

The preoperational child cannot see that one class may be included within another (**class inclusion**). For example, the child is shown 10 flowers: two roses and eight daisies. The child can divide the flowers into two groups: roses and daisies. He knows that they are all flowers. When the teacher asks him if there are more flowers or more daisies, he will answer, "More daisies." He is fooled by what he sees and centers on the greater number of daisies. He is not able to hold in his mind that daisies are also flowers. This problem is shown in **Figure 7-14**.

Hierarchical classification involves classes within classes. For example, black kittens ⊂ kittens ⊂ house cats ⊂ cats ⊂ mammals (here "⊂" denotes "subgroup" or "are contained within"). As can be seen in **Figure 7-15**, this forms a *hierarchy*, or a series of ever larger classes. Basic-level concepts are usually learned first. This level includes categories such as dogs, monkeys, cats, cows, and elephants (see Figure 7-15). Superordinate-level concepts such as mammals, furniture, vehicles, and so on, are learned next. Finally, children learn subordinate categories, such as domestic cats and wild cats, or types of chairs such as dining room, living room, rocking, kitchen, folding, and so on.

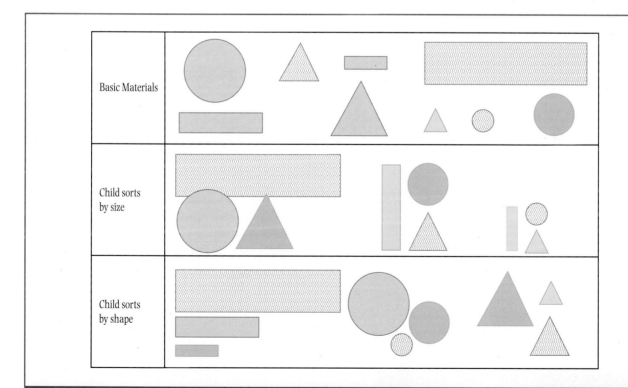

FIGURE 7-12 Multiple classification involves sorting one way and then sorting again using different criteria.

© Cengage Learning®

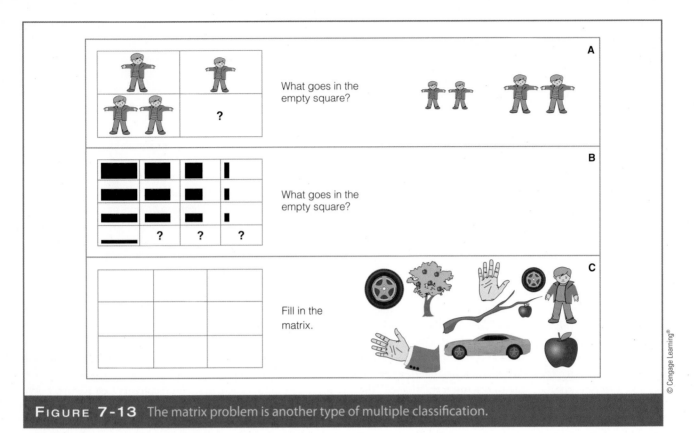

FIGURE 7-13 The matrix problem is another type of multiple classification.

Another interesting aspect of young children's concept learning is their view of which characteristics the members of a class have in common. Although preoperational-level children tend to be perceptually bound when they attempt to solve many types of conceptual problems, they can classify based on category membership when they are shown things that are perceptually similar. For example, 4-year-olds were shown pictures of a blackbird; a bat, which looked much like the blackbird; and a flamingo. They were told that the flamingo gave its baby mashed-up food and the bat gave its baby milk. When they were asked what the blackbird fed its baby, they responded that it gave its baby mashed-up food. In this case, the children looked beyond the most obvious physical attributes.

Another interesting type of characteristic to ask young children about is their view of what is inside members of a class. When young children are asked whether all members of a class have the same "stuff" inside, preschoolers tend to say that, yes, they have; that is, all dogs, people, chairs, and dolls are the same inside. Children are aware of more than just observable similarities. By second grade, they can discriminate between natural and synthetic items. They realize that living things such as dogs, people, or apples are, for the most part, the same inside as other dogs, people, or apples. However, the insides of different types of chairs, dolls, or other manufactured items are not necessarily the same. For younger children, category membership overwhelms other factors.

The following classification activities will help the transitional child (usually ages 5 to 7) to enter concrete operations.

Roses   Daisies

Flowers

FIGURE 7-14 Class inclusion is the idea that one class can be included in another.

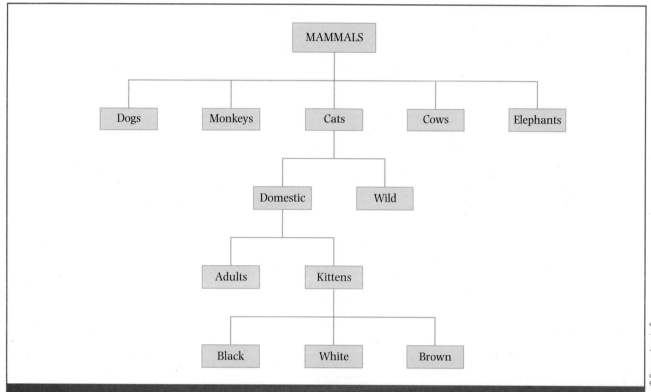

FIGURE 7-15 In a hierarchical classification, all things in each lower class are included in the next higher class.

ACTIVITIES

HIGHER-LEVEL CLASSIFICATION: MULTIPLE CLASSIFICATION, RECLASSIFY

Objective: To help the transitional child learn that groups of objects or pictures can sometimes be sorted in more than one way.

Materials: Any group of objects or pictures of objects that can be classified in more than one way, such as pictures or cardboard cutouts of dogs of different colors (brown and white), sizes (large and small), and hair lengths (long and short).

Activity: Place the dogs in front of the child. **"Which dogs belong together?"** Or, **"Are they the same?"** Note whether she groups the dogs by size, color, or hair length. **"Now, what is another way to put them in groups? Can they be put like [name another way] ?"** Put them in one pile again if the child is puzzled. **"Okay, now try to sort the [one type of object] from the [other type of object]."** Repeat this, using different criteria each time.

Follow-up: Set up other groups of materials. Set them up in boxes where the child can get them out and use them during center time. Make some felt pieces to use on the flannelboard.

Digital Download

ACTIVITIES

HIGHER-LEVEL CLASSIFICATION: MULTIPLE CLASSIFICATION: MATRICES

Objective: To help the transitional child see that things may be related according to more than one criterion.

Materials: Purchase or make a matrix game. Start with a 2×2 matrix and gradually increase the size (3×3, 4×4, etc.).

Use any of the criteria from Chapter 3 such as color, size, shape, material, pattern, texture, function, association, class name, common feature, or number. Make a game board from poster board or wood. Draw or paint permanent lines. Use a

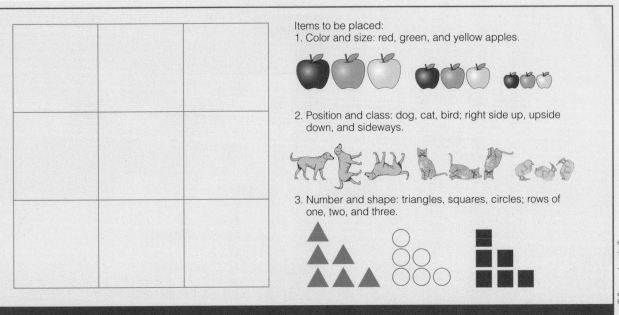

Items to be placed:
1. Color and size: red, green, and yellow apples.

2. Position and class: dog, cat, bird; right side up, upside down, and sideways.

3. Number and shape: triangles, squares, circles; rows of one, two, and three.

© Cengage Learning®

FIGURE 7-16 A matrix game.

flannelboard, and make the lines for the matrix with lengths of yarn. **Figure 7-16** shows an example of a 3 × 3 board. Start with three-dimensional materials, and then move to cutouts and then cards.

Adult-guided activities: Start with the matrix filled except for one space. Ask the child to choose from two items the one that goes in the empty space. **"Which one of these goes here?"** After the item is placed, say, **"why does it belong there?"** Once the child understands the task, leave more spaces empty until it is left for the child to fill in the whole matrix.

Follow-up: Add more games that use different categories and larger matrices.

Digital Download

ACTIVITIES

HIGHER-LEVEL CLASSIFICATION: CLASS INCLUSION

Objective: To help the transitional child see that a smaller group may be included within a larger group.

Materials: Seven animal figures or cutouts, including two kinds (such as horses and cows, pigs and chickens, dogs and cats): four of one animal and three of the other.

Activity: Place the animals within an enclosure (a yarn circle or a fence made of blocks). **"Who is inside the fence?"**

Children will answer "horses," "cows," "animals." **"Show me which ones are horses [cows, animals]. Are there more horses or more animals? How do you know? Let's check [use one-to-one correspondence]."**

Follow-up: Play the same game. Use other categories such as plants, types of material, size, and so on. Increase the size of the groups.

Digital Download

ACTIVITIES

HIGHER-LEVEL CLASSIFICATION: HIERARCHICAL

Objective: To help the transitional child see that each thing may be part of a larger category (or group of things).

Materials: Make some sets of sorting cards. Glue pictures from catalogs and/or workbooks onto file cards or poster board. For example:

- One black cat, several house cats, cats of other colors, one tiger, one lion, one panther, one bobcat, one dog, one horse, one cow, one squirrel, one bear

- One duck, three swans, five other birds, five other animals

- One teaspoon, two soupspoons, a serving spoon, two baby spoons, three forks, two knives

Adult-guided activities: Place the cards where they can all be seen. Give the following instructions:

1. **"Find all the animals. Find all the cats. Find all the house cats. Find all the black cats."** Mix up the cards, and lay them out again. **"Put them in groups the way you think they should be."** When the child is done, ask, **"Why did you put them that way?"** Mix them up, and lay them out. **"If all the animals were hungry, would the black cat be hungry? If the black cat is hungry, are all the animals hungry?"**

2. **"Find all the animals. Find all the birds. Find the waterbirds. Find the duck."** Mix up the cards, and lay them out again. **"Put them in groups the way you think they should be."** When the child is done, ask, **"Why do they belong that way?"** Mix them up, and lay them out again. **"If all the birds were cold, would the duck be cold? If the duck were cold, would all the waterbirds be cold? If all the animals were cold, would the waterbirds be cold?"**

3. Find all the things that we eat with. Find all the knives. Find all the forks. Find all the spoons. Mix them up, and lay them out again. **"Put them in groups the way you think they belong."** When the child is done, **"Why do they belong that way?"** Mix them up, and lay them out again. **"If all the spoons are dirty, would the teaspoon be dirty? If all the things we eat with were dirty, would the big spoon be dirty? If the teaspoon is dirty, are all the other things we eat with dirty, too?"**

Follow-up: Make up other hierarchies. Leave the card sets out for the children to sort during play. Ask them some of the same kinds of questions informally.

Digital Download

ACTIVITIES

HIGHER-LEVEL CLASSIFICATION: MULTIPLE CLASSIFICATION

Objective: To help the transitional child learn to group things in a variety of ways using logical reasoning.

Materials: *What to Wear?* is an emergent reader book by Sharon Young (1998b). The book depicts a boy who has two shirts, two pairs of shorts, and two caps, with each item a different color. The problem presented to the reader is to figure out how many different outfits the boy can put together. A similar problem can be found online at illuminations.nctm.org.

Adult-guided activities: The *Harry's Math Books*, *Set B, Teacher Guide* (Young, 1998a) suggests a number of activities that can be done to support the concepts in *What to Wear?* Here are some examples.

1. Have the children discuss the ways they can sort clothes, such as school clothes, play clothes, and dress-up clothes, or clean clothes and dirty clothes.

2. Use cutouts to see that, although only two of each type of clothing are in the book, the children can construct more than two outfits.

3. Make connections with other areas such as meal combinations with two main dishes, two vegetables, two potatoes, two desserts, and two drinks.

4. Have the students draw the eight different outfits they can derive from the book.

Follow-up: Provide real clothing in the dramatic play center. Note how many combinations of outfits the students can put together.

Digital Download

Shape. Once the child can match, sort, and name shapes, she can also reproduce them (**Photo 7-6**). This can be done informally. Here are some materials that could be used.

- Purchase or make a **geoboard**, a square board with headed screws or pegs sticking up at equal intervals. Give the child a supply of rubber bands and have her experiment in making shapes by stretching the rubber bands around the pegs.

- Put out a container of pipe cleaners, Wikki Stix, or straws. Ask the children to make as many different shapes as they can. Have them glue the shapes onto construction paper. Strips of paper, toothpicks, string, and yarn could also be used to make shapes.

- Pattern blocks are an important material for children to use in exploring shape (Wilson, 2001). For beginners, provide puzzle frames that indicate the shapes to be used to fill the frame. For more advanced students, provide frames where the pattern block shapes are only partially indicated. If some children can select pieces to fill in the puzzle without trial and error, give them puzzle frames with no hints as to which pattern block shapes will fill the frame. Offer children who master these advanced frames the challenge of filling the frames in more than one way. Virtual pattern blocks can be found at the Illuminations website http://illuminations.nctm.org.

Spatial Relations. After playing the treasure hunt game described in Chapter 4, children can learn more about space by reproducing the space around them as a floor plan or map. Start with the classroom for the first map. Then move to the whole building, to the neighborhood, and to the town or city. Be sure the children have maps among their dramatic play props.

ACTIVITIES

HIGHER-LEVEL ACTIVITIES: SPATIAL RELATIONS, FLOOR PLANS

Objective: To relate position in space to symbols of position in space.

Materials: A large piece of poster board or heavy paper, markers, pens, construction paper, glue, crayons, scissors, some simple sample floor plans.

Adult-guided activity:

1. Show the children some floor plans. **What are these? What are they for? If we made a floor plan of our room, what would we put on it?"** Make a list.

2. Show the children the large piece of poster board or heavy paper. **"We can make a plan of our room on here. Each of you can make something that is in the room, just like on our list. Then you can glue it in the right place. I've marked in the doors and windows for you."** As each child draws and cuts out an item (a table, shelf, sink, chair), have him show you where it belongs on the plan, and either you or the child can glue it on.

Follow-up: After the plan is done, leave it up on the wall so that the children can look at it and talk about it. They can also add more things to the plan. Use the same procedure later to make a plan of the building. Teacher and children should walk around the whole place. They should talk about which rooms are next to each other and which rooms are across from each other. Use sticks or straws to lay out the plan.

Digital Download

ACTIVITIES

HIGHER-LEVEL ACTIVITIES: SPATIAL RELATIONS, MAPS

Objective: To relate position in space to symbols of position in space.

Materials: Map of the city, large piece of poster board or heavy butcher paper, marking pens, construction paper, glue, crayons, scissors.

Adult-guided activity: Show the children the map of the city (or county in a rural area). Explain that this is a picture of where the streets would be if the children were looking down from a plane or a helicopter. Label each child's home on the map, and mark where the school is. Talk about who lives closest to the school and who lives farthest away. Print each child's address on a card, and have her review it each day. Help the children mark out the streets and roads. Lay out a large background map made with butcher paper that the children can use to copy the printed map. Have the children cut out and glue down strips of black paper for the streets (and/or roads). Each child can draw a picture of her home and glue it on the map. Keep the map on the wall for children to look at and talk about. As field trips are taken during the year, add each place to the map.

Follow-up: Encourage the children to look at and talk about the map. Help them add new points of interest. Help children who would like to make their own maps. Bring in maps of the state, the country, and the world. Try to purchase U.S. and world map puzzles.

Digital Download

Design Technology/Engineering. Chapter 4 described design technology/engineering as a natural component of children's play. Kindergartner Josh is constructing with Marbleworks. He tells his friends, "This is my invention," as he admires his work and tests its functioning with marbles. A small group is engaged in creating art projects with recycled materials (Eichinger, 2009). The more advanced 5- and 6-year-olds may be challenged by more complex design technology/engineering problems. In these more advanced projects, children go through several steps:

- A problem is identified.

- Ideas are generated for ways of investigating and solving the problem.

- A plan of action is devised.

- A product is designed.

- The product is made and tested.

- Students reflect on the results of their process and product.

Either individuals or small groups can work on problems.

The youngest children should start with simple projects that focus on one item, such as designing an airplane, building a house, or constructing a miniature piece of playground equipment. Supplied with small boxes and other recycled materials, tape, and glue, children's imaginations take off. The Virginia Children's Engineering Council website provides detailed instructions for design technology projects. For kindergarten, plans are provided for four designs: Building a Letter, Shapes All Around Us, Magnet Motion, and Old-Fashioned Paper Dolls.

Children Designing and Engineering (n.d.) provides samples of more complex long-term projects. For example, students decide to construct a safari park. They investigate the types of animals to be included and their size, habitats, and diets. The students then plan how to construct an appropriate habitat, and they proceed with construction. Next, they identify the needs of the workers and visitors. Then, they design and build an official safari vehicle. Finally, they plan an opening day event. At each step, the students reflect on the results and offer constructive criticism.

Budding engineers can join the Kids Design Network, a website sponsored by the Dupage Children's Museum in Naperville, Illinois. Children are presented with design problems that encourage investigation, invention, problem solving, design, and the actual building of a product. Members can communicate with an engineer through text chat and an interactive whiteboard. There is no cost to belong.

DeVries and Sales (2010) and Van Meeteren and Zan (2010) describe how their ramps and pathways projects provide a constructivist approach to presenting physics to young children. Children explore the movement of marbles and other objects along sections of tracks called *pathways* and along

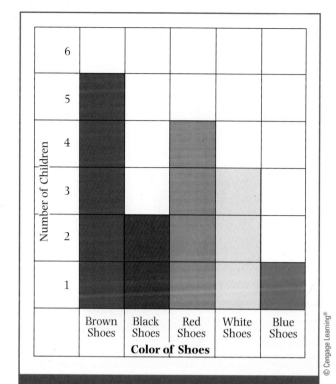

FIGURE 7-17 The child who has had experiences with simpler graphs can make square paper graphs.

inclined pathways called *ramps*. Children place their ramps at different levels of steepness. They learn that, as they make the ramp steeper, an object, such as a marble or a ball, rolls faster and farther. As they experiment with different arrangements, they come to understand the effect of slope, connections, targets, and other variations that influence pathway designs.

Graphs. The fourth level of graphs introduces the use of square paper. The child may graph the same kind of things as discussed in Chapter 5. Now, however, he uses square paper with drawn-in squares that can be colored or filled in with smaller, glued-on paper squares. These squares should be introduced only after the child has had many experiences of the kinds described in Chapter 5. The squares should be large. A completed graph might look like the one shown in **Figure 7-17**.

Concrete Whole Number Operations Problems. Once children have a basic understanding of one-to-one correspondence, number and counting, and comparing, they can sharpen their problem-solving skills with **concrete whole number operations**. They can solve simple addition, subtraction, division, and multiplication problems, using concrete materials. You could devise some simple problems to use as models, as described in Chapter 1. Some examples are in the section that follows. Provide the children with 10 counters (pennies, chips, Unifix Cubes, etc.) or with the real items or replicas of the real items described in the problems (**Figure 7-18**). The children will gradually catch on and begin devising their own problems.

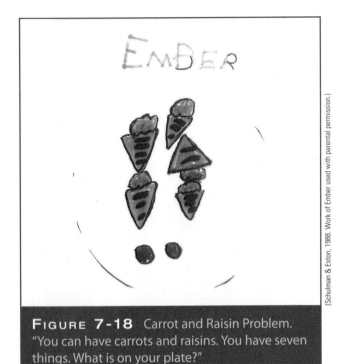

FIGURE 7-18 Carrot and Raisin Problem. "You can have carrots and raisins. You have seven things. What is on your plate?"

(Schulman & Eston, 1988. Work of Ember used with parental permission.)

FIGURE 7-19 Cookie Problem: Mother baked 12 cookies. Divide them fairly among four children.

(Based on Hutchins, 1986. Work of Rhett used with parental permission.)

As children grow and develop and have more experiences with whole number operations, they learn more strategies for solving problems. They gradually stop using the less efficient strategies and employ the more efficient ones. For example, 4- and 5-year-olds usually begin addition with the *counting all* strategy. For example, suppose the problem is. "John has three cars and Kate gives him two more, how many does John have now?" The 4- or 5-year-old counts all the cars (one-two-three-four-five). Five-year-olds gradually change to *counting on*; that is, considering that John has three cars, they then count on two more (four-five). Addition can begin with counting on (Brain POP, 2013). The website BrainPOP (www .brainpop.com) provides activities for parents and teachers to help children develop the concept of adding on as the road to equations.

Even older children who are using recall (3 + 2 = 5) check their work by counting all and counting on. When observing children doing division, note whether they make use of their concept of one-to-one correspondence. For example, when giving three people equal numbers of cookies, does the child pass out the cookies one at a time, consecutively, to each of the three recipients? Teacher-guided activities require the students to draw problem solutions, as in the following example (**Figure 7-19**). Boston Children's Museum provides an online STEM teaching guide called *STEMsprouts* (2013). Activities are provided in each of the STEM content areas.

The Symbolic Level. Children who can connect groups and symbols, identify numerals 0 to 9, and do concrete addition and subtraction problems are ready to move to the next step: connecting groups and symbols in written addition and subtraction.

As children continue to create their own problems and work on teacher-created problems, encourage them to communicate their findings. Suggest that they draw, write, and use numerals to show their results. They can use cards with numerals written on them and gradually write the numerals themselves. Children can work in pairs on problems and trade problems with other students.

Addition

- If Mary has three pennies and her mother gives her one more penny, how many pennies will Mary have?

- George wants two cookies for himself and two for Richard. How many cookies should he ask for?

Subtraction

- Mary has six pennies. She gives three pennies to her sister. How many does she have now?

- George has six cookies. He gives Richard three. How many does he have left?

Multiplication

- Mary gives two pennies to her sister, two to her brother, and two to her friend Kate. How many pennies did she give away?

- Tanya had three friends visiting. Mother said to give each friend three cookies. How many cookies should Tanya get from the cookie jar?

Division

- Lai has three dolls. Two friends come to play. How many dolls should she give each friend so that each has the same number?

- Naman's mother gives him a plate with nine cookies. How many cookies should Naman and each of his two friends take so that each has the same number?

Problems can be devised with stories that fit thematic topics.

As the children work with these concrete symbol/set addition and subtraction problems, they begin to store the **basic facts** in their memories and retrieve them without counting. They can then do problems without objects. However, have the objects on hand in case they are needed to check the answers.

Some resources for games and materials are listed here:

- *Games for Early Number Sense* (Fosnot & Cameron, 2007).

- *Minilessons for Early Addition and Subtraction* (Fosnot & Uittenbogaard, 2007).

- *The Young Child and Mathematics* (Copley, 2009).

- *Navigating through Problem Solving and Reasoning in Prekindergarten–Kindergarten* (Greenes, Dacy, Cavanagh, Findell, Sheffield, & Small, 2003).

- *Hands-on Standards* (Learning Resources, 2007).

- *A Head Start on Science: Encouraging a Sense of Wonder: Grades PreK–2* (Ritz, 2007)

Children can be encouraged to develop their own problems. Chapter 8 provides a more detailed description of the procedure for introducing the symbols needed for whole number operations. Calculators are also useful as tools for experimentation. Children will learn to make connections between problem solving and the signs on the calculator (i.e., +, −, ×, ÷, and =).

Quantities Above 10. Once children can count 10 objects correctly, can identify the numerals 1 to 10, have a good grasp of one-to-one correspondence, and can accurately count by rote past 10, they are ready to move on to counting **quantities above 10**. They acquire an understanding of quantities above 10 by exploring the relationship of groups of 10 with additional amounts. Preschoolers are just beginning to conceptualize the place value for two-digit numbers

(McGuire & Kinzie, 2013), whereas kindergartners can move on further. By first grade, students can deal with place value as described in Chapter 9. Preschoolers can count out 10 Unifix Cubes and stick them together. Then they can pick one more Unifix Cube. Ask whether they know which number comes after 10. If they cannot provide an answer, tell them that 11 comes after 10. Have them take another cube. Ask whether they know what comes after 11. If they do not know the answer, tell them 12. Go as far as they can count by rote accurately. When they get to 20, have them put their cubes together, lay them next to the first 10, and compare the number of cubes in the two rows. See whether they can tell you that there are two 10s and no 1s. Give them numeral cards for 11 to 19. See whether they can discover that the right-hand numeral matches how many more 1s than 10 that numeral stands for.

Once the children understand numerals 10 through 19, they can move on to 20, 30, 40, and so on. By exploring the number of 10s and 1s represented by each numeral, they discover the common pattern from 20 to 99: The 2 in 20 means two 10s, and no 1s; the 2 in 21 means two 10s and the 1 means one 1; and so on. They should also see that the same pattern holds true through 99. For games, see Fosnot and Cameron (2007) and Fosnot and Uittenbogaard (2007).

Estimation. *Estimation* for young children involves making a sensible and reasonable response to the problem of how many are in a quantity or how much of a measurement something is. It is the "process of thinking about a 'how many' or 'how much' problem and possible solutions"; it's not just a wild guess (Lang, 2001, p. 463; Van de Walle, Karp, & Bay-Williams, 2013, p. 229). Children might estimate how many objects (e.g., candies, teddy bears, screws) are in a jar or how many shoes tall the bookcase is. To come up with a reasonable response, children must already have developed number, spatial, and measurement sense. Without these prerequisite concepts, they make wild guesses rather than reasonable estimates. Estimation is the foundation for more advanced math skills.

Lang (2001) suggests several ways to assist children so that they can make reasonable estimates.

- A *referent* can be used, such as, "If I know how tall John is, I can estimate how tall the bookcase is if he stands next to it."

- *Chunking* involves taking a known measurement and using it as a guide for estimating a larger measurement. For example, if the children know how long 10 Unifix Cubes are, they can use this information to estimate the length of the table in cubes.

- *Unitizing* is another type of chunking where, if one part is known, then the whole can be estimated. For example, if a cup of pennies half fills a jar, then two cups will fill the whole jar. If the number of pennies in the cup is known, then the number to fill the jar can be estimated.

Children need to understand the language of comparison (Chapters 3 and 6) to give and receive communications regarding their estimates.

Robotics. Robotics is discussed in Chapter 9 and conventionally is a third-grade activity because it includes coding to program robot activities. However, simple programming of robots is now possible for preschoolers (Kazakoff, Sullivan, & Bers, 2013). Kazakoff et al. had young children use CHERP, a programming language designed for kindergartners. CHERP software can be used with robotics kits. Sequencing is an important aspect of programming in that instructions must be put in the correct logical order. Children not only learned to program their robots but also increased in general sequencing ability through their coding experiences.

7-3c Helping Children with Special Needs

Chapter 8 describes a progression suggested by Kathy Richardson (1984, 1999) for moving from concrete arithmetic to algorithms. For some children, a useful step for beginning arithmetic is to play a thinking game. Using numbers 2 to 9, the children are asked a series of questions. The children are asked. "What number comes *after* 6?" Next, "What number comes *before* 6?" Finally, "What is 6 and one more?" Patterns are also useful in helping children move into arithmetic. For example, when making a bead pattern, the child must think, "How many more beads will I need to complete my pattern?" Children who have difficulties with mathematics can benefit from this type of game.

Bilingual teachers Higinio Dominguez and Melissa Adams (2013) noticed that their bilingual fourth-grade students were not using estimation properly to check on the reasonableness of their answers. They were using rounding to arrive at estimations, but not doing it correctly. By having the students explain what they were doing and the reasons behind their methods, the teachers discovered there was a language problem related to translation from previous grades to the current grade. The teachers realized that language plays an important part in students understanding of mathematics.

7-4 END-OF-KINDERGARTEN SCIENCE STANDARDS AND EXPECTATIONS

Children in this transitional stage apply and develop fundamental concepts as they are exposed to higher-level experiences. As they near the concrete operational stage of development, they will continue to develop these concepts. The higher-level experiences described in this part of the chapter offer opportunities to build on many of the ideas presented in the previous sections of this chapter.

In line with NGSS (NGSS Lead States, 2013) and the *Framework* (NRC, 2012), there are performance expectations to be reached by the end of each grade level in each of the science areas: Life Science, Physical Science, Earth and Space

Science, and Engineering, Technology, and Science Applications. Use of the eight practices essential for learning science and engineering is stressed. The eight practices are as follows:

1. Asking questions for (science) and defining problems (for engineering)
2. Developing and using models
3. Planning and carrying out investigations
4. Analyzing and interpreting data
5. Using mathematics and computational thinking
6. Constructing explanations (for science) and designing solutions (for engineering)
7. Engaging in argument from evidence
8. Obtaining, evaluating, and communicating information (NRC, 2012, p. 42)

Understanding how scientists and engineers work will help students appreciate what scientists and engineers accomplish. Several concepts that crosscut science and engineering disciplines have already been discussed.

7-4a Concepts That Crosscut Science and Engineering Content Areas

The Next Generation Science Standards has listed seven basic concepts that crosscut all areas of science and engineering. This list includes concepts and materials from both science and engineering. These seven concepts are as follows (NRC, 2012, p. 84):

1. Patterns
2. Cause and effect: Mechanism and explanation
3. Scale, proportion, and quantity
4. Systems and system models
5. Energy and matter: Flows, cycles, and conservation
5. Structure and function
6. Stability and change

Of these, six are especially apropos for preschool and kindergarten programs. These six, slightly reworded to form a good fit with early childhood programs, are as follows:

1. Patterns and classification
2. Cause and effect
3. Scale, proportion, and quantity
4. Systems and system models
5. Groups and symbols
6. Structure and function

Patterns and Classification. Patterns are everywhere, as discussed in Chapter 5. Patterns occur in nature in the symmetry of flower petals and snowflakes. The question of how and why patterns occur in nature is often the first step in developing a scientific question. Pattern recognition is a major aspect of classification. Recognition of the similarities and differences among organisms is a major factor in grouping. Patterns are also examined in engineering design systems. Young children can note patterns that classify animals and plants.

Cause and Effect. Children are full of "why?" and "how?" questions. Scientists also come up with "why?" and "how?" questions that point them toward important findings. Repeating patterns in nature and pairs of events can lead to a scientific investigation of cause and effect. Young children may seek answers to questions such as: "Why do seeds need water?" "Why do balls bounce?" or "Why do different objects go down ramps at different speeds?"

Scale, Proportion, and Quantity. Systems and processes vary in size, time span, and energy flow. Young children understand scale in terms of relative size (large and small), weight (heavy and light), speed (fast and slow), and other informal measurements. Scale is usually introduced relative to length. Understanding of ratio and proportion begins with young children's comparisons of size and other measurements through estimation and counting. Gradually, these data are transferred to graphs. Number sense is an important part of the ability to interpret data.

Systems and System Models. The world is so complex that it can't all be studied at once. Scientists define small areas of investigation that can be referred to as systems. Boundaries are defined for any system. Organisms and machines are examples of systems. Within a system are subparts that interact with each other.

Structure and Function. The relationship between form and function is explored informally by young children. As they build with blocks, they discover that shape and stability are important factors in building. They discover that each type of animal has a different way of obtaining food and that wheels and gears are necessary for the movement of vehicles.

7-4b NGSS Performance Expectations in Kindergarten

The NGSS performance expectations for kindergarten focus on questions such as these: "What happens if you push or pull an object harder? Where do animals live and why do they live there? What is the weather like today and how is it different from yesterday?" (NRC, 2013, p. 3). Students are expected to apply the crosscutting concepts and use the eight practices to answer questions about motion and stability of the earth and planets, the effects of sunlight on the Earth's surface, the patterns of what plants and animals need to survive, and the science and engineering topics listed above. Here are some examples of the performance expectations for kindergarten:

- **Physical Science.** Plan and conduct an investigation to compare the effects of different strengths or

PHOTO 7-6 This girl is matching her wild animal toys to the wild animal pictures in the book.

different directions of pushes and pulls on the motion of an object.

- **Life Science.** Use observation to describe patterns of what plants and animals, including humans, need to survive (**Photo 7-6**).

- **Earth Systems.** Use and share observations of local weather conditions to describe patterns over time (NRC, 2013, pp. 4–8).

There are many resources that provide examples of appropriate science investigations. The NAEYC publication *Exploring Science*, edited by Amy Shillady (2013), was referred to in earlier chapters. The NSTA publication *Science and Children* includes in each issue an early childhood feature, which usually focuses on preschool activities. Frequently, articles that focus on kindergartners' projects are included.

7-4c Activities

The following are a variety of activities that focus on higher-level science concepts using mathematics skills and concepts.

Vegetable Time. Although children are asked to bring vegetables from home for this lesson, you need to prepare a variety of vegetables for maximum learning. Seed and garden catalogs and magazine pictures can provide illustrations of how the vegetables grow. Three major categories of vegetables that work well with children are leaf and stem vegetables (cabbage, lettuce, spinach, mustard, parsley), root vegetables (sweet potatoes, carrots, beets, turnips, onions), and seed vegetables (cucumbers, peas, beans, corn, soybeans). Mrs. Nevin conducts the following activity in the fall with her first-grade class.

Following is an activity that can be done with a kindergarten or first-grade class on the topic of vegetables. Mrs. Nevin first invites the children to join her on a rug to examine the different vegetables. Then she asks her class to describe the vegetables in front of them. They answer using words like *long, rough, smooth, peeling, hard, scratchy, lumpy, bumpy, crunchy, white, orange*. Mrs. Nevin holds up a potato and asks, "Can someone describe this potato?" "I can," Abigail says. "The potato is bumpy and brown." "Good," says Mrs. Nevin. "Who can find another vegetable that is bumpy?" "A pea is a little bumpy," suggests Sara. Mrs. Nevin writes the word *bumpy* on a card and groups the potato and pea together. Then she holds up a carrot and asks, "Is there another vegetable that looks like this one?" Joshua studies the assortment of vegetables and says, "How about the pumpkin?" "Yes, the pumpkin and the carrot are both orange." Mrs. Nevin writes the word *orange* on a card and places the carrot and pumpkin together with the card. The children continue to classify by characteristics until each vegetable is in a group. Mrs. Nevin refrigerates the vegetables overnight and readies them for a series of activities that emphasize a variety of concepts.

1. *Where do they grow?* The class discusses how the different vegetables looked while they were growing. Consider that, as far as most children know, potatoes come from produce sections of supermarkets and corn comes from a can. The children have fun matching the vegetable with pictures of the vegetable growing. Mrs. Nevin makes a game of matching actual vegetables with how they look as they grow.

2. *Digging for potatoes.* After matching actual vegetables with pictures of growing vegetables, children practice digging for potatoes. Mrs. Nevin fills the sandbox with rows of potatoes, and children take turns digging. Carrots, beets, and turnips are planted with their leafy tops above the soil, and children take turns gardening.

3. *What is inside?* Bowls of peas are set out to be opened and explored, and the idea of starting a garden begins to occur to children.

4. *Under, on, and above.* Mrs. Nevin makes a bulletin board backdrop of a garden, and the children match cutout vegetables to where they grow. Onions are placed under the ground; peas, beans, and corn are shown above the ground; and lettuce, cabbage, and parsley are displayed on the ground.

1. *Patterns.* Children place the vegetables in patterns. Abigail makes a pattern of potatoes, pumpkins, celery, and cucumbers. She says, "Bumpy, bumpy,

bumpy, smooth. Look at my pattern. Joshua, can you make a pattern?" Joshua begins his own pattern. "I am not going to tell you my pattern," says Joshua. He lays out mustard, carrots, peas, cabbage, potato, and beans. Abigail smiles and continues the pattern. "On the ground, under the ground, and above the ground, spinach, onion, corn," she says.

Stone Soup. Children can also learn about vegetables through literature and cooking. After vegetables are identified as members of the vegetable and fruit food group, read the book *Stone Soup* (Paterson, 1981), and act out the story.

Print the recipe on poster board (see Chapter 6); add picture clues; and have the children wash vegetables for cooking. The children will quickly learn to use vegetable peelers and table knives as they cut the vegetables into small pieces. Then, act out the story once again. This time, really add the stone and vegetables to a slow cooker to cook for the day. Bouillon cubes, salt, and pepper will spice up the soup. Do not be surprised if younger children think that the stone made all of the soup.

Prepare a set of cards with pictures of the ingredients, and have students put the cards in the correct sequence of the cooking activity (**Figure 7-20**). The children will want to

FIGURE 7-20 "What did we add to the soup first? Then what did we add?"

© Cengage Learning®

make an experience chart of preparing the stone soup. They could even graph their favorite parts of the soup.

Animal Groups. Stuffed animals are familiar to children and can be grouped in many ways. One way is to group stuffed animals on a table by number: a group of one, two, three, and so on. Ask the children to draw the set of animals at their table on a piece of white paper. After the children have drawn the animals, include early literacy experiences by having them dictate or write a story about the animals. Staple the drawings at each table into a book. The children at each table have made an animal book of 1s, 2s, and so on. Read each book with the children, and make all books available for independent classroom reading.

More First Mapping Experiences. The everyday experience of reading maps is abstract and takes practice to develop. The following mapping activities include the use of symbols and build on the mapping experiences in Chapter 5 and those suggested in Chapter 4, as well as the earlier ones in this chapter.

1. *Tangible mapping.* Children will not be able to deal with symbols on maps if they have not had experience with tangible mapping. Observe children as they create roads, valleys, and villages in clay or at the sand table. As children place objects on a huge base map, remind them of the perspective of looking down. Such a map can be made from oilcloth and rolled up when not in use.

2. *Pictorial mapping.* Take children to the top of a hill or building, and ask them to draw what they see. This activity can emphasize spatial relations and relative locations. After you have returned from a field trip, discuss what was seen on the bus ride. Use crayons or paint to construct a mural of the trip.

3. *Semipictorial mapping.* Children will use more conventional symbols when they construct a semipictorial map. As they discover that pictures take up a lot of room, they search for symbols to represent objects. Colors become symbolic and can be used to indicate water and vegetation.

4. *Base map.* The base map is an outline made by the teacher, containing the barest minimum detail—that is, key streets and buildings. This is a more abstract type of map; thus the children must know the area. Add tangible objects to the abstract base, such as toy objects and pictures. A flannel base map is a variation.

5. *Caution.* Never use one map to do many things. If your mapping experience tries to do too much, children cannot rethink the actual experience and relationships. Each mapmaking experience must fulfill some specific purpose. Each map must represent something in particular that children look for and understand.

6. *Start small.* Begin with maps of the children's block constructions. Next, move to mapping a center in the classroom before moving to something larger. Gradually increase the size of the space you are planning to map. Remember to discuss directionality.

Exploring Pumpkins: October Science. If you live where pumpkins grow, take a field trip to purchase some; if not, buy some at the grocery store. You will need a pumpkin for each child. Plan to organize the children in groups, each with an adult helper. The following activities use the senses to apply and integrate the skills and fundamental concepts used in measuring, counting, classifying, and graphing into the exploration of pumpkins.

1. *Time to Explore.* Give children time to examine their pumpkins and their stems. Ask: "What do you know about pumpkins? " "How does the pumpkin feel?" "How does it smell?" "Do all pumpkins have stems?" and "What do think is inside the pumpkins?" Later, when the pumpkins are carved, encourage the children to describe the differences in texture between the inside and outside of their pumpkins. Have them count the seeds.

   Ask: "Which pumpkin is the heaviest?" "Who has the lightest pumpkin?" After the children decide, bring out a scale, and make an accurate measurement. The children probably cannot comprehend what the scale means or read the numbers, but they like to weigh things anyway. Tape the weight (mass) on the bottom of each pumpkin. Then, when jack-o'-lanterns are created, the children can compare the differences in mass of all the pumpkins.

   Have children measure the circumference of a pumpkin with yarn. Ask: "Where shall we put the yarn on the pumpkin?" "Why?" Instruct the children to wrap the yarn around the middle of the pumpkin. Then help children cut the yarn and label it. Write the child's name on masking tape, and attach it to the yarn length. After the children have measured their pumpkins and labeled their yarn, have them thumbtack the yarn length to a bulletin board. Ask: "Which pumpkin is the smallest around the middle?" "Which is the largest?" "How can you tell?" Have the children refer to the yarn graph (**Figure 7-21**). Some kindergarten children might be ready to lay the yarn length along a measuring stick and draw horizontal bar graphs instead of yarn ones.

   Children will want to measure height as well as circumference. The major problem to solve will probably be where to measure from when the top is cut off. Provide some pieces of cardboard that will fit the top of the pumpkins. Ask the children how the cardboard could be used to measure height. This time, cut a piece of yarn that fits the height of the pumpkin. Label the yarn and attach it to pieces of masking tape. Order the yarn lengths from shortest to tallest. Ask: "Which yarn is the longest?" "Can you tell me who has the tallest pumpkin?"

FIGURE 7-21 "How big is your pumpkin?"

2. *Observing Pumpkins.* Mrs. Jones has kindergarten children count the number of curved lines along the outside of the pumpkin. She asks, "How many lines are on your pumpkin?" She instructs the children to help each other. One child places a finger on the first line of the pumpkin, and another child counts the lines. Then Mrs. Jones asks, "Do all the pumpkins have the same number of lines?" "No," answers Emily. "My pumpkin has more lines than Lai's pumpkin." Some children even begin to link the number of lines with the size of the pumpkin as they compare findings.

Mrs. Jones asks, "How does your pumpkin feel?" Ryan says his pumpkin is rough, but Sam insists that his is smooth. "Yes," Mrs. Jones observes. "Some pumpkins are rough, and some are smooth." "Are they the same color?" This question brings a buzz of activity as the children compare pumpkin color. Mrs. Jones attaches the name of each child to his or her pumpkin and asks the children to bring their pumpkins to the front table. She asks the children to group the pumpkins by color variations of yellow, orange, and so on. Some of the children are beginning to notice other differences in the pumpkins, such as brown spots and differences in stem shapes.

The children gather around Mrs. Jones as she empties the seeds and pulp from a class pumpkin. She carefully puts the seeds and pulp on separate plates and asks the children to compare the inside color of the pumpkin with the outside color. She asks, "What colors do you see?" and "What colors do you see inside the pumpkin?" "I see a lighter color," Emily says. "Do all pumpkins have light insides?" Ryan is more interested in the stringy fibers. "This looks like string dipped in pumpkin stuff." "I

am glad you noticed, Ryan," Mrs. Jones comments. "The stringy stuff is called fiber. It is part of the pumpkin." Students learn the word *pulp* and compare the seeds for future activities.

Children will also notice that pumpkins smell. Ask them to describe the smell of their pumpkins. Have them turn their pumpkins over and smell all parts. Then ask them to compare the smell of the inside of their pumpkins with the outside rind and with the seeds, fiber, and pulp. "Does the pumpkin smell remind you of anything?" Record dictated descriptions, and create an experience chart of pumpkin memories. Ask, "What do you think of when you smell pumpkins?"

As children make jack-o'-lantern faces, discuss the shapes they are using. Then ask them to draw faces on the surfaces of their pumpkins, using a felt-tip pen. Apple corers work well for carving the pumpkins' eyes. After the jack-o'-lanterns are cut and have been admired, Mrs. Jones begins a measurement activity. She asks, "How can we tell whether the pumpkin is lighter than it was before it was carved?" "Lift it," say the children. "Yes," says Mrs. Jones, "that is one way to tell, but I want to know for sure." Ryan suggests, "Let's use the scale again." But before the pumpkins are weighed, Mrs. Jones asks the children to whisper a prediction in her ear. She asks, "Do you think the pumpkin will weigh more or less after it has been carved and the seeds and pulp removed? Whisper 'More,' 'Less,' or 'The same.'" As the children respond, Mrs. Jones writes their responses on paper pumpkins and begins a *more, less,* and *the same* graph of predictions (**Figure 7-22**).

Last, but not least, in a series of pumpkin activities is tasting. Pumpkin pulp can be made into

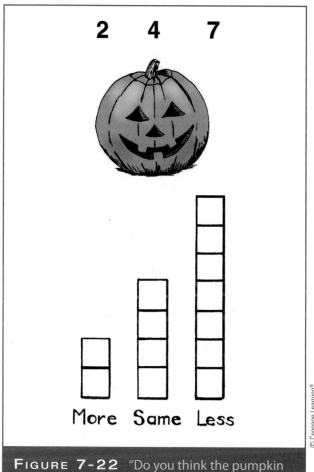

FIGURE 7-22 *"Do you think the pumpkin will weigh more than, less than, or the same after the seeds are removed?"*

© Cengage Learning®

pumpkin bread, or at Halloween party time, make drop cookies with raisins for eyes, nose, and mouth. For a tasty snack, cut some of the pumpkin pulp into chunks for cooking. Once cooked, dot the pieces with butter, and add a dash of nutmeg. Try roasting some pumpkin seeds. Have the children wash the seeds to remove the pulp and fiber. The seeds can be dried between layers of paper towels and then roasted in a single layer on a cookie sheet. Bake in a 350° oven for 30–40 minutes. The children can tell when the seeds are ready by their pale brown color. To make a comparison lesson, show them seeds that you have previously roasted, and invite them to tell you when the color of the roasting seeds matches yours. Cool the seeds; then have a snack. Before cooking the seeds, have each child count the seeds found in his or her pumpkin and compare to see which pumpkin had the most and least. If the seeds are not being eaten, they can be dried and used for counting and making groups.

Measuring the World Around Us. Playgrounds, yards, and sidewalks provide many opportunities for measuring in science. The following activities emphasize the science and measurement in outdoor adventures.

1. *How far will it blow?* After talking about air and how it moves, take the children outside to determine how far the wind will blow dandelion seeds. Draw bull's-eye–like circles on the playground with chalk. Label the circles. Have a child stand in the middle of the circle, and hold a mature dandelion up to the wind. Record which direction the wind blows the seeds and the circle in which most of them landed. This would be a good time to discuss wind as a way of dispersing seeds. If dandelions are not available, then small pieces of tissue paper with seeds drawn on them can be used.

2. *Weed watch.* Place a stick next to a growing plant such as a dandelion or similar weed. Have the children mark the height of the weed on the stick. Check the weed each day for a week, and see how tall it gets. (You might have to talk to the groundskeeper before trying this activity.) Children enjoy seeing the weeds grow. Discuss differences and possible factors in weed growth.

3. *How much do they hold?* After students have had time to explore the water center, select some of the containers used in the center. Lead the children to an area that has pinecones, acorns, pebbles, or other natural objects available. Give a container to each group of children, and instruct them to fill it with specific objects. Have each group count the number of objects that fill the container. Vary the activity by assigning different groups of contrasting objects (e.g., small, big, rough, etc.) with which to fill the containers. Compare the number of objects of each size, it takes to fill each container.

4. *Line them up.* Have children count the objects that they have collected in the containers. Ask each group to line up the objects. Compare the number of objects that it took to fill each container. If the objects collected were different, compare the number of each type of object that was needed to fill the container.

5. *How can we tell?* Children will probably find many ways to compare objects they have found (**Photo 7-7**). After they have examined and compared their objects visually, encourage them to weigh several of the objects. Ask: "Which container is the heaviest?" "How can we tell?" A balance provides an objective measure. Balance the content of one container (acorns) against the content of another (walnuts). Have children predict which will be heavier. Some could draw a picture of what they think will happen.

Popcorn Time. Children will sequence events as they act out a favorite snack. Ask the children what makes the popcorn pop. Have pairs or groups of three share their ideas. Have each group report to the class. Have two or three children become popcorn by asking them to crouch down in the middle of a masking tape circle or hula hoop. As you pour imaginary oil on them, have the rest of the class make sizzling

PHOTO 7-7 These boys are visually comparing the objects they've found.

noises and wait for them to pop. When ready, each child should jump up, burst open like a popcorn kernel, and leap out of the popper circle. Children will want to take turns acting out the popcorn sequence.

Then place a real popcorn popper on a sheet in the middle of the floor. Seat the children around the popper, remove the popcorn lid, and watch the popcorn fly. Before eating the popcorn, measure how far the popcorn popped with Unifix Cubes or string. (Be careful of the hot popper.) You could use several different brands of popcorn and ask, "Which popcorn flew the farthest?" "Which flew the shortest?"

Spatial Relations. Young children are curious about their bodies. They are familiar with outside body parts, which they can see and touch, but they are just beginning to notice that things happen inside their bodies.

1. *Inside and Outside.* To increase this awareness and reinforce the concepts of inside and outside, a teacher whom we will call Mrs. Jones, has children look at, feel, and listen to what is going on inside their bodies in the following scenario.

   Mrs. Jones fills a garbage bag with an assortment of items: a wound-up alarm clock, rubber balls, a book, a few sticks, and a bunch of grapes in a small sandwich bag. She places the bag on a chair in the front of the room, allowing it to drape down to show the outlines of some of the objects inside. She asks, "What is on the chair?" Grant says, "A garbage bag." "Is anything on the chair besides the bag?" asks the teacher. "No," the children respond. Mrs. Jones invites the children to gather around the bag and feel it. She asks, "Do you hear or feel anything?" "Yes," Alison says. "I feel something sharp." "And squishy," adds Sam. Grant is certain that he

hears a clock ticking, and Lai feels a round and firm object that moves.

After the children guess what might be in the bag, Mrs. Jones opens it and shows the children what was inside. "Did you guess correctly?" "I did," says Grant. "I heard something ticking." "Good," answers Mrs. Jones. "How did you know that sticks were in the bag?" Alison says, "I could feel them poking through the plastic." "Yes," Sam adds, "the grapes must have been the squishy stuff."

After the children discuss the contents of the bag, Mrs. Jones takes the bag off the chair, asks the children to return to their places, and invites Alison to sit in the chair. She asks, "Now, what is on the chair?" The class choruses, "Alison." "Yes, Alison is on the chair," says Mrs. Jones. "How is Alison like the bag?" After a few responses, Grant says, "Alison has something inside her, too." The children come up to look at Alison but do not touch her. Mrs. Jones asks, "Do you see what's inside showing through the way it did with the bag?" The children notice bones, knuckles, the funny bone, kneecap, and some veins. Mrs. Jones asks Alison to flex her arm muscles so the children can see muscles moving beneath her skin.

Mrs. Jones encourages the children to discover other muscles and feel them working (**Photo 7-8**). She has them stretch out on mats on the floor, curl up tightly, then slowly uncurl. "What have your muscles done?" Then she has them stretch out like a cat and curl up into a ball. Facial muscles are fun for the children. Mrs. Jones asks them to find and use all the muscles that they can on their faces. They wiggle noses, flutter eyelids, tighten jaws, and raise eyebrows. The teacher asks: "Does your tongue have muscles in it?" "How do you know?" Finally,

PHOTO 7-8 This boy works with his muscles.

the children move to music as they focus on what is happening inside their bodies. Mrs. Jones has them dancing like marionettes, stiffly with a few joints moving; then bending and curling the way rag dolls do; and finally, dancing like people, with muscles, joints, and bones controlling their movements.

The children are fascinated with the thought of something important inside of them. They make toy stethoscopes from funnels and rubber tubing and take turns finding and listening to their heartbeats. Some begin to count the beats; others enjoy tapping a finger in time with the sound of their hearts.

Mrs. Jones has the children simulate the way a heart works by folding their hands one over the other and squeezing and releasing them rhythmically. (This motion is somewhat like the way the heart muscles move to expand and contract the heart, pushing blood through.) She has them place their clasped hands close to their ears and asks: "What do you hear?" "Is this squeezing sound like the soft thumping you heard through the stethoscope?" "How is it different?"

7-4d Technology

Technology can be used to expand and supplement your science program. It can and should be used to enhance the understanding of beginning math and science concepts. The two main uses of technology in early childhood classes are software and the Internet. Software is usually used to support the acquisition and practice of concepts and skills. The Internet is often used to research topics of interest, connect with people in other locations, and illustrate concepts that children are unable to experience directly.

Appropriate software should reinforce what children are learning in the classroom. It should not be used as the sole method of instruction or take the place of actual hands-on experience. When choosing software, teachers should ask themselves the following questions.

1. Does the software ask children to engage in activities appropriate for their age?

2. Is the software interactive? The more interactive choices a child is able to make, the more appropriate the software will be.

3. Does the software come in multiple languages and utilize diverse populations in their graphics?

4. Does the software have a range of complexity that can be tailored to individual children?

Some examples of appropriate software are *Sammy's Science House* and *KidWare*. The Internet is another form of technology that is often used in early childhood classrooms. Before accessing the Internet, be sure the computers in the classroom are equipped with filtering software, so the children will not be exposed to undesirable websites. If the school or center is networked, one should always check to see whether the server is protected with a firewall that will filter inappropriate websites.

Internet websites should be used to reinforce topics under study. For example, if the class is unable to visit a pumpkin patch, then do a virtual tour. If the class is studying weather, then the class can track the changes in weather by accessing the weather channel. Apps are also available that have games and information in science.

SUMMARY

7-1 Number Symbols and Concepts: Standards and Explanations

Numerals are the symbols used to represent amounts. Most number symbols are learned through naturalistic and informal experiences.

Number Symbol Skills. The child must learn the name of each numeral. The sequence, or order, must also be learned. The child needs to understand that each numeral represents a group that is one larger than the one before (and one less than the one that comes next.

Informal Pre-Assessment. Observe how students show awareness of number symbols in the environment.

Activities. Attend to children's naturalistic attention to numerals. Many excellent self-correcting materials can be bought or made for informal activities. Any adult-guided activities should be brief.

Post-Evaluation. Observation, informal questioning, and interview tasks can be used.

7-2 Groups and Symbols: Standards and Explanations

The CCSSM standards indicate that by the end of kindergarten students should be able to match numerals 0–20 to groups. When working with groups and symbols, the child puts together the skills and ideas that have been already learned. He must match, count, classify, compare, order, and associate written numerals with groups. Students learn to match groups to symbols and symbols to groups. The also learn to write each number symbol.

Informal Pre-Assessment. Note children's behaviors during naturalistic and informal activities. Interviews may also be used.

Activities. The child employs mostly materials that can be used informally on his own. He can also learn from more structured kinds of game activities: board games, number books, computer, tablet, and online games, and calculator activities.

Informal Post-Evaluation. Observe children's group and numeral behaviors during naturalistic and informal activities. At the end of the kindergarten year, use the interview tasks included in this chapter and Appendix A.

7-3 Standards and Explanations of Higher-Level Concepts

The 12 areas included are **algebra, classification, shape, spatial relations, concrete whole number operations, graphs, symbolic level activities, quantities above 10, estimation, problem solving, design technology/engineering, and robotics**. It is suggested that the standards addressed should be reached by the end of kindergarten.

Informal Pre-Assessment. Children can be individually interviewed using the interview tasks in the previous chapters and in Appendix A.

Activities, Skills, and Concepts. Each of the areas listed in 7-3 is reviewed, and the more advanced levels described.

7-4 End-of-Kindergarten Science Standards and Expectations

Children in the transitional stage develop fundamental concepts in sets and symbols, classification, shape, spatial relations, measurement, and graphs as they are exposed to higher-level experiences. As children near the concrete operational level of development, they continue to need hands-on exploration. Performance expectations are guided by NGSS and by the science education Framework.

Concepts That Crosscut Science and Engineering Content Areas. Patterns and Classification, Cause and Effect, Scale, Proportion and Quantity, Structure and Function, and Groups and Symbols are some of the fundamental concepts that cut across all science and engineering disciplines.

Performance Expectations in Kindergarten. The performance expectations for kindergarten focus on questions such as "What happens if you push or pull an object harder? Where do animals live and why do they live there? What is the weather like today and how is it different from yesterday?" (NRC, 2013, p. 3). Students are expected to apply the crosscutting concepts and use the eight practices to answer questions about motion and stability, the effects of sunlight on the Earth's surface, and the patterns of what plants and animals need to survive, as well as use the prescribed science and engineering practices.

Activities. A variety of activities are suggested.

Technology. Technology can be used to expand and supplement the science program. Appropriate software should reinforce what children are learning in the classroom.

FURTHER READING AND RESOURCES

Byrge, L., Smith, L. B. (2014). Beginnings of place value: How preschoolers write three-digit numbers. *Child Development, 85*(2), 437–443.

Children's Engineering Journal, http://www.vtea.org.

Copley, J. V. (2011). *The young child and mathematics*, 2nd ed. Washington, DC: National Association for the Education of Young Children and New York: Teachers College Press.

Cwikla, J. (2014). Can kindergartners do fractions? *Teaching Children Mathematics, 20*(6), 354–364.

Eisenhardt, S., Fisher, M. H., Thomas, J., Schack, E. O., Tassell, J., & Yoder. M. (2014). Is it counting, or is it adding? *Teaching Children Mathematics, 20*(8), 498–507.

Greenes, C. E., Cavanagh, M., Dacey, L., Findell, C. R., & Small, M. (2001). *Navigating through algebra in prekindergarten–kindergarten*. Reston, VA: National Council of Teachers of Mathematics.

Outhred, L., & Sarelich, S. (2005). Problem solving by kindergartners. *Teaching Children Mathematics, 12*(3), 146–154.

Pollman, M. J. (2010). *Blocks and beyond*. Baltimore, MD: Brookes.

Thom, E. E., & Sandhofer, C. M. (2014). How symbolic experience shapes children's symbolic flexibility. *Child Development, 85*(2), 738–754.

REFERENCES

Adler, D. A. (2011). *Mystery math: A first book of algebra*. New York: Holiday House.

Aker, S. (1990). *What comes in 2's, 3's, & 4's?* New York: Aladdin.

Ballenger, M., Benham, N. B., & Hosticka, A. (1984). Children's counting books. *Childhood Education, 61*(1), 30–35.

Baratta-Lorton, M. (1972). *Workjobs*. Menlo Park, CA: Addison-Wesley.

Baratta-Lorton, M. (1979). *Workjobs II*. Menlo Park, CA: Addison-Wesley.

Brain POP. (2013). *Counting on: Background information and activities*. http://www.brainpopjr.com.

Boston Children's Museum. (2013). *STEMsprouts*. http://www.bostonchildrensmuseum.org.

Children Designing and Engineering. (n.d.). *What is CD&E?* http://www.childrendesigning.org.

Common Core State Standards for Mathematics (July 2010). http://www.corestandards.org.

Copley, J. V. (2004). *Showcasing mathematics for the young child*. Reston, VA: National Council of Teaches of Mathematics.

Copley, J. V. (2009). *The young child and mathematics*, 2nd ed. Washington, DC: National Association for the Education of Young Children.

Creno, C. (2013, March 5). *Kindergartners get head start on algebra.* Azcentral.com.

Curcio, F. R., & Schwartz, S. L. (1997). What does algebraic thinking look like with preprimary children? *Teaching Children Mathematics, 3*(6), 296–300.

DeVries, R., & Sales, C. (2010). *Ramps & pathways.* Washington, DC: National Association for the Education of Young Children.

Dominguez, H., & Adams, M. (2013). Mas O Menos: Exploring estimation in a bilingual classroom. *Teaching Children Mathematics, 20*(1), 36–41.

Dougherty, B. J. (2010). *Developing essential understanding of number and numeration for teaching mathematics in prekindergarten–grade 2.* Reston, VA: National Council of Teachers of Mathematics.

Eichinger, J. (2009). *Activities linking science and math K–4.* Arlington, VA: National Science Teachers Association. (Activity 7).

Fosnot, C. T., & Dolk, M. (2001). *Young mathematicians at work: Constructing number sense, addition, and subtraction.* Portsmouth, NH: Heinemann.

Fosnot, C. T., & Cameron, A. (2007). *Games for early number sense.* Portsmouth, NH: Heinemann.

Fosnot, C. T., & Uittenbogaard, W. (2007). *Minilessons for early addition and subtraction.* Portsmouth, NH: Heinemann.

Gillanders, C. (2007). An English-speaking prekindergarten teacher of young Latino children: Implications of the teacher-child relationship on second language learning. *Early Childhood Education Journal, 35*(1), 47–54.

Goldman, B. (2013, April 16). Scientists pinpoint brain's area for numeral recognition. *Stanford School of Medicine News.* http://med.stanford.edu.

Greenes, C. E., Dacey, L., Cavanagh, M., Findell, C. R., Sheffeld, L. J., & Small, M. (2003). *Navigating through problem solving and reasoning in prekindergarten–kindergarten.* Reston, VA: National Council of Teaches of Mathematics.

Hutchins, P. (1986). *When the doorbell rang.* New York: Greenwillow.

Kazakoff, E. R., Sullivan, A., & Bers, M. U. (2013). The effect of a classroom-based intensive robotics and programming workshop on sequencing ability in early childhood. *Early childhood Education Journal, 41*(4), 245–255.

Lang, F. K. (2001). What is a "good guess" anyway? Estimation in early childhood. *Teaching Children Mathematics, 7*(8), 462–466.

Learning Resources. (2007). *Hands-on standards.* Vernon Hills, IL: Author.

Marshall, J. (2006). Math wars 2: It's the teaching, stupid! *Phi Delta Kappan, 87*(5), 356–363.

McDonald, J. (2007). Selecting counting books. *Young Children, 62*(3), 38–40.

McGuire, P., & Kinzie, M. B. (2013). Analysis of place value instruction and development in pre-kindergarten mathematics. *Early Childhood Education Journal, 41*(5), 315–400.

Moses, B. (1997). Algebra for a new century. *Teaching Children Mathematics, 3*(6), 264–265.

National Research Council (NRC). (2012). *A framework for K–12 science education.* Washington, DC: National Academies Press.

NGSS Lead States. (2013). *Next generation science standards.* Washington, DC: National Academies Press.

Paterson, D. (1981). *Stone soup.* Mahwah, NJ: Troll Associates.

Pinczes, E. J. (1993). *One hundred hungry ants.* New York: Scholastic Books.

Richardson, K. (1984). *Developing number concepts: Using Unifix cubes.* Menlo Park, CA: Addison-Wesley.

Richardson, K. (1999). *Developing number concepts: Addition and subtraction* (Book 2). Parsippany, NJ: Seymour.

Ritz, W. C. (Ed.). (2007). *A head start on science: Encouraging a sense of wonder: grades preK–2.* Arlington, VA: NSTA Press.

Sayre, A. P. & Sayre, J. (2006). *One is a snail, ten is a crab: A counting by feet book.* Cambridge, MA: Candlewick.

Schulman, L., & Eston, R. (1998). A problem worth revisiting. *Teaching Children Mathematics, 5*(2), 73–77.

Shillady, A. (Ed.). (2013). *Exploring science.* Washington, DC: National Association for The Education of Young Children.

Slate, J. (1998). *Miss Bindergarten celebrates the 100th day of kindergarten.* New York: Puffin Books.

Sparks, S. D. (2013, February 4). Number sense, not counting sills, predicts math ability, says study. *Education Week blogs.* http://blogs.edweek.org.

Van de Walle, J. A., Karp, K. S., & Bay-Williams, J. M. (2013). *Elementary and middle school mathematics,* 8th ed. Boston: Pearson.

Van Meeteren, B., & Zan, B. (2010, Fall). Revealing the work of young engineers in early childhood education. SEED Papers. *ECRP, Beyond this issue.* http://www.ecrp.uiuc.edu/beyond/seed/zan.html.

Virginia Children's Engineering Council. (n.d.). *Inspiring the next generation.* http://www.vteea.org.

Wilson, D. C. (2001). Patterns of thinking in pattern block play. *Building Blocks News, 3,* 2.

Young, S. (1998a). *Harry's math books, Set B Teacher Guide.* Columbus, OH: Zaner-Bloser.

Young, S. (1998b). *What to wear?* Columbus, OH: Zaner-Bloser.

PART 5
**MATHEMATICS CONCEPTS
AND OPERATIONS FOR THE
PRIMARY GRADES**
CHAPTER 8 Whole Number Operations, Patterns, and Fractions
CHAPTER 9 Place Value, Geometry, Data Analysis, and Measurement

CHAPTER

8

WHOLE NUMBER OPERATIONS,
PATTERNS, AND FRACTIONS

OBJECTIVES

After reading this chapter, you should be able to:

8-1 Assess, plan, teach, and evaluate primary grade whole number and algebraic thinking lessons in line with national standards.

8-2 Assess, plan, teach, and evaluate pattern lessons in line with national standards.

8-3 Assess, plan, teach, and evaluate fraction lessons in line with national standards.

STANDARDS ADDRESSED IN THIS CHAPTER

NAEYC Professional Preparation Standards

5. Use content knowledge to build meaningful curriculum.

5a. Understand content knowledge and resources in mathematics and science.

5c. Design, implement, and evaluate developmentally meaningful and challenging curriculum for each child.

DAP

DAP Guidelines

2c. Know desired program goals.

3c. Use the curriculum framework to ensure there is attention to important learning goals.

Common Core State Standards for Math

Examples of Standards for operations and algebraic thinking, grades 1–3:

1.OA.1	Represent and solve word problems involving addition and subtraction within 20.
1.OA.3	Apply properties of operations as strategies to add and subtract.
2.OA.1	Use addition and subtraction within 100 to solve one- and two-step word problems, for example, by using drawings and equations, and equations with a symbol for the unknown number to represent the problem.
2.OA.2	Fluently add and subtract within 20 using mental strategies. By the end of grade 2, know from memory all sums of two 1-digit numbers.
3.0A.A.1	Interpret products of whole numbers.
3.OA.A.3	Use multiplication and division within 100 to solve word problems, for example, by using drawings and equations with a symbol for the unknown number to represent the problem.
3.OA.C.7	Fluently multiply and divide within 100, using strategies such as the relationship between multiplication and division or properties of operations. By the end of grade 3, know from memory all products of two 1-digit numbers.
3.OA.D.9	Identify arithmetic patterns.
3NFA.1	Understand a fraction $1/b$ as the quantity formed by 1 part when a whole is partitioned into b equal parts; understand a fraction a/b is the quantity formed by parts of size $1/b$.

8-1 BACKGROUND AND BASICS OF PRIMARY GRADE MATHEMATICS

This part of Chapter 8 looks at arithmetic, which includes the areas that were conventionally the core of the elementary grades mathematics program, that is, the **whole number operations** of addition, subtraction, multiplication, and division (Charlesworth & Senger, 2001). Today algebraic thinking is also integrated into operations. Currently the term *mathematics* refers to all the related concepts and skills included in this text: algebra, geometry, number sense, data analysis, and so on. Elementary and early childhood mathematics is a much more inclusive content area than it used to be. The Common Core State Standards (National Governors Association Center for Best Practices, 2010) must be attended to in planning for the primary grades. Today, answers to complex calculations can be done with calculators and computers. However, teachers encourage children to also use estimation and mental computation to check their problem solutions. To understand each operation, children must learn how to solve problems using conventional and/or invented **algorithms**, which are step-by-step procedures for solving problems (Warshauer & Warshauer, 2001, p. 23). Once children establish this understanding, they accomplish more by working on how to set up problems and then using technology to do the calculations. This chapter describes methods for introducing children to whole number operations and to whole number notation at a basic level and to fractions, which are introduced at grade 3 at a basic level. When children understand the concepts, they can move on to more complex operations, using calculators and computers to perform calculations.

Children naturally engage in the whole number operations of addition, subtraction, multiplication, and division before reaching the primary grades. Chapter 7 describes the beginnings of whole number operations as the operations grow out of naturalistic and informal experiences. Prior to entering first grade, young children also usually have an understanding of number symbols as they represent quantities. During the primary period (grades 1–3), children gradually learn the meaning of **action symbols** such as **add** (+), **subtract** (−), **multiply** (×), **divide** (÷), **equals** (=), **less than** (<), and **greater than** (>).

Teachers are expected to use state and locally developed lists of objectives, which today are becoming more in line with the Common Core State Standards (2010). Teachers are also expected to use state and/or school system selected textbooks to provide a structure for planning instruction. Unfortunately, primary teachers often tend to rely too heavily on textbooks, workbooks, and photocopied support materials. Conventionally, students are expected to be able to do paper-and-pencil arithmetic even though it might be developmentally inappropriate. Opportunities for using exploration

as a route to constructing concepts and operations are too seldom observed in the primary classroom. Students usually sit at individual desks with social interaction kept at a minimum (if allowed at all). One objective of the CCSSM is for children to take more initiative in their own learning and to engage in group problem solving.

Constance Kamii is a major critic of the conventional approach to mathematics instruction in the primary grades. She presents her point of view in her books *Young Children Reinvent Arithmetic* (2000), *Young Children Continue to Reinvent Arithmetic, Second Grade* (2003), and *Young Children Reinvent Arithmetic, Third Grade* (1994). As a Piagetian, Kamii believes—just as our ancestors did—that children reinvent arithmetic through their own actions and needs rather than learning through what someone else tells them. Children need to reinvent arithmetic through naturalistic and informal exploration with naturally occurring problems and through group games. Adults should encourage them to invent their own procedures and use their own thinking. Kamii explains that paper-and-pencil worksheet approaches remove the children from the logical thinking that is the heart of arithmetic. Kamii's emphasis on group games and social interaction as the basis for understanding arithmetic has its roots in Piaget's view that social interaction is essential as a stimulus for constructing knowledge. The following are examples of children solving problems through peer interaction:

- Three nonconservers are going to drink juice. The server pours juice into glass A. Now he must pour equal amounts into glasses B and C, which are different in size and shape from each other and from glass A. The children discuss how to do this in a fair manner and arrive at a solution: Use glass A as a measuring cup to fill the other two glasses.

- Derrick has written 7 + 4 = 10, and Brent has written 7 + 4 = 12. Their teacher has them explain to each other why they think that their respective answers are correct. Soon they discover that they are both wrong.

A danger in primary math instruction is that students will be pushed too fast before they have developed the cognitive capacity to understand the logical reasoning that underlies the operations. Keep in mind that children must be in the concrete operations period before they can successfully meet primary-level expectations. Beginning in kindergarten, standardized testing is performed each year, and teachers are pressured to teach the concepts and skills included in the tests. This pressure leads teachers to instruct arithmetic as a rote memory activity that has no logical meaning to the children. Children should be allowed to move at their own pace through primary math just as they did before entering first grade. They should also be allowed to invent their own procedures for solving problems. Herbert Ginsburg (1977) claims that young children naturally invent their own methods and should be able to use and experiment with them. For example, young children usually learn on their own to use counting methods for addition. When adding 2 + 2, the child might say, "One, two, three, four" using fingers or objects. If left on their own, they will eventually stop counting because they've internalized 2 + 2 = 4.

Carpenter, Carey, and Kouba (1990) point out that children enter first grade with informal concepts of the whole number operations. They also state the importance of observing the processes children use in solving problems. The authors believe that symbols should be introduced only to represent concepts that children already know. Instruction should begin with observations of naturalistic and informal activities.

Fuson, Grandau, and Sugiyama (2001) support the importance of informal teaching. "Such informal teaching can be done while children play, eat, get dressed, go up and down stairs, jump, and otherwise move through the day" (p. 522). During these activities, adults and more advanced peers can model mathematical concepts and skills, which children can then combine with understandings obtained during adult-guided mathematics activities. Games can support the transition into formal mathematics (see Fosnot & Dolk, 2001; Fosnot & Uittenbogaard, 2009).

This text describes a sequence of concept instruction with the caution to the teacher to bear in mind that children move at their own pace. As in previous chapters, this chapter describes, naturalistic, informal, and adult-guided activities. Adult-guided activities emphasize the use of concrete materials, with paper and pencil introduced through children's natural interests when they are ready.

8-1a Basic Combinations (Facts) and Algorithms

Isaacs and Carroll (1999) pose several questions about the value and purpose of learning the **basic facts** (or combinations) in the early grades. Will making first graders learn the addition facts interfere with their mathematical thinking? What kinds of instructional practices can build understanding and quick recall? Can children learn the facts through problem-solving activities, or are drill and practice needed? Isaacs and Carroll go on to provide answers to these questions. Knowing the facts is certainly essential to furthering mathematical understanding, but drill and practice and timed tests lead only to stress and anxiety. We should instead build on the knowledge children bring to school and support children in developing strategies for learning the basic facts. Children enter the primary grades with counting skills and an understanding that quantities can be broken down into parts. They can learn facts through solving problems using their understanding of counting and parts and wholes. Building concrete models supports understanding and remembering. Having students share strategies will move them toward more efficient ones. Useful practice that is brief and nonstressful—such as games, computers, or even flash cards—can support the learning of basic facts.

Baroody (2006) contrasts the conventional drill and practice approach to instruction with the number sense approach to learning the facts with understanding. Children usually learn the facts in three phases (Baroody, 2006, p. 22) as follows:

- *Phase 1.* Uses object counting (blocks, fingers, tally marks) or verbal counting—for 5 + 2 the child says 5 and then counts on, using two fingers, to get 7 (typical first grader).

- *Phase 2.* Uses reasoning strategies to arrive at the answer to an unknown combination—for 5 + 4 the child thinks 4 + 4 = 8, and so one more would be 9 (typical second grader).

- *Phase 3.* Mastery is achieved as answers come quickly and accurately—"5 + 4 = 9" the child responds without counting and reasoning (typical third grader).

The number sense view promotes learning the facts through discovering patterns and relationships that interconnect the basic combinations. Phases 1 and 2 serve this purpose by supporting the exploration and discovery that lead to seeing the patterns in each group of number facts. Adults should support children's use of informal strategies and focus on families of facts and their relationships. Children will gradually become more efficient. According to Baroody (2006), practice should be meaningful and should allow for flexible strategies.

Assessment should be process oriented in the primary grades; that is, children can use a number of strategies for solving problems. By the end of third grade and the beginning of fourth grade, children should be able to recall the addition and subtraction facts quickly and automatically.

Algorithms may be thought of as procedures, efficient methods, or rules for computation (Curcio & Schwartz, 1998). Several questions arise when it comes to instructional practice. Should algorithms be taught before, along with, or after children have had the opportunity to invent some of their own strategies? Curcio and Schwartz suggest that we begin with the children's own strategies and, through questioning, guide their reasoning toward more efficient and possibly conventional methods.

8-1b Computational Fluency

An important goal for the primary grades is developing **computational fluency** with whole numbers (NCTM, 2000). Russell (2000) provides guidelines for developing computational fluency. Fluency involves three ideas: efficiency, accuracy, and flexibility. *Efficiency* means the student can proceed directly without being distracted from his goal. *Accuracy* depends on being careful and double-checking results. *Flexibility* means being able to try out more than one strategy for solving problems. Fluency goes beyond memorizing one procedure or algorithm. As they learn more basic facts, they can apply this knowledge to recording their methods of problem solving. Children in grades K–2 should be encouraged to invent computational methods as they invent strategies to solve problems (Reys & Reys, 1998). Children in the early grades should be encouraged to invent their own problem-solving procedures (Heuser, 2005).

8-1c Action and Relational Symbols

At the primary level, children are usually introduced to the action and relational symbols. *Action symbols* show that some quantities have been or will be acted upon, or changed, in some way (+, −, ÷, ×); **relational symbols** show that quantities are in some way related (=, <, >). These symbols appear in **number sentences** that symbolize an operation, such as:

- 2 + 3 = 5 (two things put together in a group with three things is the same amount as five things).

- 5 > 2 (five is more than, or greater than, two).

Kamii and DeClark (Kamii, 1994, 2003; Kamii & DeClark, 2000) and others have found that young children often learn to deal with these symbols without a genuine understanding of how they relate to real quantities. Children should work with operations mentally through concrete experiences before connecting these operations to symbols and using complete conventional written number sentences such as 1 + 5 = 6, 5 − 3 = 2, 6 > 2, and so on.

Kamii suggests that full number sentences (e.g., 4 + 2 = 6) should not be introduced until second grade (Kamii, 2003; Kamii & DeClark, 2000). Children should be encouraged to devise their own notation systems and apply them as a bridge to formal notation. Children need experiences in joining and separating quantities and verbalizing about their actions before really understanding what symbols represent. Just filling in blanks in a workbook or marking answers in a standardized test booklet does not indicate that children understand the deeper meaning of number sentences.

In summary, formal number sentences should be introduced gradually. First, children should have extensive exploratory experiences that provide them with opportunities to invent their own solutions to everyday problems. They should be encouraged to find their own systems of recording solutions, using their own notation. Teachers should develop the language of number sentences through word problems that come from real-life experiences. They should introduce formal number sentences when children have developed to the level where they can understand that number sentences are a shorthand representation for words (see **Photo 8-1**). Teachers should introduce numeral notation first, then operational signs, and finally relational signs. Richardson's books (1984, 1999) are excellent resources for methods and materials that can be used for accomplishing these tasks. Hildebrandt, Biglan, and Budd (2013) describe an activity based on everyday experience that can be adopted at any age/grade level. The activity focuses on license plates. From the Internet the teacher developed a collection of license plates with at least five digits. The children were at tables in groups of three. First

PHOTO 8-1 The bead frame bridges from semiabstract to abstract.

each child added up her plate. Then the students added their table total to find which table had the largest amount. The class moved on to other number activities and some spelling activities using the letters on their license plates. The class moved on to PowerPoint journeys that followed highway road signs, which also included many numerals. Discussions that follow describe some ideas for introducing formal symbolic notation.

8-1d Instructional Strategies

Fraivillig (2001) outlines instructional strategies for advancing children's mathematical thinking. Effective teaching includes three aspects: eliciting, supporting, and extending children's solution methods. This framework is called *advancing children's thinking* (*ACT*). *Eliciting* (p. 456) involves supporting a variety of solutions for any problem by listening to children, encouraging elaboration, being accepting of errors, promoting collaborative problem solving, and being sure everyone has an opportunity to report. *Supporting* (p. 457) involves pointing out problems that are similar, providing background knowledge, supporting students as they review their strategies, putting symbolic representations of solutions on the board, and encouraging children to ask for help. *Extending* (p. 457) requires maintaining high standards and expectations for all children, encouraging the drawing of generalizations, listing all solutions on the chalk board or Smart Board to promote reflection, encouraging children to try alternative solutions and more efficient solutions, and promoting enthusiasm for challenge. Overall, the learning must take place in a safe environment in which all students feel comfortable and respected.

Informal Pre-Assessment. Observations and interviews can be used to assess children's progress in constructing operations with whole numbers. Assessment should be done through concrete activities with real-life or pretend situations. Assessment should be incorporated into instruction.

Paper-and-pencil tests are not appropriate for primary students until they can read and comprehend story problems on their own. Assessment examples will be provided as each whole number operation is discussed.

To find out whether children are ready to move on to whole number operations, use the assessment interviews in Appendix A, Concrete Operations: Level 8. These tasks include conservation of number, knowledge of symbols and sets, multiple classification, and class inclusion.

8-1e Algebraic Thinking

Schifter, Russell, and Bastable (2010) and Chappell (1997) outline the roots of algebraic thinking in the primary grades. Chappell points out that primary children are not ready for formal algebraic equations such as $x + 5 = 8$, but they can learn patterns using geometric shapes as variables. For example, in the guess-my-rule game, $\square + \square$ can indicate two $\square$ s. When doing missing addend problems (e.g., Tonio has 12¢ and needs 25¢ to buy a candy bar), a triangle can represent the missing addend: $12 + \Delta = 25$. Or counters can be used to set up the problem. Set out and write, "12 counters + empty cup = 25." Ask, "How many counters do we need to put into the cup in order to have 25?" A balance could also be used to demonstrate the problem. Chappell believes that the gate to algebra can be opened during the elementary years. The following is a sample activity adapted from those in the NCTM special issue. Additional activities are included in Greenes, Cavanagh, Dacey, Findell, and Small (2001).

ACTIVITIES

ALGEBRAIC THINKING: BUILDING RECTANGLES*

Objective: To introduce the patterns that determine the area of a rectangle, using nonstandard units.

Materials: Square tiles from sets such as TexTiles (Creative Publications) or Algebra Tiles (Cuisinaire).

Activity: Provide each child with a group of 20 tiles. Say, **"Use some of your square tiles to make a rectangle with a base of two tiles."** Ask the following kinds of questions.

1. "Did you all make the same rectangle?"
2. "How many tiles did you use in your rectangle?"
3. "How did you figure out how many tiles you used?"
4. "What is the height of your rectangle?"
5. "How would you build a rectangle that uses 18 tiles?"
6. "Can you figure out how high it would be without actually making it?"
7. "If you know how high you want a rectangle to be, can you figure out how many tiles you will need?"

Evaluation: Note the different strategies the students use (counting one by one, counting by twos, or others).

Follow-up: Try some of the other activities described in the articles suggested at the end of the chapter.

*Adapted from Yackel (1997).

Digital Download

8-1f Addition

Constructing the concept of addition requires children to understand that adding is putting together groups of objects to find out how many there are. It also involves learning the application of terms such as **total**, **sum**, and **equals**, as well as the operation signs (+ and =) that represent these terms, and connecting these amounts to symbols. Before children make these connections, they must understand quantity and what happens when quantities are combined.

Assessment. Assessing children's understanding of addition is more than finding out whether they know the so-called number facts. It is important to observe the process each child goes through in dealing with quantities. Observing the process and questioning children regarding what they have done will reveal what they do and do not understand. Their mistakes are informative and can be used to help them develop a more accurate knowledge of arithmetic.

Observations can be made during naturalistic and informal activities. Dean figures out that if he has two dimes and his grandmother gives him four more, he will have six dimes. Liu Pei decides that if three children are at one table, two at another, and four at a third, then she will need nine pieces of paper to pass out. Ann realizes that, instead of counting everyone to find out whether there are enough pencils, she can record the number at each table, find the total, and compare it with the number of pencils in the box.

Observations can also be made during adult-guided activities. Sara's teacher tells her to take groups of six cube blocks and place them in as many combinations of group sizes as she can. Does Sara realize that, however she arranges six objects (in groups of three and three; one and five; two, two, and two; two and four; or six and zero), there are still six altogether? The children are playing a card game called "Double War." Each player has two stacks of cards, which are turned over two cards at a time. The player with the higher sum gets the other player's two cards. The teacher can observe the children's strategies and whether they help one another. He can also suggest that they write and/or draw descriptions of their strategies.

As with the assessment of other math concepts, addition can also be measured using an interview approach. The following is a sample task.

SAMPLE ASSESSMENT TASK

9A   CONCRETE OPERATIONS AGES 6–8

ADDITION, COMBINING GROUPS UP TO 10: CHAPTER 8

METHOD Interview.

SKILL Child is able to combine groups to form new groups up to 10.

MATERIALS Twenty counters (cube blocks, Unifix Cubes, chips): 10 of one color and 10 of another.

PROCEDURE Have the child select two groups of counters from each color, so the total is 10 or less. Say, **"Put three yellow cubes over here and five blue cubes over here."** When the child completes the task, say, **"Now tell me, if you put all the cubes in one bunch, how many cubes do you have altogether? How do you know?"** Do this with combinations that add up to 1 through 10.

EVALUATION Note whether the child is able to make the requested groups with or without counting. Note the strategy the child uses to decide on the sum.

1. Does he begin with one and count all the blocks?

2. Does he count on? That is, in the example given, does he put his two small groups together and then say, "Three blocks, four, five, six, seven, eight. I have eight now"?

3. Does he just say, "Eight, because I know that three plus five is eight"?

INSTRUCTIONAL RESOURCE
R. Charlesworth, *Math and Science for Young Children*, 8th ed. San Francisco, CA: Cengage Learning, 2016.

Digital Download

Instruction. Instruction begins with naturalistic and informal experiences that familiarize children with quantities and how they relate to one another. Students can be guided toward constructing their own concepts if they are provided with games and word or story problems to solve and are encouraged to make up their own problems.

In *Young Children Reinvent Arithmetic* (2000), Kamii and DeClark describe a number of games that can support the development of addition concepts. The following are examples of activities.

ACTIVITIES

ADDITION: DOUBLE WAR

Objective: To construct combinations of addends (i.e., 1 + 1, 1 + 2, etc.) up to four.

Materials: Two decks of cards with different patterns on the back.

Playing the game: Start using the cards with addends up to four (aces, twos, threes, and fours). Have two children play together. To play the game, ask the children to begin with half the cards in each of the two decks, which are stacked facedown next to each other in front of them. Without looking at the cards, ask them to simultaneously turn over the top two cards from each deck. Have each find the total of her two cards. Have the child with the highest total keep all four cards.

Follow-up: Add the cards with the next higher addends as the children become adept with the first four. If the game takes too long, remove some of the smaller addends as the larger ones are included. Have the students write and/or draw descriptions of their strategies.

ADDITION: BOARD GAMES

Objective: To construct combinations of addends up to six.

Materials: A pair of dice, a marker for each player (four), and a board game. Purchase or make board games. Design games with themes that fit units in science and social studies. Some basic board-game patterns and the materials needed for construction are described in Chapter 7. Design board games at the primary level with more spaces than those in Chapter 7 because older students may move farther on each turn and will have longer attention spans.

Playing the game: Each player, in turn, rolls the dice, finds the sum of the roll, and moves the marker that many spaces.

Follow-up: Bring in new games as the students become skilled at playing the old ones. As the students become adept at playing board games, purchase or make some with pitfalls. In other words, on some spaces the player might have to move backward or lose a turn (e.g., when a player lands on a red space, he rolls the dice again, and the player moves backward the sum of the dice; or when a player lands on a certain space, he loses a turn).

Digital Download

Chapter 1 describes the importance of problem solving. Placing operations in the context of real-life situations makes them come alive for the students so they can see the practical applications of mathematics. Richardson (1984, 1999) suggests that children act out stories using real objects from around the room as props. For example, Derrick brings six books from the library center, and Theresa brings four. "How many did they bring altogether?" Derrick and Theresa actually demonstrate by going to the library center and obtaining the number of books in the problem. Trang Fung joins Dean and Sara. "How many children were there to start with?" "How many are there now?" Again, the children act out the situation. Richardson (1999) provides resources for acting out story problems with Unifix Cubes and other objects.

Carpenter et al. (1990) identify four types of addition problems:

- *Join, result unknown.* Kim has two cars. Mario gives her five more cars. How many does Kim have altogether?

- *Separate, start unknown.* Kim has some cars and gives two to Mario. Now she has five cars. How many cars did Kim have to start with?

- *Part–part–whole, whole unknown.* Kim has two yellow cars and five blue cars. How many cars does she have?

- *Compare, compare quantity unknown.* Mario has two cars. Kim has five more cars than Mario. How many cars does Kim have?

The authors caution that textbooks often contain only join and separate problems even though all four types should be introduced. A further caution is that these types are not formulas to be memorized, but just problem variations that children need to explore.

As children become more advanced, the numbers can be larger, and more addends can be included. More complex, nonroutine problems should also be used (Chapter 1, part 3).

Once the children have had some experiences with teacher-made problems, they can create their own problems.

ACTIVITIES

ADDITION: STORY PROBLEMS

Objective: To construct the concept of addition by solving story problems.

Materials: Twenty small toys that fit a current theme, for example:

- Miniature dinosaurs during a dinosaur study theme

- Miniature dogs, cats, horses, and so on, during a pet study theme

- Miniature farm animals during a farm study theme

- Miniature vehicles during a safety study theme

Developing the problems: Let the students act out the problems as you tell the stories.

- "Find three plant-eating dinosaurs. Find four meat-eating dinosaurs. How many dinosaurs do you have?"

- "Mary has some puppies. She sells three puppies. Now she has two puppies left. How many did she have to start with?"

- "Officer smith gave tickets to the drivers of two cars for speeding. Officer vargas gave the drivers of three cars tickets for going too slow on the interstate. How many tickets did the officers give?"

- "Farmer smith has five horses. Farmer valdez has three more horses than Farmer smith. How many horses does Farmer valdez have?"

- "Four puppies went out to play. Two puppies jumped in a mud puddle. How many muddy feet were there? How many dry feet?"

Follow-up: Create problems to fit projects and other activities and events.

ADDITION: CREATING PROBLEMS USING DICE OR A FISHBOWL

Objective: To create their own addition problems.

Materials: A pair of dice or a container (fishbowl) full of numerals written on small pieces of cardboard cut into fish shapes; objects such as cube blocks, chips, or Unifix Cubes.

Playing the game: Either by rolling the dice or picking two fish, have each child obtain two addends. Have her count out the amount for each addend and then tell how many objects or fish she has.

Follow-up: Once students are having an easy time making up problems using the dice or the written numerals as cues, suggest that they write or dictate their favorite problem, draw it, and write or dictate the solution. For example, Brent's dog is expecting pups. He writes, "I have one dog. I hope she has five pups." Then he draws his dog and the five pups. He writes, "Then I will have six dogs."

Using number symbols is referred to as **notation**. Gradually, you can connect number symbols to problems as you find that the children understand the process of addition and understand class inclusion. Although most first graders can fill in the blanks correctly on worksheets, they do not necessarily really understand what notation means. To find out whether a child really understands notation, present a problem such as the following.

Show the child several (four, five, or six) counters. Then show how you add some (two, three, or four) more. Then say, "Write on your paper what I did." Even at the end of first grade, you will find very few children who will write the correct notation (i.e., $5 + 3 = 8$). It is very common for first graders to write the first and last numeral (5 8) or to write all three (5 3 8) and omit the action symbols. They may also be unable to tell you what they did

and why. It is important that the use of notation be an integral part of concrete problem-solving activities. CCSSM standards include placing unknowns in beginning equations, such as $5 + 3 = ?$.

Richardson (1984, 1999) suggests that formal instruction in connecting symbols to the process of addition begin with modeling of the writing of equations. After acting out a problem such as the one described previously, write the problem on the chalkboard or Smart Board, explaining that this is another way to record the information. For example, "Another way to write three cows plus six cows makes nine cows is: $3 + 6 = 9$ (three plus six equals nine)." Help the children learn what the plus sign means by playing games and doing activities that require the use of the plus sign with the equals sign. For example, try the following activity.

ACTIVITIES

ADDITION: USING NOTATION AT THE CONNECTING LEVEL

Objective: To connect symbols to problems, using numerals and the plus operation symbol.

Materials: Objects to count and one die.

Playing the game: Have children take turns rolling the die to find out how many to add. For example, a three is rolled. Have each child count out three counters. Write "3" on the

board. A five is rolled. The students count out groups of five to put with their groups of three. Write "3 + 5" on the board.

Follow-up: After working with you in small groups, students can work independently with problems written on cards: 2 + 3, 4 + 6, and so on. As you go by, observe what they do, and ask them to read the problems to you.

Digital Download

Children sometimes look upon the equals sign as indicating that the answer is coming next rather than understanding that it indicates there is the same amount on each side of the equation. This concept can be clarified by using a balance scale to explore equality.

When the children are comfortable with connecting the symbols to the problems and using the plus symbol, they can begin to write the notation themselves. Start with problems in which you write the notation, and have the children copy what you do before they go on to independent work. For example, have everyone pick five groups of five counters each. Then tell them to separate each group of five counters as many ways as they can, and you write the results.

$1 + 4 = 5$	1	2	1	2	5
$2 + 3 = 5$	+4	+3	1	2	+0
$1 + 1 + 3 = 5$	5	5	+3	+1	5
$2 + 2 + 1 = 5$			5	5	
$5 + 0 = 5$					

After you write each equation, have the children write it on a piece of paper and put it next to the counters they have counted out. Follow up by having the students work independently, finding out how many ways they can break the amounts,

up to six, and write the equations. When they are doing well with amounts up to six, have them move on to seven and above.

8-1g Subtraction

To conceptualize subtraction is to develop an understanding that subtracting involves taking objects away to find out how many are left or comparing groups of objects to find out the difference between them. It also involves learning the application of terms such as *minus, difference,* and *equal* as well as the action signs ($-$ and $=$) that represent these terms. Subtraction also involves thinking about **more than** ($>$) and **less than** ($<$) and the symbols that stand for these relationships. It also includes connecting to symbols as a shorthand notation for concrete operations. As with addition, before children make the connections to and between symbols, they must understand quantity and what happens when something is taken away from a group or when two groups are compared.

Assessment. Assessing children's understanding of addition is more than finding out whether they know the so-called number facts. It is important to observe the process each child goes through in dealing with quantities (**Photo 8-2**). Observing the process and questioning children regarding what they have done will reveal what they do and do not understand. Their mistakes are informative and can be used to help them develop a more accurate knowledge of arithmetic.

PHOTO 8-2   It is not uncommon for primary grade students to use their fingers as support when adding or subtracting.

© 2016 Cengage Learning®

minutes until school is out and if Ms. Hebert says that they will start to get ready to leave in five minutes, then they will have five minutes to get ready. Jason has 10 bean seeds. He decides that he can give Ann 4 because the 6 he will have left will be enough for his seed-sprouting experiment. Six children are allowed to work in the science center at one time. Brent notices that only four children are at the science center now. He suggests to Derrick that they hurry over while there is room for two more. Vanessa observes that there is room for eight children in the library center, whereas six at a time may work in the math center. Thus there is room for two more in the library center than in the math center.

Observations can be made during adult-guided activities. Dean is trying to figure out how many different amounts he can take away from five. Mrs. Williams notes that Dean is well organized and systematic as he constructs one group of five after another and takes a different amount away until he has the combinations five minus zero, one, two, three, four, and five. Derrick and Liu Pei are playing "Double War." They have to subtract the amount that is smaller from the amount that is larger. Mr. Wang can note whether the children can figure out the correct differences and whether they help one another.

As with addition, assessing children's understanding of subtraction should involve more than mere number facts. Observing and questioning children about their processes for dealing with quantities will indicate the level of their knowledge.

Observations can be made during naturalistic and informal activities. Chan figures out that if there are 10 more

Subtraction can be assessed using an interview approach. The following is a sample task.

SAMPLE ASSESSMENT TASK

9B   CONCRETE OPERATIONS AGES 6–8

SUBTRACTION, GROUPS OF 10 AND LESS: CHAPTER 8

METHOD Interview.

SKILL Child is able to subtract groups to make new groups using groups of 10 and smaller.

MATERIALS Twenty counters (cube blocks, Unifix Cubes, chips): 10 of one color and 10 of another and a small box or other small container.

PROCEDURE Pick out a group of 10 or fewer counters. Say, "I have seven cubes. I'm going to hide some in the box." (Hide three in the box.) "Now how many do I have left? How many did I hide?" If the child cannot answer, give her seven of the other color cubes, and ask her to take three away and tell you how many are left. Do this with amounts of 10 and less. For the less mature or younger child, start with five and less.

EVALUATION Note whether the child is able to solve the problem and understands the process used. Note whether the child has to count or whether she just knows without counting.

INSTRUCTIONAL RESOURCE R. Charlesworth, *Math and Science for Young Children*, 8th ed., San Francisco, CA: Cengage Learning, 2016.

Digital Download

Instruction. Just as with addition, instruction should involve informal experiences that familiarize children with how quantities are related to each other. Again, providing students with games or story problems can help them to construct their own concepts and problems. Once the students evidence an understanding of addition, introduce subtraction. Children can work with both addition and subtraction problems so that they can learn the clues for deciding which operation to use.

The game "Double War" can be modified and played as a subtraction game by having the player with the largest difference between her pair of cards keep all four cards. As with addition, begin with numbers up to four and then gradually include higher numbers as the children become adept at the game. Purchase or devise board games that use subtraction as the operation that indicates which way to move. Make a board game in which all the moves are backward. The theme might be running away from a wild animal or going home from a friend's house. Or dice could be thrown, and each move would be the difference between the two.

Of course, word or story problems are an essential ingredient in the instruction of subtraction, just as they are for addition. Set or act out problems in real-life contexts. For example, suppose Derrick and Theresa have brought 10 books from the library center. Continue the activity by asking children to take different numbers of books back to the library center and to find out how many are left after each trip. Place children in groups of different sizes. If there are five children in this group and three in this group, ask them, "Which group has more? How many more? How will we find out?"

A number of different basic patterns can be used for subtraction story problems. Carpenter et al. (1990) identify seven types of subtraction problems:

- *Join, change unknown.* Kim has three cars. How many more cars will she need to have eight altogether?

- *Join, start unknown.* Kim has some cars, and Mario gives her three more cars. Now she has eight cars. How many cars did Kim have to start with?

- *Separate, result unknown.* Kim had eight cars and gave Mario three cars. How many cars does Kim have left?

- *Separate, change unknown.* Kim had eight cars and gave some to Mario. Now she has five cars. How many did she give to Mario?

- *Part–part–whole, part unknown.* Kim has eight cars. Five are yellow, and the rest are green. How many are green?

- *Compare, difference unknown.* Kim has eight cars, and Mario has three cars. How many more cars does Kim have than Mario?

- *Compare, referent unknown.* Kim has eight cars. She has five more cars than Mario. How many cars does Mario have?

As with addition, once the children have experiences with teacher-devised story problems, they can dictate or write their own. The dice/fishbowl game can be modified for subtraction. Children can also dictate or write original problems, draw them, and write or dictate the solutions.

Introduce subtraction notation gradually. Connect number symbols to problems as you find that the children have understood the process of subtraction. To find out whether a child really understands notation, use the same type of procedure as for addition. In other words, show the child several counters (five, six, or seven). Have her tell you how many you have. Hide one or more of the counters, and ask the child to show you on paper what you did. Do not be surprised if very few late first graders and only some second graders will be able to write the correct equation.

Formal introduction of subtraction can begin with modeling. Act out a problem, and then explain that there is another way to record the information. Write the number sentence for the problem on the whiteboard or Smart Board. For example, "Another way to write five rabbits take away three rabbits is $5 - 3 = 2$ (five minus three equals two)." Help the children learn what the minus sign means by playing games and doing activities that require its use with the equals sign. For example, try the activity on the next page. Unknowns for subtraction can also be indicated with a symbol such as $5 - 3 = \Delta$.

As with addition, when the students are comfortable with connecting the symbols to the problems and using the minus symbol, they can begin to write the notation themselves. Start with problems where you write the notation, and have the children copy you before they go on to independent work. For example, have everyone pick six counters. Have them see what kinds of problems appear as different amounts are taken away. After each problem, take a new group of six so that the problems can be compared. You write the results of each takeaway on the whiteboard or Smart Board (e.g., $6 - 1 = 5$); have the children copy it on a piece of paper and put it next to the counters they have counted out. Follow up by having the students work independently. Find out how many subtraction problems they can discover, starting with groups of different amounts up through six. When they are doing well with amounts up to six, have them move on to amounts of seven and above.

ACTIVITIES

SUBTRACTION: USING NOTATION AT THE CONNECTING LEVEL

Objective: To connect symbols to problems, using numerals and the minus action symbol.

Materials: Objects to count and dice.

Playing the game: Have the children take turns rolling the dice to find out which numbers to subtract. Have them first identify the larger number and count out that amount of counters. The teacher writes "[larger number] −" on the whiteboard. Then have the children remove the smaller number of counters. The teacher continues writing: "[larger number − smaller number]." Then have the children identify how many are left in the original pile. The teacher completes the equation:

"[larger number − smaller number = difference]." For example, the children roll a six and a two. They make a group of six counters, and you write "6 −." Then they remove two counters, and you continue writing: 6 − 2. Then they identify the difference (four). You finish the equation: "6 − 2 = 4."

Follow-up: After working with you in small groups, students can work independently with problems written on cards: 5 − 1, 3 − 2, and so on. Have them make up problems, using dice or pulling numbers out of a fishbowl. As you observe what the children are doing, stop and ask them to read the problems to you.

The notations for greater (or more) than (>) and less than (<) are conventionally introduced in first grade along with subtraction, but children do not usually really understood them until grade 3. For the most part, students in early primary grades work with *more* and *less* using concrete materials such as those described in Chapter 3. As they begin to understand the concepts, the children can apply them in playing games. For example, lotto and bingo boards (see Chapter 7) can be used. For bingo, the players can roll a die and cover a square on their card that contains a number or set that is more than or less than the number rolled. For lotto, they would pick a numeral or set card and again cover a card on the board that was either more than or less than the numeral or set on the card. As students become familiar with the action symbols, cards could be used that indicate that they pick an amount or numeral that is > (more or greater than) or < (less than) one of those on the card. They could then move on to using cards that indicate an amount such as [__ > 2] or [__ < 5] and thus be required to use addition or subtraction to arrive at a selection.

Children need to understand that addition and subtraction are related (Fosnot & Dolk, 2001). They may both apply to the same problem. For example, in a problem where people get on and off a bus, people must be added to the passengers, and people getting off may be subtracted from the passengers to get the total at the end of the ride. Some problems might look like addition when they really involve subtraction. For example, Juan needs $5.00 to buy a toy. He has $3.00. How much more does he need? Addition and subtraction should be taught at the same time so that children can develop an intuitive understanding of their relationship.

8-1h Multiplication

Conceptualizing multiplication requires that the students understand what equal quantities are (Photo 8-3). Then, they can proceed to learn that multiplication is a shorthand way of adding equal quantities; for example, 4×3 is the same as $3 + 3 + 3 + 3$. Multiplication also involves learning the application of terms such as **factors** (the two numbers that are operated on) and **product** (the result of the operation). Students also learn the action terms **times** and *equals* and connect them to the action signs ($\times$ and $=$). Multiplication with concrete objects was introduced before the primary level and continues at this level for most primary students. Notation and the more formal aspects may be introduced toward the end of the primary level, but students are not usually proficient at the most fundamental level until fourth grade.

Assessment. Assessment of children's understanding of multiplication, as with the other whole number operations, is more than finding out whether children know the number facts. It is important to observe the process each child goes through in dealing with quantities and to ask questions that will reveal the thoughts behind his actions (Photo 8-4).

Observations can be made during naturalistic and informal activities. Use the terms *rows*, *stacks*, and *groups* to refer to equal groups that will be added. There is no rush to

PHOTO 8-3 The checkerboard and beads support multiplication.

© Cengage Learning®

PHOTO 8-4 Student reviews multiplication facts.

Charlesworth

use the term *times*. Many children learn to recite the times tables by heart without any understanding of what *times* really means. Children must first understand that, when they multiply, they are not counting individual objects, but rather groups of objects. Watch for incidents when children work with equal groups. For example, Dean comments that every child at his table has three carrot sticks. Theresa makes sure that each of the six children working in the science center receives four bean seeds to plant. Chan tells Ms. Hebert that he has purchased three miniature dinosaurs for each of the five friends invited to his birthday party. She asks him whether he can figure out how many he bought altogether.

Multiplication can also be assessed using an interview approach. The following is a sample task.

SAMPLE ASSESSMENT TASK

9F **CONCRETE OPERATIONS AGES 7–8**

MULTIPLICATION, READINESS: CHAPTER 8

METHOD Interview.

SKILL Child is able to demonstrate readiness for multiplication by constructing equal groups of different sizes from groups of the same size.

MATERIALS Twenty counters (cube blocks, Unifix Cubes, chips).

PROCEDURE Make two groups of six counters each. Ask the child, "**Make three groups of two chips (blocks, cubes) each with this bunch of six chips (blocks, cubes).**" When the child finishes (right or wrong), point to the other group of counters. **Now make two groups of three with these chips (blocks, cubes).**

EVALUATION Note whether the child is able to make the two different subgroups. Children who are not ready for multiplication become confused and do not see the difference between the two tasks.

INSTRUCTIONAL RESOURCE
R. Charlesworth, *Math and Science for Young Children*, 8th ed., San Francisco, CA: Cengage Learning, 2016.

Digital Download

Instruction. Just as with addition and subtraction, instruction in multiplication begins with naturalistic and informal experiences that familiarize children with quantities and how they relate to each other. Students can be guided toward constructing their own concepts if they are provided with games and story problems to solve and are encouraged to make up their own problems. Richardson (1984, 1999) suggests that the children should first be asked to look for equal groups in the environment. How many tables have four chairs? How many girls have two barrettes in their hair? How many children have three cookies for dessert? How many parts of the body can they identify that come in groups of two? What parts do cars have that come in groups of four?

Of course, word or story problems are an essential ingredient in the instruction of multiplication, just as they are for subtraction and addition. Set or act out problems in real-life contexts. Dean gives four children two crayons each. How many crayons did he pass out? Chan makes three stacks of books. He puts three books in each stack. How many books does he have? Ann gives each of the five people at her table four pieces of paper. How many pieces of paper did she pass out?

Build models of multiplication problems with the students. Stack counters put the stacks in rows and place them in groups as illustrated in **Figure 8-1**. For example, working with inch cubes:

- Make three stacks of four cubes each.

- Make four rows of five cubes each.

- Make six groups of two cubes each.

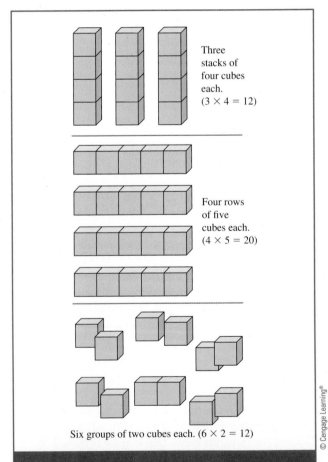

Three stacks of four cubes each. ($3 \times 4 = 12$)

Four rows of five cubes each. ($4 \times 5 = 20$)

Six groups of two cubes each. ($6 \times 2 = 12$)

FIGURE 8-1 Equal rows, stacks, and groups are the basis of multiplication.

Introduce notation gradually. Connect number symbols to problems as you find that the children understand the process of multiplication. The formal introduction of multiplication can begin with modeling. Act out a problem, and then explain that there is another way to record the information. Write the number sentence for the problem on the chalkboard or Smart Board. For example, explain that another way to write "Dean gave four children two crayons each" is [4 groups of 2 = 8]. Another way to write "Chan has three stacks of three books" is [3 stacks of 3 = 9]. Do several problems in this manner. Do problems with a symbol for the answer such as 3 stacks of three blocks = Δ. Then introduce the multiplication sign. First model. Explain that there is an even shorter way to write problems. Erase "stacks of" or "groups of" and write "×" in its place. Then write problems on the board and have the children work them out with their counters. Include symbols for the solutions such as 4 × 2 = Δ. Next, have children work out problems and copy you as you write the whole equation, that is, "4 × 2 = 8." Finally, have them make models and write the equations on their own.

Following is an example of an independent activity that can be done with multiplication using notation.

To find out whether a child really understands notation, use the same type of procedure you use for addition and subtraction. For example, show the child three or more equivalent groups, and explain that you are going to put the groups together into one group. Ask him to write what you did. If you showed three groups of four, he should write, "3 × 4 = 12."

ACTIVITIES

MULTIPLICATION: USING NOTATION AT THE CONNECTING LEVEL

Objective: To connect symbols to problems, using numerals and the times action symbol.

Materials: Counters, a die, several small containers, a sheet for recording the problems.

Activity: Have children work on their own writing equations. First let them decide how many containers to use. Have them roll the die or just pick a number. Have them line up the cups and then, starting with zero and one at a time, fill the cups and write the resulting equation. For example, if they pick four cups, they would first put zero blocks in each cup and write the equation, then one block in each, then two, three, and so on. Their work would look like that shown in **Figure 8-2**.

Follow-up: Develop some more independent activities, using the resources suggested for this unit.

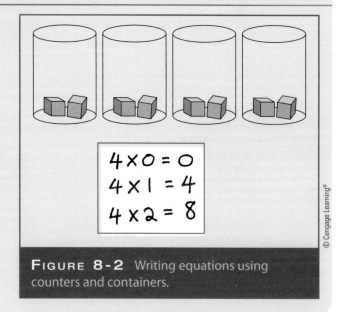

FIGURE 8-2 Writing equations using counters and containers.

© Cengage Learning®

Digital Download

8-1i Division

Division is an activity that children engage in frequently during their natural everyday activities (see Chapter 7). They are encouraged to share equally, and they are often asked to pass out items so that everyone has the same amount. Formal instruction in division is usually introduced toward the end of the primary period during the third grade, but children are not expected to be proficient in doing division problems until the fifth grade. Division is used to solve two types of problems.

- *Grouping* is the process used to find out how many subgroups of a particular size a larger group contains. For example, George has 15 blocks. He wants to make towers that are five blocks high. How many can he make?

- *Sharing* is the process of dividing a larger group into a particular number of groups to find out

how many items will be included in that number of subgroups. Six children will work in the science center, exploring the reaction of different types of items when magnets touch them. There are 32 items. How many will each child get? Are there any left over?

The children do not have to distinguish between these types of problems, which serve mainly as a guide for making up problems for them to explore. Eventually they will learn the terminology of division: **dividend ÷ divisor = quotient** and, if some are left over, **remainder**.

Assessment. Assessing children's understanding of division focuses on the processes they use to group and to share. The task on the following page can be used to assess the child's understanding of grouping and sharing.

Technology for Young Children

Voice and video recorders can be used to capture children's thinking and communication (Lapko, 2013). Children's reporting of their problem solutions and explanations can provide documentation of their performance. Interactive whiteboards such as Smart Boards have a recorder feature that allows for simultaneous auditory and visual recording. This mode can be used by students to share problem solutions.

Instruction. Division also begins with naturalistic and informal experiences. The teacher can give children many tasks that give them division experiences. Passing out items, putting items into groups to be shared, and finding out whether there is enough for everyone are opportunities for children to develop the division concept. The teacher could use games and story problems as guides in supporting the child's construction of the concept of division as she ventures into more formal activities.

SAMPLE ASSESSMENT TASK

91   CONCRETE OPERATIONS AGES 7–8

DIVISION, BASIC CONCEPT: CHAPTER 8

METHOD Interview.

SKILL Child can demonstrate an understanding that division consists of grouping or sharing objects.

MATERIALS Thirty counters (cube blocks, Unifix Cubes, chips) and five small containers (such as clear plastic glasses).

PROCEDURE Put out eight chips and four containers. Say, **"Divide up the chips so that each cup has the same amount."** When the chips are divided ask, **"How many cubes do you have in each cup?"** The child should respond "Two in each cup" rather than "I have two, two, and two." Try the same procedure with more cups and larger amounts to divide. Then try it with uneven amounts. Note whether the child becomes confused or can recognize that there are more cups than are needed. Also, do some sharing problems; for example, put out 16 chips. Ask,

"I want to give three friends the same amount of chips. How many will each one receive? Are there any left over?"

EVALUATION Note how the children handle the problem. Do they proceed in an organized fashion? Can they deal with the remainders?

INSTRUCTIONAL RESOURCE R. Charlesworth, *Math and Science for Young Children*, 8th ed., San Francisco, CA: Cengage Learning, 2016.

Digital Download

As with the other whole number operations, begin formal instruction by doing concrete problems. As Richardson (1984) suggests, tell the children stories and have them act them out. Start with real objects from the classroom. Here are two examples.

- Ann has 16 pieces of paper. Each child in her group needs four pieces. How many children can receive four pieces of paper?

- Jason, Chan, and Vanessa want to feed the guinea pig. The guinea pig gets six pellets of food. How many pellets can each child give it?

Next, have the children act out similar stories, using counters to represent real objects. Have the children make many models by constructing rows and stacks and dividing them into groups.

ACTIVITIES

DIVISION: MAKING MODELS

Objective: To construct models of division.

Materials: Counters (cube blocks, Unifix Cubes, chips) and several 16-ounce clear plastic cups.

Activity: Using different amounts initially and having the children divide them up into groups of different sizes and into different numbers of groups, have the students do many problems using the following patterns:

1. **"Make a row (train) with [number of] blocks [cubes, chips]. How many stacks of [number] can you make? Divide your row [train] of [number] into [number of] rows. How many cubes [blocks, chips] are in each row?"**

2. **"Get [number] cups. Divide [number] cubes into each cup so that there is the same amount of cubes in each cup."** Continue with different numbers of cups and counters.

Follow-up: Develop some more independent activities, using the resources suggested for this chapter.

Digital Download

Introduce division notation with modeling. Act out problems just as you did with the other whole number operations.

- "John has twelve crackers." Write "12" on the board. "He has three friends. He wants to give himself and each friend the same number of crackers." Write "12 ÷ 4." "Each child got three crackers." Write "12 ÷ 4 = 3."

- "The children are going to explore how pendulums work. There are four pendulums and eight children. How many children will have to share each pendulum? Eight children (write "8"), divided by four pendulums (write "8 ÷ 4") equals two children must share each pendulum (write "8 ÷ 4 = 2")."

After you have modeled several problems, let the children go to the next step by acting out the problems and copying what you write. Next, give them problems that they can act out with counters and write the equations themselves. When the children have completed the equations, write them on the board, and they can check theirs. Check each child's model and equation. Note whether there are any difficulties, and help children figure out how to act out and write the equation correctly. Move on to giving the children written problems (e.g., 10 ÷ 2 = ?), and ask them to act the problems out, using counters. Finally, have them make up their own problems, act them out, draw them, and write them.

To find out whether a child really understands notation, use the same procedure as suggested for the other whole number operations. Namely, act out division and then ask the children to write what you did. For example, count out 15 counters, and divide them into five groups of three. See whether the children can write "15 ÷ 5 = 3" and tell you that 15 divided into five groups makes three in each group.

8-1j Integration with Other Content Areas

Whole number operations can be applied in the other major content areas, as depicted in **Figure 8-3**. With an art project, for example, students can create squared paper designs, count the number of each color used in their design, and add the total number of squares included. For science, they can do environmental math such as graphing the contents of the trash can in the classroom and determining which type of trash is found in the largest amount. Social studies offers many opportunities, such as adding up the cost of a meal in a restaurant, dividing food into equal portions, or finding out how many of an item will be needed if each person in the group gets a fixed amount. Books, as previously described in Chapter 6, offer many opportunities for solving whole number problems.

8-1k Technology

Computers and hand calculators are useful tools for supporting the exploration of whole number operations and the properties of whole numbers. A multitude of software and Internet resources are available for working with basic whole number operations. Most of these programs are designed to help children remember the basic addition, subtraction, multiplication, and division facts. Many have interesting graphics that catch the children's attention and make drill and practice fun. With the capability of letting the children know right away whether the response is correct, the programs give the children immediate feedback and allow them to move along at their own pace.

During preprimary activities, children have explored some of the basic calculator capabilities. During primary activities, the calculator can be used for further exploration, for checking and comparing with manual calculations, and for problem solutions. A basic activity with the calculator is the exploration of multiples. Young children are fascinated with rhymes such as "Two, four, six, eight, who do we appreciate?" This type of counting is called **skip counting**. Skip counting in this example defines the multiples of two, that is, all the numbers that result when a series is multiplied by two (2 × 2 = 4, 2 × 3 = 6, 2 × 4 = 8, etc.). Children can explore these properties with the calculator through calculator counting (**Figure 8-4**).

8-1l Helping Children with Special Needs

In the primary grades, children are expected to become proficient readers. This is a special challenge for ELLs, and the challenge is compounded when they are given written or oral math problems to solve. Garrison, Ponce, and Amaral (2007) explored how mathematics teachers can find ways to help ELLs understand both the language and the mathematical concepts. Garrison and colleagues studied the results of a problem-based approach featuring adaptations for English Language Learners, compared with more traditional instruction—with no ELL adaptations—in two first-grade classrooms that included ELLs. "Our study found that students in the problem-based class were better and more persistent problem solvers than their peers in the traditional mathematics class" (Garrison et al., 2007, p. 13).

Often overlooked are the more able learners who fall in the gifted category (King, 2013). They may be achieving below their potential. Even the most able learners may have weaknesses. They may stick to one method of finding problem solutions when they should be encouraged to try others. Rather than following simple rules, they should be encouraged to play with numbers and be problem solvers. They should be given complex problems that are challenging.

The teacher started the year with simple problems using familiar vocabulary. These first problems were in the present tense, and any new words were discussed. Children first worked independently and then were put into pairs. A successful child was paired with a struggling child. Finally, children shared their strategies with the whole class. Gradually, the problems became more complex. By combining the teaching of English with mathematics, the class gained in both areas.

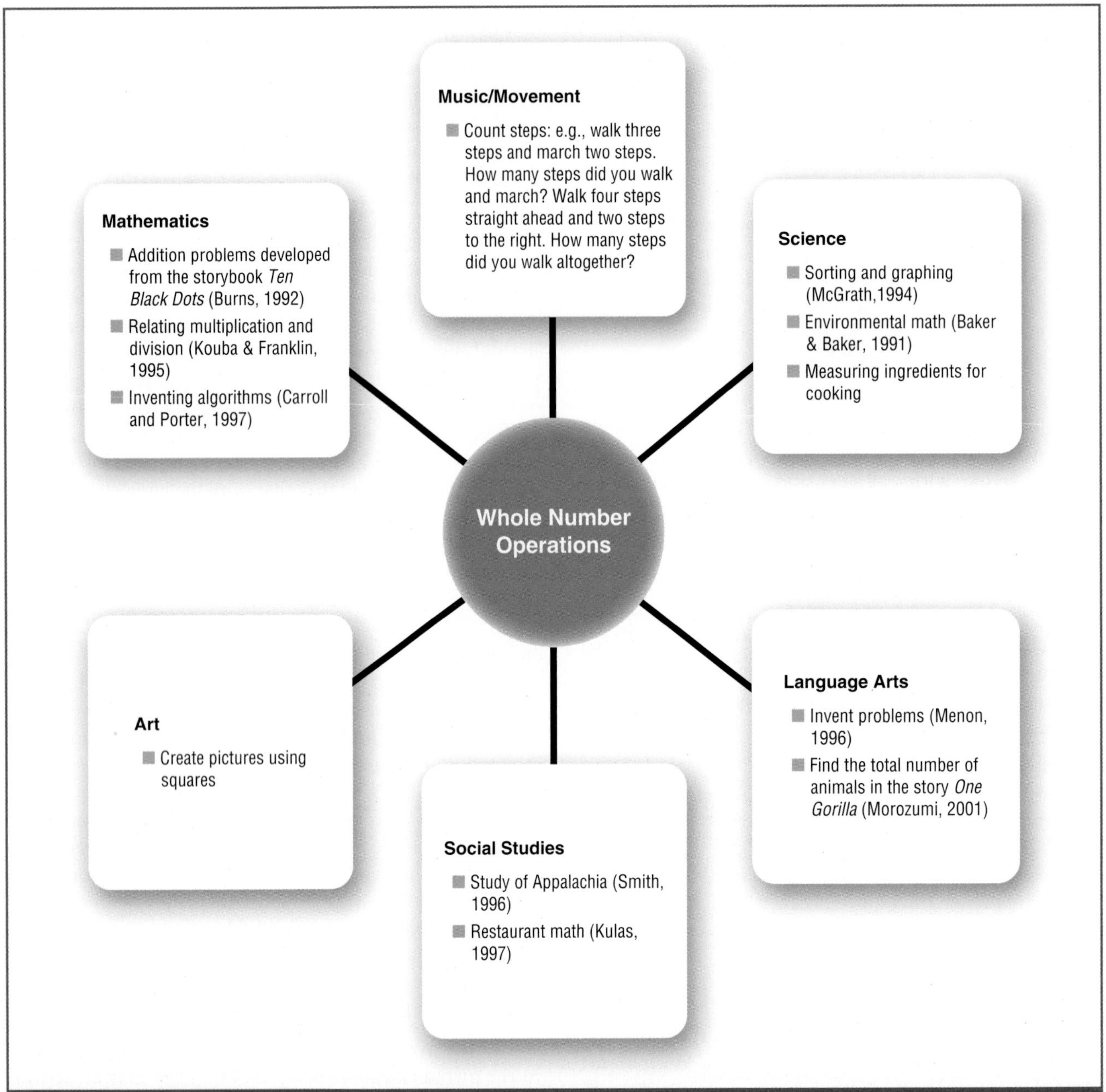

Music/Movement

■ Count steps: e.g., walk three steps and march two steps. How many steps did you walk and march? Walk four steps straight ahead and two steps to the right. How many steps did you walk altogether?

Mathematics

■ Addition problems developed from the storybook *Ten Black Dots* (Burns, 1992)
■ Relating multiplication and division (Kouba & Franklin, 1995)
■ Inventing algorithms (Carroll and Porter, 1997)

Science

■ Sorting and graphing (McGrath,1994)
■ Environmental math (Baker & Baker, 1991)
■ Measuring ingredients for cooking

Whole Number Operations

Art

■ Create pictures using squares

Language Arts

■ Invent problems (Menon, 1996)
■ Find the total number of animals in the story *One Gorilla* (Morozumi, 2001)

Social Studies

■ Study of Appalachia (Smith, 1996)
■ Restaurant math (Kulas, 1997)

FIGURE 8-3 Integrating whole number operations across the curriculum.

© Cengage Learning®

Tabor and Canonica (2008) were challenged to teach division to their special education students. These students had many misconceptions and computational difficulties. They focused on division as sharing and as the inverse of multiplication. Students shared objects and then wrote equations that illustrated their sharing. Then they moved on to writing sharing stories. They drew models of their problems and described their solutions. These and other tasks provided the students with the freedom to select numbers they felt comfortable with at their level.

8-1m Post-Evaluation

Evaluation, just as with assessment, should be done first with concrete tasks and should involve observing both the process and the product. The tasks in Appendix A and in this chapter can be used for evaluation as well as for initial assessment. Standardized achievement tests should not be administered until the students have the concepts internalized with concrete activities. For guidelines for testing young children, see the National Association for the Education of Young Children and the National Association of Early Childhood Specialists in State Departments of Education (NAEYC & NAECSSDE, 1991) position statement on standardized testing of children ages 3 to 8.

COUNT WITH YOUR CALCULATOR

Push ⬚C⬚ ⬚0⬚ ⬚+⬚ ⬚2⬚ ⬚=⬚

What do you see? _____

Push ⬚=⬚ again

What do you see? _____

What will the calculator show if you

push ⬚=⬚ again? _____

Do it. Were you correct? _____

Push ⬚=⬚⬚=⬚⬚=⬚.

Guess what the calculator will show each time. _____ _____ _____

What happened? _____

Complete the following. Then use your calculator to see if you are correct.

Push ⬚C⬚ ⬚0⬚ ⬚+⬚ ⬚3⬚ ⬚=⬚

The calculator will show _____

Push

⬚=⬚ _____

⬚=⬚ _____

⬚=⬚ _____

Push ⬚C⬚ ⬚0⬚ ⬚+⬚ ⬚4⬚ ⬚=⬚

The calculator will show _____

Push

⬚=⬚ _____

⬚=⬚ _____

⬚=⬚ _____

© Cengage Learning®

FIGURE 8-4 The calculator can be used to count equal multiples.

COMMON CORE
STATE STANDARDS

8-2 DESCRIPTION AND EXPLANATION OF PATTERNING

As described in Chapter 5, the expectations for prekindergarten through grade 3 patterning include that students will order objects by size, number, and other properties; recognize and extend patterns; and analyze how patterns are developed. Young children learn repetitive rhymes and songs and hear stories with predictive language. They develop patterns with objects and eventually with numbers. They recognize change, such as in the seasons or in their height as they grow. During the primary grades, children make a transition into more complex patterning activities, such as comparing patterns, learning number patterns, extending complex patterns, and gaining an understanding of **equality** (that two quantities are the same amount). By grade 3, students should be able to identify arithmetic patterns and explain them (CCSSM, 2010).

During first grade, problem solving connects number and operations and algebra. Children also learn about number patterns such as odd and even and those discovered in the 1-to-100 and 0-to-99 charts (**Photo 8-5**). At the second-grade level, children use number patterns to extend their understanding of number and operations. During third grade, a part of pre-algebra readiness is the understanding of multiplication and the relationship between multiplication and division.

Ordering, or putting things into a sequence, is basic to patterning. Patterning is the process of discovering auditory, visual, and motor regularities. Children must understand the many regularities in the number system. During the primary

© Cengage Learning®

PHOTO 8-5 Number patterns can be identified on the Hundred Board.

years, children work with more complex problems with concrete materials, connect concrete patterns to symbols, and learn to recognize some of the patterns and higher-level sequences in the number system.

By the end of third grade, the (National Governors Association, 2010) expectation for patterns is that children can identify arithmetic patterns and explain them using properties of operations. For example, children understand that 2 times a number is always an even amount and can be decomposed into two equal addends. This chapter focuses on extending the concept of patterning to more complex patterns and to connecting symbols and patterns. It also describes activities for looking at patterns in the environment.

8-2a Informal Pre-Assessment

Refer to Chapter 5 for a description of naturalistic and informal patterning behaviors that can be observed during children's activities. By the primary grades, children should be able to copy and extend patterns with ease. During the primary grades, they develop the ability to extend patterns, make more complex patterns, become more adept at describing patterns with words, build their own patterns, and see patterns in numbers. See Chapter 5 for a sample assessment task procedure for pattern copying, extending patterns, and describing patterns and more difficult extensions. The previous were examples of higher-level assessment tasks.

SAMPLE ASSESSMENT TASK

9K   CONCRETE OPERATIONS AGES 6–8

PATTERNS, EXTENSION IN THREE DIMENSIONS: CHAPTER 8

METHOD Interview.

SKILL The child can extend complex patterns in three dimensions by predicting what will come next.

MATERIALS Inch or centimeter cubes, Unifix Cubes, or other counters that can be stacked.

PROCEDURE Present the child with various patterns made of stacked counters. Ask the child to describe the pattern and to continue it as far as he can. Stack the blocks as shown in the following figure, one pattern at a time:

For each pattern ask, **"Tell me about this pattern. What comes next? How do you know? Continue the pattern for me."**

EVALUATION Note whether the child can continue each pattern and state his rationale. Note where the child might need further help and practice.

INSTRUCTIONAL RESOURCE R. Charlesworth, *Math and Science for Young Children*, 8th ed., San Francisco, CA: Cengage Learning, 2016.

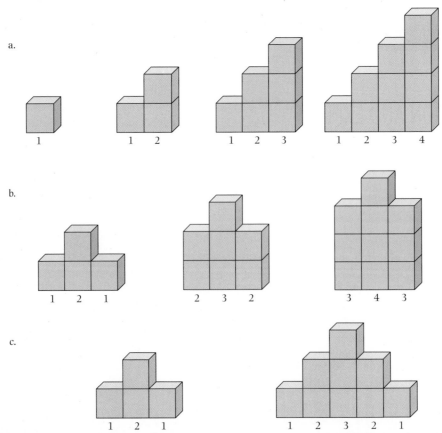

SAMPLE ASSESSMENT TASK

9M   CONCRETE OPERATIONS AGES 7–9

PATTERNS, MULTIPLE NUMBERS: CHAPTER 8

METHOD Interview.

SKILL The child can use a 1-to-100 chart to discover and predict number multiple patterns.

MATERIALS Inch or centimeter cubes, Unifix Cubes, or other counters, and a 1-to-100 chart (**Figure 8-5**).

PROCEDURE Start a pattern using multiples of two blocks. Tell the child, "**Circle or mark the amount in my group on the chart.**" If the child has a problem, show her the numeral 2, and circle it for her if necessary. Next to the group of two blocks, construct a group of four blocks. Use the same procedure. Continue up to 10. Then say, "**Show me which numbers you would circle if I kept continuing with this pattern.** " When children can predict accurately with multiples of two, try threes, fours, fives, and so on.

EVALUATION Note whether the children can connect the numbers in the pattern to the numerals on the chart and whether they can predict what comes next. If they cannot accomplish these tasks, note where their errors are:

Do they need more help with basic pattern construction? With counting? With connecting sets to symbols? With finding numbers on the chart?

INSTRUCTIONAL RESOURCE
R. Charlesworth, *Math and Science for Young Children*, 8th ed., San Francisco, CA: Cengage Learning, 2016.

1	2	3	4	5	6	7	8	9	10
11	12	13	14	15	16	17	18	19	20
21	22	23	24	25	26	27	28	29	30
31	32	33	34	35	36	37	38	39	40
41	42	43	44	45	46	47	48	49	50
51	52	53	54	55	56	57	58	59	60
61	62	63	64	65	66	67	68	69	70
71	72	73	74	75	76	77	78	79	80
81	82	83	84	85	86	87	88	89	90
91	92	93	94	95	96	97	98	99	100

FIGURE 8-5 1-to-100 chart.

© Cengage Learning®

Digital Download

DAP   naeyc

ACTIVITIES

PATTERNING: INCREASING PATTERNS

Objective: To copy and extend patterns using objects.

Materials: Counters such as chips, cube blocks, or Unifix Cubes; paper and pencil.

Activity: Examples of patterns that can be developed are given in the following figure. In each case, model the first three elements in the pattern; then ask the children to predict what comes next and to extend the pattern as far as they can. Have the children write down the pattern in numerals under each element and compare the patterns with both the objects and the numeral representations.

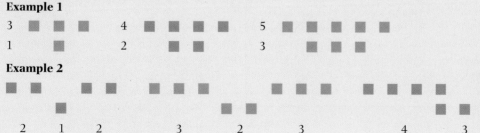

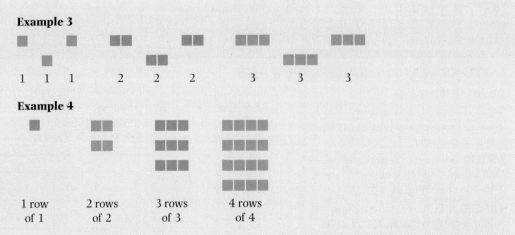

Follow-up: Have children work with various types of patterns until you believe they have grasped the concept.

Then, present the higher-level pattern activities that follow.

Digital Download

8-2b Activities

Children who have reached concrete operations are in a stage of cognitive development where they are naturally seeking out the rules and regularities in the world. Patterning activities fit the natural inclinations and interests of children in this stage. While they are engaged in calendar and 100-days activities, children are challenged to note number patterns and count by multiples (e.g., two, four, six, eight, …). They also enjoy arranging paper shapes into quilt patterns. The following examples are activities adapted from Richardson (1984, 1999) and Baratta-Lorton (1976). Patterning examples are also included in Greenes, Cavanagh, Dacey, Findell, and Small (2001) and in DeBellis, Rosenstein, Hart, and Kenney (2009).

ACTIVITIES

PATTERNING: TASK CARDS

Objective: To copy and extend patterns, using task cards.

Materials: Counters such as chips, inch or centimeter cubes, or Unifix Cubes; task cards with the first few steps (e.g., three) in a pattern.

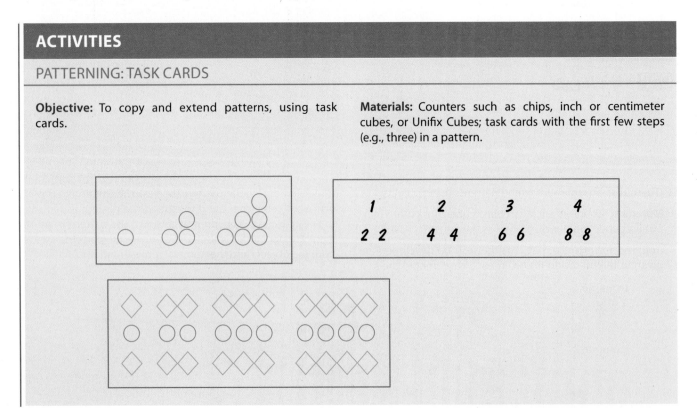

Task cards with the first step in a pattern.

Activity: Task cards with the first step in a pattern. Provide the models and then proceed to extend the patterns. With the three-step models, the pattern is set. With the one-step models, ask the children to create their own rules for extending the patterns. Always have them explain their patterns to you.

Follow-up: When the children have the concept of working from the abstract to the concrete with the task cards, have them create their own patterns, first with objects and then by drawing them, using the objects as models.

PATTERNING: ACTIVITIES WITH THE 1-TO-100 CHART

Objective: To perceive patterns on the chart in pictorial form. For children who have the concept of place value (see Chapter 9) for the 1s and 10s places, activities using the 1-to-100 chart activities are appropriate.

Materials: Copies of the 1-to-100 chart (see Figure 8-5) and counters.

Activity: On the chart, ask the children to color in or mark the amounts in their patterns, such as the one shown in the figure.

Ask the children then to mark off on the chart the amount in each part of the pattern: 5, 10, 15, 20, and so on.

Follow-up: Have the children transfer to the charts from patterns you provide and then move on to patterns that they devise themselves.

PATTERNING: EXPLORING NATURAL MATERIALS

Objective: To be able to observe and describe patterns in natural materials.

Materials: Fruits and vegetables such as cabbage, onion, orange, lemon, grapefruit, and apple; magnifying glass; pencil and paper.

Activity: Let the children explore and examine the whole fruits and vegetables. Encourage them to describe what they see and feel. Suggest that they examine the fruits and vegetables with the magnifying glass and draw them

if they wish. After a few days, ask them to predict what each item looks like inside. Then cut each one in half. Talk about what they discover. Compare what they see with what they predicted. Suggest that they draw the inside patterns.

Follow-up: Have each child use his pictures to make a *What's Inside?* book. Have him write or dictate what he knows about each item.

PATTERNING: MULTIPLES GRAPHS

Objective: To collect data regarding natural patterns and to depict the data on graphs.

Materials:

1. Number line templates made from heavy tagboard with the numbers written across. A hole is cut or punched below each one so that the numbers can be copied.

2. Large sheets of manila paper, rulers, crayons, markers, and picture magazines.

Activity: With the children, discuss the following questions:

■ "How many eyes do five people have among them?"

■ "How many legs do three chairs have among them?"

Have the children use their rulers to draw horizontal about 3 to 4 inches apart on a large piece of manila paper. Have them copy their number line at the bottom of the paper, using a template. The children draw or cut out pictures and paste them on their paper, as shown in **Figure 8-6**. Then they record the number of eyes [legs] down the right side of the paper, and circle the corresponding numerals on the number line. Ask them to examine the number line and describe the pattern they have made.

Follow-up: Have the children think of other items they could graph in multiples to create patterns.

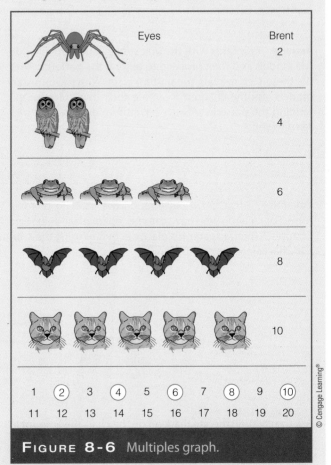

FIGURE 8-6 Multiples graph.

PATTERNING: DIVISION

Objective: To make division patterns.

Materials: Large (11 × 18-inch) pieces of paper, smaller (4¼ × 5½-inch) pieces of paper, scissors, crayons or markers, and glue.

Activity: With the whole group, start with a large piece of paper. Have a child cut the paper in half and give one half to another child. Then, have each child cut the paper in half and give one part away. Keep a record of the number of cuts and the number of children until everyone has a piece of paper. Next, give each child a large piece of paper and a small piece of paper. Have them glue the smaller piece at the top of the larger sheet (**Figure 8-7**). Have them take another small piece, cut it into halves, and glue the two parts on the large paper below the first whole piece (see Figure 8-7). Have them take another small piece, cut it into halves, and then cut each half into halves. Glue these four parts on the large sheet. Let them continue as long as they wish. Have them record the number of pieces in each row on the right-hand side of the chart.

Follow-up: Have the more advanced children cut three parts each time to see what kind of pattern they make.

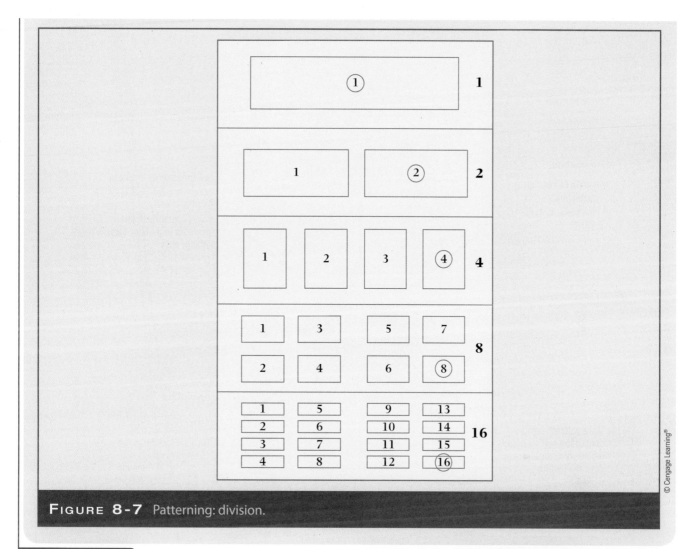

FIGURE 8-7 Patterning: division.

Digital Download

Other patterning activities can be developed using manipulatives such as pattern blocks. Pattern blocks are available in a variety of sizes, thicknesses, and colors. Many supplementary materials are also available, such as tracing templates, stickers, rubber stamps, and puzzles (see the Creative Publications catalog, address in Chapter 12). You can also make your own materials. Pattern blocks can be used to make quilt designs. Patterning activities can also be developed from children's literature (see Appendix B for the book list). As with other concepts, patterning activities can be integrated across the curriculum (**Figure 8-8**).

As was described earlier in this chapter, calculator activities are interesting ways to look at number patterns (**Photo 8-6**). After some practice with patterns, as suggested in section 8.1, have the children discover and extend patterns with their calculators; for example, make up some more patterns for the children to explore with calculators.

Clements and Sarama (2000) describe the predict-and-cover activity, which can be done both on and off

PHOTO 8-6 Calculators can provide opportunities to explore number patterns.

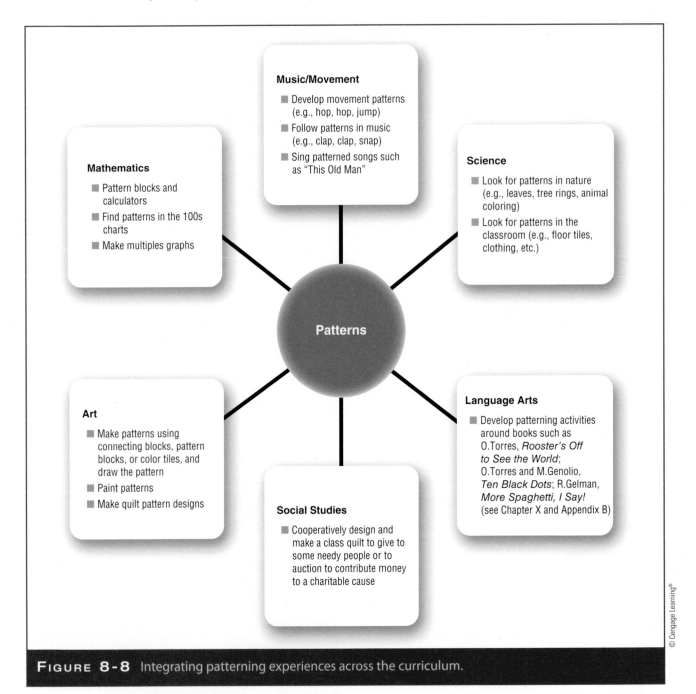

Music/Movement
- Develop movement patterns (e.g., hop, hop, jump)
- Follow patterns in music (e.g., clap, clap, snap)
- Sing patterned songs such as "This Old Man"

Mathematics
- Pattern blocks and calculators
- Find patterns in the 100s charts
- Make multiples graphs

Science
- Look for patterns in nature (e.g., leaves, tree rings, animal coloring)
- Look for patterns in the classroom (e.g., floor tiles, clothing, etc.)

Patterns

Art
- Make patterns using connecting blocks, pattern blocks, or color tiles, and draw the pattern
- Paint patterns
- Make quilt pattern designs

Social Studies
- Cooperatively design and make a class quilt to give to some needy people or to auction to contribute money to a charitable cause

Language Arts
- Develop patterning activities around books such as O.Torres, *Rooster's Off to See the World*; O.Torres and M.Genolio, *Ten Black Dots*; R.Gelman, *More Spaghetti, I Say!* (see Chapter X and Appendix B)

© Cengage Learning®

FIGURE 8-8 Integrating patterning experiences across the curriculum.

the computer. First, the children explore pattern blocks, developing their own designs. Then, they are provided with specific shapes and asked to predict and select which pattern blocks will cover the shapes provided. Patterning activities can be found online on the Virtual Manipulatives website and on the Illuminations website. Several advantages of doing the activity on the computer are listed here:

- It gives children more flexibility.
- Work can be saved and retrieved.
- Children can design their own patterns.
- Tasks are broken down in ways that clarify mathematical mental actions.

You may access the online resources for relevant links to websites and online activities.

BRAIN CONNECTION

HOW PATTERNS HELP OUR THINKING

Through repetition we learn to recognize the patterns in our environment (D'Souza, 2010). We learn that distinctive features provide the rules for objects that define the pattern. Talented people see patterns at a faster speed than most of us. Visual patterns light up more in autistic people's brains than in the general population (Chan, 2011). These brain regions are called the temporal and occipital areas.

People with autism spectrum disorder have less brain activity in the frontal brain regions associated with planning and decision making. People with autism perform strongly on visual tasks. Thus, they can learn best when symbols are taught in groups, such as families of numerals, as related patterns.

A. Chan, "Autistic Brain Excels at Recognizing Patterns," Livescience, April 4, 2011, www.livescience.com.
S. D'Souza, "Understanding Patterns: How Your Brain Thinks," Psychotactis.com, June 24, 2010, http://www.psychotactics.com.

8-2c Helping Children with Special Needs

Included in Chapters 8 and 9 are descriptions of the practical developmental implications of different disabilities. This part focuses on the blind child (Lewis, 2003). In the case of any disability, the teacher must avoid stereotypes; every child is an individual.

Children with visual disabilities must depend on their other senses for information. Rhymes and routines are therefore essential for the visually impaired young child. The adult should talk during routines, describing what is happening.

Give-and-take games can be very educational. Objects can be incorporated into routines and rhymes, because touch is an important element in a blind child's learning about the environment. The adult should label and explain toys.

Spatial relationships (such as putting a cup on the table or climbing on a chair) should be practiced. In the classroom, the blind child needs time to explore. A peer can be helpful as a mentor. Consistent routines are very important. During the primary grades, reading is a major focus, and children who are blind learn Braille.

The concrete materials used in mathematics instruction are extremely useful for the blind child. She may need extra time to become familiar with materials and learn to organize them. Texture can be very helpful. For example, patterns using rough and smooth or pattern blocks of different shapes are appropriate adaptations.

FIND THE RULE AND FINISH THE PATTERN

Use your calculator.

<u>7</u>, <u>9</u>, <u>11</u>

PRACTICE PATTERN: 1, 3, 5, _____, _____, _____   RULE: +2

1. Rule: +2

   Pattern: 2, 4, 6, _____, _____, _____

2. Rule: +3

   Pattern: 3, 6, 9, _____, _____, _____

3. Rule: _____

   Pattern: 2, 5, 8, _____, _____, _____

4. Rule: _____

   Pattern: 12, 16, 20, _____, _____, _____

5. Rule: _____

   7, 9, _____, 13, _____, _____, _____

6. Rule: _____

   5, _____, 15, _____, _____, 30, 35, _____,

8-2d Informal Evaluation

Note how the children deal with the suggested pattern activities. Do they count each part out loud? Do they seem to be doing the patterning logically by applying their number sense concept (e.g., through subitizing)? When asked, can they explain the pattern? Use the assessment tasks in Appendix A for individual evaluation interviews.

8-3 STANDARDS AND DESCRIPTIONS OF FRACTIONS

In Chapter 4, it was explained that young children have a natural understanding and interest in parts and wholes that can be used later as a bridge to understanding fractions. By the end of grade 3, according to the Common Core State Standards (2010) expectations, children should develop an understanding of fractions as numbers. Specifically, they should

- Understand that $1/b$ is the quantity formed by one part when a whole is divided into b parts and that a/b is more than 1 part.

- Understand a fraction as a number on the number line and represent fractions on a number line diagram.

- Explain the equivalence of fractions in special cases and compare fractions by reasoning about their size.

Understanding and manipulating fractions is essential to moving on to more advanced mathematics (Shellenbarger, 2013; Siegler, Fazio, Bailey, & Zhou, 2013; Sparks, 2013). Many students hit a barrier in fourth grade, when fractions become a central part of the mathematics curriculum. Therefore, with the National Governors Association (2010), as fractions move down into third grade, children need to get off to a good start.

As described in Chapter 4, the fundamental concept of *parts* and *wholes* is the basis for understanding fractions. Through naturalistic, informal, and adult-guided experiences, preprimary children become familiar with three aspects of the part–whole concept:

- Things have special parts.

- A whole object can be divided into parts.

- Groups of things can be divided into smaller groups.

Children also become familiar with the application of the terms *more*, *less*, and *same*. During the primary level, young children expand on the concrete activities they engaged in during the preprimary level. It is important not to introduce notation and symbols too soon, but to allow time for children to conceptualize fractions at the concrete level before adding symbols. Even 9-year-olds have difficulty with fractions at the symbolic level. Thus, for most children, fraction symbols cannot safely be introduced until the end of the primary period (the latter part of grade 3) and may not be fully understood until well into the intermediate level (grade 4 or higher). Fraction problems cannot be solved by counting, as can whole number problems. This fact makes them much more abstract and thus more difficult.

At the presymbolic level, children's work with fractions should be limited to **halves**, **thirds**, and **fourths**. We deal with these fractions the most frequently in life, and, once children understand them, they should be able to transfer their knowledge to fractions in general. Children can learn fraction terminology relative to concrete experiences without being concerned with the corresponding symbols. Terms such as *one-half, one-third*, and *one-fourth* can be associated with parts of concrete objects and subgroups of large groups of concrete objects, as well as parts of a number line. During the primary period, children continue to work with fractions as part–whole relationships. They can work with volume, regions, length, and groups.

- Experiences with foods (such as cutting up a carrot) and cooking (measuring ingredients) involve *volume.*

- *Regions* are concrete and easy to work with. They involve working with shapes such as rectangles, squares, and triangles. (See Pieces of cake problem, Foster, 2011/2012.)

- *Lengths* can also be divided into parts. Long, narrow pieces of paper, string, thread, ribbon, and number lines are useful for this type of activity.

▶❚❚ **TeachSource Video**

WHEN THE DOORBELL RANG

The teacher and students discuss fractions as they relate to the children's book *When the Doorbell Rang* by Hutchins. The story focuses on sharing cookies first with two children and eventually more. The students have previously shown in pictorial form how 12 cookies could be divided into two equal groups. In small groups the students write and discuss possible number sentences and then share their results with the whole class.

1. What other curricular areas are integrated?

2. What did the students understand about fractions?

3. How did the teacher include discussion?

- A whole *group* of objects serves as the unit to be divided into smaller subgroups. (See "Fair Share, Matey," Wilson, Myers, Edgington, & Confrey, 2012.)

Siegler, Carpenter, Fennell, Geary, Lewis, Okamoto, et al. (2010) and Siegler, Fasio, Bailey, and Zhou (2013) examined the research base for effective fractions instruction from kindergarten through eighth grade. Research indicates that most children lack a conceptual understanding of fractions. Here are five recommendations for fraction instruction:

1. Build on students' informal understanding of sharing and proportionality to develop initial fraction concepts. When they enter school, most children have a basic understanding of sharing, which can serve as a foundation for learning about fractions.

2. Ensure students' understanding that fractions are numbers that expand the number system beyond whole numbers. Use number lines to represent this concept.

3. When symbols are introduced, help students understand why the procedures for computation with fractions make sense—for example, why common denominators are necessary for addition and subtraction but not for multiplication and division.

4. Assist students in seeing how fractions apply in everyday life.

5. Urge teacher education and professional development programs to emphasize how to improve students' understanding of fractions.

The research evidence is strongest for recommendations two and three.

8-3a Informal Pre-Assessment

Chapter 4 described both observational and interview tasks for assessing part–whole concepts. Children are ready to understand fractions when they understand that a whole can be divided into parts, that when a quantity is divided its whole is conserved, and that the size of each part gets smaller as the number of equal divisions increases. If children evidence some of the behaviors described in Chapter 4, indicating that they understand the part–whole concept and are able to respond successfully to the Chapter 4 assessment tasks, then try the following kinds of higher-level assessment tasks.

SAMPLE ASSESSMENT TASK

9N   CONCRETE OPERATIONS AGES 6–8

FRACTIONS, EQUIVALENT PARTS: CHAPTER 8

METHOD Interview.

SKILL The child can divide a rectangle into smaller equal parts.

MATERIALS A supply of paper rectangles of equal size (8½ × 2¾ inches) in four different colors; a pair of scissors.

PROCEDURE Show the child a paper rectangle. **"This is a rectangle."** Place two more rectangles of a second color below the first one. **"Here are two more rectangles. Are all three the same size?"** Be sure the child agrees. Let him compare them to be sure. **"Now I'm going to fold one of the [second color] rectangles so that both parts are the same."** Fold the rectangle. **"Now you fold this other one that's also [the second color] just like I did."** Offer assistance if necessary. The three rectangles should look like this:

Color 1

Fold — Color 2₁

Fold, then cut — Color 2₂

"Are the parts of the [name the second color] rectangle the same size as the parts of this one?" [also the second color] **"Show me how you know. I'm going to cut this one [second color] on the fold. How many parts do I have now? If I put them back together, will they be the same size as this whole rectangle? As your [name the first color] rectangle? What is a special name for this amount of the whole rectangle?"** Point to the half. If the child's response is one-half, go through the procedure again with one-third and one-fourth, using the third and fourth colors, respectively.

EVALUATION Note whether the child has to check on the equivalency of the three rectangles. Can he keep in mind that the parts still equal the whole, even when cut into two or more parts? Does he know the terms *one-half, one-third,* and/or *one-fourth?*

INSTRUCTIONAL RESOURCE
R. Charlesworth, *Math and Science for Young Children*, 8th ed., San Francisco, CA: Cengage Learning, 2016.

SAMPLE ASSESSMENT TASK

90   CONCRETE OPERATIONS AGES 6–8

FRACTIONS, ONE-HALF OF A GROUP: CHAPTER 8

METHOD Interview.

SKILL The child can divide a set of objects into smaller groups when she is given directions using the term *one-half*.

MATERIALS Ten counters (cube blocks, chips, Unifix Cubes, or other concrete objects).

PROCEDURE Place the counters in front of the child. Say, **"I have some** **[name of counters]. Divide these so that we each have one-half of the group."** If the child completes this task easily, go on to nine counters, and ask her to divide the group into thirds. Then go on to eight counters, and ask her to divide the group into fourths.

EVALUATION Note the method the child uses. Does she use counting, or does she pass the counters out: "One for you and one for me"? Does she really seem to understand the terms *one-half, one-fourth, and one-third*?

INSTRUCTIONAL RESOURCE R. Charlesworth, *Math and Science for Young Children*, 8th ed., San Francisco, CA: Cengage Learning, 2016.

Digital Download

8-3b Activities

Chapter 4 emphasized naturalistic and informal activities as the foundation for adult-guided experiences. These activities should be encouraged and continued. Primary children continue to need time to explore materials and to construct their concept of parts and wholes through their own actions on the environment. Children can explore many materials independently to develop the foundations for understanding fractions. Children can organize any of the usual kinds of counting objects as a group, which they can divide (or partition) into smaller groups. Some materials for dividing single objects or shapes into parts are available from companies such as Lakeshore and ETA/Cuisinaire. These companies have a variety of fraction bars and number lines. Open-ended materials include Unit Blocks (Community Playthings), Cuisinaire Rods (ETA/Cuisinaire), puzzles (Lakeshore), and Legos. It is now recommended that fractions not be introduced as parts of geometric shapes, especially circles, but on number lines which show relationships more clearly (**Photo 8-7**). Placing fractions on a number line in third grade is the best predictor of their fourth-grade fraction skills.

Following are adult-guided activities that can be used to develop fraction concepts.

PHOTO 8-7 The parts of the fraction circles can be copied and recorded for later reference.

For the more advanced third-grade students, notation may be introduced on number lines or on fraction bars. Show the students how one-half can be written as ½, which means one part out of two. Then ask how they think they might write one-third as one part out of three, two-thirds as two parts out of three, and so on. (Shellenbarger, 2013; Siegler, Fazio, Bailey & Zhou, 2013; Sparks, 2013), Have them write the numerical fractions that match the parts of some of the materials suggested earlier in the chapter.

ACTIVITIES

FRACTIONS: COMPARING LENGTHS ON NUMBER LINES

Objective: To compare sizes of halves, thirds, and fourths.

Materials: Same as in previous activity.

Activity: Put out the models one set at a time. Ask the children, **"Which is longer—a half, a third, or a fourth? How many fourths make one-half?"**

Follow-up: Provide models of other fractions for children who have a good understanding of halves, fourths, and thirds. Provide sets of commercial fraction number lines.

FRACTIONS: PARTS OF GROUPS

Objective: To divide groups of objects into subgroups of halves, thirds, and fourths.

Materials: Draw, color, and cut out a mother rabbit, four child rabbits, and twelve carrots (see **Figure 8-9** for patterns).

Activity: Place the mother rabbit, two child rabbits, and four carrots in front of the children. Say, "**Mother rabbit has four carrots and wants to give each of her children half of the carrots. Help her by dividing the carrots between the two children so that each has half.**" Give the child time to complete the task. Say, "**Now suppose she has four carrots and four children.**" Bring out two more children. "**Show me how they can share the carrots so that each has one-fourth of the carrots.**" As long as the children are interested, continue the activity, using different numbers of child rabbits and different numbers of carrots. Emphasize that the carrots must be shared so that it is fair to everyone.

Follow-up: Make other groups of materials (such as children and apples, or dogs and bones, or children and cookies, using *The Doorbell Rang* book as in the TeachSource video). Move on to other fractions when the children can do these problems easily.

Figure 8-9 Patterns for the parts-of-groups activity.

© Cengage Learning®

FRACTIONS: LIQUID VOLUME

Objective: To compare fractional parts of liquid volume.

Materials: Several sets of color-coded standard measuring cups, if available, and a pitcher of water. If color-coded cups are not available, mark each size with a different color (e.g., 1 cup with blue, ½ cup with red, ⅓ cup with yellow, ¼ cup with green).

Activity: Give each child a set of measuring cups. Let the children examine the set and tell you what they notice. After discussion and examination, have the children pick up their 1-cup size and their ½-cup size. Ask, "**How many of these small cups of water will fill the large cup?**" Let the children predict. Say, "**Fill your small cup with water. Pour the water into your large cup. Is the large cup full? Pour in another small cup of water. Is the large cup full now? How many of the smaller cups were needed to fill the larger cup?**" Follow the same procedure with the ⅓- and ¼-size cups.

Follow-up: Reverse the procedure. Starting with the full 1-cup measure, have the children count how many ½, ⅓, and ¼ cupfuls it takes to empty the full cup. Do the same activity using rice, birdseed, or sand instead of water.

FRACTIONS: LENGTH

Objective: To compare fractional parts of lengths.

Materials: Cuisinaire Rods.

Activity: Provide the children with a basket full of Cuisinaire Rods, and let them explore the rods. Then, suggest that they select a long rod and find out which lengths of rods can be placed next to it to show halves, thirds, and fourths.

Follow-up: Follow the same procedure with whole straws and with straws cut into halves, fourths, and thirds. Try the activity with other materials such as string, ribbons, and paper strips.

FRACTIONS: NUMBER LINES (END OF SECOND GRADE)

Objective: To represent a fraction 1/*b* on a number line diagram by defining the interval from 0 to 1 as the whole and partitioning it into *b* equal parts. Recognize that each part has the size 1/*b*.

Materials: A laminated 0–1 number line for each child, a large laminated 0–1 number line that can be used for demonstration (or a permanent number line on the whiteboard), and objects to use as markers to indicate places on the number line.

0   >--------------------------------------→ 1

Activity: Ask the children, "If 1/*b* is ½, how many parts would your line be divided into? Place your marker at 1/*b*."

Note whether the children place a marker halfway between 0 and 1. Select a child to point to 1/*b* on the demonstration line. Using the same procedure, go on to *b* = 3 and *b* = 4.

Follow-up: Try the Ribbon Factory problem from PBS Mathline. Five customer complaints are presented:

1. The ribbon sent is ½ as long as it should be.
2. The ribbon sent is twice as long as it should be.
3. The ribbon should be ¾ as long as the one sent.
4. The ribbon is too short; it should be 6½ times as long as the ribbon sent.
5. This ribbon should be ⅛ the length sent.

FRACTIONS: USING LITERATURE

Objective: To analyze the fractional components of relevant children's literature as an application of the concept of fractions.

Materials: Children's trade books that contain fractional concepts; writing and drawing implements; paper; chalk and chalkboard.

Activity: Read books such as *When the Doorbell Rang* (Hutchins, 1986). Provide problem situations such as making a chart that shows how, as more children arrive, each

gets fewer cookies. Have the children draw pictorial representations of what is happening. For further suggestions and a list of additional books, see Conaway and Midkiff (2004), Colker (2005), and Whitin and Whitin (2004), as well as others listed in Chapter 6 or Appendix B.

Follow-up: Use additional books. Children will become more independent and see more and more ways of looking at fractions.

FRACTIONS: STORY PROBLEMS

Objective: To create and solve fraction story problems.

Materials: One or more model problems; paper, pencils, crayons, markers, and scissors; chart paper for model problems.

Activity: Have the students brainstorm real-life situations in which things must be divided into equal parts. Encourage them to write or dictate their own problems, draw a picture of the problem, and write out the solution. If they cannot come up with their own problems, provide one or two models that they can work through with you. Here are some models (have each problem written on chart paper):

1. **"Two children found six pennies. One child took three pennies. What fractional part of the pennies was left for the other child?"** Draw two stick-figure children. Draw six pennies on another piece of paper. Glue three pennies by one child and three by the other. Ask, **"What part of the pennies does each child have? Yes, one-half."** Write, **"Each child has one-half of the pennies"** (**Figure 8-10**).

2. **"Brent invites three friends over for a cake that is square. If each child gets a fair share, how will the cake look when it is cut up?"** Give each child a paper square. Ask the children to fold the squares into the right size and number of parts. Cut up one of the cakes, and glue the parts on the chart. Write, **"Each child gets one-fourth."**

Follow-up: Encourage the children to create and illustrate their own fraction problems.

"Each child has one-half of the pennies."

FIGURE 8-10 The teacher can write and illustrate a model story problem that involves the partitioning of a group.

© Cengage Learning®

FRACTIONS: GEOBOARD SHAPES

Objective: To divide geoboard shapes into equal parts.

Materials: Geoboards, geoboard shape patterns, and rubber bands.

Activity: Have the children use rubber bands to make rectangles and squares on their geoboards, and then divide the shapes into equal parts, using additional rubber bands.

Follow-up: Question the children regarding how they know that their shapes are divided into equal parts. Note whether they use the number of geoboard pegs as a clue to making their parts equal. *To Half or Half Not* is a collection of geoboard activities that can be found at Mathline. Another online resource for geoboard fraction activities is at Geoboard Activities Socrates. Also online is Lesson Seed—Understanding Equivalent Fractions Using Geoboard.

Digital Download

Children can make the connection between fractions and decimals through further concrete activities. Avoid placing any emphasis on decimal points. Work with 10ths and 100ths, using models and diagrams in the same manner as you did with the larger fractions. With models, show how 1/10 and 1/100 can also be written as 0.1 and 0.01. Students with a strong conceptual foundation can move into operations with fractions and decimals by the fourth grade. Fraction concepts can be integrated across the curriculum, as depicted in **Figure 8-11**.

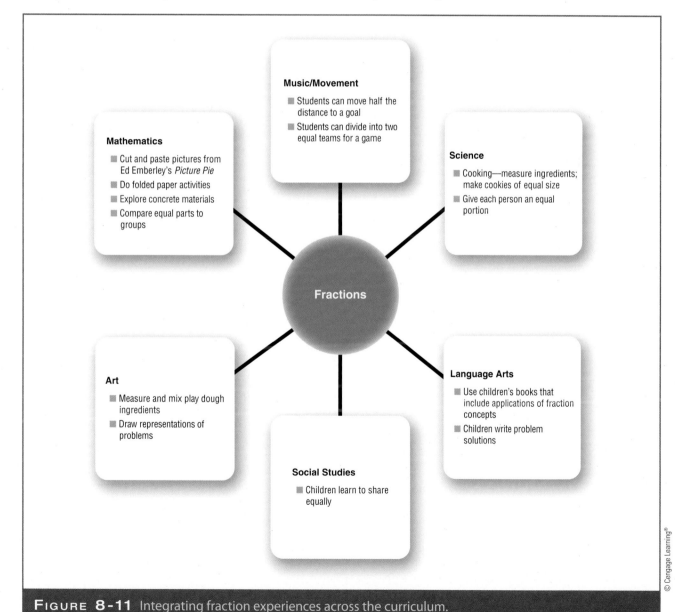

FIGURE 8-11 Integrating fraction experiences across the curriculum.

8-3c Helping Children with Special Needs

With deaf children, communication is a major consideration (Lewis, 2003). Being able to communicate with sign language provides many advantages for the deaf child. Deaf children who sign have been found to be academically and socially advanced. In a regular classroom, deaf children need an interpreter. Bilingual deaf children—those who are proficient in sign and oral language—have an advantage. Deaf children should be introduced to written language at an early age. Allen and Cowdery (2015) make a number of recommendations for teachers of young deaf children, including the following:

- While speaking, look children directly in the face. Get down to their level.

- Speak slowly and clearly.

- Use some gestures, but not so many that the child is distracted from lip reading.

- In a group, seat the child across from the teacher.

- Get the child's attention by tapping softly on the shoulder or hand.

- Use concrete examples when giving instructions.

- Read storybooks with clear, brightly colored illustrations.

- Keep routines sequenced and on a regular schedule.

Using concrete materials for math and science is essential for communicating concepts to the deaf child.

8.3d Informal Evaluation

Continue to note whether the children apply what they have learned about fractions during their everyday activities. Be sure to provide situations in which the children have to share individual items or groups of items equally with others. Note whether they can use their concept of fractions in these situations. Also note whether the children apply their concept of fractions during measuring experiences that are a part of food preparation and science investigations. Administer the assessment tasks described in Appendix A.

SUMMARY

8-1 Background and Basics of Primary Grade Mathematics

Children begin to develop the whole number operations of addition, subtraction, multiplication, and division through naturalistic and informal experiences during the preprimary years. As children's cognitive development takes them into the concrete operational level, they are ready to move into learning about action symbols and written notation.

Instructional Strategies. Problem solving with whole numbers involves the learning of basic facts and algorithms as well as developing computational fluency. Conventionally, children start with addition and subtraction in the beginning of the primary period (grade 1). They move on to more complex addition and subtraction and are introduced to multiplication in the second grade. They start with division in the third grade. Children begin each operation with informal activities and acting out problems, using concrete objects, and then move gradually into using formal notation and written problems. Story or word problems that put the operations into real-life contexts are the core around which the whole number operations are constructed in the young child's mind. ELLs can improve mathematical skill and increase their knowledge of English language skill through a problem-solving approach to mathematics.

8-2 Description and Explanation of Patterning

Primary-level children extend the work they did with patterning at earlier levels. Now they begin to identify and work with patterns in the number system as they connect numerals to patterns and develop number patterns using counting and calculators. Number patterns are the basis for multiplication and division.

Informal Pre-Assessment. Observation and interview can be used.

Activities. Activities using manipulatives are especially important for patterning. For the visually impaired tactual and shape materials enhance learning.

Informal Post-Evaluation. Observation and interview can be used.

8-3 Standards and Descriptions of Fractions

During the primary years, young children expand their informal concept of parts and wholes of objects and groups to the more formal concept of fractions, or equal parts. Primary children learn the vocabulary of fractions and work with fractions at the concrete level.

Informal Pre-Assessment. Use observation and assessment tasks.

Activities. Usually, they do not go beyond halves, thirds, and fourths, and most are not ready to understand fraction notation until the latter part of the primary period. Do not rush young children into the abstract use of fractions until they are ready, because fractions are much more difficult to work with than whole numbers. Teaching children who are deaf requires some special considerations.

Informal Evaluation. Observation and interview tasks can be used.

FURTHER READING AND RESOURCES

Billings, E. M., Tiedt, T. L., & Slater, L. H. (2007/2008). Algebraic thinking and pictorial growth patterns. *Teaching Children Mathematics, 14*(5), 302–308.

Cadzow-Wardell, L. (2009/2010). White trillium. *Teaching Children Mathematics, 16*(5), 264–266.

Cavey, L. O., & Kinzel, M. T. (2014). From whole numbers to invert and multiply. *Teaching Children Mathematics, 20*(6), 374–383.

Dubon, L. P., & Shafer, K. G. (2010). Storyboards for meaningful patterns. *Teaching Children Mathematics, 16*(6), 325–329.

Eichinger, J. (2009). *Activities linking science with math K–4.* Arlington, VA: NSTA press.

Fisher, E. C., Roy, G., & Reeves, C. (2013). The functionator 3000: Transforming numbers and children. *Teaching Children Mathematics, 20*(4), 254–260.

Jong, C., & Magruder, R. (2014). Beyond cookies: Understanding various division models. *Teaching Children Mathematics, 20*(6), 366–371.

Kidd, J. K., Pasnak, P., Boyer, C. E. & Carleson, A. (2014). Instructing first-grade children on patterning improves reading and mathematics. *Early Education and Development, 25*(1), 134–151.

Moss, E. R. (2013). Pattern blocks. *Teaching Children Mathematics, 20*(3), 136–142.

Murphy, M. S., (2009). Mathematics and social justice in grade 1: How children understand inequality and represent it. *Young Children, 64*(3), 12–17.

Piasta, S. B., Pelatti, C. Y., Miller, H. I. (2014). Mathematics and science learning opportunities in preschool classrooms. *Early Education and Development, 25*(4), 445–468.

Polly, D., & Ruble, L. (2009). Learning to share equally. *Teaching Children Mathematics, 15*(9), 558–563.

Science for all. [Focus Section]. (2014). *Science and Children, 51*(5).

Thomas, J. N., Tabor, P. D., & Wright, R. J. (2010/2011). First graders' number knowledge. *Teaching Children Mathematics, 17*(5), 298–308.

Wu, Z., An, S., King, J., Ramirez, M., & Evans, S. (2009). Second grade "professors." *Teaching Children Mathematics, 16*(1), 34–40.

See also the monthly issues of *Teaching Children Mathematics* for activities, materials, and reviews of software and websites.

REFERENCES

Allen, K. E., & Cowdery, G. E. (2015). *The exceptional child,* 8th ed. Stamford, CT: Cengage Learning.

Baratta-Lorton, M. (1976). *Mathematics their way.* Menlo Park, CA: Addison-Wesley.

Baroody, A. J. (2006). Why children have difficulties mastering the basic number combinations and how to help them. *Teaching Children Mathematics, 13*(1), 22–31.

Carpenter, T., Carey, D., & Kouba, V. (1990). A problem-solving approach to the operations. In J. N. Payne (Ed.), *Mathematics for the young child* (pp. 111–131). Reston, VA: National Council of Teachers of Mathematics.

Chan, A. (2011, April 4). Autistic brain excels at recognizing patterns. Livescience. www.livescience.com.

Chappell, M. E. (1997). Preparing students to enter the gate. *Teaching Children Mathematics, 3,* 266–267.

Charlesworth, R., & Senger, E. (2001). Arithmetic. In L. S. Grinstein & S. I. Lipsey (Eds.), *Encyclopedia of mathematics* (pp. 37–43). New York: RoutledgeFalmer.

Clements, D. H., & Sarama, J. (2000). Predicting pattern blocks on and off the computer. *Teaching Children Mathematics, 6*(7), 458–462.

Colker, L. J. (2005). *The cooking book.* Washington, DC: National Association for the Education of Young Children.

Conaway, B., & Midkiff, R. B. (2004). Connecting literature, language and fractions. In D. Theissen (Ed.), *Exploring mathematics through literature* (pp. 69–78). Reston, VA: National Council of Teachers of Mathematics.

Curcio, F. R., & Schwartz, S. L. (1998). There are no algorithms for teaching algorithms. *Teaching Children Mathematics, 5*(1), 26–30.

DeBellis, V. A., Rosenstein, J. G., Hart, E. W., & Kenney, M. J. (2009). *Navigating with discrete mathematics in kindergarten–grade 5.* Reston, VA: National Council of Teachers of Mathematics.

D'Souza, S. (2010, June 24). Understanding patterns: How your brain thinks, Psychotactis.com, http://www.psychotactics.com.

Fosnot, C. T., & Dolk, M. (2001). *Young mathematicians at work: Constructing number sense, addition, and subtraction.* Portsmouth, NH: Heinemann.

Fosnot, C. T., & Uittenboaard, W. (2009). Minilessons for early addition and subtraction. Portsmouth, NH: Heinemann.

Foster, C. (Ed.). (2011/2012). The unusual baker. *Teaching Children Mathematics, 18*(5), 278–280.

Fraivillig, J. (2001). Strategies for advancing children's mathematical thinking. *Teaching Children Mathematics, 7*(8), 454–459.

Fuson, K. C., Grandau, L., & Sugiyama, P. A. (2001). Achievable numerical understandings for all young children. *Teaching Children Mathematics, 7*(9), 522–526.

Garrison, L., Ponce, G. A., & Amaral, O. M. (2007). "Ninety percent of the game is half mental." *Teaching Children Mathematics, 14*(1), 12–17.

Ginsburg, H. (1977). *Children's arithmetic.* New York: Van Nostrand.

Greenes, C., Cavanagh, M., Dacey, L., Findell, C., & Small, M. (2001). *Navigating through algebra in prekindergarten–grade 2.* Reston, VA: National Council of Teachers of Mathematics.

Heuser, D. (2005). Teaching without telling: Computational fluency and understanding through invention. *Teaching Children Mathematics, 11*(8), 404–412.

Hildebrandt, M. E., Biglan, B., & Budd, L. (2013). Let's take a rod trip. *Teaching Children Mathematics, 19*(9), 548–553.

Hutchins, P. (1986). *When the doorbell rang.* New York: Greenwillow.

Isaacs, A. C., & Carroll, W. M. (1999). Strategies for basic-facts instruction. *Teaching Children Mathematics, 5*(9), 508–515.

Kamii, C. K. (1994). *Young children reinvent arithmetic, third grade.* New York: Teachers College Press.

Kamii, C. K. (2003). *Young children continue to reinvent arithmetic, second grade,* 2nd ed. New York: Teachers College Press.

Kamii, C. K., & DeClark, G. (2000). *Young children reinvent arithmetic.* New York: Teachers College Press.

King, S. (2013, May 7). Gifted in maths: Six ways to keep your high achievers engaged. *Theguardian.* Retrieved http://www.gardian.co.uk.

Lapko, B. S. (2013). Using voice recorders to capture their thinking. *Teaching Children Mathematics, 19*(8), 524–526.

Lewis, V. (2003). *Development and disability,* 2nd ed. Malden, MA: Blackwell.

National Association for the Education of Young Children (NAEYC) and National Association of Early Childhood Specialists in State Departments of Education (NAECSSDE). (1991). Guidelines for appropriate curriculum content and assessment in programs serving children ages 3 through 8: A position statement. *Young Children, 46*(3), 21–38.

National Governors Association Center for Best Practices, Council of Chief State School Officers. (2010). *Common Core State Standards for Mathematics.* Washington, DC: Author. www.corestandards.org.

Reys, B. J., & Reys, R. E. (1998). Computation in the elementary curriculum: Shifting the emphasis. *Teaching Children Mathematics, 5*(4), 236–241.

Richardson, K. (1984). *Developing number concepts using Unifix Cubes.* Menlo Park, CA: Addison-Wesley.

Richardson, K. (1999). *Developing number concepts: Book 2. Addition and subtraction.* Parsippany, NJ: Seymour.

Russell, S. J. (2000). Developing computational fluency with whole numbers. *Teaching Children Mathematics, 7*(3), 154–158.

Schifter, S., Russell, S. J., & Bastable, V. (2009). Early algebra to reach the range of learners. *Teaching Children Mathematics, 16*(4), 230–237.

Shellenbarger, S. (2013, September 24). New approaches to teaching fractions. *Wall Street Journal.* http://online.ws/com.

Siegler, R. S., Carpenter, T., Fennell, F., Geary, D., Lewis, J., Okamoto, Y., et al. (2010). Developing effective fractions instruction for kindergarten through 8th grade: A practice guide (NCEE 2010-4039). Washington DC: National Center for Education Evaluation and Regional Assistance, Institute of Education Sciences, U.S. Department of Education. Retrieved at http://ies.ed.gov/ncee/wwc/pdf/practice_guides/fractions_pg_093010.pdf.

Siegler, R. S., Fazio, L. K., Bailey, D. H., & Zhou, S. (2013). Fractions: The new frontier for theories of numerical development. *Trends in Cognitive Sciences*, *17*(1), 13–19.

Sparks, S. (2013, July 18). Federal research suggests new approach to teaching fractions. *Education Week*. http://www.edweek.org/ew/articles/2013/07/18 /37fractions.h32.html.

Tabor, S. B., & Canonica, M. (2008). Sharing "cat games" and cookies: Special education students investigate division. *Teaching Children Mathematics*, *15*(1), 55–61.

Warshauer, H. K., & Warshauer, M. L. (2001). Algorithms. In L. S. Grinstein & S. I. Lipsey (Eds.), *Encyclopedia of mathematics* (pp. 23–24). New York: RoutledgeFalmer.

Whitin, D. J., & Whitin, P. (2004). *New visions for linking literature and mathematics*. Reston, VA: National Council of Teachers of Mathematics.

Wilson, P. H., Myers, M., Edgington, C., & Confrey, J. (2012). Fair shares, matey, or walk the plank. *Teaching Children Mathematics*, *18*(8), 482–489.

Yackel, E. (1997). A foundation for algebraic reasoning in the early grades. *Teaching Children Mathematics*, *3*, 276–280.

PLACE VALUE, GEOMETRY,
DATA ANALYSIS, AND MEASUREMENT

OBJECTIVES

After reading this chapter, you should be able to:

9-1 Assess, plan, teach, and evaluate primary grade place-value lessons in line with national standards.

9-2 Assess, plan, teach, and evaluate primary grade geometry, data collection, and analysis lessons in line with national standards.

9-3 Assess, plan, teach, and evaluate primary grade measurement lessons in line with national standards.

STANDARDS ADDRESSED IN THIS CHAPTER

naeyc

NAEYC Professional Preparation Standards

5.   Build meaningful curriculum.

5a. Understand content resources in mathematics and science.

5c. Design, implement, and evaluate developmentally meaningful and challenging curriculum.

DAP Guidelines

2c. Teachers know what the desired goals for the program are.

3c. Teachers use the curriculum framework in their planning for CCSSM.

Common Core State Standards for Math

Number and Operations in Base 10, Grades 1 to 3

1.OA.1   Count to 120, starting at any number less than 120.

2.NBT.1   Understand that the three digits of a three-digit number represent amounts of 100s, 10s, and 1s.

3.NBT.A.2   Fluently add and subtract within 1000.

Geometry, Grades 1 to 3

1.G.A.1   Distinguish between defining attributes versus nondefining attributes of shapes.

1.G.A.3   Partition circles and rectangles into two and four equal shares.

Measurement and Data, Grades 1-3

1.MDC4   Organize, represent, and interpret data with up to three categories

2.MD.A.1   Measure the length of an object, using tools such as rulers, yardsticks, meter sticks, and measuring tapes.

Next Generation Science Standards

1-PS4-1, 2-PS-1, and 1-PS4-3   Plan and conduct investigations collaboratively to produce data to serve as the basis for evidence to answer a question.

1-PS4-4, 2-PS1-2   Use tools and materials provided to design a device that solves a specific problem.

9-1 STANDARDS AND DESCRIPTION OF PLACE VALUE AND NUMBERS ABOVE 10

According to the Common Core State Standards for Mathematics (2010) for the primary grades, by the end of third grade, children should have an understanding of place value and be able to solve problems involving place value. The standards include the following:

- *Grade 1, Number and Operations in Base 10.* Extend the counting sequence; understand place value; and use place value to add and subtract.

- *Grade 2, Number and Operations in Base 10.* Understand place value and properties of operations to add and subtract.

- *Grade 3, Number and Operations in Base 10.* Use place-value understanding and properties of operations to perform multidigit arithmetic, round numbers to the nearest 10 or 1000, fluently add and subtract within 1000, and multiply one-digit whole numbers by multiples of 10 in the range of 10 to 90.

During the latter part of the preoperational period (see Chapter 7), children who are adept at manipulating quantities up to 10 can move on to working with quantities above 10. Through manipulating groups of 10 and quantities between zero and 10, children move through the teens and up to 20. Some will pick up the pattern of the 20s, 30s, and so on, up through the 90s. As children enter concrete operations, they perfect their informal knowledge of numbers above 10 and move on to whole number operations with such numbers.

To fully understand what they are doing when they use whole number operations involving numbers above 10, children must be able to conceptualize **place value**: the understanding that the same numeral represents different amounts, depending on its position. For example, consider the numbers 3, 30, and 300. In the first instance, 3 stands for three 1s and is in the 1s' place. In 30, 3 stands for three 10s and is in the 10s' place. In 300, 3 stands for three 100s and is in the 100s' place. In the latter two numbers, 0 indicates that there is no quantity in the place it holds. In the number 32, 3 is in the 10s' place, and 2 is in the 1s' place.

An understanding of place value underlies the comprehension of certain trading rules that govern place value and that enable whole number operations to be accomplished. Examples of trading rules include the following:

- Ten 1s can be traded for one 10.

- One 10 can be traded for ten 1s.

- Ten 10s can be traded for 100.

- One hundred 1s can be traded for 100.

The place-value concept enables us to represent any value, using only 10 numerals (0–9).

Place value is one of the most difficult concepts for young children to grasp. Being able to rote- and rational-count above 10 is only a beginning step on the way to understanding place value. To develop the place-value concept, children need many counting experiences (as described in Chapter 3) and many experiences with concrete models. All too often, children are rushed into the place-value operations involved in regrouping (formerly called "borrowing" and "carrying") as a rote memory activity without the necessary underlying conceptualization. By understanding place value, children will realize that when they take one from the 10s' column, they are actually taking one group of 10 and that, when they add numbers in the 1s' column and arrive at a sum above nine, the amount they move to the 10s' column represents one or more groups of 10.

Understanding place value will also help children to see that the placement of numerals is critical in determining value. For example, sixty-eight can be written as 68 (six 10s and eight 1s) and as 60 + 8, but not as 86. In other words, "Ball boy the throws" does not follow the conventions of correctly written English. In the same fashion, one hundred twenty-one is not written as 10021. This chapter focuses on how to guide children to an understanding of this concept.

9-1a Informal Pre-Assessment

For young children, understanding place value is a difficult task. They normally flounder for a while, seeming to understand the concept in some situations and not in others. Teachers should be patient and accepting, giving the children time and appropriate experiences. The following examples of assessment tasks can be used to discover where the children are on the road to understanding two-digit numbers and the concept of place value.

On average, first graders can learn to read, write, and understand two-digit numbers; second graders, three-digit numbers; and third graders, four-digit numbers. However, a broad range of normal variation exists within any particular group. The best rule of thumb in assessment is to be sure that children understand one-digit numbers before going on to two-digit numbers, two-digit numbers before three-digit numbers, and so on.

9-1b Activities

The following activities are adapted from the some of the relevant publications in the selection of resources listed at the end of this chapter. Young children need many experiences

SAMPLE ASSESSMENT TASK

9P   CONCRETE OPERATIONS AGES 7–8

PLACE VALUE, GROUPS OF 10: CHAPTER 9

METHOD Interview.

SKILL Child is able to count groups of 11 or more objects and tell how many 10s are in the groups.

MATERIALS A container of 100 counters (e.g., chips, cubes, or sticks).

PROCEDURE Place the container of counters in front of the child. Say, **"Here are a bunch of counters. Count out as many of them as you can."** If the child counts out 11 or more ask, **"How many 10s do you think you have? How many 1s?"**

EVALUATION If the child answers correctly, then she probably has the concept of place value for 10s. An incorrect answer indicates that although she may be able to rational-count groups of objects greater than 10, she does not yet understand the meaning of each of the numerals in her response.

INSTRUCTIONAL RESOURCE
R. Charlesworth, *Math and Science for Young Children*, 8th ed., San Francisco, CA: Cengage Learning, 2016.

Digital Download

SAMPLE ASSESSMENT TASK

9Q   CONCRETE OPERATIONS AGES 7–8

PLACE VALUE, GROUPING TO IDENTIFY AN AMOUNT: CHAPTER 9

METHOD Interview.

SKILL The child is able to form two or more subgroups of 10 objects, each with some remaining from the original group, and then tell how many he has without counting each individual object.

MATERIALS A container of 100 counters (e.g., chips, cubes, or sticks).

PROCEDURE Place a pile of counters (start with about 35) in front of the child. Say, **"Make as many groups of 10 as you can. How many [counters] do you have altogether?"**

EVALUATION Note whether the child either can come up with the answer by counting the number of groups of 10 and adding on the number of 1s or instead must count each object to be sure of the total. Being able to determine the answer without counting by 1s indicates that the child is developing the concept of place value.

INSTRUCTIONAL RESOURCE
R. Charlesworth, *Math and Science for Young Children*, 8th ed., San Francisco, CA: Cengage Learning, 2016.

Digital Download

with place value and in manipulating objects whose number exceeds 10 before proceeding to two-digit whole number operations. Start with counting activities such as those suggested in Chapter 3. Then move on to the kinds of activities described in the following pages. The first two activities focus on constructing an understanding of the properties of amounts greater than 10. Once children have a good understanding of counting and subdividing groups greater than 10, they are ready for activities that gradually move them into the complexities of place value.

DAP **naeyc**

ACTIVITIES

NUMERALS GREATER THAN 10: CONSERVATION OF LARGE NUMBERS

Objective: To understand, given a group of more than 10 objects, that the number of objects remains the same, no matter how they are arranged.

Materials: Each child needs a container with 50 or more counters (e.g., cubes, chips, or sticks) and a place-value board (cf. Richardson, 1984, p. 212). A place-value board is a piece of paper divided into two sections so that groups can be placed on one side and loose counters on the other side. To make a place-value board, take a 9 × 12-inch piece of paper or tagboard and then glue or staple a 6 × 9-inch piece of colored paper on one half. Draw a picture in the upper right-hand corner of the white side so that the child knows how to place the board in the correct position.

Unifix Cubes are excellent for this activity because they can be snapped together. However, cubes or chips that can be stacked or sticks that can be held together with a rubber band may also be used.

Activity: Tell the children to put some number of counters greater than 10 on the white side of their place-value board. Suggest the children work in pairs so that they can check each other's counting. When they agree that they have the same amount, say, **"Make a group of 10 [counters] and put it on the [color] side of your board. How many loose [counters] do you have left? How many [counters] do you have altogether?"** Note how many children realize that they still have the same number of counters. Ask, **"Do you have enough [counters] to make another 10?"** Note whether they respond correctly. If they do make another 10, ask again how many loose cubes they have and whether the total is still the same. To connect their arrangements to number symbols, write the arrangements on the board: "Three 10s and four 1s" and "two 10s and fourteen 1s."

Follow-up: Do the same activity, using containers to put the counters in. Label each container "10." Using small counters such as tiny chips or bottle caps is a more efficient way to keep the groups separated. A similar activity can be done with base-10 blocks (described later in this chapter). See Richardson (1984, 1999a, 1999b) for additional variations on this activity.

NUMERALS GREATER THAN 10: MEASURING

Objective: To work with large numbers through nonstandard measurement activities (see Chapter 5 for background information).

Materials: Small objects that can be used as nonstandard units, paper and pencil to record measurements, and measurement cards (as suggested by Richardson, 1984). Each measurement card depicts something in the classroom that can be measured.

Activity: Have the children measure the items with the objects, group the objects into 10s, and then figure out how many they have used. Ask them to record the results on their paper.

Follow-up: Have the children measure the same items, using different nonstandard units, and compare the number of units. See Richardson (1984, 1999a, 1999b) for further activities.

> The chair is 24 paper clips tall.
>
> The table is 36 paper clips wide.

DAP   naeyc

ACTIVITIES

PLACE VALUE: CONSTRUCTING MODELS OF TWO-DIGIT NUMBERS

Objective: To develop models of two-digit numbers, using the place-value board.

Materials: Place-value board (described in previous activity) and a supply of cards with individual numerals, 0–9, written on each card. Provide each of the children with at least two sets of numerals and a supply of counters that can be readily stacked, snapped, or bundled into groups of 10. One child working alone will need 100 counters. If children are working in small groups and sharing the counters, add 50 counters per child.

Activity: Have the children put the place-value boards in front of them. Provide them with an ample supply of numerals in a small container, and place the container of counters where it is convenient for everyone to reach. Say, **"Close your eyes and pick two numerals. Put one on your board on the [color] side and one on your board on the white side. Make a model of the numeral you have selected."**

Follow-up: Have the students repeat this activity with different number combinations. Have them work alone, in pairs, and/or in small groups. Have them do the same activity, using base-10 blocks after they have been introduced. (Base-10 blocks are described later in this chapter.) The same activity can be adapted to work with 100s and 1000s

when the children are ready. The activity could also be done using spinners, one for each place value.

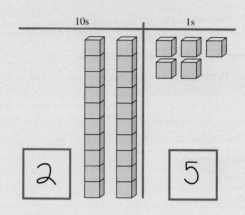

PLACE VALUE: ESTIMATION WITH COMMON ITEMS

Objective: To estimate amounts and to apply knowledge of place value to finding out how close the estimate is.

Materials: A container of common items such as a bag of peanuts or cotton balls; a box of paper clips, rubber bands, or cotton swabs; or a jar of bottle tops, clothespins, pennies, or other common items. Also, some small cups, bowls, or plastic glasses; flip chart numerals or paper and pencil to write results. (Flip chart numerals can be made by writing numerals 0–9 on cards, punching two holes at the top of each card, and putting the cards on rings.)

Activity: *Estimating* is the math term for guessing or predicting the answer to a math problem. Show the children the container of objects. Let them hold it, examine it, but not open it. Say, **"Look closely at this [container]."** Ask, **How many [items] do you think are in this [container]?"** You record or have the children record each child's guess. Open the container. **"Count out groups of 10 [item], and put them in the [cups, glasses, and so on]. Find out how**

many groups of 10 there are altogether. Each time you count out 10, turn over a number on your flip chart."** Or, if the children can write, say, **"Write the number that tells how many 10s you have."**

Follow-up: Once the children catch on, record their estimates over the course of a week. Have the children record their guesses on a chart. Then, on Friday have them open the container and find out the actual amount. Make a graph showing the distribution of estimates.

4					59	
3			39		56	64
2		27	39	45	55	63
1		25	32	40	51	60
	10s	20s	30s	40s	50s	60s

Digital Download

Base-10 blocks provide a different kind of model for working with the place-value concept. Children need to work with various types of materials in model construction so that they do not think there is only one way to view place value with concrete materials. So far we have described making models with discrete items. Base-10 blocks depict each place with 10 unit cubes stuck together in a row. Flats (or 100s) are the equivalent of 10 rods stuck together, and cubes (or 1000s) are

the equivalent of 10 flats stacked and glued together (see **Figure 9-1**).

Burris (2013) reported a study comparing the thinking of pairs of third-grade students who used concrete base-10 blocks and those who used virtual base-10 blocks. The students interacted in a similar manner with each type of material. Burris concludes that both the concrete and virtual manipulatives are of equal value in the classroom (**Photo 9-1** and **Photo 9-2**).

ACTIVITIES

PLACE VALUE: BASE-10 BLOCKS

Objective: To work with place value using base-10 blocks.

Materials: A classroom set of base-10 blocks.

Activity: The base-10 blocks can be used for the activities previously described by adding on another step. Each time the child makes a group of 10, she can record this by selecting a rod. She can then count the rods at the end to find out how many groups of 10 she has found.

Follow-up: Many auxiliary materials can be purchased that provide activities with base-10 blocks besides those that come with a teacher's guide. Base-10 blocks and teachers' guides can be purchased from suppliers such as Dale Seymour, Creative Publications, ETA/Cuisinaire, and DIDAX Educational Resources (see the addresses in Chapter 12).

Digital Download

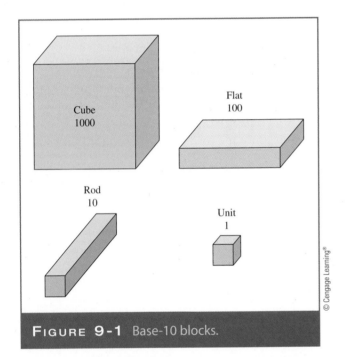

FIGURE 9-1 Base-10 blocks.

Trading is another procedure for working with place value. Primary children need many experiences counting piles of objects, trading for groups of 10, and describing the results. Once they can do these activities with ease, they can move on to regrouping and renaming. Too often they are pushed into regrouping and renaming without an adequate conceptual base built on counting and constructing many groups of 10 and relating them (and any 1s remaining) to written numerals.

Regrouping happens when one or more items are added or taken away so that an amount moves to the next 10, next 100, next 1000, and so on. For example, a group might break down into two 10s and six 1s, or 26. Five more units are added so that there are now 11 units. Ten units are then moved to the 10s' place, leaving one unit in the 1s' place. There are now three 10s and one unit, or 31. **Renaming** of the group has also occurred. It has now been renamed 31.

Reverse trading takes place if units are removed. For example, suppose seven units are to be taken away from the

PHOTO 9-1 Blocks and beads can be selected and arranged to show a large number.

PHOTO 9-2 In the computer laboratory, students can experiment with virtual mathematics place-value activities.

three 10s and one unit; a 10 would be moved over to the units, making 11 units, and 7 units could then be removed, leaving two 10s and four 1s, or 24. Primary-grade children need to do many trading activities with concrete materials before moving on to paper-and-pencil computations. These trades can be practiced with concrete items, such as cubes and chips, the beads on an abacus, or base-10 blocks. Chip trading materials can be purchased from Dale Seymour.

When the children practice trading to regroup and rename on their place-value boards, they are actually adding and subtracting informally. Richardson (1984) explains how to carry this activity over to the addition and

ACTIVITIES

PLACE VALUE: TRADING ACTIVITIES

Objective: To construct the concepts of regrouping and renaming through trading activities.

Materials: A supply of paper squares consisting of 100 reds (units) and 30 blues (10s); a place-value board with a 1s' and 10s' place.

Activity: Have the children put their place-value boards in front of them. Place a supply of red and blue paper squares where they can be easily reached. Say, **"The blue squares are 10s, and the red squares are 1s."** Hold up a large 27. **"Show me how you can make a model of this number on your board."** Have the children try several examples. When you are sure they understand that the reds are 1s and the blues are 10s, go on to regrouping. Go back to 27. **"Make 27 on your boards again. Now, suppose someone gives you five more 1s. Take five more. What happens to your 1s?"** Encourage the children to describe what happens. Remind them that there cannot be more than nine in the 1s'

place. Eventually, someone will realize that 32 should be modeled with three 10s and two 1s. Have the children discuss what they might do to get a model that has three 10s and two 1s by trading. Say, **"Suppose you trade 10 reds for 1 blue. Where should the blue be placed?"** Once everyone has the blue in the 10s' place, ask, **"Suppose someone needs four 1s. How could you give them four?"** Encourage them to discuss this problem with one another, and ask your questions until someone discovers that another trade has to be made. Have all the children trade in a blue for 10 reds, take four away, and see that they now have two blues and 8 reds (28).

Follow-up: Create some story problems, and have the children solve them using trading. Then, move on to adding and taking away two-digit quantities. Also, provide students with pairs of two-digit numbers, and have them invent problems using the numbers.

subtraction of two-digit numbers. Richardson believes that it is confusing to begin two-digit addition and subtraction with numbers that do not have to be regrouped, such as

$$
\begin{array}{cccc}
22 & 53 & 46 & 18 \\
+35 & +14 & -34 & -13 \\
\hline
57 & 67 & 12 & 5
\end{array}
$$

This type of addition and subtraction may lead children to believe that adding or subtracting with two digits is exactly the same operation as with one digit. The result may be responses such as the following:

$$
\begin{array}{cccc}
25 & 48 & 72 & 37 \\
+16 & +34 & -35 & -28 \\
\hline
311 & 712 & 43 & 11
\end{array}
$$

Note in these examples that the children have added or subtracted each column as though it were an individual one-digit problem. Introduce two-digit addition as follows:

"Put 26 cubes on your board."

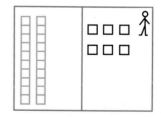

"Now get 18 cubes, and put them next to your board."

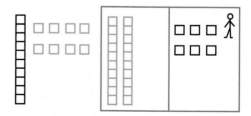

"Now put them together. How many 10s? How many 1s? Yes, we have three 10s and fourteen 1s. Do we have enough to make another 10?"

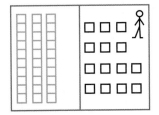

(Give them time to move 10 cubes.) **"Now we have four 10s and four 1s. How many is that? Yes, that is 44."**

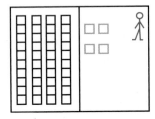

Repeat this process several times with different pairs of two-digit numbers. Sometimes the sum contains more than nine units, and sometimes it does not. When the children understand the process without symbols, connect the symbols by writing them on the board as you go through the process (see **Photo 9-3**).

Introduce subtraction of two-digit numbers in a similar way. For example, have the children put out 42 cubes, and then tell them they need to take away 25. They will discover that they have to break up a 10 to accomplish this task. After doing many examples without written numbers, go through some problems in which you connect the quantities to numbers at each step, thus gradually introducing the notation. Then have them do mixed sets of problems. Finally, move on to story problems. Problems and activities that apply place-value concepts can be integrated across the curriculum (**Figure 9-2**).

9-1c Kamii's Approach

The activities suggested in this unit follow a fairly structured sequence while promoting the construction of concepts through exploration. Kamii and colleagues (Kamii, Lewis, & Livingston, 1993) have been working with primary children, using open-ended activities that provide for more child trial and error and self-sequencing. Interviewing primary students who had been through conventional workbook/textbook instruction, they discovered that students were able to do regrouping and renaming as a rote process without really knowing the meaning of the numbers they were using. For example, when the students were asked to do a two-digit problem such as 28 + 45, they could come up with the correct answer:

$$
\begin{array}{r}
1 \\
28 \\
+45 \\
\hline
73
\end{array}
$$

However, when asked what the 1 in 13 means, they said it meant "1" rather than "10." Kamii has had greater success in communicating this concept to primary children by using games and letting them discover the relationship of the digits on their own. No workbooks or worksheets are used, and neither are the kinds of concrete activities described in this unit. Problems are written on the board, children contribute answers, and every answer is listed. Then, the children give their rationales for their answers. When working with double-digit addition, their natural inclination is to start on the left. They add the 10s, write the answer, add the 1s, and, if necessary, move any 10s over, erasing the original answer in the 10s' column. Through trial and error and discussion, they develop their own method and construct their own place-value concept. Place value is not taught as a separate skill needed before doing double-column addition. This method sounds intriguing and is more fully described in Kamii (2003).

PHOTO 9-3 Place-value squares can be used to solve large-number addition and subtraction problems.

Charlesworth

Technology for Young Children

Online Resources

Counting and Place Value (grades 2–5): PBS Learning Media

Virtual Manipulatives for Number & Operations: National Library of Virtual Manipulatives

Place Value Made Simple (grades 3–5): National Security Agency

Tenth Planet: Grouping & Place Value: Sunburst Digital, Inc.

Grouping and Grazing; Basically Base Ten: Discovering Place Value Meaning Using Base Ten Blocks; Chip Trading: Illuminations: Resources for Teaching Math

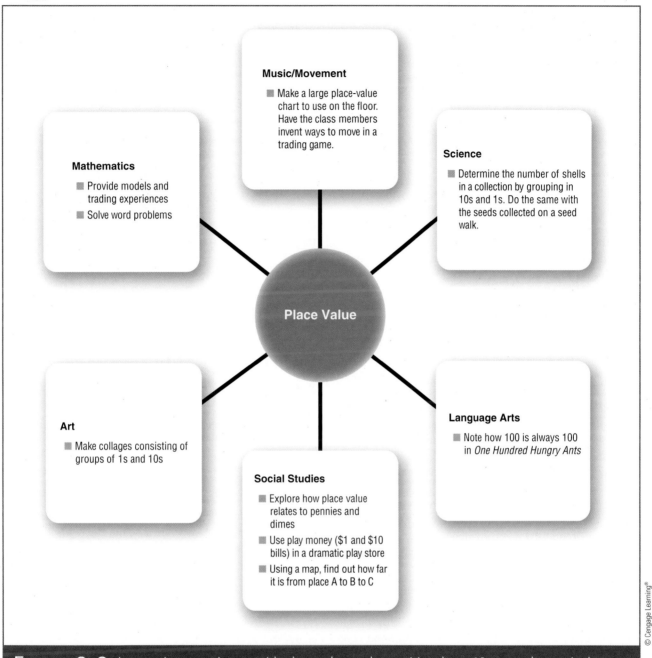

Music/Movement
- Make a large place-value chart to use on the floor. Have the class members invent ways to move in a trading game.

Mathematics
- Provide models and trading experiences
- Solve word problems

Science
- Determine the number of shells in a collection by grouping in 10s and 1s. Do the same with the seeds collected on a seed walk.

Place Value

Art
- Make collages consisting of groups of 1s and 10s

Social Studies
- Explore how place value relates to pennies and dimes
- Use play money ($1 and $10 bills) in a dramatic play store
- Using a map, find out how far it is from place A to B to C

Language Arts
- Note how 100 is always 100 in *One Hundred Hungry Ants*

© Cengage Learning®

FIGURE 9-2 Integrating experiences with place value and quantities above 10 across the curriculum.

9-1d Calculators

When children explore calculators for counting, they notice that the number on the right changes every time, whereas the other numbers change less frequently. Calculators provide a graphic look at place value and the relation of each place to those adjacent. Suggest that the children input 10 and then press 1 several times and note what happens—that is, which place changes and by how much each time? This activity will assist children in seeing what the 10s' place means. Concepts constructed using manipulatives can be reinforced with calculator activities.

By adding 1 to numbers that end in 9 and subtracting 1 from numbers that end in zero, students can see immediately what happens. Suggest that they guess which number follows 9, 29, and 59. Then have them use their calculators to check their predictions. Using the same procedure, have them predict what will happen if they subtract 1 from 20, 40, and 70.

9-1e Helping Children with Special Needs

Children with motor disabilities, such as spina bifida (SB, cerebral palsy (CP), or developmental coordination disorder (DCD), are challenged by any type of motor skills task

(Lewis, 2003). Depending on the degree of their disability, they may not be able to interact with objects in any conventional way. However, they can develop cognitive understanding with the right kind of support. Ways have to be found for them to act on their environment. Technology can be designed that allows children with motor disabilities to use whatever movement they have available to assist them in learning and communicating. These children require close attention from adults, who should provide prompting and cueing as they work. In class, teachers need to emphasize the children's strengths.

Children with perceptual problems may have difficulties perceiving the commonalities among numbers above nine. They may need to have the teens lined up vertically so that the common element of 1 (in the 10s' place) can be seen. Color-coding can be helpful. These children commonly make reversals (e.g., confusing 13 and 31). With numbers of two or more symbols, children need to understand spatial terms such as *left, right, middle, first, last,* and *beginning.* Some children may need extra help with auditory memory. The teacher may say "fifty-two" but the child may perceive only the "two."

Children may find it interesting to learn how we arrived at base 10 for our number system and how other cultures devised their systems for recording and calculating. Zaslavsky (1996) explains how finger counting is a common practice in many cultures. In others, both fingers and toes are used, and so the base is 20. Once large amounts become involved, each culture has had to invent a method of recording and calculating. Tally marks on bone or wood have been used for thousands of years. The bar codes used so commonly today are based on groups of tally marks of two heights. Knots on string are another method used to record amounts. The abacus, first developed in China, allows for calculating large numbers, using rows of beads.

The Pueblo of Jemez in north-central New Mexico took charge of its education program in 2000 (Shendo, 2013). The objective was to have an education program with a priority on the Jemez language and culture. The common core opens up the opportunity to use the community outside of the classroom as an extension of the classroom.

9-1f Post-Evaluation

An evaluation technique suggested by Kamii (2003) shows whether children really understand place value in two-digit numbers.

> *Show the child a 3 × 5-inch card with "16" written on it. Ask, "**What does this say?**" After the child says "16," count out 16 chips. With the top of a pen, circle the 6 of the 16. "**What does this part (the 6) mean? Show me with the chips what this part (the 6) means.**" Circle the 1 of the 16. "**What does this part (the 1) mean? Show me with the chips what this part (the 1) means.**" (p. 161)*

Kamii reports that, after conventional instruction with workbooks and possibly some manipulatives, all first and second graders can answer correctly regarding the 6. However, of the primary children Kamii interviewed, none of the late first graders, 33% of late third graders, and only 50% of late fourth graders said that the 1 means 10. Children who learned about place value through constructing it themselves using Kamii's method did considerably better. At the end of the second grade, 66% said that the 1 means 10, and 74% said that the 5 in 54 means 50.

Whichever instructional method you use, be sure to observe carefully the process that each child uses. Question children frequently about what they are doing, to be sure they really understand the concepts and are not just answering by rote.

9-2 STANDARDS AND DESCRIPTIONS OF GEOMETRY, ENGINEERING AND DATA ANALYSIS

This section of Chapter 9 provides an overview of primary grade geometry, engineering and data collection, and analysis. The Common Core State Standards (2010) include the following emphases:

9-2a First Grade

Geometry. Reason with shapes and their attributes. Be able to explain which attributes define each specific shape. Use shapes to develop new shapes. Decompose shapes into shares.

Data Analysis. Represent and interpret data with up to three categories. Explain the numbers in each category, and compare which categories are more and less.

9-2b Second Grade

Geometry. Reason with shapes and their attributes. Recognize and draw shapes with specific attributes. Identify triangles, quadrilaterals, pentagons, hexagons, and cubes. Partition shapes into equal shares.

Data Analysis. Represent and interpret data. Draw a picture graph and a bar graph to represent data with up to four categories. Solve simple problems related to the graphs.

9-2c Third Grade

Geometry. Reason with shapes and their attributes. Recognize that shapes in different categories may share attributes. Recognize rhombuses, rectangles, and squares as example of quadrilaterals. Partition shapes into parts with equal areas.

Data Analysis. Represent and interpret data. Draw a scaled picture graph and a scaled bar graph to represent data with several categories. Solve problems using the information in the graphs.

The Next Generation Science Standards (NGSS Lead States) (2013) and the Framework for K–12 Science Education (NRC, 2012) focus on science and engineering as partners. Whereas science asks questions, engineering seeks problems.

The following example shows how data collection and graphs relate. Weather is the current science topic in Mr. Gonzales's third-grade class in northern Utah. This morning, the children are huddled over copies of the past week's weather forecasts that they clipped out of Ogden's local morning paper. They are reading the forecast section to find out what kind of information is included and to discuss how they might organize some of the data presented. They note that the day's forecast is included along with the normal highs and lows for that date. The paper has a regional forecast for Utah and a forecast map and description of the weather for the entire United States. Selected national and global temperatures along with precipitation and outlook are included in a table. The nation's highs and lows are also reported. The children compile a list of this information and discuss what they can learn and what information might be interesting to record.

Chan's great-great-grandparents came to Utah from Beijing, in what is now the People's Republic of China. Chan has noticed that Ogden and Beijing are at about the same latitude. He decides to record the high temperatures in Beijing for eight days and compare them with the high temperatures in Ogden for the same time period. First, Chan makes a chart, and then he makes a graph to depict the information from the chart. Then, he writes a description of the information obtained from the graphs. To complete this activity, he applies his mathematical knowledge (measurement, counting, graph making) to an activity that integrates science (the topic of weather), social studies (geography), and reading and language arts (reading and comprehending the article and writing about the information obtained). **Figure 9-3** depicts what Chan might have produced.

Groundwork for this type of activity was laid in concepts included in several previous chapters: Chapter 4 (early geometry: shape and spatial sense), Chapter 5 (interpreting data using graphs), and Chapter 7 (higher-level concepts and activities). Primary children must have this groundwork before moving on to the activities described in this chapter. Children need a basic understanding of shape and space, which they apply to the early graphing and mapping experiences during the preoperational period before they can move on to higher-level graphing and geometry concepts. When they enter the primary level, children should

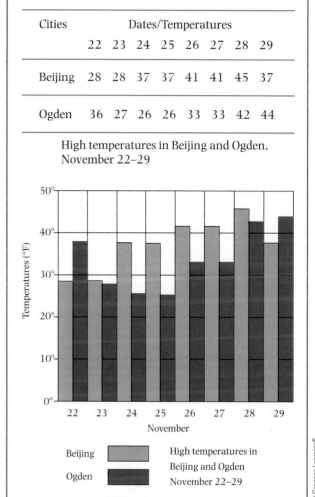

Cities	Dates/Temperatures							
	22	23	24	25	26	27	28	29
Beijing	28	28	37	37	41	41	45	37
Ogden	36	27	26	26	33	33	42	44

High temperatures in Beijing and Ogden, November 22–29

FIGURE 9-3 Chan's data table and bar graph.

know the basic characteristics of shape and be able to identify geometric shapes such as circles, triangles, squares, rectangles, and prisms. They should also have the spatial concepts of position, direction, and distance relationships, and they should be able to use space for making patterns and constructions. During the primary years, they should continue with these basic experiences and be guided to more complex levels.

Children study geometry in a general, informal way during the elementary grades. Spatial concepts are reinforced, and the senses are sharpened. During the primary years, children continue to develop geometric concepts mainly at an intuitive level. However, geometric figures are used to teach other concepts, so children should be familiar with them. For example, multiplication is frequently illustrated in a rectangular grid.

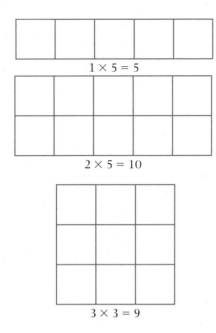

$1 \times 5 = 5$

$2 \times 5 = 10$

$3 \times 3 = 9$

Fractions are illustrated using number lines or sometimes using geometric shapes (see Chapter 8), such as the following:

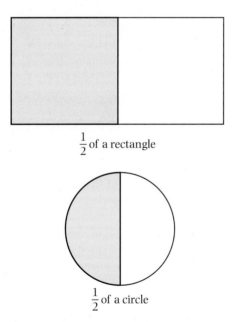

$\frac{1}{2}$ of a rectangle

$\frac{1}{2}$ of a circle

Number lines (described in Chapter 8) are conventionally used to help children visualize *greater than, less than,* the concept of *between,* and the rules of addition and subtraction. For example, the number line shown in the following figure is used to illustrate that $2 + 3 = 3 + 2$.

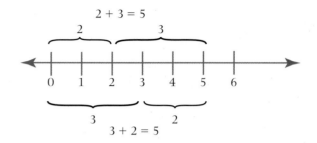

Collecting and organizing data continue to be important applications of mathematics. Graphing is closely related to geometry in that it makes use of geometric concepts such as line and shape. Note that the graphs depicted in this book are based on squares and rectangles. More advanced graphs are based on circles, and others involve the use of line segments to connect points. Tables are the necessary first step in organizing complex data prior to illustrating it on a graph. Charts are closely related to graphs.

Carraher and Schliemann (2010) explain how algebraic thinking (discussed in Chapter 8) begins in the early primary grades through problem-solving experiences. When children have the opportunity to discuss problems and see that they may have more than one solution, they are thinking algebraically (Cavanagh, 2009). Students can identify geometric and number patterns as they explore relationships. Schifter, Russell, and Bastable (2009) looked at children's early algebraic thinking—"learning representations, connections, and generalizations in the elementary school grades." Discussing and providing reasons for their problem solutions increased children's mathematical understanding and achievement.

Technology can also be used to support the development of algebraic thinking because it involves applications of a broad base of skills. As previously pointed out, design technology is an integration of technology, engineering, mathematics, and science. The STEM (Science, Technology, Engineering, and Mathematics) movement is growing in strength. See the March 2010 issue of *Science and Children*, which focuses on STEM. Another integration is the application of a variety of skills and concepts in the development of robotics projects (Clark, 2002; Murray & Bartelmay, 2005). In sum, knowledge of geometry, constructing tables and graphs, and algebraic thinking are closely related basic tools for organizing data. The remainder of the chapter describes geometry, graphing using charts and tables, and engineering at the primary level. Also described are Legos and their relationship with LOGO programming, estimation, and probability.

9-2d Informal Pre-Assessment

Children's readiness for the following primary-level activities should be assessed using the assessment tasks that accompany Chapter 4. Readiness is also measured by observing children's capacities to accomplish the graphing activities in

Chapter 5 and the higher-level graphing and spatial relations (mapping) activities in Chapter 7. Do not assume that children have had all the prerequisite experiences before they arrive in your primary classroom. You might have to start with these earlier levels before moving on to the activities suggested in this chapter.

9-2e Activities

This section begins with geometry and mapping; it then describes LOGO computer applications to mapping and to robotics and design technology/engineering. This part of the chapter then goes on to the topics of charts and tables, estimation, and probability.

Geometry. Primary children are not ready for the technicalities of geometry, but they can be introduced informally to some of the basic concepts. They can learn about **points** as small dots on paper or on the whiteboard. During a story or a mapping activity, the children are introduced to **curves** as smooth, but not straight, paths that connect two points. **Lines** appear as number lines, in measurement activities, and as the sides of geometric figures. Children perceive *angles* (space made by the meeting of two straight lines) in geometric figures. *Congruency*, or sameness of size and shape, is what children deal with when they match and compare the sizes and shapes of various figures, such as when they sort attribute blocks or make collages from paper shapes. Children are working with **symmetry** (the correspondence of parts of a figure on opposite sides of a point, line, or plane) when they do the paper folding suggested in Chapter 8. The terms *point(s)*, *line(s)*, and *curve(s)* may be used with young children without going into the technicalities. The terms *congruency*, *symmetry*, and *angle* will be introduced to them beyond the primary level and are not essential to working with the concepts informally. Working with inch cubes, children can begin to perceive how the volume of solids can be conceptualized. Blocks are excellent for developing and using spatial reasoning. Second graders in New York City designed and built bridges, buildings, and other structures with unit blocks (Shumway, 2013).

▶❚❚ **TeachSource Video**

© 2016 Cengage Learning®

HOW MANY CUBES? A QUESTION REGARDING VOLUME: STUDENT INTERVIEWS 1, 2, AND 3

Three different students are interviewed regarding volume, using drawings and plastic cubes.

The three students can be compared regarding their understanding of volume.

Questions:

1. Compare the understanding levels of the three students. Which one is the most advanced? Least advanced?

2. How does moving student #3 from concrete to semi-concrete and then to abstract help his ability to solve for volume?

3. Considering the three students, what misconceptions did you observe?

The readings and resources at the end of the chapter contain ideas for activities that lay the basis for the formal study of geometry. Following are some examples.

DAP

ACTIVITIES

GEOMETRY: GEOBOARD ACTIVITIES

Objective: To provide experience exploring the qualities of plane figures.

Materials: Geoboards and rubber bands. Geoboards may be purchased or made. A geoboard is a square board with round-head screws or smooth, slender cylinders (pegs) made of plastic or wood and placed at equal intervals so that it appears to be made up of many squares of equal size. Commercial geoboards have five rows of five pegs each.

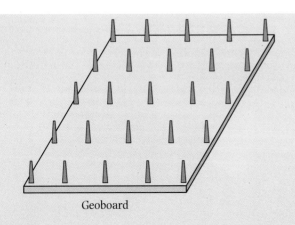

Geoboard

Activities:

1. Put out the geoboards and an ample supply of rubber bands of different sizes and colors (special rubber bands may be purchased with the geoboards). Allow plenty of time for the children to explore the materials informally.

2. Give each child a geoboard and one rubber band. Tell the children, **"Make as many different shapes as you can with one rubber band."** Encourage children to count the sides of their shapes and to count the number of pegs in each side. Suggest that they make a drawing of each shape.

3. Give each child a rubber band and an attribute block. **"Make a shape just like the block's shape."** Start with squares and rectangles, then triangles and hexagons.

4. On graph paper made to match the geoboard, draw patterns that the children can copy with their rubber bands. An example follows:

5. Have the children draw patterns on graph paper that matches the size of the geoboards. Demonstrate on the chalkboard first to be sure they realize that they need to make their lines from corner to corner. Have them try out their capabilities on some laminated blank graphs first. Then have them copy their own patterns on the geoboards. Encourage them to exchange patterns with other children.

Follow-up: Provide more complicated patterns for the children to copy. Encourage those who are capable of doing so to draw and copy more complicated patterns, possibly even some that overlap. Have them draw overlapping patterns with different-colored pencils or crayons and then construct the patterns with rubber bands of matching colors.

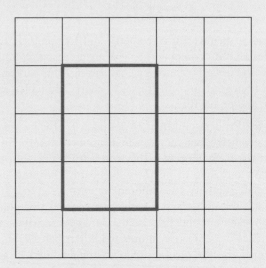

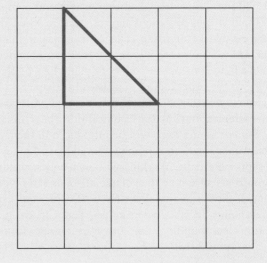

GEOMETRY: ACTIVITIES WITH SOLIDS

Objective: To explore the characteristics of solid geometric figures.

Materials: A set of geometric solids (available from Kaplan, Nienhuis Montessori, DIDAX Educational Resources, Creative Publications, Dale Seymour, ETA/Cuisinaire, and other vendors).

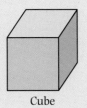

Cube

Cylinder

Cone

Pyramid

Sphere

Activities: Let the children explore the solids and note the similarities and differences. Once they are familiar with them, try the following activities.

Put out three of the objects. Describe one and see whether the children can guess which one it is.

- ■ **"It is flat all over, and each side is the same."** [cube]

- ■ **"It is flat on the bottom. Its sides look like triangles."** [pyramid]

- ■ **"It is flat on the bottom; the top is a point; and the sides are smooth."** [cone]

- ■ **"Both ends are flat and round, and the sides are smooth."** [cylinder]

- ■ **"It is smooth and round all over."** [sphere]

Follow-up: Have the children take turns being the person who describes the geometric solid. Put up a ramp. Have the students predict which solids will slide and which will roll. Then try them out. See whether the children realize that some may roll or slide, depending on how they are placed.

GEOMETRY: SYMMETRY

Objective: To provide experiences for exploring symmetry.

Materials: Construction paper symmetrical shapes (see Figure 9-4 for some suggested shapes; use your imagination to develop others).

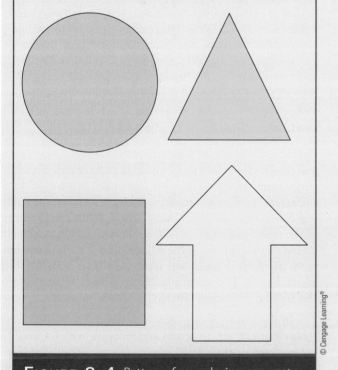

FIGURE 9-4 Patterns for exploring symmetry.

© Cengage Learning®

Activity: Give the children one shape pattern at a time. Have them experiment with folding the shapes until the halves match.

Follow-up:

1. Have the children use the shapes they have folded to make a three-dimensional collage. Say, **"Put glue on just one half of your folded paper."**

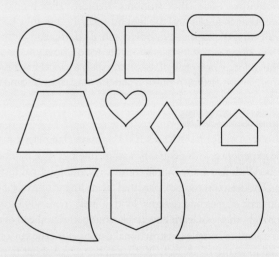

2. Give the children paper squares and rectangles. Show them how they can fold them in the middle and then cut the sides so that they come out with a figure that is the same on both halves. These figures can also be used to make three-dimensional collages.

GEOMETRY: NUMBER LINES

Objective: To apply the concept of a line as a visual picture of addition and subtraction and of *more than* and *less than*.

Materials: A laminated number line for each child; a large laminated number line that can be used for demonstration (or a permanent number line on the whiteboard); markers (e.g., chips) to mark places on the number lines.

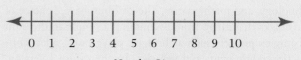

Number Line

Activities:

1. *Greater and less than.* "**Put a marker on the 4. Find a number that is greater than 4. Put a marker on it.**" Discuss which numbers were selected. How did they know which numbers were greater than 4? Go through the same procedure with the other numbers. Then, go through the procedure looking for numbers less than a given number.

2. *Addition.* Ask, "**How can we show two plus four on the number line?**" Encourage the children to try to figure it out. If they cannot, then demonstrate. Say, "**First I'll put a marker on 2. Now I'll count over four spaces. Now I'm at 6. How much is two plus four?**" Have the children try several problems with sums of 10 or less.

3. *Subtraction.* Ask, "**How can we show five minus two on the number line?**" Encourage the children to try to figure it out. If they cannot, then demonstrate. Say, "**First I'll put a marker on the 5. Now which way should I go to find five minus two?**" Have them try several problems using numbers 10 or less.

Follow-up: Have the children illustrate equivalent sums and differences on the number line (e.g., $3 + 4 = 1 + 6$, $8 - 4 = 7 - 3$). Have them also make up number line problems for themselves. Suggest that they use the number line to find the answer whenever they need help with a one-digit problem.

GEOMETRY: COMPARING ROAD AND STRAIGHT-LINE DISTANCES

Objective: To see the relationship between a direct route and the actual route between points on a map. (This activity is for the more advanced primary students who have learned how to use standard measurement tools.)

Materials: Maps of your state for everyone in the class, 1-foot rulers, and marking pens.

Activities: Have the students explore the maps. See whether they can find the legend and whether they can tell you what the various symbols mean. Be particularly sure that they know which kinds of lines are roads, how you find out the mileage from one place on the map to another, and how many miles an inch represents on the map. Spend some time finding out how far it is from your town or city to some nearby towns and cities. Have the class agree on two places in the state they would like to visit. Using their rulers and marking pens, have them draw straight lines from your city to the nearest place selected; from that place to the other location selected; and from there back home. They should then have a triangle. Have everyone figure out the mileage by road and then by direct flight by measuring the lines. Add up the three sides of the triangle. Add up the three road routes. Find the difference between the road trip and the direct route. Discuss why the roads are not as direct as the lines.

Follow-up: Encourage interested students to compare road and direct distances to other points in the state.

Digital Download

Robotics: Lego and LOGO. LOGO computer language can provide experience with geometry and technology at a number of levels. With just a few simple commands and minimal instruction, children can explore, play, and create an infinite number of geometric shapes and designs. With a little more adult-guided approach, they can learn how to plan out patterns ahead of time and use more complex instructional commands. The cursor, referred to as the **turtle** in LOGO, can be moved about in many directions and at different angles to make straight or curved lines. Children develop problem-solving skills when they work on figuring out how they will make the turtle go just where they want it to in order to come up with a particular design or figure.

Children's building with Lego building bricks and their exploration of LOGO are combined in connection with math/science/technology in the form of **Lego/LOGO**, Lego Mindstorms, and Lego Dacta robotics. These programs provide children with the opportunity to explore physics, technology, and mathematics. The children have a choice of many tasks that range from assembling a simple traffic light to complex projects such as bridges, playground rides, construction equipment, and vehicles. In the original version, the computer was programmed to control the operation of the Lego machines. More recently, National Instruments, Lego Dacta, and Tufts University have developed a Robolab system that enables students to write computer programs and transfer them into programmable Lego bricks. Even kindergartners can create their own robot designs. Lego Mindstorms includes several robotics products with sets for building *Star Wars* robots and many others. With the invention of the programmable bricks, the robots no longer need to be bound to the computer. The Mindstorms EV3 kit can communicate with iPhones and iPads as well as with Android smartphones. Seventeen possible creations are available in the EV3 kit, including "Reptar," a robotic snake.

In the Warwickshire schools in Great Britain, humanoid robots that can see, hear, and communicate with humans are helping support the STEM subjects (Curtis, 2012). The NAO robot includes cameras, microphones, pressure sensors, a voice synthesizer, and two high-fidelity speakers. The NAO robots are being introduced in the primary schools to get young children acquainted with robots. The children can interact with the robot with voice commands or by touching its head, arms, or legs.

Design Technology/Engineering. Design technology was introduced in Chapters 6 and 7 (see also Dunn & Larson, 1990; Petroski, 2003). Primary-grade students can follow more adult-guided directions and work on projects individually or in small cooperative groups. The Virginia Children's Engineering Council, the Virginia *Children's Engineering Journal*, and Children Designing and Engineering provide information and activities that provide problems for design technology. Some samples of more complex long-term projects are provided by Children Designing and Engineering (n.d.) and the Virginia Children's Engineering Council (n.d.). Chapter 7 described an example of a safari park project obtained from Children Designing and Engineering. The same site includes several additional projects. The Virginia Children's Engineering Council website also provides projects for students in kindergarten through third grade. As already mentioned, the STEM movement is increasing interest in projects relating to science, technology, engineering, and mathematics. STEM projects might include designing gravity racers (Wilcox, Roberts, & Wilcox, 2010), designing an insect keeper (Moore, Chessin, & Theobald, 2010), building houses (Bautista & Peters, 2010), exploring ramps and pathways (DeVries & Sales, 2010), or building with sand (Ashbrook, 2010). The engineering design process is described by Lottero-Perdue, Lovelidge, and Bowling (2010).

The 2012 Framework for K–12 Science Education moves beyond the conventional areas of science: physics, chemistry, biology, earth and space, and environmental science. The framework includes engineering and technology as they relate to applications of science. The term *engineering* is used "in a very broad sense to mean any engagement in a systematic design to achieve solutions to particular human problems" (NRC, 2012, p. 11). The term *technology* is used to include "all types of human-made systems and processes" (NRC, 2012, p. 11). The purpose of including engineering and technology is to demonstrate the application of science. Each issue of the *Children's Engineering Journal* contains examples of children's engineering projects. For example, kindergartners designed and built a community (Deal, 2012); second graders redesigned their classroom (Sweet, 2012); third graders designed and constructed animals using pneumatics (Stadler, 2012); and first graders constructed spider pop-up books (Willey, 2013).

Collecting and Analyzing Data and Constructing Graphs. Students can collect data, categorize the results, and depict the results in a graphical representation for analysis (**Photo 9-4**). Graphing includes constructing graphs, reading information on graphs, and interpreting the information on a graph (**Figure 9-5**). The data used for making graphs need to be something of interest to the students. Chapter 5 presents a list of possible graphing subjects that young children might enjoy working on. Other subjects will grow out of their current interests and activities. Morgan and Ansberry (2011) provide suggestions for getting K–3 graphing started and progressing. The teacher may begin with a question. If the class is studying animals, he might ask, "If you were a scientist studying animals, which animal would you study?" You then list the animals and narrow the choices down to five or six. Morgan and Ansberry then go on to design a graphing activity around the book *The Great Graph Contest* by Loreen Leedy (2005). Children can make charts and graphs tracking their own accomplishments (Forsyth, 2013). This can be a motivational activity. Second graders charted their collections for a canned food drive (Brown, 2013).

The four most popular types of graphs are picture graphs, bar graphs or histograms, **line graphs**, and circle or pie graphs. The graphs described in previous chapters fall into the first two categories and are the easiest for young children to construct and interpret. Although pie graphs are beyond the primary level, some primary-level children can begin to work with line graphs.

Line graphs require concrete operational thinking because children must focus on more than one aspect of the data at the same time. Line graphs are made on a square paper grid and enable children to apply the basic skills that they would learn

PHOTO 9-4 The student sorts shapes by color and graphs the results.

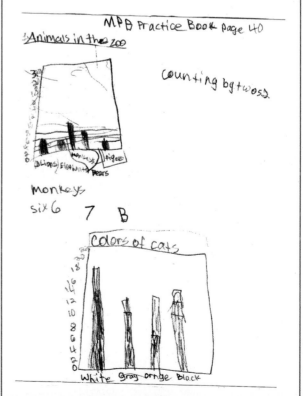

FIGURE 9-5 Third graders' homework includes constructing graphs.

by first doing the squared-paper activities with the geoboard. These graphs are especially good for showing variations such as rainfall, temperature, and hours of daylight. In **Figure 9-6**, Chan's temperature data are translated from the bar graph to the line graph. Note that the left side and the bottom are called the **axes** and that each must be labeled. In this case, the left side is the temperature axis, and the bottom is the axis representing days of the week. To find the correct point for each temperature on each day, the child has to find the point where the two meet, mark the point, and connect it with lines to the previous point and to the next point. If two or more types of information are included on the same graph, then usually geometric symbols are used to indicate which line goes with which set of data. Vissa (1987) suggests some creative ways to introduce the use of coordinate (or line) graphing to young children.

Charts and Tables. **Charts** and **tables** are constructed to organize data before they are graphed. A simple chart consists of tally marks such as those depicted in the chart on floating and sinking objects in Chapter 3 (see Figure 3-17. This information could be translated into a single-variable graph showing the frequency of floating or sinking for each object or into a double-variable graph (i.e., a double-bar or double-line graph) showing both tendencies. The simple tables shown in Figure 9-3 were used to organize the temperature data before constructing the graphs.

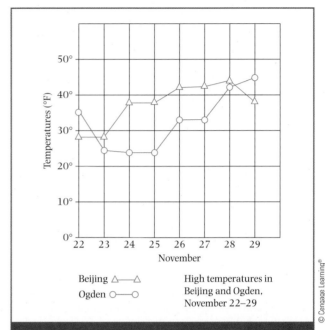

FIGURE 9-6 Chan's data depicted in a line graph.

ACTIVITIES

GRAPHING: INTRODUCING COORDINATES

Objective: To introduce finding coordinates on a graph.

Materials: A large supply of stickers of various kinds. On the bulletin board, construct a large 5 × 5 square coordinate graph. Make the grids, using black tape. Place stickers at the intersections of various coordinates (Figure 9-7).

Activities: Say, **"This is the city. Driving into the city, the corner is here, at 0, 0. I want to go to [name one of the stickers]. Tell me how many blocks over and how many blocks up I will have to go."** Suppose that the sticker is on 2, 3. Say, **"Yes, I have to go over two blocks and up three. This point is called 2, 3."** Draw the children's attention to how the numbers on the bottom and the sides correspond to the point. Go back to 0, 0, and have the children direct you to other points on the graph. Let the children take turns telling you the coordinates of a sticker they would like to have. When they are able to give the correct coordinates, they get a matching sticker to keep.

Follow-up: During center time, encourage children to explore the coordinate map on their own or with a friend. Suggest they trace trips to different "corners" with their fingers. Let the children who understand the concept of coordinates use coordinate paper to complete symmetrical shapes (Figure 9-8) and name the coordinates.

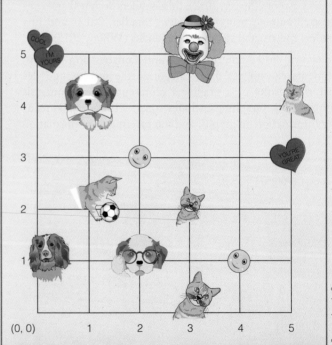

FIGURE 9-7 Coordinate graphing can be introduced using a grid with stickers placed at points to be identified.

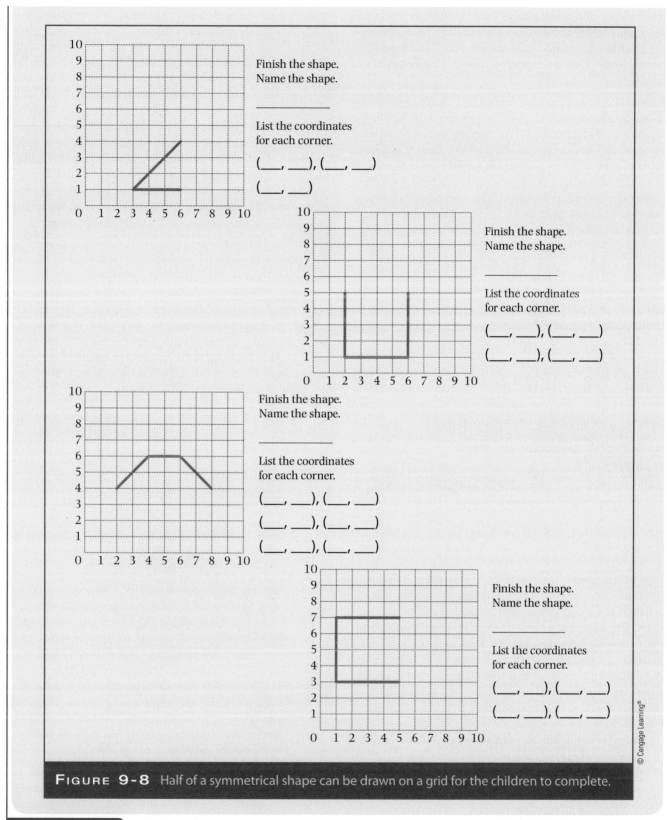

Finish the shape.
Name the shape.

_____

List the coordinates
for each corner.

(___, ___), (___, ___)

(___, ___)

Finish the shape.
Name the shape.

_____

List the coordinates
for each corner.

(___, ___), (___, ___)

(___, ___), (___, ___)

Finish the shape.
Name the shape.

_____

List the coordinates
for each corner.

(___, ___), (___, ___)

(___, ___), (___, ___)

(___, ___), (___, ___)

Finish the shape.
Name the shape.

_____

List the coordinates
for each corner.

(___, ___), (___, ___)

(___, ___), (___, ___)

© Cengage Learning®

FIGURE 9-8 Half of a symmetrical shape can be drawn on a grid for the children to complete.

Digital Download

Estimation. Estimation is an important activity at the primary level. As children enter the concrete operations period, they can begin to make rational estimates (Lang, 2001; see also Chapter 7). You could fill a jar with pennies, and have students predict how many they can hold in one hand and then compare their estimates. Each student then takes a handful, counts them, and compares the actual amounts with his or her estimate (Olson & Easley, 1996). Finally, using their handfuls as a base, students estimate how many pennies the jar holds. Show the students a jar filled with interlocking cubes. Have them guess how many are in the jar. Then, remove 10 cubes and connect them in a train. Now the students have more information. Ask them to make a new estimate. Continue making trains of 10 cubes until the jar is empty (Burns, 1997).

Probability. According to NCTM (2000), the concept of probability is extremely informal at the primary level. Challenge children to answer questions about what is *most likely* and what is *least likely*. For example, in Minnesota in January, is it more likely to snow or rain? Children can tally throws of the dice or the results of tossing a small group of two-sided discs (yellow on one side and red on the other). The children note that some numbers or colors come up more often than others, though they are not yet ready to learn how to calculate probabilities.

9-2f Integration Across the Content Areas

The concepts described in this chapter can be applied across the content areas. Some of the articles suggested at the end of the chapter provide examples of activities that integrate mathematics with other content areas.

9-2g Helping Children with Special Needs

Children with Down syndrome (DS) also need special attention and accommodations (Lewis, 2003). They tend to be relatively slow in language development as a result of poor short-term memory, especially for auditory material, and poor long-term memory for verbal and spatial material. Such children need lots of repetition of new skills, along with reviews of previously learned skills. Lessons need to be simple and should include a minimum number of materials and instructions. The range of DS abilities is broad, so careful assessment is necessary for appropriate planning. Breaking tasks into small steps is a technique used effectively with DS children (Gargiulo & Kilgo, 2014).

9-2h Informal Post-Evaluation

Note whether children can follow directions and maintain involvement in the activities. Observing the process in these activities is critical. When children are not able to do an activity, it is important to note where the process breaks down. Does the child have the basic idea but just need a little more practice and guidance? Does the activity seem to be beyond the child's capabilities at this time? These activities require advanced cognitive and perceptual motor development, so children should not be pushed beyond their developmental level. If children work in pairs or small groups of varied ability, the more advanced can assist the less advanced.

9-3 STANDARDS AND DESCRIPTION OF MEASUREMENT

Measurement is one of the most important aspects of mathematics (Kepner, 2009). It is a practical activity that is used in everyday life during experiences such as cooking, shopping,

building, and constructing. In the primary curriculum, it is essential to gathering data in science and can also be applied in other areas. Measurement is a major vehicle for integrating mathematics with other content areas. It is also a vehicle for reinforcing other math skills and concepts. The number line is based on length; a popular multiplication model is much like finding area; and measurement is a topic that lends itself naturally to problem-solving activities. Counting, whole number operations, and fractions are used to arrive at measurements and provide results. This part of Chapter 9 builds on the basic concepts of measurement described in Chapters 5 and 6. It focuses on the instruction and activities for introducing the concept of standard units and for applying that concept to length, volume, area, weight, temperature, time, and money measurement.

During the primary grades, measurement is an important connection from number and operations to algebra and geometry. During first grade, measurement is a means for obtaining data to be analyzed to solve problems. During second grade, linear measurement is a focal point that connects with geometry. During third grade, children use their knowledge of fractions as they connect to making finer measurements. Measurement of area and of volume is also a focus in third grade.

The Common Core State Standards (2010) include measurement expectations for the primary grades as follows:

1. *First Grade: Measurement.* Children should be able to order three objects by length and compare the length of two objects indirectly by using a third object. They should also understand and use length units accurately. In addition, they should be able to tell and write time in hours and half hours, using analog and digital clocks.

2. *Second Grade: Measurement.* Children should be able to measure and estimate lengths in standard units and relate addition and subtraction to length. They should be able to use rulers, yardsticks, meter sticks, and measuring tapes. They should also be able to work with time and money. They should be able to tell and write time to the nearest five minutes, using the terms *a.m. and p.m.* Children should be able to solve word problems involving dollar bills, quarters, dimes, nickels and pennies, using dollar and cents symbols correctly.

3. *Third Grade: Measurement.* Children should be able to solve problems involving measurement and estimation of intervals of time, liquid volumes, and masses of objects. They should tell and write time intervals in minutes. Children should understand and measure areas of geometric shapes and perimeters of plane figures and solve problems based on measuring these plane figures.

Chapter 5 (see Figure 5-6) described five stages in the development of the measurement concept. During the sensorimotor and preoperational periods, children's measurement activities center on play and imitation and on making comparisons (e.g., long–short, heavy–light, full–empty, hot–cold, early–late, rich–poor). During the transition period, from ages 5 to 7, children enjoy working with arbitrary units. During concrete operations (which an individual usually enters at age 6 or older), children can begin to see the need for standard units (Stage 4) and begin to develop skills in using them (Stage 5). Standard units are not introduced for each concept at the same time. In general, the following guidelines can be observed.

- *Length (linear measure).* The units of inch/foot and centimeter/meter are introduced at the beginning of primary and are used for measurement during second grade.

- *Area.* Area is introduced informally with nonstandard units in first grade and ties in with multiplication in third grade.

- *Time.* Time measurement devices and vocabulary are introduced before primary, but it is generally the end of primary before conventional time is clearly understood and an analog clock can be read with accuracy.

- *Volume (capacity).* Volume is learned informally during pouring activities, and accuracy is stressed during preprimary cooking. The concept of units of volume is usually introduced in second grade.

- *Weight.* The standard measurement for weight is usually introduced in third grade.

- *Temperature.* Temperature units are identified in second grade, by which time children may begin to read thermometers, but it is usually beyond primary before children can measure temperature with accuracy and understanding.

- *Money.* Coins and bills are identified before primary. Symbols are associated in early primary, but value does not begin to be understood until the end of primary.

The goal in the primary grades is to introduce the meaning of measurement, needed terminology, important units, and most common measurement tools.

Both **English units** (customary in the United States) and **metric units** are introduced during the primary years. Although the metric system is much easier to use because it is based on 10s and is used as the principal system in most countries, it has not been adopted as the official measure in the United States. In the 1970s, there was a movement toward the United States adopting the system, but it died out, and the US Metric Commission was abolished in 1984. However, children must learn the metric system because it is so widely used around the world in industry and science.

9-3a Informal Pre-Assessment

Concrete operational thinking is essential for children to understand the need for and the use of standard units. Conservation tasks for length, weight, and volume were illustrated earlier in the text. Chapter 5 suggested observational assessment guidelines for finding out what children at the early stages of understanding measurement know about volume, weight, length, and temperature. Interview tasks for time can be found in Chapter 5. Be sure that children can apply nonstandard measure before moving on to standard measure.

9-3b Instruction

The concept of measurement develops through measurement experiences. Lecture and demonstration are not adequate for supporting the development of this concept. Also, the teacher needs to take a sequenced approach to the introduction of standard units. Adhere to the following steps.

1. Do comparisons that do not require numbers (see Chapter 3)

2. Use nonstandard arbitrary units (see Chapter 5).
   a. Find the number of units by counting.
   b. Report the number of units.

3. Compare the thing measured to the units used (e.g., a table's width is measured with paper clips or drinking straws).

4. Introduce standard units appropriate for the same type of measurement.
   a. Find the number of units, using standardized measuring instruments (i.e., ruler, scale, cup, liter, thermometer).
   b. Report the number of units.

The introduction of new standard measurement techniques and instruments should always be preceded by comparisons and nonstandard measurement with arbitrary units. Naturalistic and informal measurement experiences should be encouraged at all levels.

The Concept of Unit. Children's ability to measure rests on their understanding of the concept of **unit**. Many children have difficulty in perceiving that units can be other than one. In other words, one-half foot could be a unit; three centimeters could be a unit; two standard measuring cups could be a unit; one mark on a thermometer equals two degrees; and so on.

The concept of unit can be developed by first using nonstandard units of measurement. Children learn that measurement can be made with an arbitrary unit, but that the arbitrary units must be equal to one another when making a specific measurement (**Photo 9-5**). For example, when paper clips are used for measurement, each clip must be the same length. A paper clip is not the unit; rather, a paper clip of some consistent length is the unit. Through the use of arbitrary but equal units to measure objects, children construct the concept of a unit. The concept is reinforced by using different arbitrary units (one kind at a time) and then comparing the results in terms of the number of units. For example, the children measure Lai's height using Unifix Cubes, identical drinking straws, and the class math textbook. Soon they realize that measurement with smaller units requires more units than measurement with larger units. When the students move on to standard units, they can compare the number of units needed to measure, using teaspoons versus a standard cup measure, inches versus a yardstick, and so on.

Children should be aware that they must be accurate when using units, whether arbitrary or standard. For example, there cannot be gaps or spaces between units when measuring length (a good reason to start with Unifix Cubes, Hurricane's Toy Links or some other units that can be stuck together and easily lined up). Once children are able to measure using as many units as needed to measure the whole length, capacity, and so on, then they can advance to using one or more units that must be moved to make a complete measurement. For example, they could make a 10-Unifix-Cube unit for length measure, place it on the item to be measured, mark where it ends, move the measure to that point, keep going until finished, and then add the 10s and any remaining cubes to arrive at the length in cubes. For capacity, they can fill individual measuring cups and then count the number of empties after a larger container is filled. Or one cup could be used and a record kept of how many cupfuls filled the larger container. As children discover these shortcuts to measurement, they become able to transfer this knowledge to standard unit measure and understand the rationale behind foot rulers, meter- and yardsticks, and quart and liter measures.

Measuring Instruments. With the introduction of standard units comes the introduction of measuring instruments. Rulers, scaled instruments (scales, graduated cylinders, thermometers), and clocks are the tools of standard measurement. Children have problems with these instruments unless they understand what they are measuring and what it means to measure. Begin with simple versions of the instruments, which are marked with only the unit being used. For example, if the unit is the centimeter, use a ruler that is marked only with centimeters (no millimeters). If the unit is an inch, use a ruler marked only with inches (no ½, ¼, or smaller parts of each inch). Be sure the children understand how units are marked. For example, on a ruler, the numbers come after the unit, not before. Most 9-year-olds will say the ruler illustrated in **Figure 9-9** is 5 inches (rather than 6 inches) long. You must be sure that children understand that each number tells how many units have been used.

Children need many experiences measuring objects shorter than their ruler before they move on to longer objects that require them to measure, mark, and move the

PHOTO 9-5 The children discover which weights will result in balance.

© Cengage Learning®

ruler. They also need to be able to apply their addition skills. For example, if a child is using a 12-inch ruler and measures something that is 12 inches plus 8 inches, can she add 12 + 8? Measuring to the nearest quarter, eighth, or sixteenth of an inch requires that the child understand fractions.

Scaled instruments present a problem because not every individual unit is marked. For example, thermometers are marked every two degrees. A good way to help children understand this concept is to have them make their own instruments. They can make graphs using different scales or make their own graduated cylinders. They can do the latter by taking a large glass and putting a piece of masking tape down the side, as shown in **Figure 9-10**.

Take a smaller container, fill it with spoonfuls, count how many it holds, and empty it into the glass. Mark the level of the water and the number of spoonfuls. Fill the small container, empty it into the glass, and mark again. In the example, the small container holds 5 teaspoons of water. This measure can be used to find out how much other containers will hold.

Analog clocks are one of the most difficult instruments for children to understand. Although there are only

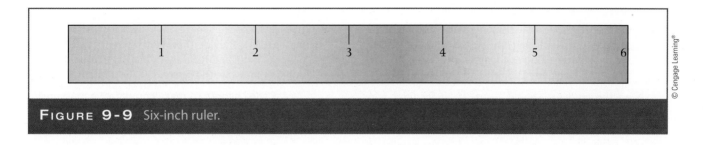

FIGURE 9-9 Six-inch ruler.

three measures (hours, minutes, and seconds), the circular movement of the hands makes reading the face difficult. McMillen and Hernandez (2008) describe a method used to help second-grade students understand the meanings of the short and long hands on the analog clock. Two one-handed clocks were used. The activities were designed to help the students understand the relationship that minutes and seconds have to each other, to groups of 5 hours, and to 12 hours. For example, to get a feeling for 1 minute, students predicted how many times they could bounce a ball, how far they could run, and how many Unifix Cubes they could connect in 1 minute. Children vary greatly as to when they are finally able to read a clock face accurately. There is no set age for being able to tell time. Skills needed to tell time must be learned over many years and through practice with clock faces with movable hands (Photo 9-6). Digital clocks are easier to read but do not provide the child with a visual picture of the relationship between time units.

Money also offers difficulties because the sizes of the coins do not coincide with their value (e.g., the dime is smaller than the penny and the nickel). Bills provide no size cues but do have numerical designations that relate one bill to the other. Relating the coins to the bills is a difficult task for young children (Photo 9-7).

9-3c Measurement Activities

This section includes activities that help children construct the concepts of measuring length, volume (capacity), area, weight (mass), temperature, time, and money, using standard units (Figure 9-11). Refer to previous units in this text for the comparison and arbitrary (nonstandard) measurement experiences that must occur before introducing standard units of measurement. Also, remember to work on the concepts of the units used for each type of measurement as well as on actual measurement.

DAP naeyc

ACTIVITIES

STANDARD MEASUREMENT: LINEAR

Objective: To be able to use standard units of measurement to compare lengths of objects; to discover that the smaller the units are, the more will be needed to measure a distance; and to use a ruler for measuring objects.

Materials: Rulers (inch or foot, yardstick, centimeter, meter stick); tape measures; paper, pencils, crayons, markers, and poster board; and the book *How Big Is a Foot?* by Myller (1972).

Activities: Introduce these activities to children, following many exploratory experiences that involve comparing objects visually and with arbitrary units. Have children measure the same objects, using both arbitrary and standard units to emphasize the need for standard units. The first activity is designed to develop an understanding of this need.

1. **"You have measured many things around the room, including yourselves, and made comparisons. What you compare against is called your *unit of measurement*. What are some units of measurements you have used?"** The children should name items used such as paper clips, Unifix Cubes, books, and the like. **"When you tell how long or how tall something is, you have to tell which unit of measure you used. Why? What problem could occur if you are telling this information to someone who cannot see your unit of measure?"** Encourage discussion. For example, the children might suggest that, if they are measuring with Unifix Cubes, they send the person a cube; or if they are measuring with a piece

of string, they send the person a piece of string of the same length. Next, read *How Big Is a Foot?* and discuss the problem the king encountered. For ideas on how to use this book, see Lubinski and Thiessen (1996).

Now the students should begin to understand why standard units of measurement are necessary. Clarify this point by summing up: "**If everyone knows exactly what the units of measurement are, it is much easier to explain how long, wide, and tall something is. That is why we have *standard* units of measure. We use inches, feet, and yards.**" Pass around foot rulers and yardsticks for the children to examine and compare. "**In most places in the world and in science laboratories and factories, centimeters, decimeters, and meters are used.**" Pass around metersticks. Point out that the base-10 blocks they've been using are marked off in centimeters (1s units) and in decimeters (10s units) and that ten 10s placed end to end make a meter. Have them test this statement with the meter sticks and the base-10 blocks. "**These units are the same everywhere and do not change. Get into pairs and measure each other's body parts, using your rulers and tape measures. Before you start, make a list of the parts you plan to measure.**" Have the students call out the names of the parts they plan to measure. When they finish, have them compare their results.

2. Have the children use their foot rulers and two other units (such as a shoe and a pencil) to measure the same objects. Have them record the results in a table.

Object	Length			
	Feet	Inches	Shoes	Pencils
Table	____	____	____	____
Windowsill	____	____	____	____
Bookshelf	____	____	____	____

Discuss the results and what they mean.

3. Have the children make their own inch and centimeter rulers. Provide them with strips of cardboard 6 inches long, and have them mark the results off in units, as shown in the figure.

Ask the children to make comparative measures around the classroom. Then send the rulers home along with a note to the parents.

Dear Parents,

We are working with different ways of measuring length. Your child is bringing home an inch ruler and a centimeter ruler and is supposed to measure six things at home with each ruler and record the results. Please help your child if necessary. Have your child share the results with you and explain the differences in the number of inches versus the number of centimeters of length found for each object. Thanks for your help with this project.

Sincerely,

Jon Wang, second-grade teacher

Object	Length	
	Inch Ruler	Centimeter Ruler
1.	_____	_____
2.	_____	_____
3.	_____	_____
4.	_____	_____
5.	_____	_____
6.	_____	_____

Follow-up: Do many more linear measurement activities using standard units, as suggested in the resources at the end of the chapter.

STANDARD MEASUREMENT: VOLUME

Objectives: To be able to use standard units of measurement to compare volumes of materials; to learn that the smaller the units are, the more will be needed to measure the volume; to learn how to use standard measures of volume such as teaspoons, tablespoons, cups, pints, quarts, and liters.

Materials: Containers of many different sizes (boxes, baskets, buckets, jars, cups, bowls, pans, bottles, plastic bags, etc.) and standard measures of volume (a set of customary measuring cups and a set of metric cups; liter and quart measures; customary and metric measuring spoons).

Activities: Introduce these activities to children, following many exploratory experiences of comparing volumes visually and with arbitrary units. Have children measure the same container's capacities with both arbitrary and standard units to emphasize the need for standard units. The first activity is designed to develop an understanding of this need.

1. Discuss volume, following the same format as was used for linear measurement. **"You have explored the volume or space inside many containers by filling and emptying containers of different sizes and shapes. What kinds of units have you used?"** Encourage them to name some of the smaller units that they used to fill larger containers. See whether they can generalize from the length discussion that problems in communication arise when standard units are not used. Pass around the standard measurement materials. Encourage the children to talk about the characteristics of these materials. Do they recognize that they have used these types of things many times to measure ingredients for cooking? Do they notice the numbers and scales marked on the materials?

2. Using the standard units, have the children find out the capacities of the containers previously used for exploration. Have them use materials such as water, pebbles, and/or sand for these explorations. They should record their findings in a table like the following one:

	Number of Units to Fill	
Container	Using Standard Cup Measure	Using Small Juice Glass
1.	_____	_____
2.	_____	_____
3.	_____	_____
4.	_____	_____
5.	_____	_____
6.	_____	_____

Follow-up: Continue to do exploratory measurement of capacity. Also, continue with cooking activities, giving the children more responsibility for selecting the needed measuring tools.

STANDARD MEASUREMENT: AREA

Objective: To explore area in a concrete manner and its relationship to linear measurement.

Materials: Inch and centimeter cubes, two-dimensional patterns (with and without squares), paper grids, and paper squares (or purchase Measuring Center from Lakeshore).

Activities: Long before formal instruction, children can explore area with squared paper and cubes. Remember that area-type activities are frequently used as the visual representations of multiplication.

1. On poster board, make some shapes, such as those shown in the following figure, that are in inch or centimeter units. Have the children find out how many inch or centimeter cubes will cover the whole shape.

2. Make a supply of paper grids (inch or centimeter squares, about 5 × 4 squares) and construction paper squares. Have the children make up their own areas by pasting individual squares on the grid. Have

them record on the grid how many squares are in their area (or use Measuring Center).

SHAPES WITH SQUARES MARKED

SHAPES WITHOUT SQUARES MARKED

Follow-up: If you have introduced rulers to the children, ask them to measure the lines on the grids and patterns with their rulers. Discuss how they might figure out how many square inches or centimeters are on a plane surface, using their rulers.

STANDARD MEASUREMENT: WEIGHT

Objective: To be able to use standard units of measure to compare the weights of various materials and to use balance and platform scales.

Materials: Balance scales with English and metric weights, a set of platform scales, a metric and/or customary kitchen scale, paper and pencil for recording observations, and many objects and materials that can be weighed.

Activities: The children should have already explored weight, using comparisons.

1. **"When you look at two objects, you can guess whether they are heavy or light, but you don't really know until you lift them, because size can fool you. You could easily lift a large balloon, but a rock of the same size would be too heavy to lift."** Have a balloon and a rock available for them to lift, if possible. **"A marshmallow would be easier to lift than a lump of lead of the same size. The lead and the rock have more stuff in them than the balloon and the marshmallow. The more stuff there is in something, the harder a force in the earth, called gravity, pulls on it. When something is weighed, we are measuring how hard gravity is pulling on it. You have compared many kinds of things by putting one kind of thing on one side of a balance scale and another on the other side. Now you will work with customary and metric weights in your pan balance on one side and things you want to weigh on the other side."** Discuss the sets of pan balance weights, and have them available for the children to examine. Explain that all of them are made of the same material so that size is relative to weight. Have the children weigh various objects and materials (water, sand, pebbles, cotton balls, Unifix Cubes, etc.). Compare the weights of a cup of water versus a cup of sand or a cup of pebbles. Which weighs more? How much more? Remind the children that they will have to add the amounts for each weight to get a total. Suggest that they work in pairs so they can check each other's results.

2. Show the children how to read the dial on the kitchen scale. Provide a variety of things to weigh.

3. If a platform scale for people is available, have everyone in the class weighed, record the results, and have the children make a graph that depicts the results.

4. Have the children go through the newspaper for grocery store advertisements and cut out pictures of items that have to be weighed at the store to find their cost.

5. Have the children weigh two objects at the same time. Remove one, and weigh the remaining object. Subtract the weight of the single object from the weight of the two. Now weigh the other object. Is the weight the same as when you subtracted the first weight from the total for both objects?

Follow-up: Continue putting out interesting things to weigh. Make something with a metric recipe that specifies amounts by weight rather than by volume.

STANDARD MEASUREMENT: TEMPERATURE

Objective: To be able to use standard units of measurement to compare temperatures and to learn how to use a thermometer to measure temperature.

Materials: Large demonstration thermometer, small thermometers for student use, outdoor thermometer.

Activities: These activities assume that children have talked about and have had experiences with hot, warm, and cold things and with hot, comfortable, and cold weather.

1. Let the children examine the demonstration thermometer. Have them decide why there are two scales (Fahrenheit and Celsius) and how each is read. Discuss their experiences with thermometers (e.g., when they are ill or go to the doctor for a checkup; measuring outdoor and indoor air temperatures; controlling the thermostat on their furnaces and air conditioners).

2. Provide some hot water and ice cubes. Ask the children to measure the temperature of the water and record the result. Have them add an ice cube, let it melt, measure again, and record the result. Keep adding ice cubes and recording the results. Have the children make a line graph to illustrate how ice affects the temperature. Is any other factor affecting the water temperature? (Answer: the air temperature.) Compare the results with the temperature of tap water.

3. If possible, post an outdoor thermometer outside the classroom window, and have the children record the temperature each day in the morning, at noon, and at the end of the day. After a week, have them make some graphs depicting what they found out. Ask interested students to write daily weather reports for posting on the bulletin board.

Follow-up: Have interested children record the daily weather forecasts from the radio, TV, or newspaper. Compare the forecast temperatures with those recorded at school.

STANDARD MEASUREMENT: TIME

Objective: To be able to use standard units of time measurement and to read time accurately from an analog clock.

Materials: Large clock model with movable hands (e.g., the well-known Judy Clock), miniature model clocks that can be used individually during small group activities, a 60-minute timer that can be used to help develop a sense of time duration, a class monthly calendar (teacher-made or purchased).

Activities:

1. Children should have some sense of time sequence and duration once they reach the primary level. A timer is still useful to time events such as "Five minutes to finish up" or "Let's see if anyone can finish before the 10-minute timer rings." The major task for the primary child is to understand the clock and what it tells us and to eventually to learn how to work with time in terms of the amount of time from one clock reading to another. Children can work together with

the Judy Clock or with their smaller models, moving the hands to different positions at random and identifying the times. Much clock knowledge comes from everyday activities through naturalistic and informal experiences. You can support these experiences by having a large wall clock in your classroom and having visual models of important times during the day that the children can match to the real clock. For example, the daily schedule might be put on the wall chart with both a conventional clock face and the digital time indicated for each major time block, as shown in the following figure:

 Arrival 8:30 a.m.  Lunch 11:30 a.m.  Depart 3:00 p.m.

2. Clock skills may be broken down as follows:

    a. Identify the hour and the minute hands and the direction in which they move.

    b. Be able to say the time on the clock at the hour, and be able to place the hands of the clock for the hour. Know that the short hand is on the hour, and the long hand is on 12.

    c. Identify that the time is after a particular hour.

    d. Count by 5s.

    e. Tell the time to the nearest multiple of 5.

    f. Count on from multiples of 5 (10, 15, 20, . . .).

    g. Write time in digital notation (3:15).

    h. Tell time to the nearest minute, and write it in digital notation.

    i. Match the digital clock's time to the analog clock's time.

    j. Identify time before a particular hour, and count by 5s to tell how many minutes it is before that hour.

3. Each child can make a clock to take home. Use a poster board circle or paper plate. Provide each child

with a paper fastener and a long and short hand. Have them mark the short hand with an *H* and the long hand with an *M*. Send a note home to the parents, suggesting some clock activities they can do with their child.

4. Each month, provide the children with blank calendars that they can fill in with important dates (holidays, birthdays, etc.).

Follow-up: Continue to read children stories that include time concepts and time sequence. For more advanced students who understand how to read clocks and keep track of time, have them keep a diary for a week, recording how much time they spend on activities at home (eating, sleeping, doing homework, reading, watching TV, using computer, playing outdoors, attending soccer practice, going to dancing lessons, etc.). Ask them to add up the times at the end of the week and rank the activities, in terms of time spent on them, from most to least. They might even go on to figure out how much time per month and year they spend on each activity if their activities are consistent from week to week. See McMillen and Hernandez (2008) for more lessons on understanding the analog clock.

STANDARD MEASUREMENT: MONEY

Objective: To be able to tell the value of money of different denominations, associate the cent symbol (¢) with coins and the dollar sign ($) with dollars, find the value of a particular

set of coins, and be able to write the value of particular sets of coins and bills.

Materials: Paper money and coin sets, pictures of coins, and Money Bingo game (Trend Enterprises).

Activities: Money is always a fascinating subject for young children. Money activities can be used not only to learn about money but also to provide application for whole numbers and later for decimal skills.

1. Dramatic play continues to be an important vehicle of learning for primary children. First graders enjoy dramatic play centers such as those described in Chapter 6. Second graders and third graders begin to be more organized and can design their own dramatic play activities, using available props. They enjoy writing plays and acting them out. Play money should always be available in the prop box.

2. Make some price tags (first with amounts less than $1, later with more). Have the children pick tags out of a box, one at a time, and count out the correct amount of play money.

3. Have the children go through catalogs and select items they would like. Have them list the items and their prices and then add up their purchases. Younger children can write just the dollar part of the prices.

Follow-up: Play Money Bingo. The bingo cards have groups of coins in each section. Cards with different amounts of cents are picked, and the children have to add up their coins to find out if they have a match. Download from the Illuminations website, Primary Economics, which contains activities for primary students to practice consumer roles such as earning money and saving for a future purchase. Coin Box, also at the illuminations site, provides activities designed to help children learn to count, collect, exchange, and make change with coins.

Digital Download

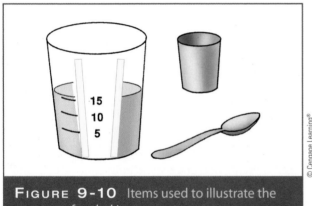

FIGURE 9-10 Items used to illustrate the concept of scaled instruments.

9-3d Ideas for Children with Special Needs

The last disability considered in this section of the book includes the autism spectrum disorders (ASD). This group of developmental disabilities includes autistic disorder, pervasive developmental disorder, and Asperger's. The incidence of these disorders is ever increasing (Gargiulo & Kilgo, 2014). The symptoms of these disorders vary, but afflicted children typically have social and communication disorders and may display challenging behaviors. The focus for teaching ASD children is getting them socially involved. Intellectually, they range from gifted to severely challenged.

According to Lewis (2003), communication with these children must be clear and simple. Tasks need to be broken down into small steps. The environment, materials and equipment, must be carefully structured (Gargiulo & Kilgo, 2014). All these methods require constant attention to the child.

PHOTO 9-6 Written time is matched with analog clock face time.

PHOTO 9-7 Children can figure out which coins and bills make a specific amount.

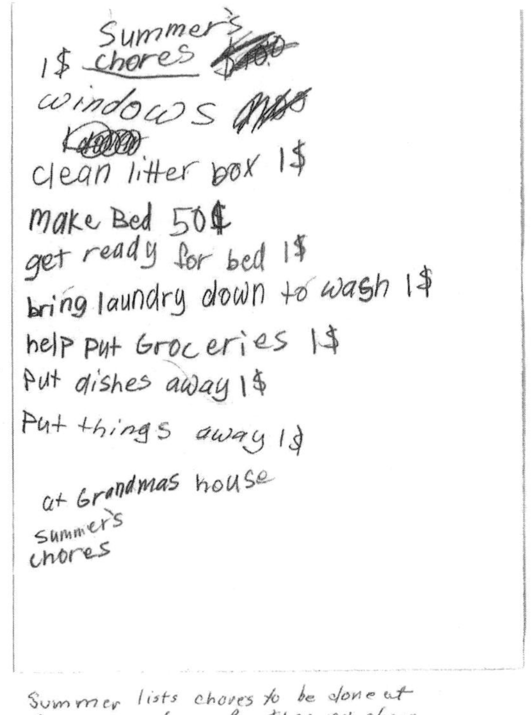

FIGURE 9-11 Summer (age 9) is very interested in making money. She makes a list of chores she can do at Grandma's house to earn some money.

We have looked at the wide variety of disabilities that children may display. Some typical children may have difficulties with mathematics that can be identified in the early grades. Mathematics Recovery (MR) (Wright, Martland, Stafford, & Stanger, 2002) is a program for helping first graders (6- or 7-year-olds) who are struggling with mathematics. The one-on-one instruction is individualized and problem based. Wright and colleagues present a detailed plan for working with difficult students.

9-3e Evaluation

Evaluate children's progress with measurement, using concrete tasks; here are some examples:

- Give the children a list of three items in the classroom to measure. Arrange a set of measuring cups, material to measure, and a container to measure into. Then ask each child to turn in his answer.

- Set up a scale with three items of known weight, and have each child weigh each item individually and record the amount.

- Put out three model thermometers with different temperatures and have each child, in turn, tell you the readings and whether they indicate hot, comfortable, or cold.

- Show the child the time on a model clock and ask her to tell you the time and explain how she knows it.

- Have each child identify coins and then put them together to make various amounts, making the amounts appropriate to the child's level at the time.

SUMMARY

9-1 Standards and Description of Place Value and Numbers Above 10

Learning about place value and working with two-digit whole number operations that require regrouping and renaming are two of the most difficult challenges the primary-level child faces. These concepts should be taught initially with concrete or virtual manipulatives. Most mathematics educators believe that children learn the concepts and skills needed to understand place value—as well the processes of regrouping and renaming—through practice in solving problems that use concrete materials.

Informal Pre-Evaluation. Should be done using interview assessment tasks that employ concrete materials to determine prior knowledge.

Activities. Both concrete and virtual manipulatives can be used. Kamii (2003) takes a different approach, using no concrete materials, but guiding children through trial and error and discussion. Children with perceptual and/or motor disabilities need special assistance. As the common core is implemented, it should be adapted to culture and community.

Post-Evaluation. Kamii provides a questioning/interview approach.

9-2 Standards and Descriptions of Geometry, Engineering, and Data Analysis

Primary experiences with geometry, spatial sense, graphs, tables, charts, algebraic thinking, estimation, and probability build on preprimary experiences with shape, spatial sense, simpler graphs and charts, and patterns. Science, engineering, and technology work together.

Informal Pre-Assessment. See Chapters 4, 5, and 7.

Activities. Primary-level geometry is an informal, intuitively acquired concept. Children gain familiarity with concepts such as line, angle, point, curve, symmetry, and congruence. Geoboard activities are basic at this level. Geometric and number concepts can be applied to graphing. Advanced children can develop more complex bar graphs and move on to line graphs. Charts and tables are used to organize data, which can then be visually depicted in a graph. Lego/LOGO, Lego Mindstorms, Lego Dacta robotics, and design technology and engineering provide opportunities for more complex experiences combining mathematics, science, and technology.

Informal Post-Evaluation. Note children's process activities. Are they involved? Do they demonstrate understanding? Do they need scaffolding?

9-3 Standards and Description of Measurement

Measurement skills are essential for successful everyday living. People need to know how to measure length, volume, area, weight, temperature, time, and money. These concepts develop gradually through many concrete experiences, from gross comparisons (e.g., long–short, heavy–light, hot–cold, early–late) to measurement with arbitrary units, and finally to measurement with standard English (customary) and/or metric units.

Informal Pre-Assessment. Observation and interview tasks.

Instruction. Measurement concepts are acquired through practice with real measuring tools and real things to measure. Lecture and demonstration alone are not adequate methods of instruction.

Activities. Measurement activities are valuable opportunities for applying whole number skills and knowledge of fractions (and later decimals), as well as for obtaining data that can be graphed for visual interpretation.

Informal Post-Evaluation. Provide students with informal tasks to accomplish.

FURTHER READING AND RESOURCES

Barker, L. (2009). Ten is the magic number! *Teaching Children Mathematics, 15*(6), 336–345.

Burgess, C. R. (2014). Untangling geometric ideas. *Teaching Children Mathematics, 20*(8), 508–515.

Castle, K., & Needham, J. (2007). First grader's understanding of measurement. *Early Childhood Education Journal, 35*(3), 215–222.

Cengiz, N., Grant, T. J. (2009). Children generate their own representations. *Teaching Children Mathematics, 15*(7), 438–444.

Christy, D., Lambe, K., Payson, C., Carnevale, P., & Scarpelli, D. (2008). Alice in numberland: Through the standards in wonderland. *Teaching Children Mathematics, 14*(8), 436–446.

Crawford, H. G. (2010). Economic insights through problem solving. *Teaching Children Mathematics, 17*(4), 218–219.

Dixon, J. K. (2008). Tracking time: Representing elapsed time on an open timeline. *Teaching Children Mathematics, 15*(1), 18–24.

Dougherty, B. J., & Venenciano, L. C. H. (2007). Measure up for understanding. *Teaching Children Mathematics, 13*(9), 452–456.

Eichinger, J. (2009). *Activities linking science with math.* Arlington, VA: NSTA. (Vertex graphs)

Kieran, C. (2014). *Algebraic thinking in arithmetic research brief.* National Council of Teachers of Mathematics. Retrieved May 7, 2014, from www.nctm.org/news /content.aspx?id=42315.

Kunze, S. A. (2014). *Making tens: Finding addends that sum to ten.* Retrieved April 7, 2014, from http://illuminations .nctm.org.

McDuffie, A. R. & Eve, N. (2009). Break the area boundaries. *Teaching Children Mathematics, (16)*1, 18–27.

Mokros, J., & Wright, T. (2009). Zoos, aquariums, and expanding students' data literacy. *Teaching Children Mathematics, 15*(9), 524–530.

Shultz, G. O. (2008). Making sense of time with *A Toad for Tuesday. Teaching Children Mathematics, 15*(4), 212–216.

Whitin, D. J., & Whitin, P. (2009). Why are things shaped the way they are? *Teaching Children Mathematics, 15*(8), 464–472.

Wickett, M. (2009). Tuheen's thinking about place value. *Teaching Children Mathematics, 16*(4), 256.

Yeh, C. (2014). Pattern-block puzzlers. *Teaching Children Mathematics, 20*(8), 528.

REFERENCES

Ashbrook. P. (2010). Building with sand. *Science and Children, 47*(7), 17–18.

Bautista, N. U., & Peters, K. N. (2010). First-grade engineers. *Science and Children, 47*(7), 38–42.

Brown, M. (2013, December 17). Northwood students learn through canned food donation drive. *Crestview News Bulletin.* Retrieved 12/18/13 from www.crestviewbulletin.com.

Burns, M. (1997). Number sense. *Instructor* (April), 49–54.

Burris, J. T. (2013). Virtual place value. *Teaching Children Mathematics, 20*(4), 228–236.

Carraher, D. W., & Schliemann, A. D. (2010). Algebraic reasoning in elementary school classrooms. In D. V. Lambdin (Ed.), *Teaching and learning mathematics* (pp. 23–29). Reston, VA: National Council of Teachers of Mathematics.

Cavanagh, S. (2009). Kiddie algebra. *Education Week, 28*(21), 21–23. www.edweek.org.

Children Designing and Engineering. (n.d.). What is CD&E? Retrieved November 20, 2004, at www .childrendesigning.org.

Clark, L. J. (2002). Real world robotics. *Science and Children, 40*(2), 38–42.

Common Core State Standards for Mathematics. (2010). Washington, DC: National Academies Press.

Curtis, S. (2012, November 26). Warwickshire schools get humanoid robots to promote STEM subjects. *TECHWORLD.* http://news.techworld.com.

Deal, T. (2012). Kindergarten civil engineers. *Children's Engineering Journal, 10*(Fall 2012), 2.

DeVries, R., & Sales, C. (2010). *Ramps & pathways.* Washington, DC: National Association for the Education of Young Children.

Dunn, S., & Larson, R. (1990). *Design technology: Children's engineering.* Bristol, PA: Falmer, Taylor & Francis.

Forsythe, J. (2013, December 14). 'It pushes me to do my best': Students use charts to track their own growth. *News-Democrat.* www.bnd.com.

Gargiulo, R., & Kilgo, J. (2014). *An introduction to young children with special needs,* 4th ed. Belmont, CA: Wadsworth.

Kamii, C. (2003). *Young children continue to reinvent arithmetic,* 2nd grade, 2nd ed. New York: Teachers College Press.

Kamii, C., Lewis, B. A., & Livingston, S. J. (1993). Primary arithmetic: Children inventing their own procedures. *Arithmetic Teacher, 41*(4), 200–203.

Kepner, H. (2009). Measure for measure. *NCTM News Bulletin* (May/June). www.nctm.org.

Lang, F. K. (2001). What is a "good guess" anyway? Estimation in early childhood. *Teaching Children Mathematics, 7*(8), 462–466.

Leedy, L. (2005). *The great graph contest.* New York: Holiday House.

Lewis, V. (2003). *Development and disability,* 2nd ed. Malden, MA: Blackwell.

Lottero-Perdue, P. S., Lovelidge, S., & Bowling, E. (2010). Engineering for all. *Science and Children, 47*(7), 24–27.

Lubinski, C. A., & Thiessen, D. (1996). Exploring measurement through literature. *Teaching Children Mathematics, 2,* 260–263.

McMillen, S., & Hernandez, B. O. (2008). Taking time to understand telling time. *Teaching Children Mathematics, 15*(4), 248–255.

Moore, V. J., Chessin, D. A., & Theobald, B. (2010). Insect keepers. *Science and Children, 47*(7), 28–32.

Morgan, E., & Ansbey, K. (2011). Wild about data. *Science and Children, 48*(5), 18–20.

Murray, J., & Bartelmay, K. (2005). Inventors in the making. *Science and Children, 42*(4), 40–44.

Myller, R. (1972). *How big is a foot?* New York: Athenaeum.

National Council of Teachers of Mathematics (NCTM). (2000). Principles and standards for school mathematics. Reston, VA: Author.

National Research Council. (2012). *Framework for Science Education: Crosscutting concepts and core ideas.* Washington, DC: National Academies Press.

NGSS Lead States (2013). *Next Generation Science Standards for States by states.* Washington, DC: National Academies Press.

Olson, M., & Easley, B. (1996). Plentiful penny projects to ponder. *Teaching Children Mathematics, 3,* 184–185.

Petroski, H. (2003, January 24). Early education. Presentation at the Children's Engineering Convention (Williamsburg, VA). www.vteea.org.

Richardson, K. (1984). *Developing number concepts using Unifix Cubes.* Menlo Park, CA: Addison-Wesley.

Richardson, K. (1999a). *Developing number concepts: Book 2. Addition and subtraction.* Parsippany, NJ: Seymour.

Richardson, K. (1999b). *Developing number concepts: Book 3. Place value, multiplication, and division.* Parsippany, NJ: Seymour.

Schifter, S., Russell, S. J., & Bastable, V. (2009). Early algebra to reach the range of learners. *Teaching Children Mathematics, 16*(4), 210–237.

Shendo, K. (2013, December 3). Common core from a tribal perspective. *Education Week.* www.edweek.org.

Shumway, J. F. (2013). Building bridges to spatial reasoning. *Teaching Children Mathematics, 20*(1), 44–51.

Stadler, K. (2012). Pneumatics. *The Children's Engineering Journal, 11* (Summer 2013), 8.

STEM: Science, engineering, technology, and mathematics. (2010). *Science and Children, 47*(7). [Focus issue].

Sweet, B. (2012). Room makeover-math and engineering. *The Children's Engineering Journal, 11*(Summer 2013), 7.

Virginia Children's Engineering Council. (n.d.). Inspiring the next generation. Retrieved November 20, 2004, from www.vteea.org.

Vissa, J. (1987). Coordinate graphing: Shaping up a sticky situation. *Arithmetic Teacher, 35*(3), 6–10.

Wilcox, D. R., Roberts, S., & Wilcox, D. (2010). Gravity racers. *Science and Children, 47*(7), 19–23.

Willey, S. (2013). S.T.E.M. in first grade at Henderson Elementary School. *The Children's Engineering Journal, 11* (Summer 2013). 4.

Wright, R. J., Martland, J., Stafford, A. K., & Stanger, G. (2002). *Teaching number.* Thousand Oaks, CA: Chapman.

Zaslavsky, C. (1996). The multicultural math classroom. Portsmouth, NH: Heinmann.

PART 6
INVESTIGATIONS IN PRIMARY SCIENCE

CHAPTER 10 Overview of Primary Science: Life Science, and Physical Science
CHAPTER 11 Earth and Space Sciences, Environmental Awareness, Engineering, Technology, and Science Applications

CHAPTER
10

OVERVIEW OF PRIMARY SCIENCE:
LIFE SCIENCE, AND PHYSICAL SCIENCE

OBJECTIVES

After reading this chapter, you should be able to:

10-1 Provide an overview of primary grade science.

10-2 Plan, teach, and evaluate primary grade life science lessons and projects in line with national standards.

10-3 Plan, teach, and evaluate primary grade physical science lessons and projects in line with national standards.

STANDARDS AND PRACTICES ADDRESSED IN THIS CHAPTER

naeyc

NAEYC Professional Preparation Standards

5.   Use content knowledge to build meaningful curriculum.

5a. Understand content knowledge in planning for mathematics and science.

5c. Design, implement, and evaluate developmentally meaningful and challenging curriculum.

DAP Guidelines

2C. Know desired program goals.

3C. Use curriculum framework in planning.

Common Core State Standards for Math

K.MD.B.3 Classify objects into given categories, count the numbers of objects in each category and sort the categories by count.

Next Generation Science Standards

2-LS4-3-LS4   Biological evolution: unity and diversity.

1-PS4   Waves and their applications in technologies for information transfer.

2-PS1   Matter and its interactions.

2-LS4-1   Making observations to collect data that can be used in comparisons.

10-1 NEXT GENERATION STANDARDS AND GUIDELINES FOR PRIMARY GRADE SCIENCE

Kindergarten through 12th grade science is in a state of transition from what we perceive as conventional science instruction to the next generation of teaching as outlined in the Next Generation Science Standards (NGSS). Some teachers are already involved in planning and instruction in line with the NGSS; others will be soon; and still others may be located in states that haven't adopted NGSS. Therefore we have provided instructional examples from both points of view. Science teaching is a complex activity. The Next Generation Science Standards (NGSS) (NRC, 2013) are grounded in *A Framework for K–12 Science Education* (NRC, 2012). This book highlights the important role of teachers in the development of science learning and presenting strategies for teaching science in a way that reflects how science is actually practiced. Following an overview of primary science, this chapter includes sections on the teaching of life science and physical science. In Chapter 11, the focus is on teaching earth and space science, environmental awareness, and engineering design technology and science applications. In both chapters, basic concepts of the subject matter are included; these concepts follow the NGSS standards closely. In addition, ways of teaching those concepts are included—from both the inquiry perspective, which is the thrust of the NGSS, and the traditional subject matter orientation method, which is familiar to most beginning teachers.

These chapters relate the skills needed for primary science investigations together with the fundamental process skills incorporated in the science lessons. Children in the primary grades continue to be avid explorers. Even though they are beginning to refine their inquiry skills, identify changes in observed events, and understand relationships among objects and events, they still require time to interact with and manipulate concrete objects. Students need to have many and varied opportunities for investigating, collecting, sorting and cataloging, observing, note taking and sketching, interviewing, and polling (**Photo 10-1**).

As children leave kindergarten and enter the primary level, most are also leaving the preoperational level and entering concrete operations. They begin to be able to use abstract symbols, such as numbers and written words, with understanding if they are tied to concrete experiences such as science investigations. They are also entering a period of industriousness in which they enjoy long-term projects, building things, making collections, and playing games that require taking turns, learning systems of rules, and making predictions. Peers are becoming increasingly important; thus, working in small groups becomes a basic instructional strategy.

TeachSource Video

5–11 YEARS: PIAGET'S CONCRETE OPERATIONS STAGE

Several children are presented with Piagetian conservation tasks and demonstrate their concrete operational thinking.

1. Describe the change from preoperational to concrete operational thinking.

2. How do the interview results support Piaget's theory?

© 2016 Cengage Learning®

Primary-age children may be just arriving at the stage when they can classify by more than one characteristic, transfer abstract ideas to objects and events outside their direct experience, draw inferences from data, and identify complex patterns in data taken over a long period of time. Primary-age children also may have difficulty with experimentation as a process of testing ideas and with the logic of using evidence to formulate explanations. However, they can design

PHOTO 10-1   Children work together to obtain information on kangaroos.

Charlesworth

investigations to try things to see what happens; they tend to focus on concrete results of tests and will entertain the idea of a "fair" test in which only one variable at a time is changed.

To learn science and engineering, children must develop eight essential practices that reflect the actual practices used by scientists and engineers. The eight essential practices for K–12 classrooms are as follows:

1. Asking questions (for science) and defining problems (for engineering)

2. Developing and using models

3. Planning and carrying out investigations

4. Analyzing and interpreting data

5. Using mathematics and computational thinking

6. Constructing explanations (for science) and designing solutions (for engineering)

7. Engaging in argument from evidence

8. Obtaining, evaluating and communicating information (NRC, 2012, p. 42)

Keeping in the STEM framework, it is important to note the parallels between the Framework and the Common Core State Standards in Mathematics (Mayes & Koballa, 2012). Mayes and Koballa outline the math practices that are in line with science practices, including these:

■ Making sense of problems and persevering in solving them

■ Reasoning abstractly and quantitatively

■ Constructing viable arguments and critique the reasoning of others

■ Modeling with mathematics

■ Using appropriate tools strategically

■ Attending to precision

■ Looking for and making use of structure

■ Looking for and expressing regularity in repeated reasoning

To investigate the problems included in NGSS, students must apply both science and math practices. Moyes and Kobolla emphasize the importance of elementary teachers being familiar with both the math and science standards.

Chapter 10 provides an overview of primary science containing lesson examples, strategies, and classroom vignettes of next generation and conventional science topics. This section begins with a description of how the NGSS standards could be translated into instructional strategies, as described by Roger Bybee (2013). Following is a description of conventional science instruction. The overview is followed by sections more specifically focused on life science and physical science, including examples of how some of the science topics suggested by the 2013 Standards might be taught in the primary grades. The Unifying Concepts and

Processes discussed in Chapter 2 highlight the connections between scientific ideas and are a natural part of any investigation. Children will not fully understand these powerful ideas that characterize science until they are much older, but aspects of the ideas are integrated in developmentally appropriate ways in this section.

10-1a Translating NGSS for Classroom Instruction

The major concern for teachers is how they will translate the NGSS into instruction. It is made clear that this document is not a curriculum, but a guide for what children should know and be able to do at each grade, K–12. Curriculum, instruction, and assessment are left up to those in the practice areas. Rodger W. Bybee (2013) has made an effort to develop guidelines for translating NGSS for classroom instruction.

According to Bybee, assessments will change to meet the NGSS performance expectations. Curriculum (programs) and instruction (practices) will also change. Bybee believes that development of curriculum and instruction should not be driven by assessments, but should be developed first. Bybee describes a sequence of steps in planning that can guide performance expectations for assessment. He developed a planning guide table with lessons (1, 2, 3, etc.) on the left, what the teacher does during classroom instruction in the second column, and the three dimensions of the performance expectations heading columns across the top. These include Science and Engineering Practice, Disciplinary Core Idea, and Crosscutting Concept. Bybee's goal is that student learning will be improved as curriculum, instruction, and assessment are devised so they are in line with the NGSS content standards. A major concern is the development of teaching materials for NGSS. Some current materials can be adapted, but new materials must be available. Meanwhile, Bybee provides a procedure for developing initial lessons that support NGSS.

Bybee (2013) answers frequently asked questions regarding NGSS. One of the questions is "Why use the term *practices*? Why not continue using *scientific inquiry*? As described in earlier chapters, the term *scientific inquiry* became popular from 1960 to 1990. The Framework and NGSS emphasize a broader range of practice of which scientific inquiry is one practice. The term *practice* does not replace *inquiry*, but expands and enriches the teaching and learning of science (Bybee, 2013, p. 41). Practice is a broader term that puts emphasis on teaching activities that involve several practices such as experimenting, collecting data, using models and tools, explaining and arguing, and so on. Another question is, "Why include engineering?" The practices of science and engineering are similar (see list of science practices earlier in this chapter; engineering practices are described in Chapter 11). At the elementary level, teachers already have students do engineering activities such as building bridges, dropping eggs and designing model cars. It needs to be clarified that these types of projects are engineering.

Classroom Instruction. Following is a brief description of Bybee's recommendations for planning instruction. According to Bybee, teachers should think beyond individual lessons to an integrated instructional sequence. He believes a unit should begin with an engaging lesson and then move on to exploration lesson(s), explanation lesson(s), elaboration lesson(s), and finally to the evaluation. This is much like the learning cycle described in Chapters 1 and 2.

At each grade, there are several performance expectations (PEs). Bybee is not considering each PE as a separate lesson, but suggests planning by incorporating a group of PEs into a thematic unit or project. The sequence of lessons should include a variety of experiences ("e.g., web searches, group investigations, reading, discussion, computer simulations, videos, direct instruction"; Bybee, 2013, p. 57). Bybee promotes "backward design," that is, the performance expectation should be the starting point for planning. Use the performance expectation to design assessments and then select the sequence of activities. The backward design process involves three stages:

1. From NGSS, identify desired results, standards, and performance expectations.

2. Decide on acceptable evidence of learning, that is, the performance expectations. Then design the evaluation activities.

3. Develop learning experiences and activities, that is, the activities that engage, explore, explain, and elaborate.

Instruction in the Elementary Classroom. Bybee (2013, Chapter 5, pp. 65–72) provides a sample unit plan for 2-SL4 (second-grade life science, biological evolution: unity and diversity). The PE for this standard is that students who demonstrate understanding can **make observations of plants and animals to compare the diversity of life in different habitats.** The required science and engineering practice is that K–3 students will carry out simple investigations that require making observations. They will learn the core idea described in the Disciplinary Core Idea: **There are many different kinds of living things in any area, and they exist in different places on land and in water** (NGSS, 2012, p. 19). To *engage* the students, the teacher asks them to name a plant or animal and tell where it lives. She then asks them to name a plant or animal that lives in a weird or exotic place. She asks for clarification as needed. Everyone has a turn. The *explore* phase is a trip to the schoolyard, in groups of two, to investigate where plants and animals live. The students record their observations in journals. The *explanation* phase involves the students presenting their findings. The teacher explains that the students were being scientists. For *elaboration*, the teacher has students collect pictures of three organisms that live on land and three that live in water. She challenges the teams to see which ones can come up with the most diverse groups. *Evaluation* consists of two questions relative to their experiences.

It is recommended that teachers look carefully at the NGSS, which can be purchased in hard copy from the National Academies Press or downloaded from the NSTA website.

naeyc DAP

10-1b Conventional Science Instruction

This part of the chapter begins with common examples of how young children's love of collecting can be applied in the beginning science curriculum as a means to get them interested in the science processes. Next, planning for investigations is described, followed by suggestions on how to manage the classroom.

Collecting. Primary children love to collect. They are increasingly aware of details, and their ability to compare and categorize objects is developing. They are apt to begin collecting pocketfuls of small and portable objects that they see around them. Use this natural inclination to encourage children to observe, compare, sort, and classify. Collections can consist of many things such as plants, animals, feathers, fur, rocks, sand, seashells, soils, and anything else that interests children.

However, whatever the composition of the collection, it should be viewed as a means of encouraging inquiry, not as an end in itself. In this way, simple identification of objects does not become the focal point of collecting. Instead, children will learn the basic practices of scientific inquiry. In earlier chapters, a sequence of steps for investigations was described. However, as children enter concrete operations, they can learn that there is no one right method in scientific inquiry. Today the focus is on practices such as those listed above and especially on critique and evaluation: knowing why the right answer is right and the wrong answer is wrong.

Getting Started by Using Magnifiers. A **magnifier** is useful for both collecting and classifying. Handheld plastic magnifiers are perfect for all ages, are inexpensive, and have the advantage of being mobile, for outdoor explorations (**Figure 10-1**). Magnifying boxes are hollow plastic boxes with a removable magnifier at the top. They are ideal for observing small treasures and animals such as live insects. When using

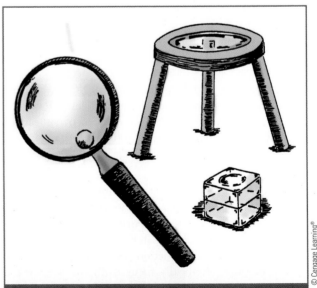

FIGURE 10-1 Introduce children to magnifiers.

magnifiers, carefully catch the insects, observe them, and then return them to their environment without injury. In this way, you will encourage humaneness as well as observation.

Safety note: Teach students how to capture insects in jars without touching them. Be sure they stay away from spider ants and spiders—caution them especially not to probe under things or in dark warm areas. Also be sure that the students can recognize poison oak, poison ivy, and poison sumac and that they stay away from these plants!

Children can also use the jumbo-sized magnifier mounted on a three-legged stand. There is no need to hold objects with this type of magnifier, and objects of different sizes can be examined at the same time. Although some dexterity is required for adjusting most magnifiers, the effort is important because the magnifiers are a bridge to using microscopes. In the following scenario, second graders are introduced to magnifiers before collecting.

Having had the students contribute various objects for the science center, Mrs. Han introduces magnifiers by making them available in the science center and suggesting to the students that they see what they can find out as they use them. Mrs. Han then lets the children explore independently for a period of time. She does not tell them what to look at; rather, she gives them time to "mess around" with the magnifiers. "Wow!" observes Annie. "Look how big the hair on my arm looks." As she continues to look around at objects close to her, Hayden motions her over to his table. "Look, Annie. Look at the sleeve of my shirt. It looks different. Something is in my shirt," he says.

"Mrs. Han," asks Genevieve, "Do things always look bigger with magnifiers? Can we always see more?" "Let's look through them and see," suggests the teacher.

Mrs. Han plans several opportunities to view objects in different ways. She asks the children to describe the object before viewing with a magnifier, to describe what they see while they are viewing, to compare how objects look under different powers, and to compare and contrast appearances of objects after viewing is completed. She asks, "How does the object appear under the magnifier? Why do you think it looks different?"

The teacher groups the children and has them examine different areas of the room, their clothes, lunch, and a spider web. She explains that the magnifying glass itself is called a **lens** and confirms that things look different under a magnifier. She says that this is because of the way the magnifier is constructed but does not suggest technical explanations. Primary children will enjoy noticing details not seen with the naked eye.

Focusing the Collecting. Practice collecting on the school grounds or in the neighborhood. Help children focus on their collections by giving them suggestions. After collecting, suggest classification systems; let children come up with their own; or try sorting objects in different ways. At this age, the primary purpose of collecting is not identification. Rather, collecting should be viewed as an opportunity to encourage inquiry and to become aware of the variety of similarities and differences in nature. As children collect, they observe, compare, classify, and begin to think as a scientist might think. They compare

collections and note similarities and differences. If the children have difficulties in coming up with ideas for collections, the following ideas will get the class started.

1. *Leaves.* Collect and sort leaves by color, shape, vein patterns, edges, and so on. Ask: "**How many red leaves can you find? Can you find leaves that are smooth? Do some of the leaves feel different? Try putting all of the leaves that smell the same in a pile.**" Children will want to associate the leaf with its name on a label. Suggestions for displaying collections are found in Chapter 12.

   Safety note: Be sure students recognize poison oak, poison ivy, and poison sumac and that they stay away from these plants!

2. *Shells.* Collect different types of empty shells, such as nutshells, eggshells, snail shells, or seashells. Ask: "**What kind of objects have a shell? What do you think the shells are for?**"

3. *Litter.* Collect litter around the school ground. Ask: "**What type of litter did you find most often? Where did you find it?**"

4. *Seeds.* Seeds can be found on the ground or flying in the air. Walk through a field, and examine the seeds clinging to your trouser legs and socks. Sort the seeds by size, color, and the way they were dispersed. Ask, "**What type of seed did you find most often?**" Suggestions for setting up a center on seeds are found in Chapter 12.

5. *Spider webs.* Spider webs are all around us, but children will need practice and patience to collect them. Spray powder on the web, and then put a piece of dark paper on one side of it. Hold the web in place with hairspray. Ask: "**How are the spider webs the same? How are they different?**" Children might enjoy pulling twine through white craft glue to duplicate how a spider forms its web. Let dry and hang.

6. *Feathers.* Feathers can be found at home, at school, and on the way to school. Children will enjoy examining the feathers with magnifiers. Point out the zipper-like barbs that open and close the feathers. Ask: "**How are the feathers alike? How do they differ?**" If children are studying birds, identify the function of the different types of feathers (**Figure 10-2**).

7. *Rocks.* Collect rocks and sort them by color, size, shape, texture, and hardness. Ask: "**What size rocks do you have? What color rocks do you have? What shapes are your rocks? How do they feel? How are the rocks alike? How are the rocks different?**"

8. *Rubbings.* Another way to collect is to collect impressions of objects. Rubbings of bark and fossils are made by holding one side of a piece of paper against an object and rubbing the other side with a dark crayon. Mount the resulting patterns

FIGURE 10-2 Zipper-like barbs can be seen with the help of a magnifier.

FIGURE 10-3 Making a plaster mold of raccoon tracks. "What animal made these tracks?"

on colored construction paper, and display. Have the children compare and classify the patterns.

9. *Modeling clay.* Modeling clay can be used to create an impression of fossils, bark, leaves, and seeds. Simply press the clay against the object, remove, and compare impressions.

10. *Plaster molds.* Forming a plaster mold can preserve footprints. Mix plaster, and build a small cardboard rim around the footprint; then pour plaster into the impression that you have found. Carefully remove the plaster when dry, and return the cast to the room for comparison (**Figure 10-3**).

Collecting Small Animals Without Backbones. Mr. Wang asks his students, "What is your favorite animal?" "That's easy," Tyler says. "I like lions, seals, and cats." "Me, too," Theresa says. "But I really like horses the best." Finn chimes in that his favorite pet is a gerbil, and Greta insists that dogs are the best animals because they guard the house.

A few students mention reptiles as a favorite animal, but most of the children name mammals. To introduce invertebrates as animals and clear up a common misconception, the teacher has the children run their hands down their back. He asks, "What do you feel?" "Bones," says Theresa. "I feel my backbone." Mr. Wang asks the children whether their favorite animals have backbones. "Yes, of course they do," Finn answers.

Mr. Wang explains that animals with backbones (including us people) are called vertebrates, but not all animals have backbones; these animals are called invertebrates. He asks the students to think of some animals that do not have backbones. He then adds to their list, which includes worms,

sponges, mollusks, starfish, crayfish, spiders, and insects, and he is surprised at the children's interest.

Mr. Wang decides to plan a collecting trip to a nearby pond and field. Each student is told to wear old clothes, including long pants, and bring a washed peanut butter–sized jar. Mr. Wang prepares insect sweepers and a few catch jars (**Figure 10-4**).

Before leaving on the trip, Mr. Wang gives instructions. "We will need to be quiet and to look high and low." Tyler cuts in, "And under rocks, bushes, and fallen branches." "Yes," the teacher says, but be very careful. Don't put your hands underneath anything in the wild; you never know what might be there. You might find a surprise, some of which are exciting to look at, but some of which are poisonous or can sting us. He continued, "Look carefully where you walk."

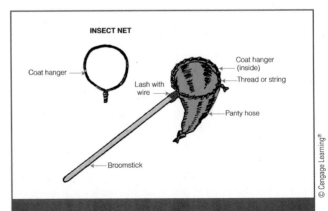

FIGURE 10-4 Making an insect sweeper from discarded nylons and a hanger.

The class worked in teams during the hunt, and each team tried to capture only one kind of animal. "Remember where you captured your animal," Mr. Wang reminded the children. "We will turn the insects loose in the same habitat that we found them."

After returning to the room, the teams used nature books to find out how to keep their captives alive. Each animal was displayed with an index card giving its name, habitat where it was found, and the collector's name. The animal was on display for two days and then released to its original habitat. Many questions were raised. "Does my worm like to eat raisins?" Tyler wanted to know. Finn was interested in knowing whether his worm was able to see, and Greta wondered whether her sow bugs would dig in the dirt of their container.

Mr. Wang encouraged close observation and investigation with such questions as, "Does the animal like rough or smooth surfaces? Does it spend most of its time in the light or in the dark?"

The next day, Greta brought in animals she had found on her way to school. The display was growing. Children classified the animals by color, number of legs, and where they were found. "Let's group the animals into those found on land and those found on water," Theresa said. "Don't forget the air," Finn suggested. Some were found in the air."

The invertebrate display was an excellent way to observe animals and their habitats. The students had an opportunity to classify, investigate characteristics, study life cycles, and expand their definition of animals. Some students developed a skit involving metamorphosis; others worked on a wall chart; and all gained an appreciation of the little creatures and their world.

A problem in engineering design might grow out of a classroom concern. For example, the students and the teacher might find that the classroom is too crowded. The problem is "How can we make more space?" The children could come up with several solutions. Cut back on the class size? Cut back on the furniture? Try to find a better arrangement? The second and third options might work. After measuring the furniture, they make a plan of the current arrangement and then cut out paper furniture they can move about on a plain floor plan. On the Internet, they research classroom floor plan ideas. In pairs, they try a variety of arrangements using their paper models. They share their arrangements with the rest of the students, and after some discussion, they decide they can remove one table and one bookcase and arrange the remaining furniture in a way that will provide for easier movement.

NGSS

10-1c Practices and Design

The scientist's major focus is investigation and empirical inquiry. The focus for the engineer is construction of explanations or designs using reasoning, creative thinking, and models. The scientist has questions about the real world. He investigates by asking questions, observing, experimenting, and measuring. He collects data and tests his solutions. The engineer works with theories and models. She imagines reasons, calculates, and predicts. She proposes solutions as she develops explanations and conclusions. Both scientists and engineers evaluate through argumentation, critique, and analysis.

Hands-on manipulative activities, just as with math, support the learning of science concepts. Yet many teachers shy away from allowing children the active participation needed to develop these skills and concepts. Messy science investigations are avoided for several common reasons. One is that some teachers do not feel comfortable teaching science. Other teachers find managing children and materials an overwhelming task, and still others believe that investigations should be reserved for older children.

Put such fears to rest. You do not need an extensive science background to guide children in science investigations. What you do need is instruction in how to do it and some background information that will allow you to answer some simple questions. What is most essential for teaching science is a teacher's sense of security and ability to say, "I don't know. How do you think we can find the answer to your question?" Explore strategies for supporting primary-age children's investigations, and try the suggested strategies for managing children and materials. Early science experiences provide the necessary background for future, more sophisticated practices and concept development.

Supporting Science Investigations. Science investigations usually begin with a question. For example, ask, **"How long can you keep an ice cube from melting?"** Children can initiate investigations by asking their own questions, such as, "How long will this ice cube last if I leave it on my plate?" After the initial question or questions, you usually predict what you think is going to happen. In the ice cube example, a child might predict, "I think the ice cube will last until lunch."

Help the students consider factors that they should consider in their investigation.

For example, ask: **"What are we trying to find out? What shall we change?"** Keep records of observations, results, procedures, information obtained, and any measurements collected during the investigation. **Conclusions**, of course, are statements that tell whether the original prediction, **hypothesis**, was rejected. Ask: **"What happened? Is this what you thought would happen? Did anything surprise you?"** This procedure resembles the conventional scientific method for a reason: Children are unconsciously using the conventional scientific method as they observe, predict, and reach conclusions. Encouraging them to investigate capitalizes on their natural interest. In fact, we could call investigations "student research." Basically, children are trying to find the answers to questions for which they do not know the answers. As they investigate, they find answers to their questions in the same way a scientist does. They are thinking like scientists.

It is not necessary to follow a fixed pattern of investigation. Scientists and engineers move aback and forth as they analyze and critique their progress and move in different directions.

Hands-on science means just that: learning from materials and processes of the natural world through direct observation and experimentation. Direct experience, experimentation, and observation are sources of students' learning about science and are essential to learning. Hands-on learning begins in infancy with sensory stimulation that hones infants' observation and discrimination skills and readies them for the more detailed explorations of toddlerhood. However, hands-on instruction alone does not constitute inquiry teaching. There is a substantial difference between an open-ended, inquiry approach to an activity and an approach that is hands-on but that does not encourage problem solving and inquiry. For example, one approach to teaching the concept that water expands when it freezes might be as follows:

1. Fill a plastic container with water.

2. Place the container in the freezer, and have the children observe the condition of the water after a period of time.

3. Ask the children: "**What happened? How would you explain this?**"

Compare this lesson to another way of approaching the same concept. Assemble materials and present the following challenge: "**Can you prove at least three things that happen or don't happen to water when it freezes? Be prepared to share what you have discovered with others.**"

Both lessons provide children with a teacher-selected topic and a hands-on experience. The first, however, offers only one strategy (procedure) that can be used to demonstrate an already given solution (water expands when it freezes). Although this is a useful strategy, the second approach promotes inquiry because it requires that children first figure out what they observe happening (or not happening) to water when it freezes and then plan a way to convince someone else of their discovery. And, as you know, material taught on any day is retained for exactly 23 hours and 59 minutes when the 24th hour is the next class period on the same topic discussed yesterday.

Although both activities are hands on, use process skills, and require physical manipulation of objects to gain an understanding of a science concept, only the second activity involves problem solving from which inquiry is most likely to spring. By listening to students who are actively engaged in conceptual problem solving and investigations, the teacher will uncover many scientific misconceptions that will provide instructional materials for years to come (refer to Chapter 2 for additional problem-solving suggestions).

DAP naeyc

10-1d Managing the Classroom

A carefully thought-out management plan supports instructional success. In addition to planning your activities, take some time to consider how you will organize your children and the materials they will work with. The following suggestions will help you get started.

Organizing Children for Learning. Organize the class into teams of no more than four children. Each child must have responsibilities on the team. Designate a team leader, who is responsible for seeing that all materials are correctly obtained, used, and put away. Pick a recorder who is responsible for obtaining and putting away records, of investigation findings such as, might be recorded in journals and notebooks, and reporting results to the class. Appoint a judge, who has the final word in any science activity–related disputes, and an investigator, who is responsible for seeing that the team follows directions when conducting the science activity. Make sure the children understand their responsibilities. Note: Be careful not to let the same students linger in the same job for long periods of time. Instead, make it a point to change responsibilities regularly so that everyone on the team gets a chance to perform all the duties associated with a particular job. These job roles are easily adaptable for use with most cooperative learning experiences.

Organizing Materials for Learning. Materials can be organized several ways. One possibility is to distribute materials from four distribution centers in your room. Each center should be labeled as 1, 2, 3, or 4 and should contain all the equipment needed for an exploration. Then, number the children in the team 1, 2, 3, and 4. The 1s are responsible for acquiring the materials at distribution center 1, the 2s at center number 2, and so on. Locate the distribution sites in separate areas of the room to reduce confusion; give a time limit for the collection of materials; and provide a materials list so that the team leaders can check to see that everything needed is on their table.

If you are teaching an adult-guided activity, you may want to make a list indicating what each individual will do during the exploration. For example, if you want the children to explore concepts of surface tension with soap and pepper, have the 1s pour the water into the cup, the 2s tap the pepper in the cup, the 3s coat the toothpick with liquid detergent, and the 4s plunge the toothpick into the pepper.

Science explorations are fun. To maintain discipline while conducting complex activities with the whole class, an organization system for children and materials is needed. Establish simple and clear rules for classroom operation. Once the children are comfortable with the rules and organization system, you need only periodically review what is expected to keep them on task.

Pocket Management Strategy. A primary teacher prepares for managing children in learning areas by making a personalized library card pocket for each child in her class. Each pocket has the child's picture on it, and each job has a distinguishing symbol, such as an orange triangle or a green square. Each morning a job symbol card is placed in each child's library card pocket. Children learn the classroom jobs and become familiar with the symbols for each job, and they review their job list each morning.

After the children are comfortable with the job symbols and pockets, the teacher introduces them to the learning areas of the room. A symbol designates each area, and the number of symbols indicates to the children how many individuals may work in an area. For example, four circles mean that four children are permitted in the area. If the teacher does not want the children to use certain equipment, she places a "closed" sign in the area.

Colored strips of laminated paper containing the child's name and that of an available learning area are kept in the child's pocket. These strips are called "tickets." When Scott wants to construct a zoo in the block center, he takes his block ticket to the block area and puts it in the pocket. When he is finished working in the block area, he removes his ticket and puts it in a basket. In this way, children rotate through the room and are exposed to a variety of learning experiences.

 NGSS

10-1e Sample Investigations

The following investigations allow children to develop science processes as they conduct scientific investigations.

 DAP naeyc

---

ACTIVITIES

HOW LONG DOES IT TAKE FOR A PAPER TOWEL TO DRY?

Concept: Water disappears into the air during evaporation.

Objective: To investigate the length of time it takes for paper towels to dry.

Materials: Bowl of water, paper towels, cardboard, pie plates, variety of fabric swatches.

Naturalistic and informal activities: Encourage children to experiment with wetting the different swatches of fabric and hanging them on the clothesline. Say: **"Are all your clothes dry? Are some drier than others? Why do you think that happened?"**

Adult-guided activity: Ask children how their clothes get dry after they are washed. Are they put in a dryer? Are they hung on a line? Say, **"Let's pretend these paper towels are clothes and see how long they will take to dry."**

1. Soak a paper towel in water.
2. Squeeze out all the water that you can.
3. Open the towel, and lay it on a pie plate.
4. Leave the plate on a table. Have children check and record the time.
5. Feel the towel at 30-minute intervals to see if it is dry. When it is dry, record the time.
6. How long did the towel take to dry? Have the groups share their findings on a class chart.

Extensions: Ask: **"Do you think it will make a difference if you put the towels in the sun or in the shade? Which wet towel do you think will dry first? Do you think wind will make a difference in how fast a paper towel dries?"** Set up a fan to create wind. Measure the difference in drying time.

CAN GOLDFISH BE TRAINED?

Concept: Animals can be trained to respond to light and other signals.

Objective: To train a goldfish to respond to light.

Materials: Goldfish (at least two), tank, flashlight, fish food.

Procedure: Ask, **"Have you ever trained a pet to do something?"** Children usually have a dog that sits or stays. **"Do you think that goldfish know when it is time to eat? How could we train the goldfish to go to a corner of their tank to eat?"** Discuss possibilities.

Shine the flashlight into a corner of the tank. Ask, **"Do the goldfish swim toward the light?"** (No.) Each day sprinkle a little food in the water as you shine the flashlight in the corner (**Figure 10-5**). Ask, **"What are the fish doing?"** (Swimming toward the light.)

Do this for several days in a row. Then, shine the light without adding food. Ask, **"What happens when you only shine the light?"** (Fish come to the light, but only for a couple of days if food is not offered.)

FIGURE 10-5 "Can a goldfish be trained to respond to light?"

© Cengage Learning®

Extensions: Ask: **"Will the fish respond to different signals? Do both fish respond in the same way? Will different types of fish respond in the same way?"** Have children record their attempts and successes. They may want to write stories about their fish, tell others, and invite other classes to see their trained fish.

ANALYSIS OF CALVIN WAFFLE'S INVESTIGATION

Concept: The organization of a science investigation.

Objective: To analyze how an investigation might have an objective, how it can be set up, how data is collected, and how to analyze data and form conclusions.

Materials: A copy of the book *Danny's Doodles* by David A. Adler (2013). Naperville, IL: Sourcebooks, Inc.

Procedure: Read the book to the students; more advanced readers could read the book themselves. In groups of 2–4 have the students discuss the following questions and report to the whole class for discussion:

- "Describe Calvin's investigation.
- "What was Calvin's design?"

- "What was Calvin's objective?"
- "What material did he use?"
- "How does Calvin apply practice?"
- "What was Danny's role?"
- "How did Calvin's friends help?"
- "What was the result of Calvin's project?"
- "What might he have done differently?"

Extensions: Have the students analyze the pros and cons of Calvin's approach to science. Have each student create a question for a science investigation.

Digital Download

Examples of Topics to Investigate. As students begin to see their roles as scientists and engineers, they will think of questions to investigate and problems that call for design solutions. Following are some questions that might get them started:

- "Can we design a container to keep an ice cube from melting?"
- "Will mold grow on bread?"
- "Can we get a mealworm to change direction?"
- "What objects in our classroom is a magnet attracted to?"
- "Can a seed grow without dirt?"
- "Which part of a wet spot dries faster: the top, middle, or bottom? Or does it all dry at the same time?"
- "How can we design and build a bird feeder?"
- "What size aquarium will we need for our goldfish?"
- "How and where will we house our pet bunny?"
- "How will we arrange our garden? What tools will we need for gardening?"

acquire firsthand knowledge of plants and animals make learning fun for both children and teacher (**Photo 10-2**). The K–12 Framework (NRC, 2012) and NGSS (NRC, 2013) emphasizes that during the primary grades, children begin to develop an understanding of biological concepts through direct experience with living things, their life cycles, and their habitats. NGSS suggests that primary grade children should be able to formulate answers to questions such as the following (NRC, 2013, pp. 9, 15, 24):

1. Questions for first graders: "What are some ways plants and animals meet their needs so that they can survive and grow?" and "How are parents and their children alike and different?"

NGSS

10-2 CONVENTIONAL AND NEXT GENERATION LIFE SCIENCE INSTRUCTION

Whether they live in large cities or small towns, children display an eagerness to learn about the living things around them. The countless opportunities that exist to

PHOTO 10-2 Students make individual lists regarding investigation of a pineapple.

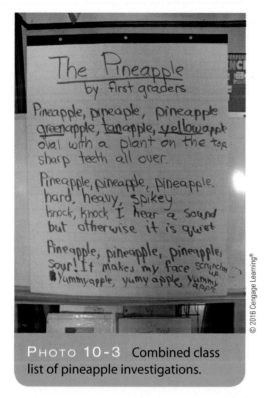

PHOTO 10-3   Combined class list of pineapple investigations.

© 2016 Cengage Learning®

2. Questions for second graders might include these: "What do plants need to grow?" and "How many types of living things live in a place?"

3. Questions for third graders might include the following: "How do organisms vary in their traits?" "How are plants, animals, and environments of the past similar or different from current plants, animals, and environments?" and "What happens to organisms when their environment changes?"

These are the first of many such questions that might begin life science investigations (**Photo 10-3**). Primary experiences lay the groundwork for the progressive development in later grades of the major biological concepts.

10-2a NGSS Life Science Performance Expectations

According to NGSS, students who demonstrate an understanding an understanding of life science in grades 1 through 3 meet the following criteria.

First Grade

- Use materials to design a solution to a human problem by mimicking how plants and/or animals use their external parts to help them survive, grow, and meet their needs.

- Read texts and use media to determine patterns in behavior of parents and offspring that help offspring survive.

- Make observations or construct an evidence-based account that young plants and animals are alike, but not exactly like their parents.

Second Grade

- Plan and conduct an investigation to determine whether plants need sunlight and water to grow.

- Develop a simple model that mimics the function of an animal in dispensing seeds or pollinating plants.

- Make observations of plants and animals to compare the diversity of life in different habitats.

Third Grade

- Develop models to describe that organisms have unique and diverse life cycles, but all have in common birth, growth, reproduction, and death.

- Construct an argument that some animals form groups that help members survive.

- Analyze and interpret data to provide evidence that plants and animals have traits inherited from parents and that variation of these traits exists in a group of similar organisms.

- Use evidence to support the explanation that the environment can influence traits.

- Analyze and interpret data from fossils to provide evidence of the organisms and environments in which they lived long ago.

- Use evidence to construct an explanation for how the variations in characteristics among individuals of the same species may provide advantages in surviving, finding mates, and reproducing,

- Construct an argument with evidence that in a particular habitat some organisms can survive well, and some cannot survive at all.

- Make a claim about the merit of solution to a problem caused when the environment changes and the types of plants and animals that live there may change.

Under most performance expectations in the NGSS book are clarification statements that suggest possible projects. Boxes below the performance objectives describe the science and engineering practices, disciplinary core ideas, and crosscutting concepts.

NGSS

10-2b Next Generation Instructional Plans

Herbert Spencer (1862), acclaimed English philosopher and scientist, wrote, "Children should be led to make their own investigations, and to draw upon their own inferences. They should be told as little as possible." For a century and a half, science educators have tried to see how it is possible for children to learn science if we don't tell them. To date, probably the most significant advance has been the Learning Cycle. The Learning Cycle was originally developed by Robert Karplus, a theoretical physicist at Berkeley. He had become upset with the factual nature of his daughter's science education in her elementary grades—the kind of science education in which the teacher tells the students what they are to learn, and the student is required to learn it. The problem was that (a) the children were not encouraged to think for themselves; (b) some of the factual material was obsolete, having been replaced by newer material as a result of advances in scientific research; (c) some of the factual material required was just plain wrong; and (d) most of the required information had little or no relevance to students' lives. The Learning Cycle partially solved this problem. It consisted originally of three phases that repeated in cyclic form as the material became more advanced and/or as new material was introduced: exploration, concept introduction, and concept application. As one of the results of the work done by Barbee and others at the Biological Sciences Curriculum

Study (BSCS) organization, the original Learning Cycle has morphed into today's cycle, which you encountered in earlier chapters.

When the research and the performance of students are considered, we find it is better for children to learn how to *do* science than it is for them to learn *about* science. The earlier guide to science teaching shifted the focus of science education to children doing science instead of memorizing facts. The present NGSS provides more detail.

You have already seen lessons constructed in the "Pre-NGSS" way. Below are lessons with a life science focus, fashioned to enable your students to think for themselves and to *do* science the way suggested by the new standards.

ACTIVITIES

FIRST-GRADE LIFE SCIENCE

Question: How can a variety of seeds be classified into groups?

Objective: To devise a classification system for a collection of seeds.

Materials: A collection of several different kinds of seeds, say 15 or 20 for each group, such as peas, lima beans, sunflower seeds, corn, radish seeds, marigold seeds, and large seeds for other flowers and vegetables. Books about seeds.

Procedure

Engage: Ask the children to examine the seeds and tell what they observe.

Explore: Ask the children how they can determine how many types of seeds are included in the seed display. Note whether they figure out that the seeds that are alike can be placed together in separate piles. Ask them to give a

descriptive name for each group of seeds, *and to explain why they chose that name.*

Explain: Ask the children to explain what they know about each type of seed. Have them explain how they can learn more. After they have looked through the seed books, have the children tell what they learned. Did they name the seeds correctly?

Elaborate: To incorporate mathematics in this activity, ask children to count the number of seeds in each of their groupings. They then record the number of each kind and draw a bar graph (histogram) of the data.

Performance expectation: Children will classify, count, and display seed information.

Follow–up: What can we do with the seeds?

Digital Download

Before you have children do the following activity, try it yourself. You may be surprised at the ambiguity of some of the suggested materials.

ACTIVITIES

FIRST-GRADE LIFE SCIENCE

Question: What Can Sprout and Grow?

Objective: To predict which object(s) in a collection of objects can sprout and grow.

Materials: Provide children with a collection of several items similar in size to seeds. Suggestions include several kinds of bean seeds, corn seeds, pea seeds, roasted peanuts, other nuts, a piece of gum, a shell, several kinds of buttons, a gum

ball, a small piece of potato, a thawed pea from a box of frozen peas, a rubber band, a screw, a crayon, and so on.

Procedure

Engage: Ask children to examine the collection of objects.

Explore: Tell children to pick out the things they think will sprout and grow. Ask why they think these items will sprout and grow. Then ask the children to pick out the things they think will *not* grow, and ask them to tell why they think they will not grow. Glue the items on the appropriate sides of a large piece of poster board labeled "Will Sprout and Grow" and "Will Not Sprout and Grow."

Further Exploration: On the next day of science, for each item which children predicted will sprout and grow, "plant" a duplicate in a wet tissue or paper towel; place the towel with the "seed" in a plastic baggie that can be sealed; seal it; and place it in a well-lit area. Ask children to check the results of their predictions each day until they see whether something happens in the bags. Each day have the students record their observations.

Explanation: Students explain what they have learned. Teacher provides additional information.

Elaboration: Students might decide they would like to plant a garden (either indoors or outdoors as space is available).

Performance expectation: Children will complete the investigation and produce data as evidence for their conclusions.

Follow-up: Obtain further information n plant growth. Read grade-appropriate texts and use media to obtain scientific information to determine patterns in the natural world. (1-LS1-2).

SECOND-GRADE LIFE SCIENCE

Question: How effective is camouflage?

Standard: Make observations of plants and animals to compare the diversity of life in different habitats (2-LS4-1).

Practice: Make observations to collect data that can be used to make comparisons (2-LS4-1).

Objective: To assess the effectiveness of camouflage, using a toothpick model.

Materials: String, meter stick (or yardstick), short pegs (such as tongue depressors), toothpicks of different colors (between 15 and 20 each of white, red, green, blue, and orange for each group), timer or watch with a second hand.

Procedure

Engage: Ask the students what they know about camouflage. List their contributions on poster board or the Smart Board. Obtain their ideas regarding how to study camouflage.

Explore: Measure a 1-meter (or 1-yard) square of grass in the schoolyard, and outline this square with string. Mark off enough squares for groups of four students. Assign each square to one team of four students. One member of each team is designated "It," and turns around, back facing the square, while the other students scatter the toothpicks of various colors fairly evenly on the grass inside the square. At a signal, "It" turns around and gathers as many toothpicks as possible in, say, 5 seconds.

The team then counts the number of each color "It" gathered, and records the results. This is repeated as many times as it takes for each member of the team to have a turn being "It." Children should record their observations.

Explanations: Typical discussion questions might include:

- "Which color did "It" pick up the most of? The least?"
- "What is the color of the grass?"
- "How does the number of toothpicks of a certain color picked up correspond to the color of the grass?"
- "From this activity, what do you think about the usefulness of camouflage by color?"
- "Can you think of other examples where camouflage by color is used? How about by people? How about by big animals? How about by insects?
- "Can you think of other examples where camouflage is used?"

Elaboration: Students might look for camouflage examples on the Internet or teacher might play a film or video that shows how various animals and/or insects are able to use camouflage.

Performance expectation: Students will make observations to collect data that can be used to make comparisons (2-LS4-1).

THIRD-GRADE LIFE SCIENCE

Question: How do whales stay warm in cold water?

Standard: Make observations of plants and animals to compare the diversity of life in different habitats (2-LS4-1).

Objective: To develop a model showing the relationship between the fat an animal possesses and its ability to survive in cold water.

Materials: Small plastic bags the size a hand will fit in (two for each student), duct tape, buckets with ice and water in them, food shortening such as Crisco.

Procedure

Engage: Children have been studying water temperature and sea life. Some students are especially interested in whales. Their teacher shows a video about the blue whale, the largest mammal to ever have lived.

Explore: The children look online for whale information. They are surprised to discover that whales can be found in every ocean on earth, including the Arctic and Antarctic.

They remember that blue whales spend much of their time near polar ice. They wonder how they stay warm.

Explain: At the Defenders of Wildlife website students find out that beneath their skin, whales have a layer of fat called blubber. Blubber is a storage area for energy and is also for insulation.

Elaborate: To demonstrate how blubber works as insulation, set up the following demonstration. Give children small plastic bags to secure over one of their hands with tape. Set up buckets of ice water around the room. Children place their gloved hand in the ice water while a partner times how long it takes before their hand gets too cold to keep in the ice water. Next, they immerse the gloved hand in another bag filled with shortening, squeezing the shortening around the gloved hand until the hand is covered with the shortening fairly uniformly. They place the hand in the ice water, and their partner again records the time it takes for their hand to get too cold to stay in the ice water. The children are constructing a model of how whales are protected from cold.

Elaboration: Typical discussion topics might include any of the following:

- "What is your answer to the question posed in the title of this activity?"
- "What is 'blubber'?"
- "Some people hunt whales for their blubber and for other parts of the animal. What are your thoughts about this practice versus conservation?"
- "Whales are mammals. What does this tell you about how the whale lives?"
- "Why do whales blow water out of their blow holes?"

Performance expectation: Students will develop models to describe phenomena (3-LS1-1).

Follow-up: Some students might be interested in doing some follow-up research on whales in books or on the Internet.

Practice: Read grade-appropriate texts, and use media to obtain scientific information to determine patterns in the natural world (1-LS1-2).

Digital Download

In kindergarten, children should have met the CCSSM objective: *Classify objects into given categories, count the numbers of objects in each category and sort the categories by count,* thus being prepared for seed sorting. The NGSS standard to be met for the following projects is *Plan and conduct investigations to produce data to serve as the basis for evidence to answer a question.* If children have not already done a seed classification activity, now is the time to have them do it. It doesn't matter which seeds you use so long as there are enough that each group can form their own system.

naeyc DAP

10-2c Conventional Life Science Instruction

This part of the chapter begins with life science concepts that are basic to primary grade learning; it then presents an example of a seed unit planned with the webbing strategy discussed in Chapter 2. Next, guidelines for animal care and a variety of investigations and learning experiences with animals are described. Finally, sources for teaching about plants, animals, and the human body are suggested.

Life Science Concepts. As a result of activities in the primary grades, all students should develop an understanding of the characteristics of **organisms**, the life cycles of organisms, and organisms and environments.

Young children's ideas about the characteristics of organisms develop from basic concepts of living and nonliving things. Piaget noted that many children associate "life" with any objects that are active in any way. Thus, movement becomes the defining characteristic of life, and **anthropomorphic** explanations are given to organisms. Eventually children's conception of the characteristics of life include other activities such as eating, breathing, and reproduction, but students must have a variety of experiences with organisms to develop this knowledge base.

Primary-age children can understand that organisms have basic needs. For example, animals need air, water, and food; plants require air, water, nutrients, and light. Organisms can survive only in environments in which their needs are met. Many different environments support the life of different types of organisms.

Children can begin to understand that each plant or animal has different structures that serve different functions in growth, survival, and reproduction. The behavior of individual organisms is influenced by internal cues (such as hunger) and by external cues (such as a change in the environment). Humans and other organisms have senses that help them detect internal and external cues.

The children should begin to understand that plants and animals have life cycles that include being born, developing into adults, reproducing, and eventually dying, and that plants and animals closely resemble their parents.

Upper primary students will begin to develop the understanding that all animals depend on plants. Some animals eat plants for food, and other animals eat the animals that eat plants. A plant or animal's behavior patterns are related to the nature of its environment, including the availability of food and resources and the physical characteristics of the environment.

Children will begin to note that all organisms cause changes in the environment in which they live. Some of these changes are detrimental to the organisms, and some are beneficial. Humans depend on their natural and constructed environments and also change the environments in beneficial and harmful ways.

Conventional Planning for Life Science. A knowledge of life science concepts is basic to planning and teaching life science to primary-age children. The fundamental life science concepts are the major ideas that we want students to understand. Thus, learning experiences are planned around them. For example, **Figure 10-6** shows a unit planning web (described in Chapter 2), which focuses learning activities around three basic concepts involving the topic of seeds. The following concepts can be used in activity planning and are basic to understanding plants, animals, and all living things.

Living Things. Living things can be distinguished from nonliving things.

1. Plants and animals are living things.

2. Animals and plants affect one another.

3. Living things have unique features that help them live in different kinds of places.

4. Most living things need water, food, and air.

Seeds and Plants

1. Seeds differ in size, shape, color, and texture.

2. Seeds germinate and grow into a specific type of plant.

3. Some seeds grow inside fruits.

4. Some seeds grow into flowers, shrubs, and trees.

5. Some seeds grow into food that we eat.

6. Seeds are dispersed in several ways.

7. Seeds need water, light, and warmth to grow.

8. Seeds and plants grow and change.

9. Leaves tend to grow toward light, and roots tend to grow into the soil.

10. Plants grow from seeds, roots, and stems.

11. Some plant forms do not have seeds, roots, or stems.

12. Some plants grow in the light, and some plants grow in the dark.

13. Some plants change in different seasons.

Animals

1. Animals need food, water, shelter, and a unique range of temperatures.

2. Animals have individual characteristics.

3. Animals have unique adaptations. They move, eat, live, and behave in ways that help them survive.

4. Animals go through a life cycle.

5. Pets are animals that depend on us for special care. We love and take care of our pets.

6. There are many kinds of pets.

7. Different kinds of pets need different types of care to grow and be healthy.

8. Aquariums are places for fish and other living things to grow.

10-2d Planning and Teaching a Seed Project

The learning experiences suggested in this plan follow the format described in Chapter 2 and are designed to meet the needs, interests, and developmental levels of primary-age children as described earlier in the chapter. Each lesson states a concept, a teaching objective based on what the child should be able to do, materials needed, and suggestions for teaching the concept. Extensions, integrations, and possible evaluation procedures are indicated in the body of the lesson when appropriate and at the end of the project.

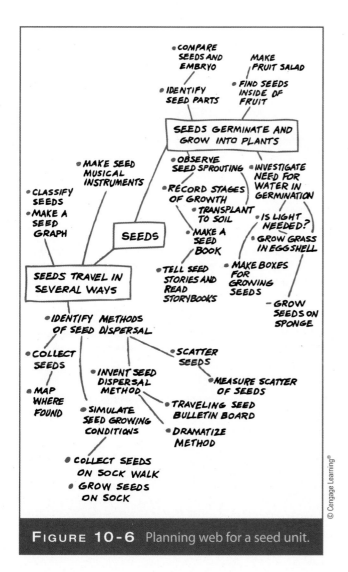

FIGURE 10-6 Planning web for a seed unit.

ACTIVITIES

SEEDS

Concept: Seeds germinate and grow into plants; seeds contain a baby plant.

Objective: To discover that a seed has three parts. Identify the embryo inside of the seed.

Materials: Lima beans that have been soaked overnight (if you soak them longer, they may rot), paper towels, a variety of seeds.

Procedure: Show the children a lima bean seed. Ask: **"What do you think might be inside this seed? Can you draw a picture of how you think the inside of the seed looks?"**

Have children open the lima bean seed with their thumbnails. Ask: **"What do you notice about your seed? How does the seed feel? Is there a smell? Does the inside of the seed look like the picture you have drawn?"** Discuss similarities and differences. Have students draw a picture of the bean after it is opened.

Point out that there are three basic parts in all seeds: the seed cover (for protection), food for the baby plant (cotyledon), and the baby plant itself (embryo) (**Figure 10-7**). Introduce the term **germinate**. (This is when the seed grows; it sprouts.) Have students paint a picture of the plant as they think it will look when it has grown.

Naturalistic and informal activities: Have a variety of seeds in the science center so that the children can soak them and then see whether they have the same parts as the lima beans. When you observe children opening the beans, ask: **"How are the seeds like the lima beans? How are they different?"** This could be done in an unstructured way as part of a seed center. Beans and peas have two seed halves. In seeds such as corn and rice, there is only one seed half, or cotyledon.

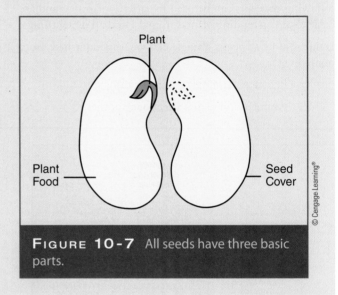

FIGURE 10-7 All seeds have three basic parts.

BABY PLANTS

Concept: Seeds germinate and grow into plants.

Objective: To observe and describe how seeds grow into plants, and to describe how the embryo grows into a plant.

Materials: Lima beans, paper towels, water, cotton, clear containers or glass tumblers.

Procedure: Say, **"Yesterday we saw a baby plant inside a seed. Do you think it will grow into a big plant? Let's find out."**

Soak lima beans overnight. Have children line the inside of a drinking glass with a wet, folded paper towel. Then stuff cotton into the glass. This holds the paper towel in place.

Put soaked seeds between the paper towel and glass. Pour water to the edge of the bottom seed in the glass (the paper towel and cotton will absorb most of the liquid). The sprouting seeds will be easy for the children to see through the clear container. Have the children draw the sprouting lima bean, and write a story about the investigation.

Ask: **"What do you see happening? What colors do you see? Which way are the roots growing? Where is the embryo getting its food?"** (It is from the cotyledon.) As the plant gets larger, the seed becomes smaller. In fact, the plant will begin to die when the cotyledon is used up.

When the food provided by the seed is used up, ask, **"What other type of food can we give the plant?"** Discuss the possibility of transplanting the young plants to soil as a continuation of the project.

Extension: This concept can be extended throughout the year. It is a good science activity, with the advantage of going from simple observation to experimentation. The concept lends itself to a short study of seeds or to an extended study of how light, moisture, heat, color, soil, air, and sound affect the growth of plants.

GLASS GARDEN

Concept: Moisture is needed for seeds to sprout.

Objective: To observe the growth of seeds.

Materials: Mung beans, cheesecloth, jar.

Procedure: Soak a handful of mung beans in a jar, and cover the jar tightly with cheesecloth. Protect the jar from light by wrapping it in a towel. Then have children simulate rain by rinsing and draining the seeds three times a day. Have children predict what will happen to the seeds. Ask: **"Did the seeds sprout even though they were in the dark?"** [Yes.] **"Do you think the seeds will sprout if we keep them in the dark but do not water them?"** [No.] Repeat the activity, and investigate what will happen if the seeds are kept in the dark and not watered.

Naturalistic and informal activities: Have a variety of seeds in the science center so that the children can experiment with them to see if they all react in the same way as the mung beans.

Extension: You may want to make a salad and top it off with the mung sprouts. Several variables can be tried—one at a time, of course—so that children can investigate variables in sprouting seeds and growing plants.

Teaching note: Lima beans usually work well, but mung beans show the speedy growth that impatient young children may demand. Mung beans will not grow as tall as others, but they will show growth. Corn, on the other hand, takes longer than lima beans to germinate.

WHAT'S INSIDE?

Concept: Seeds come from the fruit of plants.

Objective: To discover that seeds develop inside of fruit.

Materials: A variety of fruits, pinecones, flowers; plastic knives and paper towels.

Procedure: Select several fruits, and place them on a table with plastic knives and paper towels. Have children examine the fruits and ask, **"What do you think is inside of the fruit?"**

Invite children to cut the fruits open. Ask: **"What did you find? How many seeds did you find? Are all of the seeds the same color? What do you think the seeds are doing inside of the fruit?"**

Explain that a fruit is the part of a flowering plant that holds the seeds. Ask: **"Can you name any flowers in your backyard that have seeds?"** [Sunflowers, dandelions.] **"Are they fruits?"** [Yes.] Point out that not all fruits are edible.

Extension: Show a picture of a pine tree. Ask: **"Does this tree have flowers?"** [No.] **"Does it have seeds?"** [Yes.] **"Where are the seeds?"** [Cones.] Have children examine pinecones to find out how the seeds are attached. Compare the seeds enclosed in fruits to those attached to cones. Point out that seeds can grow inside of a flower, surrounded by fruit, or in a cone.

TRAVELING SEEDS

Concept: Seeds need to travel to grow.

Objective: To investigate why seeds travel by simulating growing conditions.

Materials: Two containers, soil, seeds.

Procedure: Have children bring in seeds from the school grounds or their neighborhood. Examine the seeds, and discuss where they were found. Hold up a seed, and ask: **"Do we have this kind of plant on our school grounds?"** [No.] **"How did the seed get here?"** [Wind.] **"I wonder, why did it blow away?"**

After discussing, ask: **"Do you think that seeds will get a chance to grow if they all fall at the bottom of the parent plant? Let's see what happens when seeds fall in one place."**

Fill two containers with seeds. Have children help plant seeds close together in one container and far apart in the other. Ask, **"Which container do you think will grow the most plants?"** Discuss and list suggested reasons. Have children take turns giving all of the seeds water, light, warmth. Watch them for many days. Have children measure the growth of the plants and record what they see. Then ask, **"In which container do seeds grow better?"** [Spaced apart.] In this way, children will see a reason for a seed to travel.

SCATTERING SEEDS

Concept: Seeds are adapted to disperse in several ways.

Objective: To identify several ways of dispersing seeds.

Materials: Seeds, magnifying glasses, mittens.

Procedure: Arrange seeds from weeds, grasses, and trees in a science center. Have a magnifying glass and mitten available for students to examine seeds. Give basic directions, and let children "mess around" and explore the seeds. Ask, **"Which seeds seem to catch in the mitten?"** [Hairy ones or ones with burrs.] Have children predict and draw what they think they will see when they observe a burr through a magnifying glass. Say, **"Let's look through the magnifying glass and draw what we see."** Discuss the before and after pictures, and describe the tiny hooks and

how they are used. Introduce the term *disperse* and use it in sentences and stories about the burr with tiny hooks.

Extension: Take children outside to explore how different seeds are dispersed, by shaking seeds from pods, beating grass seed spikes to release grains, brushing hairy seeds against clothes, and releasing winged seeds. Compare what happens to each seed.

INVENT A SEED

Concept: Seeds are modified to travel in a specific way.

Objective: To modify a seed for travel.

Materials: Dried bean or pea seeds, a junk box (colored paper, glue, rubber bands, tape, cotton, ice-cream-bar sticks, balloons, pipe cleaners, paper clips, string), scissors.

Procedure: Show children a coconut (the largest seed), and ask, **"How do you think this coconut travels?"** [By water.] Display pods such as milkweed to demonstrate a pod that bursts and casts its seeds to the wind. Ask, **"How will the burr travel?"** [By catching on things.] Say, **"Birds and other animals eat fruit such as berries. Then, they digest the fruit and leave the seeds somewhere else. Why did the bird want to eat berries?"** [They were good to eat.] Children will conclude that seeds have specific modifications to travel in specific ways. To reinforce the term *modify*, have students modify their clothes for different weather or activities.

Ask, **"If you were a seed, how would you like to travel?"** Discuss preferences, and then assign one of the following means of travel to each small group of children: attracts an animal, catches on fur, pops or is shot out, floats on water, or is carried by wind. Give each group seeds and junk box materials, and ask them to invent a way for their seed to travel. When the children have completed their creations, have them demonstrate how their seed travels (**Figure 10-8**).

Extension: Make a bulletin board that displays the modified seeds traveling in the way the students intended. Have children examine seeds and think of other objects that work in the same way. (For example, the burr is the inspiration for the development of Velcro.)

Concept: Seeds come from the fruit of plants.

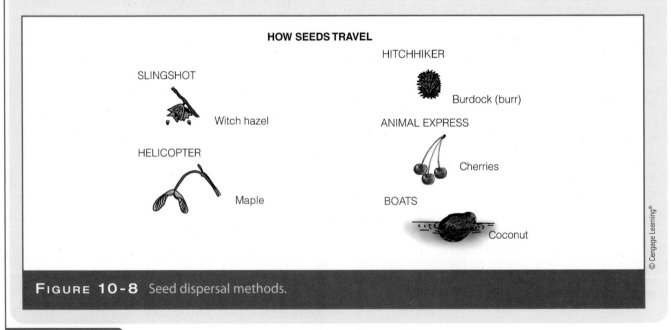

HOW SEEDS TRAVEL

SLINGSHOT — Witch hazel

HELICOPTER — Maple

HITCHHIKER — Burdock (burr)

ANIMAL EXPRESS — Cherries

BOATS — Coconut

© Cengage Learning®

FIGURE 10-8 Seed dispersal methods.

More Seed Suggestions

1. *Sock walk.* Drag a sock through a field. Then, cover it with soil and water, and wait for a variety of plants to grow from the seeds caught on the sock. Or put the sock in a plastic bag, shake the seeds out

of the sock, and examine them. Ask, **"What types of seeds did the sock attract?"**

2. *Egghead hair.* Draw a face on half of an eggshell. Place the egg in an egg carton, and fill the eggshell with moist soil. Sprinkle grass seed on top,

then water. Grass will grow in about five days. Attach construction paper feet with clay to display (plastic eggs also work well). To show the benefit of light on leaves, first grow the grass hair in the dark. Discuss the resulting pale, thin grass and ask, **"How can we make the grass green and healthy?"** Place the egg person in the light, and be prepared to trim the healthy green hair.

10-2e Subject Integrations

Science and Math

1. *Seed walk.* Take a seed walk around the school. Ask, **"Where shall we look for seeds? What do you think we might see?"** Gather seeds, and use as materials to sort, match, count, and weigh in the science center.

2. *How many ways.* Provide a box of seeds for students to classify. Compare size, shape, color, and texture of the seeds. Construct a seed graph.

3. *Greenhouse.* Simulate a greenhouse by placing a plastic bag over a container of germinating seeds. Place seeds in a jar on a moist paper towel. Put the jar inside of a plastic bag, and record the amount of time needed for sprouting. Compare sprouting time with seeds that are not placed in a plastic bag.

4. *Cooking.* Create a fruit salad with the fruits gathered for seed activities. Or measure ingredients and follow a recipe to make apple pie or other tasty dishes. By passing the seeds or nuts through a nut grinder, you can make nut butter. Store in the refrigerator to use as spreads.

Science and Social Studies

1. *Neighborhood map.* Have children bring in seeds that they have found. Make a map of where the seeds might be found.

2. *Seeds can be edible.* Try to bridge the gap between the processed food that the children eat and its raw form. Show pictures of wheat, fruit trees, and vegetables growing. Discuss edible seeds such as pumpkin, sunflower, peanuts, as well as those that are not eaten, such as watermelon and apple seeds.

3. *Woodworking.* Create boxes and planters for growing seeds.

Science and Language Arts

1. Dramatize the growth of an embryo into a plant.

2. Make a seed book (in the shape of a lima bean), and fill it with bean stories and drawings.

3. Read, tell, and dramatize stories about seeds such as "Jack and the Beanstalk," "The Story of Johnny Appleseed," or *The Popcorn Book* by Tomie dePaola (1984).

4. Share the following books aloud: *Growing Vegetable Soup* (Ehlert, 1987), *The Carrot Seed* (Krauss, 1945),

PHOTO 10-4A and B Primary grade children can research and write reports on creatures of interest.

From Seed to Pear (Mitgutsch, 1971), and *Tops and Bottoms* (Stevens, 1995). Have the children make books using a similar theme, and share it with younger children (**Photos 10-4a and b**).

Science and Music

1. Sing songs about seeds and plants from your music book.

2. Use seeds to create musical instruments, such as maracas and other types of "shaking" instruments in tubes with plastic lids.

Science and Art

1. Create landscapes that would be favorable for seed growth.

2. Make faces on moist sponges with birdseed. Trim the green growth into different patterns.

3. Design seed mosaics. Glue seeds to paper or cardboard to make pictures.

10-2f Additional Plant Activities Based on Science Concepts

When your unit on seeds is completed, you might want to develop additional concepts about plants. Here are a few suggestions.

Concept: Plants Grow from Roots and Stems. Growing plants from cuttings can be an exciting experience for primary-age children. They will enjoy observing familiar products from a grocery bag doing unfamiliar things. Investigations with cuttings are long term and provide opportunities for record keeping, process skill development, and subject integration. You will need water, light, and common vegetables to rein-force that seeds are not the only way that plants reproduce.

1. *Dish garden.* To make a dish garden, cut off the top inch of carrots, beets, or white turnips. Keep the tops in dishes of water while the children observe the roots growing. Shoots will usually appear in a week to 10 days. Ask, **"Can you tell what this plant is by the leaves?"**

2. *Hanging around.* Suspend a yam or a fresh sweet potato, tapered end down, in a jar filled with wa-ter. Insert toothpicks so that only one-third of the sweet potato is in the water. Put the jar in a warm, dark place until buds and roots grow. Then put it in a sunny place, and prepare a string trellis for the upcoming foliage to climb. Children can chart the number of days for root and foliage growth and ob-serve and record changes. Ask, **"What happens to the sweet potato as the vine grows?"**

3. *Pineapple tops.* Cut a 2½-inch section of pineapple fruit below the leaves. Put the pineapple top in a dish with water. When the roots develop, put the plant in potting soil and make a greenhouse by covering it with a plastic bag. Keep the pineapple greenhouse warm, but not in direct sunlight. In about three weeks, take the new plant out of the greenhouse, add water, and place it in the sun. Eventually, tiny pineapples may form (6 to 12 months).

Concept: Molds Grow in Dark, Moist Conditions. Children have probably seen mold in their own refrigerators or breadbaskets, but do not realize that mold is an organism called fungi. Observing a mold garden gives children an opportunity to focus on recording observations, keeping records, and writing predictions as they investigate the world of mold.

1. To begin the lesson, show the children a molding orange and ask, **"What is on the orange? Is the orange good to eat? Where have you seen mold?"** Make a list of the conditions of the places where mold has been found. There should be replies of "moist," "dark," and types of materials such as fruit and bread.

2. To make the mold garden, fill a glass jar about one-third full of sand. Sprinkle water on the sand, and place items that the children bring in on top of the sand. Screw the lid on the jar and begin observations, discussion, and predictions. Ask, **"Which objects do you think mold will grow on first? Will any objects not grow mold?"** Place the mold garden in a dark place and prepare the children to observe. Changing colors, shapes, and sizes should prove interesting.

3. You might want to mention the important role that fungus plays in breaking down materials and in returning the components to the soil.

Teaching Notes

1. Most mold of this type is harmless, but do not take any chances. Keep the lid on the jar. In addition, have children wash their hands if any moldy items are touched; do not sniff molds (check for mold allergies among students); and when the activity is completed, throw away all mold gardens without opening them and in a tightly sealed bag.

2. Growing mold in soil is speedy because soil is rich in organic materials, and for that reason some science educators recommend it. However, a teacher does not know what else might be in the soil sample, ready to grow. Thus, play it safe and slow—stick to sand.

3. Mold is a type of fungus that lacks chlorophyll. Although warmth, darkness, and moisture are ideal conditions for mold growth, neither warmth nor darkness is necessary for growth. Further investigations of conditions for mold growth may be appropriate in your classroom.

10-2g Animals in the Classroom

Caring for and studying living things in the classroom and outdoors can be an excellent way to develop a respect for and knowledge of the daily requirements of all forms of life (**Photo 10-5**). As children care for a living thing, they seem

PHOTO 10-5   The class Bearded Dragon relaxes in the sun on his rock perch.

PHOTO 10-6   During the student lunch period, the dragon walks freely around the classroom.

to develop a sensitivity and sense of responsibility for the life around them (**Photo 10-6**). As they maintain the living organism, they become aware of the conditions under which that animal (or plant) survives, as well as the conditions under which it will perish. You hope that these understandings and attitudes will carry over into the child's life and the human condition in general.

Before you think about caring for any living organisms, take the precautions listed in this chapter. It is vital that living things do not suffer from too much care, such as overfeeding and handling, and too little care, such as improper diet, water, temperature, and shelter. In other words, before allowing an animal in your classroom, be sure you know how to take care of it.

Care of the animal should begin before the animal arrives. The entire class should have an opportunity to help prepare the cage or environment. As preparations are made, discuss why and what you are doing, and so develop the children's understanding of the specific needs of a species.

When the animal arrives in class, give the new visitor time to become acclimated to its new surroundings. The expected enthusiasm and interest that an animal visitor is likely to generate may overwhelm the newcomer. Instruct children to quietly observe the animal in pairs for brief periods of time. Then, small groups can watch, always quietly, as everyone (animal and children) adjusts to the environment.

When planning for an animal visitor, ask yourself and your students the following questions:

1. "What type of cage or environment does this animal require?"

2. "What temperature must be maintained?" Some animals require a warm and a cool area of the cage.

3. "What type of food is needed, and how should that food be presented?" Some animals need live food.

4. "Will the animal be able to live in the room over weekends? What will happen to the animal during vacations?"

5. "Is this an endangered animal? Has this animal been illegally captured or imported?" For example, for each parrot of many species that a child encounters, about 10 parrots have perished in capture or transport. Or, as in the case of a species such as the ball python, some animals will never eat in captivity. Limit animal use to those bred in captivity.

6. "Does the animal need special lights?" Many reptiles must have ultraviolet light.

7. "Will this animal make a good classroom visitor? Should it be handled?" Avoid impulse purchases that will lead to future problems.

Tips for Keeping Animals in the Classroom. When animals are in the classroom, care should be taken to ensure that neither the children nor the animals are harmed. Mammals protect themselves and their young by biting, scratching, and kicking. Pets such as cats, dogs, rabbits, and guinea pigs should be handled properly and should not be disturbed when eating. For example, rats, rabbits, hamsters, and mice are best picked up by the scruff of the neck, with a hand placed under the body for support. Observe also the following precautions.

1. Check school district procedures to determine whether there are any local regulations to be observed. Personnel at the local humane society, pet stores, or a zoo are often very cooperative in assisting teachers to create a wholesome animal environment in the classroom. However, zoos receive numerous requests for adoption and usually do not want classroom animals for their collection or feeder stock when the school year is over.

2. Caution students never to tease animals or to insert their fingers or objects through wire mesh cages. Report animal bites and scratches immediately to the school's medical authority. Provide basic first aid. Usually, children follow the example set by the teacher. If you treat the animals with respect, then the children will, too.

3. Purchase fish from tanks in which all the fish appear healthy.

4. Discourage students from bringing personal pets to school. If they are brought into the room, they should be handled only by their owners and provided a place for fresh water and a place to rest.

5. Guidelines for collecting invertebrates and caring for them in the classroom are provided in the first section of this chapter.

Teaching with Animals. Entire projects can be designed around observing animals in the classroom. Science concepts and subject integrations occur naturally as children observe, categorize, and communicate their experiences with animals. The benefits of observing animals far outweigh the disadvantages and are well worth your time and energy. If possible, try to adapt your discussion of the topic through the use of available technologies. The Next Generation Science Standards work has provided a few exemplary questions for each learning objective (see NRC, 2013, pp. 2–33, for grade-level appropriate questions and suggestions for further study of physical science and life science). Following are a few questions and project integrations that lead to investigations:

1. *Describe how the animal moves.* Ask: **"Do you move that way? See if you can figure out why the animal moves in the way that it does. Does anything make it move faster or slower?"** Add children's observations to the observation list.

2. *"How does the animal eat its food?* Does it use its feet or any other part of its body to help it eat? Does it prefer a specific type of food?"* Make a chart or graph showing preferences.

3. *"What do the animals do all day?"* Keep a record of the animal's activities, or pinpoint several specific behaviors, such as recording the type of food eaten. Ask, **"Are there times when the animal is more or less active?"** Take pictures of the animal at the same time of the day. Chart the results.

4. *"What do the animals do at night?"* Children have many questions about what the classroom animals do at night. One instructional technology tool for finding an answer to the question "What does Harry the Hamster do when we leave the room?" is to set up a digital video camera that will take video and time-lapse pictures. For example, the camera can be set to take a picture every 15 minutes or to take a 5-minute video every 20 minutes. The resulting digital images can be a way for children to collect data to answer their questions.

5. *"How do animals react to different objects in their environment?"* Offer gerbils paper towel tubes, and watch them play. Help the children to write a story that sequences the actions of the gerbils.

6. *"What type of sounds do the animals make?"* Have children try to identify different taped animal sounds and decide they can tell the size of an animal by its sound. Have children tape-record different sounds made by the animal as it is sleeping, eating, playing, and drinking. Play the tape, and have children make up stories about what they think is happening.

7. *"How can we keep earthworms in the classroom?"* Have children research what is required for keeping earthworms healthy. Earthworms make good pets because they can be handled with less stress to the animal than mammals, birds, reptiles, and amphibians.

8. *"Describe the animal's body covering.* Why do you think it has this type of covering?"* Compare the body coverings of different animals. Design a center that allows children to feel objects that simulate animal coverings (refer to Chapter 12). Observe these coverings on a trip to the zoo.

9. *"How does the animal drink?* Can you think of other animals that drink in the same way?"* Categorize ways that animals drink (e.g., a cat laps water; a snake sucks water).

Although 7- and 8-year-olds are not yet ready for formal outlining, building a web is a good way to organize what they are learning about animals. This type of organization refreshes memory for what children have seen or studied and relates any information they are collecting. **Figure 10-9** presents their ideas in a loosely structured way. The teacher selects the main divisions and writes them on the chalkboard or Smart Board. Then, the children give the main points. If the children are working in committees to research different aspects, this strategy illustrates the relatedness of the entire project.

10-2h A Trip to the Zoo

A trip to the zoo is an effective way to offer children opportunities to explore the world of animals. Observing animals in a zoo setting is a high-interest activity that helps children learn about animals and their needs. The following suggestions are designed to maximize the effect of a zoo's unique setting. (Note: If a zoo is not located nearby, you might consider taking the class to a pet store. Although

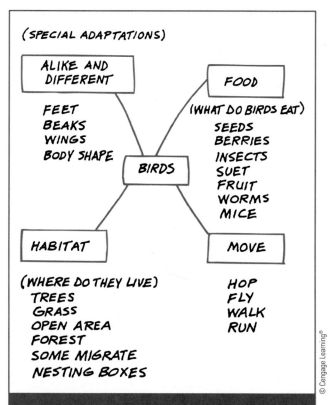

FIGURE 10-9 Webbing to review what we have learned.

the variety of animals is limited, such a trip would at least somewhat fulfill the purpose of a trip to the zoo.)

Before, During, and After. To make the most of your zoo visit, plan learning experiences that will be taught before going to the zoo, during the zoo visit, and after returning to the classroom. For example, you might want to focus your plans on the similarities and differences between reptiles and amphibians. In the following scenario, Mrs. Red Fox decides to relate class discussions and observations to turtles.

Before the Zoo Visit. Before going to the zoo, Mrs. Red Fox prepares learning stations for her class. The stations will prepare the children for their zoo visit.

- *Station 1.* Mrs. Red Fox prepares items that simulate body covering for the children to feel. To represent the dry, scaly skin of most reptiles, she rolls shelled sunflower seeds in clay. Oiled cellophane represents the moist, glandular skin of most amphibians. As children visit this station, they are invited to touch the simulated coverings and match picture cards of animals that might feel dry or slimy.

- *Station 2.* To emphasize the role of **camouflage** in both reptiles and amphibians, the teacher prepares two pieces of black construction paper. A yellow pipe cleaner is taped to one piece of paper, and a black pipe cleaner is taped to another. Ask: **"Which is harder to see? How do you think this helps the animal survive? Design camouflage for a green pipe cleaner that lives in a desert."**

- *Station 3.* Some reptiles and amphibians rely on sensing vibrations to "hear" because they do not have outer ears. Mrs. Red Fox has the children tap a tuning fork on a surface and hold it near their ear. She says, "Describe what happens. Tap the fork again, and press it against your cheek. What happens this time?" The class discusses how vibrations tell the animal what is happening. Some of the children begin comparing how birds and mammals hear and sense vibrations.

- *Station 4.* Mrs. Red Fox has the children draw what they think a turtle will look like and what kind of home it will have.

At the Zoo. Mrs. Red Fox divides her class into small groups and assigns a chaperone to each small group. Each group has a turtle task card. When the groups come to the turtle exhibit, the chaperone helps the children complete the questions. The children are asked to observe and answer the following questions:

- "How many turtles do you see?"
- "What are they doing?"
- "Are turtle toes like your toes?"
- "What are the turtles eating?"
- "Try walking around the areas as slowly as the turtle is moving. How does it feel?"

- "How are you and the turtle alike?"
- "How are you different?"
- "What other animals are living with the turtle?"
- "Is it easy to find the turtles in the exhibit?"

As the children move to an amphibian exhibit such as frogs, toads, and salamanders, they make comparisons between the turtles and the amphibians. Mrs. Red Fox makes sure that the exhibit signs are read and that questions are asked to gather additional information.

After the Zoo Visit. Mrs. Red Fox reinforces what the children have learned with a variety of learning experiences. The class makes turtle candy from caramels, nuts, and chocolate bits, and the children create a play about turtles and how they live.

Each child creates a shoebox diorama of the turtle habitat. The teacher asks, "Did the turtle live in the same way that you thought it would? What was different? What was the same?" She has the children compare what they knew about turtles before the visit to the diorama that they created after the visit. Mrs. Red Fox has storybooks and reference books available for children to find out more about reptiles and amphibians.

Additional Zoo Animal Activities. The following questions and activities can be used before, during, or after a trip to the zoo.

1. "How many toes does a giraffe have? What color is a giraffe's tongue? Can you touch your nose with your tongue?" Explain that giraffes use their tongues the way we use forks and spoons.

2. A snake is covered with scales. Ask: "Are the scales on a snake's stomach the same shape and size as those on its back? Does a snake have feathers? Does a snake have fur?"

3. "What do we use to protect our feet? How are the feet of the sheep and deer adapted to where they live?" When in front of the hoofed animal display, have students stretch out their arms and then slowly move their arms together while looking directly ahead. "When can you see your hands?" Direct the children's attention to the hoofed animals. "Where are the deer's eyes located?" Discuss the location of the eyes, and name some advantages of having eyes that can see behind you.

4. In front of the aquarium ask, "How do you think fish breathe? Do fish have noses?" Then say: "Find a fish that feeds from the top of the tank. Find one that feeds from the bottom of the tank. Do any of the fish feed in the middle of the tank?"

5. "Do any of the animals have babies?" Refer to these questions when observing animal babies. "Do the babies look like the adult? How are they different?" And: "Does the baby move around on its own? Is one of the adults taking care of the baby? What is the adult doing for the baby?"

6. Other books that can be read aloud or put in the classroom library are *The Puffins Are Back* (Gibbons, 1991); *The Salamander House* (Mazer, 1991); *Frogs, Toads, and Lizards* (Parker & Wright, 1990); *Tigress* (Cowcher, 1991); *Dear Zoo* (Campbell, 1982); *The Yucky Reptile Alphabet Book* (Pallotta, 1989); and *Look Out for Turtles* (Berger, 1992).

Learning at the zoo can be an exciting experience. For a successful trip, plan activities for before, during, and after a zoo visit. If this is your first trip to the zoo, concentrate on familiar body parts and activities. For example, how does the animal move, eat, hear, see, or protect itself? Use these questions to encourage discussion of the special abilities and adaptations of animals.

10-2i Strategies for Teaching About the Human Body

The internal anatomy of the human body is a hard concept for young children to understand. Concrete experiences on which to base understandings can be difficult to provide.

BRAIN CONNECTION

BRAIN

The BRAIN initiative (Brain Research through Advancing Innovative Neurotechnologies) is part of a government focus on revolutionizing understanding of the brain (NIH, 2014). Supported and funded by NIH (National Institute of Health), this initiative will move ahead at a rapid rate the technologies for studying the brain and our knowledge of how the brain works. The initiative is needed because, although we have learned more about the brain in recent years, we are still behind in understanding the underlying causes of neurological and psychiatric disorders such as Alzheimer's. Parkinson's, autism, epilepsy, schizophrenia, depression, and traumatic brain injury. Researchers need new advanced tools and information for understanding how the brain functions. The initiative takes a multidisciplinary approach to developing more advanced tools and obtaining more information. At the intersection of neuroscience, imaging, engineering, informatics, and other emerging science areas, it is believed new tools can be developed.

NIH (2014). Retrieved February 2, 2014, from http://www.nih.gov/science/brain

---

Inside Me. Although children cannot observe the insides of a human body, they can infer that muscles, bones, and organs are inside them. For example, bones give the body shape, help the body move, and protect the organs. Preliminary activities should include body awareness activities in which children explore, feel, and identify some of the major bones. Observation of X-ray films can further enhance the children's concept of bones. Then, trace a Halloween skeleton, cut out the bones, and assemble the skeleton, using paper fasteners as joints. Try some of the following strategies for teaching about bones with children.

Our Skeleton Has Joints. Have the children move their arms and legs in a way that explores the way joints work: marching, saluting, swinging arms and legs, and acting like a windmill. Ask: "**Do your legs bend when you march? Can you march without bending your legs? Is it easy to do?**" Point out and explore the joints that help your body move. Discover the difference between *hinge joints*, which bend one way, and *ball-and-socket joints*, which can bend, twist, and rotate (**Figure 10-10**).

Find the Joints. Have children work in pairs to make a paper body and locate joints. Have one child lie on a piece of butcher paper while another child draws the outline of the body. Then have the children locate joints on the paper body. Discuss why the type of joint used in the body is the most appropriate. Ask, "**What would happen if we had a ball-and-socket joint in our knees?**"

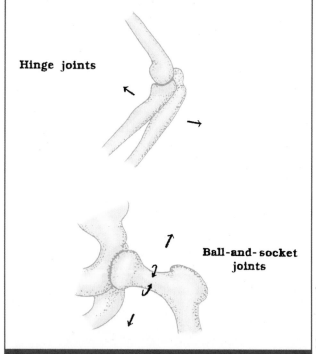

FIGURE 10-10 A hinge joint and a ball-and-socket joint.

© Cengage Learning®

Make a Muscle. Young children enjoy flexing their arm muscles and feeling the muscles they can make, but they might think that arm muscles are the only ones they have. Encourage them to discover other muscles by raising their heels off the ground in a tiptoe position. Ask, "Can you feel your muscles move as they do this?" Have the children lie on mats, stretch out like a cat, and then curl up into a ball. Ask, **"Which muscles can you feel now?"**

Explore facial muscles by wiggling noses and raising eyebrows. Ask, **"Does your tongue have muscles?"** [Yes.] Give children time to find unexpected muscles in their bodies. Then apply some of the bone and joint learning experiences to teaching about muscles.

10-3 PHYSICAL SCIENCE FOR THE NEXT GENERATION AND CONVENTIONAL PHYSICAL SCIENCE INSTRUCTION

Physical science experiences are fun and exciting for primary-age children. Even though these experiences can be dramatic and astounding for children, teaching the concepts is more foolproof than you might think (**Photo 10-7**). This is true for several reasons.

First, the physical sciences abound with opportunities for using discrepant events (discussed in Chapter 2) that put students in disequilibrium and ready them for learning. Thus, they are eager and ready to explore. Second, most experiences are instantly repeatable. In this way, the child can continue exploring without elaborate preparation. Finally, the hands-on nature of physical science explorations makes them ideal for use with primary-age children.

Charlesworth

PHOTO 10-7 **The playground equipment provides opportunities to learn about gravity, balance, and motion.**

The Framework (NRC, 2012) and the NGSS (NRC, 2013) state that, as a result of the activities in the primary grades, all students should develop an understanding of Matter and its Interactions; Motion and Stability: Forces and Interactions; and Energy. At the primary level, the NGSS content standards (NRC, 2013) focus on waves and their applications, matter and its interactions, and motion and stability. Children can best understand these topics by acting on objects and observing what happens to them. NGSS (NRC, 2013, pp. 9, 15, 24) suggests primary grade children should be able to formulate answers to questions such as the following:

1. Questions for first graders: "What happens when materials vibrate?" "What happens when there is no light?"

2. Questions for second graders: "How are materials similar and different from one another?" "How do the properties of materials relate to their use?"

3. Questions for third graders: "How do equal and unequal forces on an object affect the object?" "How can magnets be used?"

These are examples of the types of question that might begin a physical science investigation. Primary grade experiences lay the groundwork for the progressive development of the major physical science concepts that will be investigated more deeply in the later grades.

Technology for Young Children

NSTA eBooks +

NSTA has developed Multi-Touch e-books that can enrich science instruction. Several include physical science topics. *Chemical Reactions* includes more than 20 simulations and animations. *Nature of Light* describes characteristics of light such as the concept of light as waves and light and color. Life science topics include *Heredity and Variation* and *Interdependence of Life*. *Heredity and Variation* looks at the variables that influence inheritance. *Interdependence of Life* looks at the interactions between organisms and environments. They can be purchased at the iBook Store and can be viewed on iPads and Macintosh computers.

10-3a NGSS Performance Expectations

The following performance expectations are detailed in the NGSS, which says that students who demonstrate understanding can do the following:

First Grade

■ Plan and conduct investigations to provide evidence that vibrating materials can make sound and that sound can make materials vibrate.

■ Make observations to construct an evidenced-based account that objects can be seen only when illuminated.

- Plan and conduct an investigation to determine the effect of placing objects made with different materials in the path of a beam of light.
- Use tools and materials to design and build a device that uses light or sound to solve a problem of communicating over a distance.

Second Grade

- Plan and conduct an investigation to describe and classify different kinds of materials by their observable properties.
- Analyze data obtained from testing different materials to determine which materials have the properties that are best suited for an intended purpose.
- Make observations to construct an evidenced-based account of how an object made of a small set of pieces can be disassembled and made into a new object.
- Construct an argument with evidence that some changes caused by heating or cooling can be reversed and some cannot.

Third Grade

- Plan and conduct an investigation to provide evidence of the effects of balanced and unbalanced forces on the motion of an object (**Photo 10-8**).
- Make observations and/or measurements of an objects motion to provide evidence that a pattern can be used to produce future motion.
- Ask questions to determine cause-and-effect relationships of magnetic interactions between two objects not in contact with each other.
- Define a simple design problem that can be solved by applying scientific ideas about magnets.

PHOTO 10-8 Swings provide lessons in force.

© 2016 Cengage Learning®

Under each performance expectation in the NGSS are clarification statements that suggest possible projects. Boxes below the performance expectations describe the science and engineering practices, disciplinary core ideas, and crosscutting concepts.

10-3b Next Generation Instructional Plans

Following are lessons with a physical science focus fashioned to enable your students to think for themselves and to *do* science the way suggested by the new standards.

ACTIVITIES

FIRST-GRADE PHYSICAL SCIENCE

Question: What sound is louder?

Performance expectation 1-PS4-1: Plan and conduct investigations to provide evidence that vibrating materials can make sound and that sound can make materials vibrate.

Lesson objective: To differentiate accurately between loud and soft sounds.

Materials: Objects to drop on the desktop, some of which make a loud sound and some of which make a soft sound. Suggestions include pencils, paper clips, keys, coins, feathers, erasers, and the like.

Procedure

Engage: Ask children to tap their fingers lightly on a desktop. They must be very quiet to do this activity. Ask them to describe how loud or soft the sound is. Then ask them to put one ear directly on the desktop and tap their fingers the same way. Is this sound louder or softer than before?

Explore: Have children try several variations of this activity, including tapping their fingers harder and softer and using other materials such as pencils, paper clips, keys, coins, and so on.

Explain: Typical discussion questions center around children differentiating between loud and soft sounds, and the application of this activity to the wave nature of sound. Children should record their observations.

Elaborate: Move on to the exploration of pitch.

Expected conclusions: Children will accurately tell which of several sounds is the loudest.

Once you are reasonably sure that children can differentiate among various "loudnesses" of sound, they can do the following activity, which asks them to differentiate between high and low pitches.

FIRST-GRADE PHYSICAL SCIENCE

Question: Which pitch of sound is higher?

Performance expectation 1-PS4-1: Plan and conduct investigations to provide evidence that vibrating materials can make sound and that sound can make materials vibrate.

Objective: To demonstrate understanding of the difference between high and low pitches of sound.

Materials: Eight glass soda bottles, wooden stick. Guitar, ukulele, violin, harp, or another instrument that vibrates to make sound.

Procedure

Engage: Ask the children to provide example of vibrations that make sound.

Explore: Have the children explore the instruments displayed. Have them comment on the sounds. (high, low, loud, soft)

Elaborate: Provide eight identical empty glass soda bottles filled with water to different levels. Have the students tap each bottle with a wooden stick. Then have them arrange the bottles in order of ascending pitch.

Explain: Typical discussion questions center around students tapping any two bottles and telling which has the higher pitch and which the lower pitch. Why do you suppose this happens the way it does? (Note to teacher: It is the vibration of the water in the bottle—plus, to a lesser extent, the vibration of the glass itself—that produces the sounds; the more the water, the lower the pitch when you tap on the glass.)

Expected conclusions: Students will accurately tell which of several sounds has the highest pitch.

Follow-up: You can play a tune with the bottles by tapping the side of the bottles and arranging them in a line from lowest to highest pitch. Compare pitch with several different drums.

Advanced suggestion: As an interesting extension, try this. Blow across the tops of the bottles in flute-like style to see which bottle gives the highest pitch and which the lowest pitch. This is called a *discrepant event* because what actually happens is the opposite of what you think ought to happen.

SECOND-GRADE PHYSICAL SCIENCE

Question: What happens when we make mud?

Performance expectation 2-PS-1: Plan and conduct an investigation to describe and classify different kinds of materials by their observable properties (2-PS1-1).

Lesson objective: To describe what happens when water is added to different kinds of soil.

Material: Several different kinds of soil, plastic cups, stirrers.

Procedure

Engage: Read *Pigs in the Mud in the Middle of the Rud* by Lynn Plourde and John Schoenherr (1997). This is a story about animals that won't budge from the middle of the muddy road ("rud") during mud season in Maine.

Explore: In small groups, show children cups of several different kinds of dry soil. Ask children to describe what they observe: color, texture, materials in the soil, sizes of particles, and so on. Then select one of the cups of soil, and ask the students to predict what will happen if water is added. Have students take turns adding water and stirring the mixture until the water and soil are thoroughly mixed.

Explain: Ask children what they observe in the cup. Ask if they can remember the name for this material ("mud").

Elaborate: Next, provide several cups of different kinds of soil for each group of children. Also provide a cup of sand. Ask children to add water to each cup, one cup at a time, and stir gently after each addition of water. They should keep adding water until they get mud.

Explain: Ask the students to observe and describe what they observe. Ask children to do the same thing with the sand, describe what they observe, and record their observations.

Elaborate: Typical discussion questions might start with the following:

- "What does soil look like?"
- "How much water do you need to add before you get mud?"
- "Do you need to add the same amount of water to each kind of soil to get the same effect?"
- "Does the mud look like the soil? How are the mud and the soil alike? How are they different?"
- "Would the same thing happen with a different kind of soil? Let's try it and see."
- "What happens when you add water to the sand?"

- "Do you get the same results with the sand as you do when you add water to soil? Why do you suppose that happens?"

- "Do you think this is a physical change or a chemical change? Why?"

Expected conclusions: Children should tell the effects of adding water to different kinds of soil.

Follow-up: Students can use print and media resources to look for information on concrete and cement.

THIRD-GRADE PHYSICAL SCIENCE

Question: How do various materials affect tarnished pennies?

Performance expectation (science and engineering practice) 3-PS2-3: Ask questions that can be investigated based on patterns such as cause-and-effect relationships.

Lesson objective: To describe what happens when various materials are added to tarnished pennies.

Materials: A dozen or so pennies, some of which are bright and shiny and some of which are dull and corroded, transparent plastic cups, fingernail brush, soap, salt, vinegar, lemon juice, hot sauce, ketchup, and items suggested by the children for use the next day.

Procedure

Engage: Have the children examine a collection of tarnished pennies, and ask them to think of different ways they might be able to clean the pennies. Responses might include "washing them with soap," "washing them without soap," "brushing them," "soaking them," and so on.

Explain: Introduce some new ideas such as cleaning them with lemon juice, vinegar, or salt, and cleaning them with a mixture of vinegar and salt. You might also suggest trying to clean them with hot sauce, ketchup, and other spicy sauces. Have the children provide their opinions on which substances will work.

Explore: Provide the materials children would need to try these options. In small groups, or with individuals, have

the children try out each option. Provide a plastic tray to work on, and be sure children wash their hands well after they have done the activity. Children should record their observations.

Explain: Have the students report the results of their cleaning activity. Typical discussion questions might include the following:

- "What is meant by a clean penny?"

- "What method produced the cleanest penny?"

- "Would the penny get cleaner if you added more material to it?"

- "Would the penny get cleaner if you scrubbed harder? Faster?"

- "Do you think this is a physical change or a chemical change? Why?"

Note to teacher: It is imperative that children wear science lab goggles before they do this activity. Be sure children wash their hands after touching any of the liquids, especially the vinegar-and-salt mixture, which can burn hands.

Elaboration: Children will complete the investigation and produce data as evidence for their conclusions. They will use these data to describe the best way of cleaning tarnished pennies.

Digital Download

10-3c Conventional Physical Science Instruction

This part of the chapter begins with the physical science concepts that are conventionally considered to be basic to primary grade learning and presents an example of ways that the topic of air can be integrated with science concepts of movement and changes in matter, gravity, light, and color. The subject integrations and lessons are part of the webbing scheme depicted in Figure 2-10 in Chapter 2. Suggestions for the teaching sound are also included.

Physical Science Concepts. The following concepts are basic to understanding the physical sciences. Use this list to identify concepts you can use to develop a planning

web, such as those described in Chapter 2 and earlier in this chapter.

- Air takes up space.

- Air has weight.

- Air is all around us.

- Things vibrate when they make sounds (like a guitar string or a drum).

- Moving air pushes things.

- Air slows moving objects.

- Things near the earth fall to the ground unless something holds them up.

- Everything is made from material called matter.

- All matter takes up space.

- Matter can change into a solid, liquid, or gas.

- Matter can be classified according to observable characteristics.

- **Physical changes** and **chemical changes** are two basic ways of changing things.

- In a physical change, appearances change, but the substance remains the same (tearing paper, chopping wood).

- In a chemical change, the characteristics of the substance change so that a new substance is formed (burning, rusting).

- A mixture consists of two or more substances that retain their separate identities when mixed together.

- Temperature tells how hot or cold an object is.

- There are many types of energy—light, heat, sound, electricity, motion, magnetic.

- Magnets can be used to make some things move without being touched.

- Static electricity is produced when two different materials are rubbed together.

- A simple electric circuit has three parts: a source of electricity, a path for electricity to travel, and something that uses the electricity (a lightbulb or bell).

- Some materials allow electricity to pass through them.

- To see color, light is needed.

- The way to change how something is moving is to give it a push or a pull.

- Machines make it easier to move things.

- Things move in many ways, such as straight, zigzag, around and around, back and forth, and fast and slow.

10-3d Planning and Teaching a Project About Air

The learning experiences suggested in this part of the chapter follow the format described in Chapter 2 and used in the seed project (in the Life Science part of this chapter). Each lesson states a concept, an objective, materials, and suggestions for teaching the concept. Extensions, integrations, and possible evaluation procedures are indicated in the body of the lesson when appropriate and at the end of the project. The topic of air is explored with bubble and sound lessons.

Exploring Bubbles. Children love to play with bubbles. They love to create bubbles, chase bubbles, and pop bubbles. Why not take advantage of this interest to teach science concepts with a subject children already know something about?

ACTIVITIES

THE BUBBLE MACHINE

Concept: Bubbles have air inside them.

Objective: To construct a bubble machine by manipulating materials to produce bubbles.

Materials: Mix a bubble solution of half a cup) of liquid soap and 1 quart water. Punch holes about halfway down the side of enough paper cups for each child. A box of drinking straws will also be needed. Write each child's name over the hole.

Procedure: Assemble a bubble machine by inserting a straw through a hole in a paper cup and filling with detergent solution to just below the hole. Have the children observe the machine as you blow bubbles. Ask, **"What do you think is**

happening?" Have the children assemble bubble machines. Each child should insert a straw into the hole in the side of the paper cup and then pour some detergent solution into the cup just below the hole. Give children time to try bubble blowing and ask: **"What do your bubbles look like? Describe your bubbles. How many bubbles can you blow? What is inside of the bubble?"**

Extensions: Make bubble books with drawings that depict the bubble machine experiences. Encourage children to write about their pictures. Read the books to the class, and then put them in the library center for perusal.

INVENTING BUBBLE MACHINES

Concept: Many different shapes will create bubbles.

Objective: To make a shape that will create a bubble. Observe air entering bubbles and taking up space.

Materials: Mixed bubble solution; soft, bendable wire; pans for bubble solution.

Procedure: Say, **"Your bubble machine works well. Can you bend wire into shapes that will make bubbles?"** Have

children mess around with wire to create a variety of shapes for making bubbles (**Figure 10-11**). Have them test the shapes by blowing air into the bubble film or moving the wire shape through the air. Ask, **"Did you make a bubble? Was your bubble the same shape as the wire?"**

Naturalistic and informal activities: In the science center, have other materials available for making bubble machines, such as a pierced spatula, turkey baster, berry basket

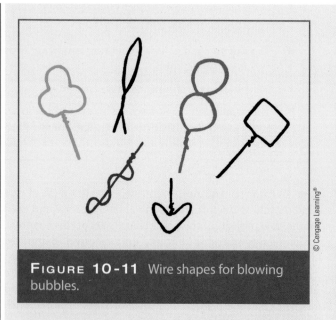

FIGURE 10-11 Wire shapes for blowing bubbles.

© Cengage Learning®

FIGURE 10-12 Kitchen shapes make interesting bubbles.

© Cengage Learning®

bottom, sieve, and other kitchen items (**Figure 10-12**). Ask, **"What shape do you think these bubbles will be? What do you notice about the size of the bubbles?"** (Different sizes.) Have children record predictions and results for the different bubble blowers.

TABLETOP BUBBLES

Concept: Air takes up space.

Objective: To use air to create bubble sculpture. Predict how the bubbles will act on top of tables.

Materials: Bubble solution, straws, cups, flat trays.

Procedure: Have children dip out a small amount of bubble solution on a tray and spread it around. Ask, **"What do you think will happen if you blow air into the bubble solution?"** [Bubbles will form.] Instruct children to dip a straw into the soap on the tray and blow gently. Give them time to "mess around" with tray-top bubble blowing. Present challenges. **"Can you blow a bubble the size of a bowl?"** Have several children work together to make a community bubble. One child begins blowing the bubble, and others join in by adding air to the inside of the bubble. (The straws must be wet to avoid breaking the bubble.) Bubble cities of the future can be made by adding more solution to the tray and blowing several bubble domes next to one another.

Extension: Bubbles inside of bubbles. Ask, **"Can you fit a bubble inside a bubble?"** Have children blow a bubble. Then insert a wet straw inside the bubble and start a new bubble. Ask, **"What happens if the sides touch?"** Make bubble chains. Have children blow a bubble with a straw. Then wiggle the straw and blow another one. Soon, a chain of bubbles will form. Ask, **"How many bubbles can you make?"**

Digital Download

Investigation Questions for Exploring Air and Bubbles

1. Will other liquids create bubbles?

2. Will adding a liquid called **glycerin** to the bubble solution make the bubbles stronger? [Yes.] Can you think of other things to add to the bubble solution to make the bubbles last longer? Test your formulas.

3. Are bubbles always round? [Yes, unless some of them stick together. Forces acting on the inside and outside of the soap film are the same all over it.]

10-3e Subject Integration

Bubbles and Science

1. *Observe bubbles.* Describe the color, movement, size, and shape. How many different colors do you see in the soap bubble? How do the colors move and change? Look at the bubbles through different colors of cellophane or polarized sunglasses. Do the bubbles change?

2. *Classify bubbles.* Classify by color, size, shape (bubble machine bubbles will stick together and take different shapes), location, and how the bubble was made.

3. *Changes in matter.* Ask children to describe some changes that they notice in bubbles. Ask, **"Did anything change?"** [Yes.] **"Did you see a physical change in the bubble solution?"** [Yes, matter changes form only in a physical change.]

Bubbles and Art

1. *Bubble painting.* Mix bubble solution with liquid poster paint. Put the mixture in a bowl. As the child blows into the paint with a straw, a paint bubble dome forms. Lay construction paper over the bubble. As the paint bubble bursts, it splatters paint on the paper.

2. *Bulletin board.* Make a background of large construction paper bubbles. Display children's writing and art activities in this way.

Bubbles and Math

1. *How high?* Measure the height of the bubbles on a tray top. Measure how long a bubble lasts, and predict and then measure how many bubbles can be blown and how far they can float. Graph the results.

2. *Lung capacity.* Make a graph of who has the largest lung capacity. Have children discover a way of determining lung capacity by blowing bubbles.

Bubbles and Language Arts

Science experiences can provide inspiration for important first steps in writing.

1. *Bubble books.* Provide paper for children to record their bubble explorations. These can be illustrated and bubble shaped.

2. *Books about bubbles.* Read storybooks about bubbles (see Appendix B).

3. *Chart story.* Have children write or dictate stories about what they observed when they examined air inside of bubbles (**Figure 10-13**).

Bubbles and Food Experiences

Children can observe the tiny air bubbles that go into various whipped mixtures. For example, whipped milk topping can be made for cookies. You will need ½ a cup of instant dry skim milk and ½ a cup of cold water.

Beat the dry milk and water with an electric mixer at high speed for 4 minutes. Have children watch the mixture change. Then, add 2 tablespoons of sugar and ½ a teaspoon of vanilla, and beat at high speed until the mixture stands in peaks. You may want to add the ingredient "air bubbles" to your recipe. Remind children that air went into what they are eating.

10-3f Concept: Air Can Move Things and Slow Things Down

The following suggestions extend science concepts.

1. *Moving bubbles.* Have children move bubbles in the direction they want them to go by fanning the bubbles with paper.

2. *Paper fans.* Make paper fans to move air. These can be accordion-pleated sheets of paper or small paper plates stapled to ice-cream-bar sticks.

3. *Glider designs.* Make gliders, and find out how far they can fly.

4. *Straw painting.* Blow paint with plastic straws. Pick up the paint with air pressure (as with the bubble solution), drop it on paper, and blow the puddles of paint into a design.

5. *Make pinwheels.* Have children fold squares of paper and then hold them in front of a fan or in the wind. Ask, **"What happens to the paper?"** [It moves.] Help children make pinwheels from typing paper or wallpaper. A pushpin will hold the pinwheel to a pencil eraser and allow it to turn freely. Ask, **"How did we produce motion?"**

6. *Air walk.* Take children on a walk to find things that are moved by air. Discuss and write about what you have seen. Local windmills are ideal, but weather socks, flags, trees, seeds, clothes on a clothesline, and other moving things work well.

7. *Exploring parachutes.* Have children make parachutes out of squares of cloth. Tie each corner with string, then thread the four strings through a wooden bead or washer. Drop the parachute from various heights, and predict what will happen. Cut a hole in the top of the parachute, and observe any

Matthew

To day we were sintest again it was a lot of fun. We were seeing if air took up space. Some people thoght that it did and some thoght it didn't. I blew a very very very very big bubble but it popped in my face. There were different colors and shapes. But they didn't taste good.

Figure 10-13 Matthew has made many observations about bubbles.

differences. Make parachutes out of different materials, such as plastic or cupcake liners, and compare their flight.

8. *Baby seeds.* Open milkweed pods in the wind and watch the wind disperse the seeds. Refer to the seed lessons in the Life Science section for further investigations.

9. *Air movers.* Have children experiment with different objects found in the room to see which is the most effective in moving bubbles.

10-3g Exploring Sound

Children love to make music, but they probably do not know anything about the nature of sound. Help them understand that sound is caused when something vibrates by using the following lessons to teach children to see, hear, and feel the sound vibrations around them (**Photo 10-9**). Then make musical instruments that reinforce the concepts.

PHOTO 10-9 The keyboard presents an opportunity to experiment with sound.

© 2016 Cengage Learning®

ACTIVITIES

GOOD VIBRATIONS

Concept: Sound is caused when something vibrates.

Objective: To observe objects vibrating and making sounds. Construct musical instruments based on the concepts of sound.

Materials: Paper plates, rubber bands, bottle tops, hole punch, paper cups, waxed paper, coffee cans, flexible tubing.

Procedure

1. *Vocal cords.* Have children begin vibration observations by gently resting their fingers over their vocal cords and saying "Ahhhh" and "Eeee." Ask, **"What do you feel?"** [Something moves.] Explain that they are feeling vibrations occurring in their vocal cords, where all sounds they make with their voices come from.

2. *Vibrations.* Then have the children place their fingertips against their lips while they simultaneously blow and hum. Reinforce the connection between vibration and sound by touring your classroom and asking children to identify things that vibrate: the aquarium pump, kitchen timer, air vent, and overhead lights. If possible, let them feel the vibrations in these objects and listen to the sounds each makes.

3. *Drum.* Make a simple drum out of a coffee can that has a plastic top. Place grains of rice on the can lid and tap lightly while your students watch and listen. Ask, **"What happens to the rice when you do this?"** [It bounces up and down to the sound of the drum.]

4. *Drumsticks.* Make drumsticks from tennis balls and dowels (**Figure 10-14**). Punch a hole in the ball, apply glue to the end and edges of the dowel or stick, and push it into the center of the ball. Or use a butter brush, wadded-up rubber bands, or a plastic lemon.

5. *Humming cup.* Make a humming cup by cutting the bottom out of a small paper cup. Then have the children cover the newly opened ends with waxed paper and secure with rubber bands. Say, **"Place your lips lightly against the waxed paper end of the cup and hum."** They will get another feel for sound. Paper towel tubes can be used in a similar way to make horns.

6. *More horns.* A yard of flexible tubing will provide an opportunity for children to whisper back and forth and feel sound traveling to their ears through

BOTTLES AND WATER

Collect eight bottles to make a scale—your job will be easier if they are all the same kind and size. To tune the bottles, you'll need to fill them to varying heights with water.

Start by dividing the volume of water that one of the bottles could accommodate by the number of notes you wish to produce. For example, if you want a one-octave scale, divide the volume by eight. Then, leaving bottle one empty, put $1/8$ of the volume into bottle two, $1/4$ into bottle three, $3/8$ into bottle four, and so on until bottle eight contains $7/8$ of its volume of water. Adjust the amount of water up and down in the bottles until the scale intervals sound (more or less) true. Use masking tape to mark the correct level on each bottle.

FIGURE 10-14 The formula for bottle music.

a talking tube. Then tape a funnel to one end and make a bugle-like horn.

7. *Tambourines.* You can construct this favorite instrument by decorating and shellacking paper plates in which you have already punched holes. Distribute bottle caps that also have holes punched in them, and have children tie two or three caps to each hole in their plates. This is a noisy but fun way to show the relationship between vibrations and sound.

Note to teacher: You should have children do the sound volume and sound pitches activities detailed above before you have them do more complex activities such as this one.

Naturalistic and informal activities: Put a variety of musical instruments in a sound center. Give the children time to explore the instruments and record their observations in their science journals.

Extensions: Build a band. Making musical instruments will give children an opportunity to observe vibrations in other ways. Make a variety of instruments and decorate them for a special occasion.

Digital Download

Wind Instruments. Wind instruments such as flutes, whistles, and panpipes depend on vibrating columns of air for their sound. The longer the column of air, the lower the *pitch*, the highness or lowness of a sound. The more vibrations per second, the higher the pitch that is produced; the fewer vibrations, the lower the pitch. The following lesson demonstrates the relationship between the length of an air column and musical pitch.

ACTIVITIES

THE PITCH OF SOUND

Concept: Pitch is the highness or lowness of a sound.

Objective: To recognize differences in sound. Construct wind instruments.

Materials: Ten bottles of the same height, water.

Procedure: Prepare by filling glass soda bottles to varying levels with water. (Plastic bottles are too easily knocked over.) Hold up an empty bottle, and ask: **"What do you think is in the bottle? What do you think will happen if the air in the bottle vibrates?"** Demonstrate by blowing across the top of the empty bottle. Teach children to direct air across the mouth of a bottle. This is worth taking the time to do. Instruct children to press the mouth of the bottle lightly against their lower lip and direct air straight across the mouth of the bottle. (They should not blow *into* the bottle; the secret is blowing straight across.) Give them time to "mess around" with their new skill. Then ask, **"What do you think will happen if you blow across a bottle with water in it?"** Pour water into bottles, and have children find out what will happen. Children will discover that the bottles make sounds that vary in pitch. They might even play a tune (Figure 10-14).

Naturalistic and informal activities: Invite musicians to the classroom to share their instruments and answer questions.

Extension: Emphasize the meaning of pitch by reading a familiar tale in which high- and low-pitched sounds figure. For example, ask children to imitate the three billy goats gruff. Dramatize differences in pitch with voice and body activities.

Digital Download

10-3h Properties of Matter

The *NGSS* suggests that young children need to understand that matter can be classified according to observable characteristics such as size, shape, color, weight, temperature, and the ability to react with other substances. Children's experience observing, manipulating, and classifying common objects provides the foundation for much of their later learning.

Children build concepts related to the properties of objects and materials by engaging in a variety of experiences requiring them to observe and describe the properties of objects, comparing objects for their observable similarities and differences, and sorting or grouping objects based on their similarities. The following activities provide early experiences with ordering and classifying according to observable characteristics using the senses.

1. *Shape and size.* For each child, make a "feely sock" that has two objects in it. One object should be the same in all socks, such as a Unifix Cube or other item that is familiar to the children. The second object should be distributed in pairs so that there are two socks that match. Ask, **"Describe the objects that are in your feely sock."** After each child has described the objects in the socks, invite the children to find the sock that matches their sock. When a child believes that he has the match, ask the children to pull out their objects out and to compare the objects to see whether their descriptions of the size, shape, and textures of their object provided accurate details.

2. *Smell.* Make "scent jars" from film canisters, pieces of sponge, and food flavorings such as cinnamon oil, peppermint, clove oil, and so on. For each scent, make three canisters. Label the canisters on the bottom with letters or colors so that the children can check to make sure they have found the correct matches to their scents. Distribute the canisters and ask the children to smell their canister and describe the scent and anything that smells like the scent.

Ask the children to find their matching canisters and discuss the descriptions that helped them find each other.

3. *Temperature.* Laminate six different colors of construction paper and lay them side by side to create a classification mat. Place cups of water of differing temperatures on the mats. Ask the children to use their sense of touch to order the cups from hottest to coolest. Children should place the hottest cup at one end and the coolest at the other end, and then try to figure out which ones go in between. When they have arranged the cups, ask them to check their work by using a thermometer or temperature probe. The activity will need to be completed quickly before the temperatures even out. Children can generate their own ways of comparing, and a table or graph can be produced.

4. *Weight.* Gather a large selection of balls, including some that are very similar in weight. The collection might include tennis balls, Styrofoam balls, Ping-Pong balls, marbles, ball bearings, softballs, golf balls, and so on. Use the colored mat system described in the Temperature section to provide students with a system for organizing the balls. Ask students to order the balls from heaviest to lightest. Once students have made their determinations, have them use a balance to see whether their predictions were correct. Children will have to work to determine the best way to use the balance. (Placing the heaviest object in one bucket on the balance and then testing all other objects to see if any are heavier works well.) Once the heaviest has been confirmed, children can continue with the next objects, comparing them all to each other until the order is established. This ordering activity can become a classification activity when objects are combined and weight is used to determine when sets of objects are to be grouped together.

ACTIVITIES

CHANGE

Concept: Chemical changes.

Objective: To explore chemical changes.

Materials: 3-ounce plastic cups, plastic bowls, 4- to 8-ounce bottles of glue (do not use washable glue), distilled water, borax.

Procedure

1. Mix equal parts of glue and distilled water into a large container.

2. In a second container, mix 1 liter of distilled water and 1 tablespoon of borax.

3. Divide the children into pairs, and have one member of each pair measure 2 ounces of the glue solution into a plastic cup.

4. Have the second child measure 2 ounces of the borax solution into a second cup.

5. Pour the solutions into the bowl and stir, being careful to keep it in the bowl.

6. Ask, "**What happened when you mixed the two solutions? Does the result look like either of the solutions before they were mixed? Is this a new substance?**"

Concept: Physical changes.

Objective: To explore physical changes.

Materials: Water, sand, bowls, paper.

Procedure

1. Have each child pour water and sand into small bowls.
2. Put the bowls in the sun.
3. Check the bowls before leaving school.
4. Ask: "**What happened to the sand and water? Has a new substance been formed? Is this a physical or chemical change?**"

Digital Download

10-3i Exploring Light

Children need many concrete experiences with light to provide the conceptual background necessary for later understanding. Help children understand the Next Generation Science Standard for light—light travels in a straight line until it strikes an object, and light can be reflected by a mirror, refracted by a lens, or absorbed by objects—with the following learning experiences.

Light Beam Tag. To encourage children to discover that light travels in a straight line, play light beam tag with mirror tiles that are at least 5×5 inches (rough edges should be covered with duct tape). Focus the beam on one student's mirror. The student must use the mirror to reflect the beam to another student's mirror. The light intensity should be enough to reflect to two or three children at one time. When two or three children are successfully reflecting each other's beams, clap the chalkboard eraser in the areas where the light is traveling. The class will be able to observe the light beams traveling in straight lines between the mirrors. This activity could also be used to reinforce the concept that a mirror can reflect light.

Instructional Technology: The Light Sensor. Young children come up with numerous questions regarding light when they are introduced to instructional technology that measures light levels. The following scenario demonstrates how a light sensor can be introduced to young children.

Early in the year, Mr. Wang had introduced his students to a sensor and probeware package that consists of software; probes and sensors that measure temperature, light, sound, motion, and other variables; and the hardware that interfaces the computer and the probes and sensors. The focus of *the probe* is to teach young children simple data collection and graphing in a developmentally appropriate manner. For instance, the first activity with the light probe involves pointing the sensor toward a bright light. The computer screen turns completely white. When the probe is covered, thus allowing no light, the computer screen turns completely black. When pointed toward varying levels of light, the computer screen turns shades of gray. Mr. Wang asked, "What do you think the sensor was sensing?" After several suggestions and trials, the children quickly realized that the amount of light striking the sensor made the changes.

Mr. Wang showed the children other ways in which the amount of light could be detected and used other features of the probe that recorded the highest and lowest reading, like an ECG. There were many opportunities to take measurements, to ask questions, and to generate interest in the "snapshots" of light levels that can be displayed in a simple table. In this way, the children could compare two or more light levels by comparing the numbers.

The children decided to use the technology to help them solve a problem. The children had been working on constructing a classroom planetarium out of cardboard boxes and glowing star stickers. They needed a curtain that would cover the entrance and block out all light during their "star shows" but that would be easy to move aside to allow light to enter and be absorbed by the glowing stickers (so they would glow brightly during the star shows). Several children brought in materials from home to use for the curtain, including old sheets, blankets, and an old tarp. The children cut the cloth into equal pieces to determine which would block the most light. One piece of cloth was a light color and a medium weave; another was a gray color and a tight weave. The last one was black and of a loose weave. Most of the children predicted that the black cloth would block the most light. Mr. Wang asked, "How could you use the light sensor to help you solve this problem?" Some of the children decided to find out by putting the cloth over a flashlight and then holding the sensor up to it. Another group decided to cover the light sensor with the cloth and hold it up to the light. Mr. Wang allowed the groups of children to try their investigations. When they were finished, several tables of data were produced.

The children were amazed that the gray cloth blocked out the most light. Mr. Wang asked, "Why do you think the gray cloth worked the best?" Liu Pei said maybe it had something to do with the color. Maybe all gray cloths worked better than white or black. Derrick thought it had to do with how close together the threads were. He held up each piece of cloth and looked through it, pointing out how much more space was between the threads on the white and black cloths. The other children also observed this and started gathering their materials and setting up additional investigations. Liu Pei wanted to test some cloths that were the same except for their color to see if the gray really worked best. Derrick thought it would be a great idea to do the same thing with some pieces of cloth that were the same color but had different amounts of space between the threads.

Charlesworth

PHOTO 10-10   The Internet is an excellent resource for report information.

Mr. Wang was pleased that the children wanted to do investigations regarding light. He knew that the children would carry out many more investigations throughout the year about concepts regarding how different colors absorb and reflect light (**Photo 10-10**). Perhaps the children would want to set up investigations testing the reflective qualities of sheets of construction paper or the amount of light allowed to pass through pieces of colored transparencies. The probes were going to be a great tool for facilitating inquiry in his classroom.

10-3j Assessment Strategies

The NGSS standards provide performance expectations that can be adapted to evaluation criteria. Evidence is a critical need for NGSS, so making models, drawing, diagrams, and creating tables and charts are important assessment tools. Because many primary children are beginning readers, simple performance assessments designed around process skills and anecdotal records can be used to determine understanding. When recording children's oral explanations of what is happening, it is better to place the emphasis on the child's ability to communicate ideas and not on the use of terminology. When children are completing a task, write down snippets of informal conversation relating to the task.

SUMMARY

10-1 Standards and Guidelines for Primary Grade Science

The standards for primary grade science are based on the NGSS and the Framework for K–12 Science. Primary grade students are entering Piaget's concrete operations stage and thus can understand more complex concepts. They must begin to learn eight practices that are basic to science,

Translating the NGSS for Classroom Instruction. Translating the NGSS for classroom instruction is a major concern for teachers. The highlights of Roger Bybee's suggested plan are described.

Conventional Science Instruction. Primary grade students are naturally dawn to collecting. They observe, sort, and compare collections and thus begin their science experiences,

Practices and Design. Scientists answer question and engineers solve problems. Both use similar practices as they investigate to find answers to questions or devise designs to solve a problem. In the past, inquiry was the major science practice; today it is still an important approach, but other practices are also important.

Managing the Classroom. Having a plan for organizing the students, materials, and classroom is essential. Suggestions are made for accomplishing these tasks. Students should be clear about when they are assigned to groups and when they have choices.

Sample Investigations. Several examples of conventional investigations are described. A list of potential primary grade topics is included.

10-2 Life Science Conventional Instruction and Life Science for the Next Generation

Teaching life science concepts on a firsthand basis is essential to planning and teaching science to primary-age children. Children display an eagerness to learn about the living things around them and have many questions that can be investigated. NGSS (NRC, 2013) includes specific performance expectations for each of the primary grades.

Next Generation Life Science Instructional Plans. Lessons fashioned to meet the NGSS standards are developed so as to give students maximum opportunity to explore for themselves and to think their way through the open-ended science activities. In this way, children are learning how to *do* science the way scientists and engineers do their work.

Conventional Life Science Instruction. This section provides activities about seeds, plants, and molds; it also contains suggestions for caring for and studying living things (both indoors and outdoors) and keeping animals in the classroom.

Animal observations capitalize on the interest of children. The benefits of these observations far outweigh any cautions. A trip to the zoo can be a meaningful experience if specific plans are made for the visit. Prepare activities to do before, during, and after the trip. An early morning nature walk can also be used to look for local wildlife. Children are also curious about what is inside their bodies.

10-3 Physical Science for the Next Generation

The Next Generation Physical Science Standards are based on the K–12 Framework. The performances are hands on and fun. Performance expectations are clearly defined and ideas for children's activities are suggested.

Next Generation Instructional Plans. Physical science lessons constructed with the NGSS in mind enable students to explore in their own directions and come up with their own observations and conclusions.

Conventional Physical Science Instruction. Conventional instruction involves the children in exploration. Areas suggested for explored in this text are air, sound, properties of matter, and light. When children explore physical science concepts, they are learning basic skills that develop future understandings. To be effective, these lessons must emphasize process skills, concrete experiences, and integrations. Thus, students see a relationship between the concepts and their world.

FURTHER READING AND RESOURCES

Ansberry, K., & Morgan, E. (2007). *More picture perfect science lessons: Using children's books to guide inquiry.* Arlington, VA: NSTA Press.

Early childhood life science. (2013). [Focus Issue]. *Science and Children, 50*(6).

Instructor. (2014, Spring). Articles focusing on NGSS.

Keeley, P. (2013). *Uncovering student ideas in primary science.* Arlington, VA: NSTA Press.

Keeley, P., & Harrington, R. (2014). *Uncovering student ideas in physical science*, vol. 2. Arlington, VA: NSTA Press.

Konicek-Moran, R. (2011). Series *Yet more everyday science mysteries* (2010); *Even more everyday science mysteries* (2009); *More everyday science mysteries* (2008); *Everyday science mysteries.* Arlington, VA: NSTA Press.

Krajcik, J. (2013). The next generation science standards: A focus on physical science. *Science and Children, 50*(7), 7–15.

Ohana, C. (2007). Creative integration [Theme issue]. *Science and Children, 44*(6), 6.

Sound [focus issue]. (2014). *Science and Children, 51*(6).

Willard, T. (2013). A look at the Next Generation Science Standards. *Science and Children, 50*(7), 16–17.

REFERENCES

Adler, David A. (2013). *Danny's doodles.* Naperville, IL: Sourcebooks, Inc.

Berger, M. (1992). *Look out for turtles!* New York: Harper Collins.

Bybee, R. W. (2013). *Translating the NGSS for classroom instruction.* Arlington, VA: National Science Teachers Association.

Campbell, R. (1982). *Dear zoo.* New York: Little Simon.

Cowcher, H. (1991). *Tigress.* New York: Farrar, Straus, & Giroux.

dePaola, T. (1984). *The popcorn book.* New York: Holiday House.

Ehlert, L. (1987). *Growing vegetable soup.* San Diego, CA: Harcourt, Brace, Jovanovich.

Gibbons, G. (1991). *The puffins are back.* New York: Harper Collins.

Krauss, R. (1945). *The carrot seed.* New York: Harper & Row.

Mazer, A. (1991). *The salamander house.* New York: Knopf.

Mayes, R., & Koballa, T. R. (2012). Exploring the science framework. *Science and Children, 50*(12), 8–15.

Mitgutsch, A. (1971). *From seed to pear.* Minneapolis, MN: Carolrhoda Books.

National Research Council. (2012). *A Framework for K–12 Science Education.* Washington, D.C.: National Academies Press.

National Research Council. (2013). *Next Generation Science Standards.* Washington, D.C.: National Academies Press.

Pallotta, J. (1989). *The yucky reptile alphabet book.* Watertown, MA : Charlesbridge.

Parker, N. W., & Wright, J. R. (1990). *Frogs, toads, and lizards.* New York: Greenwillow.

Plourde, L., & Schoenherr, J. (1997). *Pigs in the mud in the middle of the rud.* New York: Scholastic.

Spencer, H. (1862). *Education: Intellectual, moral, and physical.* New York: D. Appleton.

Stevens, J. (1995). *Tops and bottoms.* New York: Scholastic.

EARTH AND SPACE SCIENCES,
ENVIRONMENTAL AWARENESS, ENGINEERING, TECHNOLOGY, AND SCIENCE APPLICATIONS

OBJECTIVES

After reading this chapter, you should be able to:

11-1 Plan, teach, and evaluate primary grade Earth and space science lessons and projects in line with national standards.

11-2 Plan, teach, and evaluate primary grade environmental awareness lessons and projects in line with national standards.

11-3 Plan, teach, and evaluate primary grade engineering, technology, and science application lessons and projects in line with national standards.

PRACTICES AND STANDARDS ADDRESSED IN THIS CHAPTER

naeyc

NAEYC Professional Preparation Standards

5. Build meaningful curriculum.

5a. Understanding content and resources in mathematics and science.

5c. Design, implement, and evaluate developmentally meaningful and challenging curriculum.

DAP Guidelines

2c. Teachers know what the desired goals for the program are.

3c. Teachers use the curriculum framework in their planning.

Next Generation Science Standards

1-ESS1-2 Make firsthand observations to collect data.

1-ESS1-1 Use firsthand observations to describe patterns in the natural world.

K-ESS-3 Communicate solutions that will reduce the impact of humans on the land, water, air, and/or other living things in the local environment.

NGSS

11-1 STANDARDS AND GUIDELINES FOR EARTH AND SPACE SCIENCES

Earth and space sciences (ESS) include the study of processes on Earth as well as Earth's relationship to the solar system and the galaxy (NRC, 2012). Earth and space science is closely related to the physical sciences (e.g., forces, gravity, energy, magnetism), which have helped in learning about the size, age, structure, composition, and behavior of the Earth, sun, and moon. Life science is also rooted in Earth science because Earth is the only biologically active planet that we know of. Earth science is interdisciplinary in that it includes astrophysics, geophysics, geochemistry, and geobiology. However, traditional geology is the cornerstone of ESS.

The systems (atmosphere, hydrosphere, geosphere, and biosphere) that make up the Earth are closely connected. Changes in one part of the system affect the other parts. Earth is just one part of the solar system, which is itself only a small part of the galaxy.

There are three core ideas in the Earth and space sciences:

- Earth's place in the universe
- Earth's systems
- Earth and human activity

The field of Earth and space science has become much more important as astronomy and space exploration have advanced our knowledge of the universe and research has increased our understanding of the Earth's structure and surface. Today human society is much more affected by ESS than in the past. The increasing population and growth of cities makes the effects of natural hazards such as hurricanes, storms, and droughts much greater in their impact. Further the increasing population has stretched our natural resources of water, arable land, plants, animals, minerals, and hydrocarbons. Thus ESS now has a much greater science emphasis than in earlier times.

According to NGSS (NRC, 2013, pp. 9, 15, 24) primary grade children should be able to formulate answers to questions that might begin an ESS lesson, these:

1. First Graders: "What objects are in the sky, and how do they seem to move?"

2. Second Graders: "How does land change, and what are some things that cause it to change?" "What are the different kinds of land and bodies of water?"

3. Third graders: "What is typical weather in different parts of the world and during different times of the year?" "How can the impact of weather-related hazards be reduced?"

11-1a NGSS ESS Performance Expectations

Students who demonstrate understanding can:

- Use observations of the sun, moon, and stars to describe patterns that can be predicted.

- Make observations at different times of the year to relate the amount of daylight to the time of year.

- Use information from several sources to provided evidence that Earth events can occur quickly or slowly.

- Compare multiple solutions designed to slow or prevent wind or water from changing the shape of the land.

- Develop a model to represent the shapes and kinds of land and bodies of water in an area.

- Obtain information to identify where water is found on Earth and that it can be solid or liquid.

- Represent data in tables and graphical displays to describe typical weather conditions expected during a particular season.

- Obtain and combine information to describe climates in different regions of the world.

- Make a claim about the merit of a design solution that reduces the impacts of a weather-related hazard.

Under each performance expectation are clarification statements that suggest possible projects. Boxes below the performance expectations describe the science and engineering practices, disciplinary core ideas, and crosscutting concepts.

NGSS

11-1b The Constructivist Approach to the Next Generation Science Standards in Primary Earth and Space Science

As was emphasized in Chapter 10, the Next Generation Science Standards call for teaching less material but teaching it better, and teaching it such that students are called upon to *think*. Below are lesson guides in the field of Earth and space science that will enable you to teach science in the constructivist manner, which means that you will spend more time helping children validate or revise their own thinking than you spend imparting factual information.

ACTIVITIES

FIRST-GRADE EARTH SCIENCE

Question: What's in the soil?

Objective: To describe the composition of a soil sample and develop a soil classification system.

Materials: Several different kinds of soil samples, paper plates, magnifying glasses, plastic spoons.

Procedure

Engage: Obtain a bag of soil from your home or the schoolyard. Put a spoonful of the soil on a paper plate for each child or group of children. Ask the students to look carefully at their soil sample. Ask the students to tell what they think might be in the soil.

Explore: Provide magnifying glasses. Ask the children to examine the soil carefully and tell the different kinds of things they find in the soil. They can write or draw what they find, or they can communicate their findings in a different way that they themselves come up with.

Explain: Have the students tell what they found in the soil.

Elaborate: Children can bring soil from where they live, and the class can examine the soils from different places to see what is similar and what is different. You might also want to include some potting soil to show the similarities and differences. Ask children to group the soils according to some characteristic they identify.

Explain: The children can then share their category groupings with the class as a whole. The groups can chart the category characteristics observed.

Performance Expectations: Children will construct charts and/or histograms that depict the characteristics of the soil samples examined.

FIRST- OR SECOND-GRADE EARTH SCIENCE

Question: Where does soil come from?

Objective: To infer the origin of given samples of soil.

Material: One or more samples of different kinds of soil, paper plates, magnifying glasses, plastic spoons.

Procedure

Engage: Tell the children they are going to be detectives. Children put a spoonful of the soil on the plate.

Explore: Have the children examine their soil sample carefully with and without the magnifying glass to try to identify the different kinds of things that are in the soil.

Explain: Ask children to describe what they see in the soil, and ask them to infer where these things came from and also to cite their reasons for inferring what they did. Finally, ask them to deduce where the soil sample itself may have come from, based on what they found in it. Give additional samples to students who finish early.

Elaborate: Have children compile their ideas about the origin of the soil samples, discuss their agreements and disagreements, and reach agreement on the most likely sample contents.

Performance Expectations: Students will develop a chart showing the results of their investigation.

SECOND-GRADE EARTH SCIENCE

Question: How do the inhabitants of the ant farm go about their daily activities?

One of the more fascinating living laboratories is the ant farm. Constructed properly, an ant farm provides an ideal exhibit of insect behavior. The easiest way to set up an ant farm is to buy a ready-made kit; they are available at pet stores and toy stores, and come with a coupon that you send to the supplier, who then sends you a supply of live ants to put in your ant farm. You can construct your own ant farm as follows: Obtain a transparent, wide-mouth plastic container and a smaller plastic cup or jar that fits inside the container so that there is about a half inch between the large container and the smaller container all the way around. Fill the space between the two containers with damp sand, and tamp it into the space.

Objective: To infer the role ants play in cultivating soil.

Materials: Ant farm (see above), ants.

Procedure

Engage: Have the children pass the ant farm around. Have them suggest what living thing might like living in it.

Explore: Have students collect a few ants from the schoolyard and put them on top of the sand or soil in the ant farm. Then sit back and watch the ants work. The tunneling activity should start in a few days. Students should provide food for the ants on the top of the sand; food can consist of anything they might have at a picnic—bread crumbs, tiny pieces of lettuce, cookie crumbs, and so on. They must be careful, however, not to overfeed or overwater the ants; a tiny bit of food and a tiny bit of water once a week should be fine.

Elaborate: Have students write or draw what they see over a period of time, say a week or two. It might be interesting to some students to make a separate drawing every day to show what the ants do over time. Students may also want to take pictures and mount them, to show they understand what is happening. Compile an Ant Book.

Explain: Finally, ask the main question: **"How do ants help cultivate soil?"**

Performance Expectation: Students will share their Ant Books and compare observations.

FIRST-GRADE SPACE SCIENCE

Question: How big is the sun? This activity shows a size comparison between the Earth and the sun. The Earth is approximately 8,000 miles in diameter, and the sun is approximately 865,000 miles in diameter. Thus, the diameter of the sun is about 108 times the diameter of the Earth. This means that 108 "Earths" could fit across the surface of the sun if it were flat.

Objective: To demonstrate their understanding of the size of the sun compared with the size of the Earth.

Materials: Yellow poster board, meter stick or yardstick, ¼-inch adhesive circles (obtainable from office supply stores).

Procedure

Engage: Cut a circular "sun" 2 feet 3 inches in diameter, and laminate it if possible. This is a cross-sectional model of our sun. Tell the children, **"This yellow circle is a model of our sun and we are going to compare the size of the Earth and the sun."** Draw a straight line through the center of the "sun." Ask the class, **"What do we call this line?"**

Explore: The ¼-inch circular dots represent a cross section of the Earth. Ask the students to estimate how many dots will equal the size of the sun. Have children stick the dots on the straight line (diameter) that goes across the center of the sun. How many "Earths" will fit across our sun? (108)

Explain: Next, have children put a sticker on one outside edge of the sun and describe the differences in size between the sun and the Earth.

Elaborate: Take the paper sun with the Earth dots and walk away from the class as far as you can get. What happens to the Earth as you walk away? Finally, ask children to tell what the Earth would be like if it were closer to the sun; if it were farther from the sun.

Another Question: "Where is the sun at night?" Have the children individually or in groups of two to four make models of the sun and the Earth. Have the students look on the Internet for sites that show the relationship between Earth and sun.

Practices: Use observations (firsthand or from media) to describe patterns in the natural world in order to answer scientific questions.

Performance Expectations: Students will make models using information from the Internet.

SECOND-GRADE SPACE SCIENCE

Question: What is the order of the planets' distances from the sun?

Objective: To make a living model of the solar system.

Material: (Children should bring these materials from home)—winter jacket, gloves, cap, scarf, dark sun glasses, light sun glasses, hand-held fan, 4" × 6" cards with string to serve as necklace and with the name of a planet written on each, large paper "sun."

Procedure

Engage: Have the children discuss why they have been asked to bring a variety of outerwear and sunglasses. Have eight children dress as follows:

1. Dark sunglasses, fan, sun visor
2. Dark sunglasses, fan
3. Dark sunglasses
4. Light sunglasses
5. Jacket
6. Jacket and gloves
7. Jacket, gloves, and cap
8. Jacket, gloves, cap, and scarf

Explore: First, scatter the children so they are in no particular order. Then have them line up and move around a large paper "sun" in accordance with the costumes they are wearing.

Explain: Ask discussion questions such as, "How does your distance from the 'sun' affect how hot or cold you are?" "How big does the sun look from different positions?" "If you represented planets, which would be the coldest? The hottest?" "Which planet would you like to live on? Why?"

Elaborate: Have the students go to the Universe Today website and read the article "How far are the planets from the sun" by Elizabeth Howell, published on April 21, 2014. Have the children line up in order of distance from the sun.

Pass out name tags for the planets for the children to wear as they move around the sun.

Explain: Have the children dress in order of decreasing temperature. How will they know which planets are hottest and which are the coolest?

Evaluate: Draw or with clay make models of the planets, and place them in order from the sun.

Practices: Use observations (firsthand or from media) to describe patterns in the natural world in order to answer scientific questions.

THIRD-GRADE MODEL OF THE SOLAR SYSTEM

Performance Expectations: Students will make models of the planets.

Objective: To prepare a reasonably accurate living model of the solar system.

Material: Adding machine tape, large circular "sun," placards with the names of the planets written on them, paper cutouts of each planet.

Procedure

Engage: If the students have done the previous activity, then they will understand this activity. From what we have done so far think about how far each planet in our solar system is from the sun.

Explain: In the illustrations you've seen online and in books our solar system often is portrayed as eight planets clustered closely together around the sun. Is this an accurate picture? (class discusses) In actuality, in a model that is scaled accurately, if the Earth were about 13 inches from the sun, Neptune, the most distant planet in our solar system, would be over 34 feet from the sun. Of course, it is impossible to use this scale accurately in books.

Explore: This activity will need to be done in the hallway or lobby or gym of the school. Relative distances of all the planets from the sun are shown in the following chart. To portray this in a dramatic fashion, line people up in the hallway at the planet distances. Select eight students, and

give each a paper cutout representing a planet; give a ninth student a paper sun. As you measure out the planetary distances, the nine students hold up their planets and the sun so everyone can get a picture of the model. Using a yardstick, line the students up as indicated in the chart.

Planet	Approximate Relative Distance from the Sun
Mercury	5¾ in.
Venus	10 in.
Earth	13 in.
Mars	1 ft. 9 in.
Jupiter	5 ft. 11 in.
Saturn	14 ft.
Uranus	19 ft. 4 in.
Neptune	34 ft. 1 in.

Explain: Discuss the following question: What are the primary characteristics of our solar system?

Elaborate: Children can go online to look at websites such as those created by NASA.

Practices: Use observations (firsthand or from media) to describe patterns in the natural world in order to answer scientific questions.

Digital Download

DAP naeyc

11-1c Conventional Earth and Space Science Instruction

The emphasis of Earth and space science is its observational nature. In primary grades, children learn about Earth and space by making observations as they explore, collect, describe, and record information. Children investigate and gain an understanding of the properties of Earth materials such as water, soil, rocks, and minerals.

A major role of the teacher in primary Earth and space science lessons is to guide children in observing natural changes of all kinds. These include cyclical changes, such as the movement of the sun and moon, and variable changes such as the weather (**Photo 11-1**).

Most children in the primary years are able to order and group objects by a single characteristic and to communicate

PHOTO 11-1 Materials for study of plants in each season.

Charlesworth

PHOTO 11-2 Painting the hemispheres.

PHOTO 11-3 Finished Western Hemisphere.

and make comparisons about their observations (**Photos 11-2** and **11-3**).

This section begins with lessons about various Earth materials that we use in different ways. For example, soil, rocks, and other Earth materials are used for building, fuels, and growing plants. Suggestions for introducing children to Earth materials, space, and weather are included. Lessons about rocks that can be developed into a project and integrated into the classroom are suggested.

Earth and Space Science and the Environment

- Earth's materials include rocks, soils, fossil fuels, water, and the gases in Earth's atmosphere.

- Materials that make up the Earth's crust are nonliving.

- Earth's materials have properties that make them useful to us in different ways.

- Soils have properties of color and texture.

- Soils have the capacity to retain water and help plants survive.

- Rocks are formed in different ways.

- Rocks are nonliving things.

- Sand is made up of tiny pieces of rock.

- Water and wind change the surface of the Earth.

- Mountains and land are made of rocks and soil.

- **Evaporation** means a liquid changes into a gas (vapor) in the air.

- **Condensation** means a gas changes to a liquid. Dew is an example of condensation.

- The **atmosphere** is the air around us. It has conditions such as wind, moisture, and temperature. **Weather** is what we call the conditions of the atmosphere.

- There are four seasons, and each has a unique climate.

- Temperature is how hot or cold something is.

- Clouds and fog are made of droplets of water.

- Water is a liquid and is called ice when it is solid.

- The sun gives off light and heat and warms the land, air, and water.

- A light source at a great distance looks small.

- The sun, moon, stars, and clouds have properties, locations, and movements that can be observed and described.

- The sun, moon, and stars all appear to move slowly across the sky. The moon appears to change in size and shape. Sometimes the moon can be seen at night, and sometimes it can be seen during the day.

- There are many stars in the sky. They do not look the same in brightness and color and are not scattered evenly.

- The patterns of stars stay the same and appear to move across the sky.

- The quality of air, water, and soil is affected by human activity.

11-1d Planning and Teaching a Unit on Rocks

Children need a variety of concrete experiences that enable them to learn the properties of Earth materials. For example, as children begin to observe rocks, they will see that some are made up of a single substance but that most are made up of several substances (minerals). The assessment of children's skills and understanding of concepts takes place as children group a variety of rocks according to one of their properties, such as color, pattern, buoyancy, or layering.

The learning experiences suggested in this section follow the format described in Chapter 2 and used in Chapter 10. Each activity states a concept, an objective, materials, and suggestions for teaching the concepts. Extensions, integrations, and possible evaluation procedures are indicated in the body of the plan, when appropriate, and at the end of the section.

The following basic geology lessons introduce fundamental concepts and stimulate children's curiosity about rocks, minerals, and Earth processes. The strategies will acquaint primary-age children with the nature of rocks in a way that is immediate, exciting, and fun.

DAP **naeyc**

ACTIVITIES

A CARTON OF ROCKS

Naturalistic activity: In the science center, have a variety of rocks, magnifiers, and books about rocks available for the children to explore and make observations. The books can be used to identify rocks.

Informal activity: When the children begin to examine the rocks, ask: **"What color, shape, size rocks do you have? Are any of the rocks the same? How are the rocks alike? How are they different?"**

Adult-guided activity:

Concept: There are many kinds of rocks.

Objectives: To observe different types of rocks and classify rocks in different ways.

Materials: An egg carton for each child or group, small labels that can be glued on the box, pencils or pens, a handful of rocks.

Procedure: Show the children the rocks in your hand. Ask the children, **"What are these, and where are they found?"**

Give each small group of children a few rocks, and encourage them to develop classification schemes for them, such as flat, speckled, or animal shaped. Younger children will notice size and color first, then shape and the way the rock feels. Have the children develop labels for the categories.

Take the children to any place where there are rocks. Set a generous time limit, and have them search for different types of rocks to fill their egg cartons. Then have the children share and classify what they have found. Use labels to identify rocks in the egg carton collections (speckled, round, etc.).

Extension:

1. Older children are able to compare rock characteristics with pictures in rock identification handbooks.

2. Use various rocks to create a rock collage.

3. Read *Sylvester and the Magic Pebble* by William Steig (1973). A round red pebble makes a nice prop.

THINKING LIKE A GEOLOGIST

Concept: Some rocks are harder than other rocks.

Objective: To examine rocks and minerals in order to determine how hard they are. Classify rocks by characteristics.

Materials: An assortment of rocks (a rock and mineral set, if possible), roofing nails, pennies.

Procedure: Give groups of children an assortment of rocks to observe. After they have had time to observe the rocks, ask, **"Can you scratch any of the rocks with your fingernail?"** As they notice a difference in rocks, ask: **"Can some rocks be scratched in this way?"** [Yes.] **"What else could you use to scratch rocks?"**

After children try to scratch rocks with different objects, such as the penny and fingernail, explain that finding out whether a rock crumbles easily is one of the things a **geologist** does. (Even though children may not remember the term, the labeling is important.)

Tell the children that they are going to think like a geologist and determine how hard a rock is. Make a list of ways that the children will test the rocks. For example, they can see whether the rock:

- Rubbed off on fingers.
- Can be scratched with a fingernail.

- Can be scratched with a penny.
- Is hard to scratch.

Have the children test the rocks and place them with the statement that best describes the rock. Ask, **"Which rocks do you think are the hardest?"** [Those that are hard to scratch.] (See **Figure 11-1**.)

FIGURE 11-1 Labeling rocks by hardness.

© Cengage Learning®

Then, take the children outside to see which rocks can be used to draw streaks or lines on the sidewalk. Children might even see distinctive colors. Ask, **"What colors are the streaks?"** Have children compare the colors in the rocks with the colors of the streaks. Ask, **"Can we classify rocks in this way?"** [Yes.] You may want to review some of the ways that geologists classify rocks (appearance, texture, hardness, color). Graph the findings.

Extension: As children wash their hands, compare wet and dry rocks. What differences do they notice? Geologists use hardness and streak tests to identify minerals. Introduce the term **minerals** when children notice bits of color in the rocks. Explain that rocks are made up of many different ingredients (i.e., minerals).

Digital Download

11-1e How Rocks Are Formed

Primary students commonly believe that the ground is composed mostly of soil and that rocks are only what they can hold and carry in their hands. Through pictures and discussion of mountains, cliffs, and deserts, help students understand the great variety, size, and distribution of rocks on and in the Earth. Most of the Earth's crust is solid rock, a nonliving material made of different kinds of minerals. The forces that make the major types of rock are too complex for lower-level primary grades to understand. However, you may want to introduce upper-level children to a few examples that simulate the basic ways that rocks are formed.

You can make the study of rocks more meaningful for your students if you know the basic way rocks are formed and a few common examples of each (**Photo 11-4**).

Igneous Rocks. **Igneous rocks** are formed through the cooling of magma or lava. Examples of igneous rocks formed by the rapid cooling of surface lava are pumice, obsidian, and basalt. Granite is the most common example of slow, below-surface cooling of molten rock. Refer to the igneous rock fudge-cooking experience (Subject Integrations, later in this section).

Sedimentary Rocks. These rocks are formed from eroded rocks, sand, clay, silt, pebbles, and other stones. Compressed skeletons, shells, and dissolved chemicals also form **sedimentary rocks**, which are usually deposited in layers, compacted and cemented by the pressure of the overlying sediments. Examples of sedimentary rocks are conglomerate, sandstone, shale, and limestone. **Fossils** are frequently found in sedimentary rock.

Metamorphic Rocks. The term *metamorphic* means "changed in form." **Metamorphic rocks** are formed when sedimentary and igneous rocks are completely changed in form through pressure and heat. For example, limestone becomes marble, shale becomes slate, and sandstone may become quartzite. These rocks tend to be harder than other rocks.

11-1f Subject Integrations

The following are examples of integrating rocks and science with other curriculum areas such as art, language arts, math, cooking, and social studies.

Rocks and Science

1. *Smooth rocks.* Additional ideas about rocks and their formation can be introduced by walking along a beach or stream and observing the smooth stones at the bottom of the stream or on the shore. Children can collect rocks and begin to draw comparisons about what makes the rocks smooth. Have them watch the action of the waves or stream. Ask, "What is happening?" Compare using sandpaper with the action of sand against the rocks.

2. *Sand from rocks.* Many children may not make the connection between rocks and sand as broken pieces of rock (sand also contains bits of broken and worn-down sea shells). Have students use hand lenses to examine and compare grains of sand and rocks. Have children rub two rocks together to simulate wear on them. Discuss how this wear might take place in nature (water current, waterfalls, wind, etc.).

Rocks and Art

1. *Rock gardens.* Construct small rock gardens. Use pictures of Japanese gardens as inspiration.

2. *Rock necklaces.* Glue yarn to the back of flat, round rocks to make necklaces.

3. *Vegetable fossils.* Make mold "fossils" of vegetables.

PHOTO 11-4 Materials for study of rocks and minerals.

Charlesworth

Rocks and Language Arts and Reading

1. *Storybooks.* Read *Stone Soup* (Paterson, 1981) and make vegetable soup. See Chapter 7 for suggestions.

2. *My rock.* Have each child select a rock and describe it. The children can record or dictate descriptions. Encourage them by asking: "What does your rock feel like? Does your rock have a smell?" Stimulate thinking with, "My rock is as sparkly as a ..." Then have children write a biography of their rock. Following is a fun activity to help children sharpen their sense of observation.

Which Rock Is Mine? Obtain a bag full of the same kind of rock (sandstone, granite, conglomerate, basalt, etc.). You probably can find these rocks at a nursery or purchase them online. Have students reach in the bag and get one of the rocks. This rock is *theirs*. Ask them to get to know their rock very well through observing it carefully, using all their senses except taste. Then have all the children put their rock in a basket and sit in a circle. Pass the basket around and have the children pick out their own rock and explain to the class how they knew it was theirs. If a child selects someone else's rock by mistake, the real owner should remain quiet and challenge the error when his or her turn comes.

Rocks and Math

1. *Ordering rocks.* Put rocks in order of size, shape, weight, and color, and then from smoothest to roughest. Try doing this activity blindfolded.

2. *Weighing rocks.* Use a small balance to weigh rocks. Predict which rocks are the heaviest.

3. *Rock jar.* Fill a jar with rocks, and have the children estimate how many rocks are in the jar. Verify the number of rocks in the jar by counting by groups of 10.

4. *Dinosaur rocks.* Have children predict the number of rocks needed to build a dinosaur cave. Children can determine the needs of a dinosaur, such as enough rocks to shelter it and to keep larger dinosaurs out of the cave.

Rocks and a Cooking Experience

1. *Igneous rock fudge.* After showing children pictures of volcanoes, find out what children know about them. Have pumice available for the children to examine. Some children might notice that the stone is light and has air bubble spaces. Explain that *igneous* means "fire" and that the pumice stone is an igneous rock that was once hot, liquid iron in a volcano that hardened as it cooled.

   To illustrate how lava cools, make fudge in a medium-sized pan. Mix ⅓ cup of water, 1 cup of sugar, a pinch of salt, 3 tablespoons of cocoa, and 1 teaspoon of vanilla. Boil the mixture for 3 minutes, and then cool in two different ways. To cool the fudge fast and produce a shiny, smooth surface (black glassy obsidian is a good example), pour some of the mixture into a pie plate that is resting in a bowl of ice. For rough and lumpy, granite-like fudge, cool at room temperature in another pie pan. Ask, "Which way do you think the piece of granite was cooled?"

Rocks and Social Studies

1. *Geologist.* Have a geologist visit the class and discuss his or her job and the tools that are used on the job.

2. *Mapping.* Group the children into pairs, and allow them to hunt for rocks on the playground. When they return to the classroom, have each pair draw a map of where their rocks were found. Discuss each map, focusing on prominent land features in each area.

11-1g Fossils

Children will not be able to grasp the enormous time spans represented in the lessons about fossils and dinosaurs. They should be helped to understand that the dinosaurs existed long before humans; cartoon depictions of cave dwellers and dinosaurs together are inaccurate.

Fossils can be shells and bones, prints of leaves, footprints, trees that have turned to stone, or insects that were trapped in tree sap. Discuss how the fossils might have been formed and whether they came from a plant or an animal. Ask, "What living things from the past can be identified by fossils?"

One way to illustrate this is to have students wear old shoes and go outside to make footprints in mud or damp sand. Have various students walk, jump, and so on, and ask other students to figure out from the prints how each person was moving.

Fossils are most likely to be found in sedimentary rock. One way children can recognize this kind of rock is that it crumbles or scratches fairly easily and may have a smell when it gets wet. To make a fossil, give the children a few leaves and have them press them into clay. Remove the leaf and observe the imprint (**Figure 11-2**). Encourage the children to match the various leaves with the imprint that was made.

FIGURE 11-2 Making a mold fossil.

© Cengage Learning®

11-1h Soil Samples

Visiting an outdoor study site on a regular basis will encourage children to observe the properties and changes in Earth materials and vegetation. As children collect rocks and observe the vegetation, they will become aware that soil varies in texture, color, and fertility from place to place. The study site is also a good place to observe erosion and the effect of seasonal changes on the ground.

If the weather permits, take children outside to gather soil samples from different areas of the study site. Using a garden trowel, place the soil samples in separate plastic containers, and label the containers. Of course, you want to be sure there is no broken glass or other dangerous materials in the ground.

After initial observations at the study site, cover several of the classroom tables with newspapers, and distribute hand lenses for children to gain a close-up look at the small rocks, soils, and grains of sand that may be in the soil samples they gathered. After the children have had time to explore, ask them to describe the soil. Encourage them to smell the soil and to look for color and other properties. As the children describe the soil, record their responses on a chart. Encourage further observations by asking: "Is your sample wet or dry? Do you see any plants or bugs?" Children will begin to compare areas of the study sites and generate more questions.

After the students have had time to explore the study site's soil, continue the observations with a lesson on soil composition. Ask, "What do you think is in soil?" Children begin to understand that soil is made of broken and pulverized bits of rock and organic matter, such as decayed leaves and plants and the remains of animals, which provide the nutrients necessary for plant growth.

Half-fill a jar with water, then spoon in soil that has a good mixture of humus, clay, sand, and gravel (you may need to add some of these ingredients). Shake the jar well, but carefully so it doesn't break; then set it on a table for children to observe the layers of materials as they settle. As the soil settles, examine the layers with a hand lens. Discuss the color and what might be in each layer, such as bits of gravel, some sand, fine pieces of rock that form, mud and clay, and plant and insect parts. Children will enjoy exploring the soil samples used in the demonstration. Return to the question, "What do you think is in soil?"

Take a second trip to the outdoor study site. Spread the children out around the site. Use plastic hoops (sorting or hula) to create defined observation areas. Give each child a magnifier. Have the children observe their area and draw and/or describe the soil, vegetation, and insects within the space. After returning to the classroom, compare and then graph the results.

Revisit the study site before and after a rain shower. Notice how the soil types change when wet. As the children walk along, ask, "How does the hard-packed soil feel as you walk on it? How does the loose soil on the baseball field feel? How do you think the loose soil will feel after a rain?"

All living things depend in some part on soil for their food. People use soil for many purposes, including growing food and building homes. Encourage children to continue their soil explorations and to begin generating a list and picture collage of the uses of soil. As a culminating experience, either visit your local cooperative extension office or invite a staff member to visit the class and discuss soil testing.

11-1i Weather

Lessons on weather and seasons are especially appropriate for primary-age children. In addition to discussing and studying the daily weather (**Photo 11-5**), take the children on a field trip to observe weather equipment in action. Local trip opportunities might include airports, television and radio stations, or high-school or college weather stations. Visiting a weather station familiarizes children with the instruments and information they will study as they follow and record changes in weather and differences in seasons. Include the construction of weather instruments, graphing, storybooks, subject integrations, and hands-on experiences as you teach children about weather.

Temperature, rain, and snow tend to be high, medium, and low in the same months every year. Have children plot patterns of water freezing, ice melting, and water disappearing on cold surfaces (**Photo 11-6**). The following lessons in temperature and sunlight provide an opportunity for children to begin correlating changes in daily temperature with seasons.

A Lesson on Temperature. Begin a discussion of temperature by asking children to explain how they know whether it is hot or cold outside. After discussing observations, introduce the idea of using a thermometer as a way of measuring temperature. Distribute thermometers to pairs or small groups to examine, and have the children record their observations. Ask: "What happens when you hold the thermometer between your hands for a minute? Is the temperature different when you hold the thermometer at the base of the bulb?"

Photo 11-5 Children are making cloud charts.

PHOTO 11-6 Children write winter labels for the snowman.

And: "What do you think will happen if you put the thermometer in a glass of cold water? What will happen if you put the thermometer in a glass of hot water?"

Provide the groups with cups of hot and cold water, and let them investigate what will happen when the thermometers are placed in the cups of water. Have the children keep a record of their investigations and share results with other groups. Keeping records helps children articulate their observations about how the thermometer works.

Pairs or groups of children will enjoy checking and recording temperature readings at different times of the day in a chosen location in the classroom or on the school grounds. Over a period of days, they can compare the pattern that emerges and make predictions. Because the goal of this lesson is for children to be aware that the temperature varies at different times of the day and because thermometers can be difficult to read, temperature need not be measured precisely.

Keep a class temperature chart so that the patterns seen over weeks and months can be related to the changing seasons. Identify clothing, activities, and food that are associated with each season. Include them on the temperature chart. A large paper body figure could be clothed to reflect seasonal changes.

Children may enjoy brainstorming words associated with each season and creating a "Hot and Cold" book following a pattern, for example, "as hot as _____" or "as cold as _____." Encourage the sensory aspect of the seasons by discussing seasonal smells, sounds, and tastes. One way to do this is by collecting pictures from magazines that represent the sights, sounds, tastes, and activities of the season and displaying them as posters. A touch board made from objects found in the seasons provides an interesting class display. Refer to the temperature activity in Chapter 10.

Extending the Concept. To extend the concept, ask: "Do you think shadows affect temperature? How could you test your idea? Record what happens." To continue the investigation of factors that can affect an object's temperature, such as color, ask: "Do you think there will be a difference between a thermometer placed in a dark-colored envelope and one placed in a light-colored envelope? Why do you think so?" Challenge children to find the hottest and coldest location in the classroom or on the playground, and ask them to give reasons for the varying temperatures. Encourage children to design ways to test different ideas.

In the same way, the amount of sunlight on the same day each month can be recorded. Children can observe and record the daylight or dark when they come to school, eat supper, or go to bed. Discuss how the length of days affects our lives. As the year progresses, children will begin to correlate the changes in daily temperature and sunlight with the seasons.

To extend the concept of seasons, choose a tree from either the playground or an adjacent area, and conduct observations periodically throughout the year. Have the children work in pairs, using a digital video camera or a camera that utilizes still shots. The observations should include the size of the tree, the colors of the bark and the leaves, the amount of leaves (lots, few, etc.), the smell of leaves, and the feel of leaves. Play back the video (or show the series of still shots), and have the children discuss the changes in the tree over the year and the seasons associated with the different observation times.

A Thermometer Table. Construct a thermometer table by having the children collect a variety of thermometers to compare and explore, such as oven thermometers, indoor-outdoor thermometers, and the many kinds of thermometers used to measure body temperature.

A Party for All Seasons. At the beginning or the end of each season, children may want to have a season party. Planning groups will enjoy designing and creating the many aspects of the season party. The party could include single-portion recipes and samples of seasonal food, aromatic jars, touch boxes, and music and pantomime games of the indoor and outdoor activities typically done in each season. Children will enjoy painting murals and pictures of seasonal activities and constructing props for the activities.

11-1j Water

Evaporation and *condensation* signify disappearing and reappearing. Years before children begin to understand that evaporating water that seems to disappear is still present in the form of small molecules (water vapor), they can observe the process and should be provided many opportunities to explore the phenomena. The following lesson, Wet Spots, is an example that allows children to see the effect of the science concept.

The process of evaporating water spots will reinforce the experience of inquiry as well as the content of changes in matter. Mr. Wang makes a large wet spot on the chalkboard and draws a circle around it every minute. As the water disappears slowly, a series of chalk circles are left on the board. Mr. Wang asks the children, "How could you evaporate the water more quickly?" Isabella says, "Blow on it." Sarah wants to use a blow dryer. Some children want to shine a light on it. Mr. Wang encourages the children to try all of their suggestions, one variable at a time.

The Wet Spots lesson continues the next day with more questions. Children want to know if the time of day makes a difference and whether cold or hot water would evaporate faster. Some begin to invent ways to evaporate the water spot without touching it. They might suggest blowing on it, using a blow dryer, or shining a light on it. Mr. Wang challenges the children to find a way to preserve a wet spot for a long time. Refer to Chapter 10 for more ideas for more investigations.

Puddle Pictures. Ask, **"What happens to puddles on warm sunny days?"** Have children use a paintbrush to make a water puddle on the sidewalk. Carefully trace around the puddle with sidewalk chalk. After the puddle starts to dry, Ask: **"How did the water in your puddle picture change? Where do you think the water goes when it dries?"** And **"What does it change into?"** Have the children record the progress of the evaporating puddle on paper and with different colored chalk to mark the progress of the disappearing puddle. Ask, **"What caused the water to change into water vapor?"**

Relate this experience to observations of the drying process in the home. Have the children predict the fastest way to dry a shirt: lay it flat, hang it on a clothesline, or crumple it up in a bundle? Ask, "How can you be sure the water goes into the air?" Help children design an investigation that reduces a shirt's (or paper towel's) exposure to the air. Develop the idea that when water dries, it evaporates or changes into a gas called water vapor.

Ask the children to look for examples of water changing from water vapor back into a liquid such as dew on the grass, frost on the window, and fog or steam on the mirror.

Once children have observed examples of evaporation and have begun to understand the role of heat, it is time to focus on examples of condensation. Begin the experience by asking the children to predict what they think happens when cold air and hot air collide. After predictions are made, pour very hot water into a large-mouth glass jar. Make a pocket out of tin foil and insert it into the mouth of the jar. Put ice cubes into the pocket. Have the children observe and explain what they think happened.

11-1k Space Science

Space travel, the moon, the sun, and the stars intrigue young children. The children will not be able to comprehend the vastness of space or the enormity of the sun, moon, and Earth; yet they can readily observe aspects of space science.

The sun is the most observable object in the sky. (*Caution:* Children should never look directly into the sun.) Ask, "On what side of the building does the sun shine in the morning?" Then, "On what side of the building does the sun shine when we leave for the day?" Take the children for a walk around the building, and note where the sun's rays are shining at different times of the day. Draw these changes on a chart. Ask, "Why do you think that the sun's rays shine in different places?"

Take the children outside the building in the morning, and have them draw the school building and the location of the sun. Begin a bulletin board mural. Make the school building and surrounding features, and have the children place a construction paper sun where it belongs in the morning sky. Then, make paper sunrays shining on the school building.

Shadow play is natural for young children as they learn about the sun. Draw chalk outlines of the shadows cast, and then try casting shadows on a cloudy day. Ask: "Do you have a shadow today? Why not?" Discuss the color of the sun and the moon. Ask: "Is the moon the same color every night? Can you see the moon during the day?" [Yes.] Many children think that the moon goes to bed at night. Help them speculate on why the moon does not look as bright during the day.

If children think that the stars are held up with tape, do not discourage them. They are in good intellectual company. Aristotle, for example, thought that stars were embedded in concentric crystalline spheres. A primary-age child cannot understand interstellar concepts. Help the child notice that things in the sky look different at various times of the day and night.

Moon Patterns. The child's concept and grasp of the universe grows slowly over time. Ideas about light and sight are prerequisites to understanding the night sky. The priority in space-related lessons for young children is on describing what the sky looks like and identifying changes in shape and movement. The moon looks different every day and makes an ideal subject for observing and comparing.

Children can easily observe the pattern that the moon makes as it goes from one full moon to the next. Because moon phases appear at regular intervals, they can serve as a natural clock. It is not as important that children remember the names of the phases of the moon as that they see the pattern of change in the sky. As children record the differences that they see, they should describe and compare the various shapes the moon seems to have (**Figure 11-3**). The observations can be recorded in special Moon Watch books made of construction paper and writing paper in the shape of the moon.

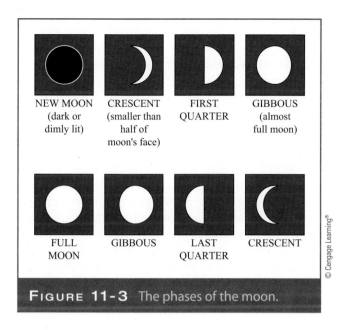

FIGURE 11-3 The phases of the moon.

The phases shown: NEW MOON (dark or dimly lit), CRESCENT (smaller than half of moon's face), FIRST QUARTER, GIBBOUS (almost full moon), FULL MOON, GIBBOUS, LAST QUARTER, CRESCENT.

© Cengage Learning®

The Dos and Don'ts of Using Binoculars. This is an ideal time to introduce the children to binoculars and telescopes. By third grade, children should know that binoculars and telescopes magnify the appearance of objects in the sky. The craters, mountains, and other features on the moon's surface provide a source of much discussion and imagination. Binoculars work especially well with young children.

The following are some binocular dos and don'ts: Do not try to find an object with the binoculars held up to your eyes. Do look at the object you want to look at, and then bring the binoculars up to your eyes. This will work better if you focus the binoculars first. To do this, look at an object, bring the binoculars up to your eyes, and then focus until the object is clear. *Caution children never to look at the sun with a pair of binoculars or a telescope.* Blindness could be the result.

Craters of the Moon. As children look at the moon more closely and more often, they will begin to notice the many interesting features that can be seen by the naked eye or with binoculars. Take advantage of children's natural interest in the night sky, and let them record and draw their observations in greater detail.

Children will enjoy creating a lunar landscape. This can be done in the sand table by dropping different size balls into very wet sand. If a sand table is not available, a box of sand makes a good substitute. The children can compare the splatter marks extending from the impression made from the ball as it hits the sand to similar marks seen on the moon. Have the children compare the drawing that they have made of their moon observations with the sand craters they have made.

Features of the moon are ideal for simulation with clay and other sculpting materials. Murals, paintings, and other art forms provide reinforcement for the children's observations. If the child does not remember how a feature looks or her drawing is not as clear as she wants it to be, she can easily look at the moon the next night.

Technology for Young Children

Eight Great Tips for Tablet Integration

Many teachers are integrating tablets into their classroom instruction. Four teachers suggested integration methods.

1. Children can take the tablets with them on a hike. For environmental exploration, they can record observations on their tablets, eliminating the need for paper.

2. Load apps that promote creativity, such as iMovie and Garage Band.

3. If the number of tablets is limited, have the students set up a system for sharing.

4. The free Educations Interactive Whiteboard app can be used for sharing information. Presentations can be posted on the class website or wiki.

5. Apps can provide a variety of tools. Groups of students can try out new apps and report on their value and utility.

6. Individually, in pairs, or in small groups, children should have time to explore apps. This promotes collaboration and sharing skills.

7. Start with free apps.

8. Jump right in to using your tablet. It can streamline your day as you record student responses, collate data, and organize activities.

Nine great tips for iPad integration, Education World, 2013, retrieved February 26, 2014, from www.educationworld.com.

Observing the moon cycle will stimulate children's natural curiosity. They will want to know more about the night sky. A variety of things in the sky can be seen at night. Planets, comets, meteors, stars, satellites, artificially created space objects such as the space station, and airplanes fill the sky. The familiar patterns of stars, called **constellations** provide much excitement. Keep in mind that it is not important for children to know the names of the constellations. They need to be aware that the pattern of stars stays the same as it appears to move across the sky. This movement in the sky is another pattern that is readily observed.

11-2 STANDARDS AND GUIDELINES FOR ENVIRONMENTAL AWARENESS

The topic of environmental awareness is not a separate section of NGSS (NRC, 2013), but is embedded in kindergarten and fourth-grade expectations:

- Communicate solutions that will reduce the impact of humans on the land, water, air, and/or other living things in the local environment.

- Obtain and combine information to describe that energy and fuels are derived from natural resources and that their uses affect the environment.

The *K–12 Framework* (NRC, 2012) includes aspects of Environmental Awareness. ESS2.E Biogeology (p. 189–190) considers how living organisms alter Earth's processes and structures. As organisms change and evolve, the makeup of Earth's geosphere, hydrosphere, and atmosphere change. The chemical makeup of the atmosphere is modified by the global carbon cycle. Greenhouse gases are of great concern. By the end of grade 2, children should know and understand that plants and animals (including humans) depend on the land, water, and air to live and grow (p. 190). Plants and animals (including humans) can change the environment. Core idea ESS3 focuses on how the Earth's surface processes and human activities affect each other. Humans depend on natural resources, some of which are renewable and some not. Natural hazards such as Earthquakes and hurricanes can alter human populations and activities. On the other hand, humans can alter the Earth's surface and can change the climate. Climate change and depletion of natural resources are of major concern. By the end of grade 2, children need to know and understand that living things need water, air, and resources from the land and need to live where these things are available (p. 192). Children need to know and understand how humans change the planet (ESS3.C, p. 194). By the end of grade 2, children should know and understand that they can make choices that reduce their impacts on the land, water, and other living things—for example, by reusing and recycling and thus reducing the amount of trash we produce. (p. 195). Children can engage in many activities that reflect environmental awareness.

Some schools have adopted the E-STEM (environment, science, technology, engineering, and math) curriculum, which enables each grade level to develop integrated unit projects in science, literacy, and social studies (STEM, February 2014). Students meet English standards by reading nonfiction science in Language Arts; they also demonstrate they can collect environmental data to solve an environmental problem, analyze and organize the data in math, and display their information using technology.

A major role of the teacher in the primary grades is to guide children in investigating and gaining an understanding of the characteristics and changes within their local and regional population, resources available in our world, and how our decisions make an impact on the availability of those resources. Primary grade children should be able to answer questions such as "How can we maintain the health of our environment?"

Students who demonstrate understanding meet NGGS Standard K-ESS-3: Communicate solutions that will reduce the impact of humans on the land, water, air, and/or other living things in the local environment.

11-2a Next Generation Environmental Awareness Instructional Plans

Environmental awareness involves understanding the nature of our environment, its destruction, and ways of protecting it. The term *environment* refers to everything that surrounds us—air, water, land, plants, animals, other people, ourselves, and anything else that is part of our lives. An environment can be global (such as the ozone hole), regional (such as flooding), local (such as dumping grounds), and even individual habitats (such as an ant hill). Although there are differences of opinion about some environmental issues (such as whether global warming is actually occurring), there is universal agreement that we must protect our environment. This calls for awareness of what our environment is and what it does for living things, both plants and animals (including us humans). The purpose of this section is to give you, the teacher, some guidance as to what to teach concerning the environment, as well as some examples of lessons you might want to use as models for your own teaching.

The Next Generation Science Standards detail topics of study and performance expectations for the exploration of environmental awareness. They are as follows (from National Research Council, 2013, pp. 8 & 41):

Title: Earth and Human Activity. Disciplinary core ideas (these are the main topics of study.)

1. Natural Resources

    - Kindergarten: Living things need water, air, and resources from the land, and they live in places that have the things they need. Humans use natural resources for everything they do.

    - Fourth Grade: Energy and fuels are derived from natural sources, and their use affects the environment. Some resources are renewable over time, and some are not.

2. Natural Hazards

    - Kindergarten: Some kinds of severe weather are more likely than others in a given region. Weather scientists forecast severe weather so that communities can prepare for and respond to these events.

    - Fourth Grade: A variety of natural hazards result from natural processes, for example, Earthquakes, tsunamis, volcanic eruptions, tornados, and hurricanes. Humans cannot eliminate the hazards, but we can take steps to reduce their impacts.

Performance Expectations: These are the overarching performance objectives; individual lessons probably will have their own performance objectives.

Kindergarten

- Use a model to represent the relationship between the needs of different plants or animals (including humans) and the places they live.

- Ask questions to obtain information about the purpose of weather forecasting to prepare for, and respond to, severe weather.

- Communicate solutions that will reduce the impact of humans on the land, water, air, and/or other living things in the local environment.

Fourth Grade

- Obtain and combine information to describe that energy and fuels are derived from natural resources and that their uses affect the environment.

- Generate and compare multiple solutions to reduce the impacts of natural Earth processes on humans.

11-2b The Constructivist Approach to the Next Generation Science Standards in Primary Grades Environmental Awareness

In the conventional instruction section, you will see several inquiry projects dealing with environmental awareness (such as Water Changes the Earth, Trash and Litter, Recycling). Below are lessons with an environmental awareness focus fashioned to enable your students to think for themselves and to *do* science in the way suggested by the new standards. In each activity, assessment should be based on the student's execution of the investigation and his or her discussion about the questions the teacher asks.

ACTIVITIES

FIRST-GRADE ENVIRONMENTAL AWARENESS

Question: What are the causes of soil erosion?

Objective: To infer causes of soil erosion in the environment around the school.

Materials: Container of dirt or sand with mound in the center, pitcher of water.

Procedure

Engage: Ask the class to tell you what erosion is. What do they know about erosion? Provide time for discussion. Ask them what will happen if water is poured on the dirt mound. Provide time for discussion. Pour water on the mound. Tell the students to observe closely. What did the students observe?

Explore: Take the class outdoors, and help them find examples of soil erosion around the school. Good places to look

are on slopes and at the ends of drainage pipes. Ask them for their observations about the soil, the general area, the slope of the ground, and so on.

Explain: Ask the students to form inferences as to what caused the soil to erode in the way they observed and to provide reasons for their inferences. Have them think of solutions that would eliminate the erosion that they observed

Elaborate: Have students draw what they see and label the pertinent features. Have them describe what they see as a problem and explain how they would solve the problem.

Performance Expectations: Students will complete the erosion assignment.

SECOND-GRADE ENVIRONMENTAL AWARENESS

Question: What kinds of materials absorb water? Which do not absorb water?

Objective: To predict whether given materials absorb water or whether they do not absorb water and list situations in which it is important that material absorbs or does not absorb water.

Materials: Wax paper, paper towels, paper bags, napkins, typing paper, plastic wrap, different kinds of cloth, oil cloth, roofing shingle, sandstone rock, limestone rock, piece of granite, and other materials that may or may not absorb water, eye dropper, other materials requested by the students.

Procedure

Engage: Ask the class what happens if you hold a piece of wood at an angle and put water drops at the highest point. Have them describe what they observe (the water starts

downhill, but some disappears). Tell the students they will be doing activities that will help them earn about absorption.

Explore: Provide an assortment of materials such as those listed above. Children place the material on a piece of cardboard held at an angle. Ask children to predict which materials will allow the water to run down the incline rapidly and which will cause the water to run down the incline slowly or be absorbed almost immediately. Children then test their predictions Using an eyedropper or a straw, children place one or two drops of water on the material at the top of the incline and observe what happens to the water. Encourage children to do many variations on this activity, such as laying the material flat on the table, holding the material over the top of an open coffee can, using oil instead of water, and other variations. Encourage children to try their own variations and to suggest different materials that might be used.

Explain: Listed here are some typical questions and topics for discussion:

- "Which material would you use for a roof on a house?"
- "Suppose you were in the woods, and you only had what nature could supply. What would you use to build a shelter? Why?"
- "A great deal of the water we use comes from *aquifers* deep within the Earth's crust. (An *aquifer* is a large body of water stored in the sponge-like spaces in porous rock deep within the Earth's crust). What material would you want between the aquifer and the surface of the ground?"

- "Why is it important that the water in the aquifers not be pumped excessively?"
- "Why is it important not to waste water?"
- "Where does our wastewater go?"

Elaborate: Have students research water conservation. Have small groups of students come up with a plan for conservation in their area and share their plans.

Performance Expectation: Students complete water conservation plans, share in small groups, and make a case for their plan.

THIRD-GRADE ENVIRONMENTAL AWARENESS

Question: What can we infer about the ages of trees and rainfall and climate from tree rings?

Objective: To infer the age of a tree and the circumstances of its growth from the tree rings in a cross section of its trunk.

Materials: Thin slices from the trunk or branches of a tree that is being cut down. Obtain both horizontal and vertical slices.

Procedure

Engage: Ask, **"What can we infer about the ages of trees and rainfall and climate from tree rings?"** Have students present ideas.

Explore: Have the children examine the tree rings and record what they notice.

Explain: A tree ring is a layer of wood produced by the tree in one year. One ring normally contains a thin layer (produced early in the growing season) and a thicker layer (produced later in the growing season). Wide rings suggest a growing season with plentiful rainfall; narrow rings suggest hard times such as draught.

Elaborate: After a discussion about the nature of tree rings and the seasonal growth of trees, which results in tree rings, give students a cross-sectional piece of a tree trunk. Ask them to count the number of complete tree rings. Have several children count the rings of the same specimen and decide which count is accurate. From this count, ask them to infer how old the tree was. Also ask them to tell *why* they came up with the age they did. Ask children to infer the length and weather conditions of the seasons during which the tree grew.

If possible, give students cross sections of branches that came from the same tree, and ask them to infer which of the branches is oldest, which is youngest, and where on the tree they came from.

Digital Download

BRAIN CONNECTION

THE TRANSPARENT BRAIN

As students solve problems and seek answers for questions, we wonder what is happening within their brains. MRIs and other technological advances allow us to look within the brain and observe which areas of the living brain are active. The brain can be dissected postmortem to try to see exactly what connections are included. At Stanford University Medical School, a new imaging process called CLARITY enables scientists to take the whole postmortem brain and with visible light and chemicals measure and probe the fine wiring and molecular structures with the brain intact. Chemical engineering served as the basis for developing CLARITY. The scientists can now obtain a three-dimensional view of the brain.

A. Myers, Getting CLARITY: Hydrogel process developed at Stanford creates transparent brain. *Stanford University School of Medicine, April 10, 2013,* http://med.stanford.edu.

DAP **naeyc**

11-2c Conventional Environmental Awareness Instruction

Concepts and Approaches

- **Environments** are the space, conditions, and factors that affect an individual's ability to survive.

- **Resources** include anything that can be used to fill a need. Natural resources include coal, water, oil, gas, and so on.

- **Recycling** is the process of recovering used materials.

Environmental investigations are a natural way for children to enjoy and explore the world around them. When children explore the environment, they will engage in active participation and cooperation as they begin developing their own understanding. Experiences are often free or inexpensive and readily accessible to a variety of audiences and learning styles.

The suggestions and lessons in this section are based on one or more of the three common approaches to environmental education outlined by Dighe (1993):

1. The *awareness* approach focuses on children's feelings and appreciation of the world around them.

2. The *environmental concept* approach introduces ideas that will lead to learning about environmental concerns.

3. The conservation approach provides opportunities for children to take action and see a result of that action.

The results of the lessons need to be observable and should not be too dramatic or controversial. To be effective, children need to see a direct result of their actions. For example, children can see a direct result of picking up trash or monitoring the use of lights in the room.

To introduce the word *environment*, use a brainstorming approach. Write the word on the chalkboard and ask, "What do you think the word 'environment' means?" List the ideas named by the children, and keep that list posted. Children may want to modify the list as their awareness of the environment progresses. Periodically, have the children return to modify the list as meaning develops.

11-2d Water

Water is everywhere. It flows in rivers and streams and makes up the oceans that cover the Earth's surface. Draw children's attention to the bodies of water around them—rivers, lakes, oceans, and the like. Show pictures of different bodies of water, and discuss experiences.

naeyc **DAP**

ACTIVITIES

WATER CHANGES

Concept: Water changes the face of the Earth.

Objective: To observe and record changes in the soil as a result of moving water.

Materials: Rocks, soil, liter soda bottles filled with water, half-gallon paper milk cartons, trays, scissors.

Procedure: Divide the children into pairs. Give each pair a milk carton, some soil and rocks, a liter soda bottle, a tray, and a pair of scissors. Have the children cut the panel of the milk carton under the spout (**Figure 11-4**). Fill the carton three-fourths full with soil and rocks. Put the carton in the tray, and place a rock under one end of the carton. Make a small channel for a stream to flow. Ask the children, **"What will happen when you pour water into the channel?"** One of the pair should slowly pour the water in the higher end of the tray. The other partner should observe and record what happens through writing or drawing. Ask the children, **"What happened when you poured water into the channel?"** After the children have discussed their observations, ask, **"What do you think will happen if we add a small amount of rocks and gravel to the channel?"**

Extension: Find a river or stream, and have the children take samples of muddy water so that they can observe the sediment when it settles.

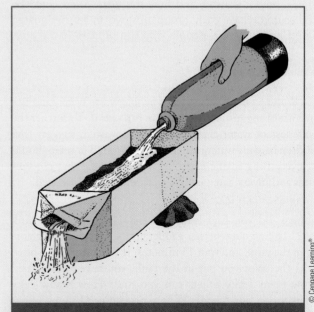

FIGURE 11-4 Water changes the face of the Earth.

© Cengage Learning®

Water Changes the Earth. Water is the single most important force that shapes the surface of the Earth. Water from melting glaciers, rain, and snow forms streams and rivers and moves sand, which gradually wears away mountains and carves hills and valleys. To explore the concept of **erosion**, try the following activity.

Take a class walk, and look for evidence of water changing the surface of the Earth. Discuss how these changes can be beneficial or harmful.

Using Water. Living things—people, plants, and animals—consist mainly of water and must have it to live. In fact, water is more important for survival than food. Ask children to name some of the ways they use water. Encourage responses by asking: **"What are some other ways people use water?**

Why is water important to business? To people who fish or raise farm animals?" Begin a chart to record children's responses to the ways living things use water. Add to the chart throughout the lesson as other uses of water are discussed.

After completing the following activity, it will emerge that the school depends on water in many ways. Children may appreciate its availability and how difficult life would be without such access to water. Encourage children to draw or cut out pictures of water uses in their home or school.

Ask children to keep a personal Water Use Log. They should record their use of water for one day, beginning from the time they get up and continuing to record their use until the time they fall asleep.

ACTIVITIES

HOW OUR SCHOOL USES WATER

Concept: People are dependent on water. Water is used in many ways.

Objective: To investigate and record how water is used.

Materials: Investigation journals, pens, pencils, cameras (optional).

Procedure: Ask the children, **"How do you think water is used at our school?"** Assign groups of children locations, such as the kitchen, bathroom, art room, cleaning closets, and water fountains. Brainstorm with the children a list of questions to be asked to find out where the water comes from, how it is used, and how the water used could be measured. Have each group observe in its designated area, and interview people who use or work in the area.

After completing their research, groups should return to the classroom, and a summary of the collected information should be made and discussed. Discuss questions such as these: **"How many water sources were found? How much water does the school use? Is water wasted? What would we do if we didn't have water?**

Extensions:

1. Have children record how their family uses water during one evening.

2. Visit a local aquarium and see how it uses water. How is its water use similar or different from that of the school?

Digital Download

Be a Water Saver. Discuss ways people waste water, and begin a list of suggestions for how we can save it. To further the awareness of water that is sometimes wasted, suggest that children become water inspectors. Each child or team should list everything in the classroom and at home that requires water and investigate possible ways that water is wasted.

When children have completed their survey, ask: "Where did you find leaky faucets? Does the toilet tank leak?" To find out whether a toilet tank leaks, put food coloring in the tank, and wait 15 minutes. If the water in the bowl turns the color you put in the tank, you have a leak. Ask: "How many leaky toilets can you find? How many leaky toilets are in our school? Whom do you need to tell about your findings?"

Water wasted from leaky faucets can be measured by placing a cup under the faucet and collecting the drips. Ask, "How much water drips from the faucet in one hour?"

Collect the water, and have the children think of a way to use the water instead of pouring it down the drain.

After investigating and studying water waste, children may then want to explain how they personally plan to conserve water. Children can illustrate one way they use water wisely. Have students pantomime a scene to show a way to conserve water at home or at school.

Water for a Day. Provide each student with a paper cup and a 1-liter bottle of water. Tell them that this is their day's water supply for drinking, washing their hands, and so on. However, tell students that they can flush the toilet. Tape faucets shut, and put a tub in the sink to collect water that would have gone down the drain. Have the children predict how much water they will use and record this information on a chart. At the end of the day, have them use a large graduated cylinder to measure any water that remains in their bottles and the water in the tub. Record the data on charts, and water the plants with the remaining water. Ask, "**Did you use as much water as you thought you would use?**"

As more people use water, there has been an increase in water **pollution**. In some areas, raw sewage is pumped into rivers and streams, or pesticides and fertilizers are washed from lawns and farmland into the water system, and pollutants such as metals and petroleum products may enter a river or an ocean. Point out that not all pollutants are visible. Some children think that because water looks clear, it is safe to drink. Emphasize to children they should never drink water unless they know it is safe.

Is It Safe to Drink? Every day, wastes are being pumped into the world's water supply, but they are not always easy to detect. To develop the idea that you cannot always see pollution in water, cut off the bottom of a piece of celery, and divide the celery in half lengthwise. Fill two glasses halfway with apple juice, and add three drops of red food coloring to one and three drops of blue food coloring to the other. Place one-half of the celery in each glass, and let it stand for several hours. Take the celery out, and cut it into slices. Ask, "What color is the celery at the top of the stalk? Taste the celery. Can you taste the apple juice?" Try this investigation with food coloring and water.

After completing this activity, read the children's book *Magic School Bus: Through the Waterworks* (Cole, 1986). Take a trip to the local water treatment facility or have a representative visit your classroom. If you have the opportunity to visit a local facility, upon returning make a class book to record the children's observations. The software version of *Through the Waterworks* can be used as a center activity. Once the children have had an opportunity to explore the software, discuss how the children's trip in *Through the Waterworks* is alike or different from that which your class experienced.

11-2e Trash and Litter

How Much Trash? It is an understatement to say that each person throws away a lot of garbage and trash in a lifetime. To provide children with an opportunity to see how much garbage they use in one day, suggest that they place the garbage they normally toss out in a day or a week in a large biodegradable trash bag. They may be able to take this trash bag with them for a day. That night, sort the garbage from the trash bag into labeled categories of use such as organic, paper, plastics, metal, glass, clothes, and mysterious items that do not seem to fit the other categories. This is an especially appropriate classroom or family experience. The bags can be weighed. Most people create at least 4 pounds of garbage each day. Ways to recycle trash can be explored. Ask: "**Which bag weighs the most? Which weighs the least?**" And: "**Which bag has the most trash in it? Who created most of this trash? Can any of the items be used again?**"

A mathematics connection is to have the children problem-solve how much garbage a family of four produces in a day, week, or month. Have children measure the area that 4 pounds of trash covers. Next, have the children problem-solve the area needed to store trash for a family of four for a day, week, or month.

Keeping the Earth Clean. Make a class book of all of the things you can do to help keep the Earth clean. Then take the class on a scavenger hunt. Put the children in pairs, and give each pair a short list of items to locate (newspaper, soda can, candy wrapper, etc.). Children can draw or plot on a map where they found each item. Have the children compare findings and discuss how the items might have ended up where they did.

Litter Collage. Gather people's litter and nature's litter (fallen leaves, twigs, seed pods, etc.), and make a collage from each. Have the children write descriptions about the human litter and nature's litter. Bury some of the litter made by people and some of the litter made by nature. After a month, dig it up, and see what happened to it.

Recycling. One of the best ways to recycle is to reuse materials instead of discarding them. Many of the items that are thrown away can be used again in the everyday classroom environment. Look around the classroom, and list the items being reused, such as boxes, Styrofoam chips, sheets of paper, larger pieces of cloth, rope, yarn, string, plastic jugs, wood scraps, old magazines, rug scraps, and many more. The symbol in **Figure 11-5** means packaged in recycled materials. Ask, "How many items in your home come in recycled packaging? How many can you find in the classroom or in the school?"

Recycling Survey. Have children brainstorm a list of suggestions for a recycling survey. Ask them what they want to know about the recycling habits of their families. Questions might include these: "Do you recycle? If so, do you recycle aluminum cans?" Additional suggestions might be grocery bags, newspapers, magazines, plastic bottles, plastic containers, and glass bottles and jars. Ask: "Do you think recycling is important? Why or why not?" After developing the survey, have the children give their survey to their family and friends. Compile the results of the survey on a bulletin board made of a huge brown paper bag, and discuss the results with the children. Ask, "Does anything about the results on our chart surprise you?"

FIGURE 11-5 Packaged in recycled materials.

Save a Tree. Making paper is a fun and inexpensive way to emphasize the recycling process. Have the children save old newspapers instead of throwing them away. You will also need the following items: a large plastic pan or wading pool filled with warm water, an eggbeater, wire mesh screens, sponges, cotton cloth, and a rolling pin.

Shred the paper into strips, and place them into water. Use the eggbeater, a whip, or an old blender to mash the paper into the consistency of oatmeal. For fancy paper, children can sprinkle bits of thread or flower petals into the pulp. To make the sheets of paper, spread and press the pulp onto a wire mesh screen, first dipping the screen under the pulp in the pan of water. Remove excess water from the sheet and underside of the screen.

Place the sheets of paper onto a cotton cloth, cover it with fabric, and squeeze out remaining moisture with a rolling pin. Let the sheets dry, trim them to a desirable size, and the children will be ready to write.

Paper Logs. Paper logs can be made for holiday treats by putting 20 or 30 sheets of recycled newspaper together and adding a cup of crushed pinecones or cedar shavings between every few pages. These sections are tightly rolled and tied loosely at the end. Fill the pool with water and enough cones and chips to cover half of the water's surface. Add three cups of salt to the mixture (for extra pretty flames), and put the logs in to soak for a week. Turn them once a day. Dry the logs, and give them as presents. Place a note on the logs that they may be burned in the fireplace or safe fire pit. Have an adult light them; then the children should note the colors of the flames and the remaining ashes. An adult should make sure the embers are put out.

Another activity that can be used to explore **biodegradable** and nonbiodegradable materials is creating a class **landfill**. Do this outside in a secure area. Have the children collect a variety of paper, Styrofoam, food products (these can be obtained from the school cafeteria), soil, and water. Divide the children into small groups, and give each group a large, black trash bag. They are to choose the materials they feel are most likely to break down. Have the children layer the materials in the trash bag and cover it with soil. Add water so that the materials are moist, but not flooded. Tape each bag shut, label the bag with the group name, and leave it for two weeks. At the end of the two weeks, open the bags and look to see what degraded and what did not. Were the children's predictions correct? This activity could be followed by a visit to a local landfill.

ACTIVITIES

DISAPPEARING PEANUTS

Concept: Biodegradable materials can be used to complete tasks previously done with nonbiodegradable materials.

Objective: To explore how biodegradable packing peanuts change form when water is applied.

Materials: Biodegradable peanuts in a bag marked "1," nonbiodegradable packing peanuts in a bag marked "2," water, trays.

Procedure: Have the children take a small amount of packing peanuts from bag 1 and bag 2 and put each in a bowl. Observe the peanuts in each bowl carefully. Ask, **"How are they alike, and how are they different? What do you think will happen when you add water to each** of the bowls?" [Add water and observe.] Ask: **"What happened when you added water? Once you finished using the packing peanuts, which would take up less space in a landfill?"**

Extension:

1. Experiment with other packing materials to see whether they are biodegradable.

2. Call local moving companies and suppliers of moving materials to see whether they use biodegradable materials. How does the information you collect affect your local landfill?

Digital Download

11-3 DESCRIPTION AND STANDARDS FOR ENGINEERING DESIGN, TECHNOLOGY, AND APPLICATIONS OF SCIENCE

As with the other disciplinary core ideas *The K–12 Framework* (NRC, 2012) provides the basis for engineering design, technology, and applications of science (ETS). When engineering practices are applied in the classroom, they help children acquire and apply science knowledge. ETS-1 Engineering Design is the main practice in engineering today. ETS-2 links engineering, science, technology, and society. The definitions of these components are as follows (NRC, 2012, p. 202):

- *Technology* is any modification of the natural world made to fulfill human needs or desires.

- *Engineering* is a systematic and orderly process to designing objects, processes, and systems to meet human needs and wants.

- *An application of science* is any use of scientific knowledge for a specific purpose such as to design a new product, a new technology, or to predict the impact of human action.

Students need to come to understand that scientists and engineers frequently work as a team to develop new products or new technologies.

The Next Generation Science Standards (NRC, 2013) build on the K–12 Framework and on children's natural interest in building and creating. By the end of second grade, students should be able to go through the engineering design three-step process:

1. Define the problem. Kindergartners learn that a problem is created when there is a situation people want changed. By the end of second grade, students know that they can make observations and gather information that will help them solve problems.

2. Develop possible solutions. Students need to learn that they should look at multiple solutions to the problem. They should also recognize that a sketch or a model could help them develop their ideas.

3. Compare different solutions. Students should be able to think of ways to compare solutions.

Kindergarteners are expected to build simple devices. First graders are expected to use tools and materials to solve a simple problem and test and compare different solutions. Second graders are expected to solve more complex problems and develop, test, and analyze data to compare different solutions (NRC, 2013, p. 22).

11-3a Engineering Design

Remember that the engineer's task is to solve problems. To solve problems engineers use several different practices (NRC, 2012, p. 204):

- Problem definition

- Model development and use

- Analysis and interpretation of data

- Application of mathematics and computational thinking

- Determination of solutions

Engineers must create goals and criteria that will determine whether the problem is successfully solved: Does the product or system work as desired? Does it meet cost limitations? By the end of second grade, students should understand several factors such as the notion that a situation that people want to change or something they want to create may be tackled as an engineering problem. Problems may have more than one acceptable solution. To think about a problem solution, one needs to make observations, ask questions, and gather information. Solutions can be compared relative to the success criteria set up in advance. Students need to understand that it is important to understand the problem. There are many global problems in need of solutions, such as the need for clean water and the need for food and for energy sources that minimize pollution. Engineering can address these problems.

How does the engineering design process work? The process may begin with brainstorming and then narrow down to a specific problem focus. Informal sketches and diagrams may then be translated into more formal models. Physical models such as such as scale models or prototypes can be tested for strength, flexibility, and other success criteria. Before the design is produced, mathematical models can be used to vary features of the design such as material components. Data from models and experiments can be analyzed to see whether it meets success criteria. By the end of second grade, students need to understand that designs can be expressed through sketches, drawings, or physical models. These representations can be used to communicate the idea to other people. A complex problem may have to be solved in small steps, which at the end can be brought together for the final solution. By the end of second grade, students need to recognize that there is always more than one possible solution to a problem, so it is useful to compare designs, test them, and discuss strengths and weaknesses. By the end of third grade, students integrate their understanding of science into design challenges that may involve magnetic forces, the needs of organisms, and the impact of severe weather.

11-3b Links Among Engineering, Technology, Science, and Society

How are these areas interconnected? New scientific knowledge can bring about new technologies, which are evolved with engineering design (**Photo 11-7**). On the other hand,

PHOTO 11-7 Advances in technology change children's lives and ways of learning.

Charlesworth

PHOTO 11-8   This boy designs a rocket ship.

Charlesworth

PHOTO 11-9   He cuts out the rocket ship.

TeachSource Video

© 2016 Cengage Learning®

GRAPHING CHANGE: A TECHNOLOGY-INTEGRATED LESSON

This video demonstrates how students collect weather data, make predictions, create a line graph, defend their results, and explain how their results compare with their predictions.

1.   How does technology support this lesson?

2.   How does communication apply to this activity?

new technologies can open the way for new science investigations. Progress in science, engineering, and technology can have a great influence on society (**Photos 11-8** and **11-9**). Big changes are taking place in agriculture, energy, and communication due to growth in available technology, engineering design, and scientific knowledge. By the end of second grade, children should understand that every day new questions about the natural world are encountered. New observation and measurement tools are produced through engineering. Every day engineers use observations and measurement to help test and refine design ideas. Students should also be aware of some of the tools and instruments (such as rulers, balances, thermometers, graduated cylinders, telescopes, and microscopes) used in scientific explorations.

Science, engineering, and technology affect the ways people live and the natural world. Humans are dependent on natural resources. Through science, engineering, and technology, humans have developed ways to use these natural resources.

Science and engineering affect areas such as agriculture, medicine, housing, transportation, energy production, water availability, and land use. Some of the new technologies and designs have had positive effects, and some have had negative effects. Any new technology must be examined for costs, benefits, and risks. Mathematical modeling is a tool that can provide a view into the future of any new problem solution. By the end of second grade, students should understand that humans depend on the technologies in their lives. Most of the technology we use is made from materials from the natural world. Thus, new technologies impact the natural world.

NGSS

11-3c Next Generation Instructional Plans

Engineering is finding a prominent place in science instruction. Following are some examples of real student projects, followed by some sample project plans.

Project Examples. This first example is one from real life. The problem was to design a community of 20 homes (Webster, 2014). In Correggio, Italy, adults and children worked together to design the community of Corindoline. All the members of the community, including the children, contributed. The children learned about architecture and about drawing and building models. They also wrote a list of their needs and desires. Examples of the homes, the models, and the drawings can be found on the Corindoline website.

Third- and fourth-grade students were provided a project of building a house access ramp for a community resident (Darrow, 2014). To fund the project, the students, with the help of college engineering students, built and sold lockers. The next step was to build a ramp for the campus gazebo. When a community recipient is selected, the final step will be to build the residential ramp. The project involves math, geometry, and engineering. The evaluation of the residents' applications applies reading and persuasive language skills.

Ashworth (2013) describes a problem tackled to meet the performance expectation 2-PS1-1: Plan and conduct an investigation to describe and classify different kinds of materials by their observable properties; and 2-PS-2: Analyze data obtained from testing different materials to determine which materials have the properties that are best suited for an intended purpose. The activity applied K-2-ETS1-1 (identify problem), K-2-ETS-1-2 (make a drawing), and K-2-ETS-1-3 (make the product and critique). The problem was to design a container to carry their favorite food. The students engaged in many experiences with different types and sizes of containers and discussed attributes such as big, small, tall, flat, round, plastic, wood, and metal. The children examined and classified many types of materials such as fabric, a variety of paper types, plastic wrap, cardboard, wood, and aluminum foil. They drew pictures of a container to carry their favorite food. They considered whether the food was hot or cold, and liquid or solid. They then made their container and analyzed whether it would work.

Third graders combined science and engineering to design parachutes (Lachapelle, Sargianis, & Cunningham, 2013). They began with a question from their teacher: "What information do you need to make sure that your team's parachute is 'mission ready'?" Students then chimed in with additional questions. The third lesson in the Designing Parachutes project centered on how the thickness of the atmosphere and the parachute design affect the speed of the falling parachute. The class discussed the importance of models. The students were then divided into three groups, with each group studying one variation in one variable: materials, size, and suspension line length. They recorded the average drop speed for each parachute. The data were recorded in one chart. Before trying out the models, students discussed their ideas about which parachute design would work best. This project met standards 3-5ETS-1 and 3-5ETS1-2. Students engaged in the eight engineering practices and two disciplinary core ideas: ETS1.A, Defining and delimiting engineering problems; and ETS1.B, Developing possible solutions.

A primary (K–2) project that took place in a kindergarten class involved designing a hamster habitat (Tank, Pettis, Moore, & Fehr, 2013). It was a project from PictureSTEM, an ongoing initiative to design curriculum that uses picture books as a stimulus to learning in elementary classrooms. The project took five days, and a book introduced each day's activity. Students drew plans for a habitat trail. They used small blocks to map out areas for the hamster to take care of his basic needs. The students tested their trails, discussed the results in class, and modified their designs, if needed.

Project Plans for Next Generation Engineering Design, Technology, and Applications of Science. Following are lessons with a focus on Next Generation Science Standards engineering design, technology, and applications of science, fashioned to enable your students to think for themselves and to *do* science in the way suggested by the new standards.

ACTIVITIES

FIRST AND SECOND GRADE

Question: What do astronauts eat in space?

Objective: To measure crumbs resulting from eating snacks and infer characteristics most appropriate for food to be eaten in space.

Materials: Cookies, crackers, potato chips, marshmallows, and M&Ms; several white paper napkins or paper towels for each student.

Procedure

Engage: Show a short video that portrays the gravity-free environment of a spaceship. (Check TeacherTube for "Drinking Tea in Microgravity," "Experiments in Microgravity," and "Fun Stuff in Microgravity." Check YouTube for "Do It Yourself Weightless Experience for Kids.") Pose a question such as: "What do you suppose astronauts eat in space?" "Would they eat cookies?" "Why do you think so?" Ask the same questions about crackers, apples, bananas, and potato chips. Use children's responses and input to extend the conversation. Pose another question: "What would happen to the crumbs if astronauts were to eat a cracker?"

Explore: Provide a small amount of each of several different kinds of snack foods such as cookies, crackers, potato chips, marshmallows, and M&Ms, and several white paper napkins for each group. Children take a small bite of each of the snacks over white napkins. They use a different napkin for each snack, put the remainder of the snack piece on the napkin, and put it to one side while they taste each snack. They then examine each napkin and make a judgment as to the quantity of crumbs that fell. If desired, they can develop a system for measuring the amount of crumbs left behind, such as estimating the number of crumbs, counting them, comparing their sizes, or arranging the napkins in order of which ones have the most crumbs, so children can identify the "crumb factor" of each snack. The specific method used by children will emerge during the lesson. If everyone agrees to use the same system, the crumbs left behind from each student can be totaled.

Explain: Finally, children infer which of these snacks is/are best for space travel, providing reasons for their responses.

Elaborate: Listed here are some typical discussion questions:

- "Which snacks made the most crumbs?"
- "Which snacks made the fewest crumbs?"

- "Which snacks would you recommend that astronauts take with them to space? Why?"
- "What other foods could astronauts eat?"
- "What foods should astronauts *not* take with them? Why?"
- "Which would you want to eat in bed?"

Performance Expectation: Student will chart and/or graph the results of their observations.

SECOND AND THIRD GRADE

Question: How can a raw egg be dropped without breaking it?

Objective: To design and build a device to hold a raw egg so that it won't break when it is dropped to the hard floor from a height of at least 5 feet.

Materials: The students will come up with their own list of materials.

Procedure

Engage: For this activity, put the students into heterogeneously populated groups; groups of four students would be ideal. They will need to work together on this project. Ask, **"What will happen to this egg if I drop it on the floor?"** Say, **"Everybody knows that if I drop an egg on the floor, it will break and spatter. Your challenge is to design and build something that will hold the egg so it will not break when it is dropped to the floor; the distance of the fall will be at least 5 feet."** The design and the construction *must* be done in school; that way you can be sure it is the students who come up with the final design and not a parent or someone else, and it is the students who build the contraption. Have each group draw the design for their tool.

Explore: Students will need a few days to complete this activity; they will need to bring materials from home. Students will explore ideas for the design of their device, draw their device, and make a model.

Of course, the real test of their design and construction will be dropping the egg without its breaking. Meanwhile, you should circulate among the students, probing for their thinking behind the design and their method of construction.

Explain: The students should test their egg-dropping devices. Each group should report on its results and explain why they succeeded or failed. Compare the factors that were the characteristics of both the successful and failed devices.

Elaborate: If the device does not work and time permits, the students could come up with a new design, build it, and test it.

Evaluate: Students meet the Performance Expectation through the engineering design practice K-2-ETS1-1: Design a simple problem that can be solved through the development of a new or improved object or tool.

THIRD GRADE

Question: How can we clean up an oil spill?

Objective: To investigate several ways of cleaning an oil slick on water and decide which method cleans the most oil with the least effort expended.

Materials: Aluminum pie plate, plastic bowl, or similar container, water, motor oil, salad oil, cotton balls, spoon, eye dropper, piece of nylon netting, piece of nylon stocking, piece of Styrofoam, piece of cardboard, piece of string, straw, Dawn liquid detergent, other materials individual students identify.

Procedure

Engage: Say, **"An oil tanker has hit a huge rock near shore, ripping open her oil storage tanks. Millions of gallons of oil have spilled out into the water and have floated to the surface. What can be done to clean up the spill and save the shoreline inhabitants?"** Have the students contribute ideas.

Explore: Place about an inch of water in the container, and place a predetermined number of drops of the motor oil onto the surface. Have the students take turns selecting any of the materials available, and use them to clean up the oil slick. Use a stopwatch or clock with a second hand to time how long it takes to clean up the spill. Use a data chart, such as the abbreviated one suggested here, to record your results.

- Repeat the simulation, using different kinds of oils.

Explain: Ask, **"Which method enabled you to clean up each kind of oil the fastest?"**

Typical collateral questions include the following:

- "What happens to sea life in and/or near the oil spill?"
- "What happens to sea birds?"
- "What happens to the coral reefs on the ocean floor?"

Data Table

Oil Spill Cleanup

Kind of Oil	Material Used	Time to Clean Up the Spill	Estimated Percentage of Oil Cleaned Up	Comments

Performance Expectation: Students will demonstrate standard K-2-ETS1-1: Ask questions, make observations, and gather information about a situation people want to change to define a simple problem that can be solved through the development of a new or improved object or tool.

Digital Download

SUMMARY

11-1 Standards and Guidelines for Earth and Space Sciences

Earth and space sciences (ESS) include the study of processes on Earth as well as Earth's relationship to the solar system and galaxy. ESS is interdisciplinary in that it relates to the other science areas and other disciplines such as math and reading. All Earth's systems affect each other. There are three core ideas in ESS. As we learn more about space and as human population grows, ESS gets more notice. NGSS includes specific performance expectations.

Next Generation Instructional Plans. Earth and space science planning that meets the performance objectives of the NGSS is broken down into manageable individual lessons, each with its own performance objective. Lessons focus on soil, its origin and its composition, helpful and harmful erosion, and our solar system, including our sun, and are constructed so as to encourage children to explore on their own.

Conventional Earth and Space Science Instruction. Conventional instruction includes the study of rocks; soil; water; sand; weather and seasons; heat; sun; light; the solar system; and air, water, and soil quality.

11-2 Standards and Guidelines for Environmental Awareness

Standards for environmental awareness are embedded within NGSS kindergarten and fourth-grade performance expectations. Students are expected to communicate solutions that will reduce the impact of humans on the land, water, air, and/or living things in their local environment. In addition, they should obtain and combine information to show that energy and fuels are derived from natural resources and that their uses affect the environment. The K–12 Framework includes descriptions of aspects of environmental awareness. Primary teachers should guide their

students in learning about a healthy local environment and acting to provide it.

Next Generation Environmental Awareness Instructional Plans. Lessons focused on raising environmental awareness encourage students to explore phenomena on their own and use their observations to come up with their own conclusions.

Conventional Environmental Awareness Instruction. Conventional instruction focuses on environment, resources, and recycling. Instruction may follow one or more of three common approaches; awareness, environmental concerns, and/or conservation. Major areas of focus include water, trash and litter, and recycling.

11-3 Description and Standards for Engineering Design, Technology, and Applications of Science

Engineering design is the main practice in engineering today. Technology is a modification to the natural world made to fulfill human needs. Scientific knowledge may be applied to help solve a design problem, Engineering Design is a three-step process: (1) Define the problem; (2) develop possible solutions; and (3) compare different solutions.

Engineering Design. The engineer's task is to solve problems. The engineer goes through several practices as he or she solves a problem. Specific goals provide the criteria for a successful solution. Brainstorming and construction of models help in the path to a solution.

Links Among Engineering, Technology, Science, and Society. New scientific knowledge can result in new technology, which may evolve in new engineering design and new science investigations. This progress can have an effect on society and the natural world.

Next Generation Instructional Plans. Several examples of ETS instructional investigations are described. Plans are outlined for additional projects.

FURTHER READING AND RESOURCES

Crismond, D., Soonyiah, M., & Cain, R. (2013). Taking engineering design out for a spin. *Science and Children, 50*(5), 52–57.

Graca, R. M. (2012). It's no problem to invent a solution. *Science and Children, 50*(4), 34–39.

High, V., & VanHorn, L. (2012). Soil science in the digital age. *Science and Children, 50*(3), 37–45.

Powell, S. (2014). *The cardboard box book*. New York: St. Martin's Press.

Sibley, A., & Kurz, T. L. (2014). iSTEM: Celebrating Earth Day with sustainability. *Teaching children Mathematics, 20*(8), 516–518.

Science and Children. (2013). The history of our planet [Focus issue on Earth Science]. *50*(8).

Spring, P., & Harr, N. (2014). Our world without decomposers: How scary! *Science and Children, 51*(7), 28–37.

Truesdell, P. (2014). *Engineering essentials for STEM instruction*. Arlington. VA: NSTA Press & ASCD.

REFERENCES

Ashworth, P. (2013). Are they getting it? *Science and Children, 51*(3), 24–25.

Cole, J. (1986). *Magic school bus: Through the waterworks*. New York: Scholastic Books.

Darrow, B. (2014, January 19). AES students to build handicap access ramp for resident. *Cookeville Herald Citizen*. www.herald-citizen.com.

Dighe, J. (1993). Children and the Earth. *Young Children, 48*(3), 58–63.

Lachapelle, C.P., Sargianis, K., & Cunningham, C.M. (2013). Engineering encounters: Engineer it, learn it: Science and engineering practices in action. *Science and Children, 51*(3), 70–76.

National Research Council (NRC). (2012). *A framework for K–12 science education*. Washington, DC: National Academies Press.

National Research Council (NRC). (2013). *Next Generation Science Standards*. Washington, DC: National Academies Press.

Paterson, D. (1981). *Stone soup*. Mahwah, NJ: Troll Associates.

Stein, W. (1973). *Sylvester and the magic pebble*. New York: Simon & Schuster.

STEM with an environmental focus. (2014, February). *NSTA Reports, 25*(6), 1, 5.

Tank, K., Pettis, C., Moore, T., & Fehr, A., (2013). Hamsters, picture books, and engineering design. *Science and Children, 50*(9), 59–63.

Webster, J. (2014, February 28). Children as architects. *ExchangeEveryDay*. Retrieved from www.childcareexchange.com.

PART 7
THE MATH AND
SCIENCE ENVIRONMENT
CHAPTER 12 Materials and Resources: Math
and Science in the Classroom and the Home

CHAPTER
12

MATERIALS AND RESOURCES:
MATH AND SCIENCE IN THE CLASSROOM AND THE HOME

OBJECTIVES

After reading this chapter, you should be able to:

12-1 Select appropriate materials and set up learning centers for math and science in line with national standards.

12-2 Plan and provide math and science experiences using blocks, woodworking, games, outdoor activities, technology, manipulatives, and other materials, in line with national standards.

12-3 Provide families with strategies and activities that support math and science learning at home.

STANDARDS ADDRESSED IN THIS CHAPTER

naeyc

NAEYC Professional Preparation Standards

1c. Create healthy, respectful, supportive, and challenging learning environments.

2a. Know and understand diverse family and community characteristics.

2b. Support and engage families and communities.

2c. Involve families and communities in children's development and learning.

4b. Know and understand effective early education strategies and tools, including technology.

5c. Design, implement, and evaluate developmentally meaningful and challenging curriculum.

DAP Guidelines

2E. Promote each child's learning and development.

5D. Acknowledge family's choices and goals, and respond with sensitivity and respect.

Common Core State Standards for Math

MP5 Use appropriate tools strategically.

Next Generation Science Standards

3-PS2-1 Science and engineering practice: Science investigations use a variety of methods, tools, and techniques.

ETS 1.A Define and delimit engineering problems.

ETS 1.B Develop possible solutions.

12-1 OVERVIEW OF MATERIALS AND ENVIRONMENT

Whether learning experiences are presented in an informal, naturalistic, or adult-guided approach (a learning cycle, discrepant event, or demonstration) or are used in learning centers or manipulated by an entire class at one time, manipulative science and mathematics require materials for children to explore. Hands-on mathematics and science require that materials be handled, stored, distributed, and replaced whenever they are used. Do not be discouraged. In the long run, once the materials are accumulated and organized, less time is needed for teacher preparation because much of the classroom instruction will be carried out by the child interacting with the materials.

Some categories of math and science materials can be used to guide selections. In Chapter 1, six categories of math materials were discussed: real objects, real objects used with pictorial representations, two-dimensional cutouts, pictures, wipe-off folders, and paper and pencil. These categories follow a developmental sequence from the concrete manipulative to the abstract representational. Preoperational children work with only the first four types of materials. During the transition to concrete operations, the last two categories may be available for children who can use them. Throughout the concrete operations period, new concepts and skills that employ concrete manipulative and pictorial materials should be introduced to children before moving on to the abstract representational. The materials must be accurate representations of the concept, and adults should carefully guide the students as they introduce the materials (McNeil & Uttal, 2009). Montessori was very adept at providing step-by-step adult guidance. Virtual manipulatives offer a more controlled approach for students who cannot get the concepts through concrete examples. For some students (both younger and older), moving from the concrete to the abstract is a difficult challenge.

Many kinds of concrete manipulative materials or tools have been introduced throughout the preceding chapters. Some are versatile, whereas others serve more specific functions. Pictorial manipulatives and other picture materials have also been suggested. Children's picture books are an especially rich source of pictorial and language information, as suggested in Chapter 6. Stories, poems, and pictures enrich the math curriculum. These materials help teach math vocabulary, illustrate the use of math in a variety of settings, and expand children's ideas of how math can be used. Carefully select books. Be sure that the illustrations accurately portray the concepts the book purports to help teach. As noted in Chapter 7, take special care when selecting counting books, because the illustrations are frequently inaccurate in their depiction of the group symbol

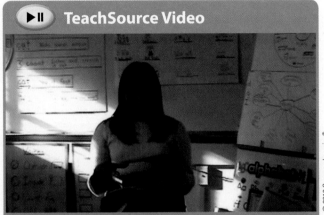

▶❚❚ TeachSource Video

© 2016 Cengage Learning®

HANDLING THE DISTRIBUTION OF TOOLS IN KINDERGARTEN

The kindergarten teacher explains how he introduces tools (manipulatives) to students, so eventually they can select the ones that work best for them.

1. How does the teacher introduce tools to children?
2. How does the teacher manage using multiple tools?
3. What method does he use so students can learn which tools are best for them?

relationships. The teacher should ask: "Which concept or concepts are illustrated in this book? How will reading this story or poem help Matthew, Lucy, or Amanda to better understand this concept?" Books should have good artwork and be colorful and well written. The National Council of Teachers of Mathematics publishes a resource catalog, which you can request from its website.

There are several general categories of science materials. The most complete listing of available materials appears each January in *Science and Children*, a journal of the National Science Teachers Association (NSTA). This useful supplement answers the question "Where do I go for help?" The publication is organized into four main sections: (1) equipment/supplies, (2) media producers, (3) computers/software, and (4) publishers. This chapter offers suggestions for the selection of basic science materials and resources and for preparing science learning centers. The guidelines for selecting math materials for young children can also be applied to selecting science materials.

DAP **naeyc**

12-1a Basic Math and Science Materials

There are two basic types of math and science materials: those you purchase and those you "scrounge." Purchased materials include textbook publishers' kits, general kits, and items purchased at supply houses or local retailers. Materials that are scrounged or contributed by parents and by other benevolent individuals are known by many teachers as "good junk," or recycled material. Regardless of how the materials are acquired, they must be organized and managed in a way that promotes learning. (Refer to Chapter 10 for additional suggestions for classroom management.)

The Good Junk Box: Things to Scrounge. Many teachers rely on boxes of miscellaneous materials that have been gathered from many sources. A junk box comes in handy. Invite children, friends, businesspeople, and others to add to yours. Once people know you collect odds and ends, they will remember you when they are ready to throw something away. Here are some examples:

- Glass containers and 2-liter bottles make good aquariums, terrariums, and places to display animals.

- Aluminum foil, pie plates, and frozen food containers are useful for numerous activities.

- Small cans with lids or medicine bottles with the labels removed can be used to make smell and sound containers.

- Hardware supplies are always welcome for the tool center; plastic tubing, garden hoses, and funnels are ideal for water play and making musical instruments.

- Candles, thumbtacks, paper clips, and other sink-or-float items come in handy.

- Refrigerator magnets are useful for magnet experiences; old, leaky aquariums make good housing for small mammals or reptiles.

- Oatmeal containers make drums; shoe boxes are great for dioramas and general organization and storage.

- Toys, clocks, and kitchen tools can be added to the machine center and used for dramatic play.

- Flashlights, batteries, and wire from telephone lines can be used for electricity experiments.

- Pipe cleaners are always useful for art; buttons and other small objects are needed for classifying and comparing.

- Straws, balloons, paper cups, pieces of fabric, and wallpaper are objects for the touch box.

- Some stores invite teachers to collect their old carpet and wallpaper sample books.

- Always keep an eye out for feathers, unusual rocks, shells, seed-growing containers, plastic eggs—the list is endless.

- Items that can be counted, sorted, graphed, and so on, such as plastic lids from bottles, jars, and other containers; thread spools, pinecones, seashells, buttons, and seeds are all useful.

- Egg cartons and frozen food containers can be used for sorting.

- String, ribbon, sticks, and so on, can be used for comparing lengths and for informal measuring.

- Small boxes can be used for construction projects.

Some teachers send home a list of junk items at the beginning of the year. Parents are asked to bring or send available items to school. Such a list will be easy to complete when you become familiar with what is good junk and have an idea of some of the items that you will use during the year. In addition, parents are usually responsive to special requests such as vegetables for the vegetable activities like those in Chapter 7 or ingredients for the cooking activities in Chapters 6 and 11.

Commercial Materials for Science. Your school district might decide to purchase a kit from a publisher when selecting a textbook for teaching science. Publisher kits are available from most major companies and contain materials specifically designed to implement the activities suggested in the textbook. These kits can be helpful in providing the hands-on component of a textbook-based science program.

General kits are available from many sources and range in size from small boxes to large pieces of furniture with built-in equipment such as sinks and cabinets. General kits contain basic materials but may not be directed to your specific needs. An advantage of the boxes or rolling tables is that they are easy to circulate among teachers.

Specific topic kits such as Mining, Minerals, and Me (suggested in Chapter 11) are boxed by topic and grade level. The idea is to provide the teacher with the materials necessary to teach a specific science topic. Teachers' manuals and materials allow teachers to use the kit as a supplement to a textbook or as the major means of teaching a science concept.

Advantages and Disadvantages of Kits. Most kits contain a limited amount of consumable supplies, usually just enough for a class to do all of the activities covered in the teacher manual. Reordering must be continuous for the kit to be used again. However, the kits also contain permanent supplies such as magnifiers, clay, small plastic aquariums, petri dishes, balances, and the like.

The major drawbacks to commercial kits of any type are maintaining the consumables in the kits and finding the money to purchase the kits. Kits are self-contained, complete, and ready for use; consequently, they are expensive.

Purchased Equipment. You might have to purchase some items to be an effective science teacher. This list includes magnifiers, eyedroppers, plastic tubing, mirrors, a rock and mineral set, magnets, batteries, and bulbs. If you select just one of these items, do not hesitate to choose magnifiers as the most useful piece of science equipment for the early childhood classroom. (Refer to Chapter 10 for suggestions on using magnifiers.)

Although they are not interactive in the same way as rollers, ramps, and constructions, magnifiers provide children with their first look at fascinating magnified objects.

Piaget was a biologist and probably would have wholeheartedly approved. It is hard to believe that he did not eagerly explore his environment up close at an early age.

There are a multitude of commercially available materials for mathematics. Some materials are versatile and can be used in the development of more than one concept. Basic materials include the following:

- Unit blocks with miniature animals, people, and vehicles
- Construction materials (**Figure 12-1**)
- Unifix Cubes
- Legos
- Multilinks
- Pegboards and pegs
- Picture lotto games
- Beads and strings
- Attribute blocks
- Geoboards
- Balance scales
- A thermometer
- A flannelboard and a magnet board with felt and magnet pieces for concept activities
- Montessori Cylinder Blocks (**Figure 12-2**)
- A manipulative clock

- Base-10 blocks
- Fraction pies
- Hand calculators and computers

Search through the major catalogs and decide what you can afford. Also, consider assembling and making materials (see the resource lists at the end of each unit).

Organizing and Storing Materials. As you collect and develop materials for teaching science and math, storage might become a problem. Most commercial kits have neat, ready-made labeled boxes, but the junk-box system will need some organizing.

One way to manage a variety of materials is to place them in shoe boxes or other similar containers. The boxes contain the equipment and materials needed to teach one or more specific concepts. If the containers are clearly marked, they can be very convenient. The trick is to keep everything you need in the designated container—for example, homemade equipment materials, task cards, materials to duplicate, and bulletin board ideas. To be effective, the box, envelope, or grocery bag should display a materials list on the outside. In this way, you have a self-contained kit for teaching science and or math (**Figure 12-3**).

Materials relating to a learning center can be stored in boxes under or near the science or math center. Materials will be handy, and older children will be able to get their own materials. Primary-age children can be effective organizers. They will enjoy and benefit from the job of inventorying and organizing materials.

3D Geoshapes	Cuisinaire® Rods	Keeptacks	Polydron
Balancing H Blocks	Disco Shapes	Klondikers	Poly-M
Baufix	Duplo®	K'Nex	Rig-A-Jig
Beads	Edu-Builder	LASY Construction Kits	Ring-A-Majigs
Beam and Boards	Flexibricks	Learning Links	Snap Blocks
Bendits	Flexo	Lego®	Snap Wall
Block Head	Floresco	Light Table and Accessories	Snap-N-Play Blocks
Blockbusters	Form-A-Tions	Lincoln Logs	Soft Big-Blocks
Bolt Builder	Free Form Posts	Lock & Stack Blocks	Space Wheels
Brio Builder	Frontier Logs'N Blocks	Locktagons	Sprocketeers
Bristle Bears	Galaxy Builder	Magnastiks	Stackobats
Bristle Blocks	Gear Circus	Magnetic Blocks	Structo-Brics
Building Clowns	Gears! Gears!	Marble Run	Struts
Building Shapes	Geo-D-Stix	Mega Blocks	Sturdiblocks
Busy Blocks	Giant Double Towers	Mobilo	Tectonic
Channel Blocks	Giant Edu-Blocks	Multi-fit	Tinkertoys
Cloth Cubes	Giant Interlockers	Multilinks®	Tower-ifics
Color Cone	Giant Structo-Cubes	Octagons	Toy Makers
Connect-A-Cube	Girders	Omnifix	Tuff Tuff Blocks
Connector	Groovy Parts	Pipe Construction	Unifix Cubes®
Construction Rug	Habitat	Play Shapes	Unit Blocks
Create It	Hex-A-Links	Play Squares	Wee Waffle Blocks
Crystal Climbers	Ji-gan-tiks	Play-Panels	Wonderforms
Crystal Octons	Jumbo Cuisinaire Rods	Poki Blocks	Wood'n Molds

FIGURE 12-1 Construction materials for math and science.

© Cengage Learning®

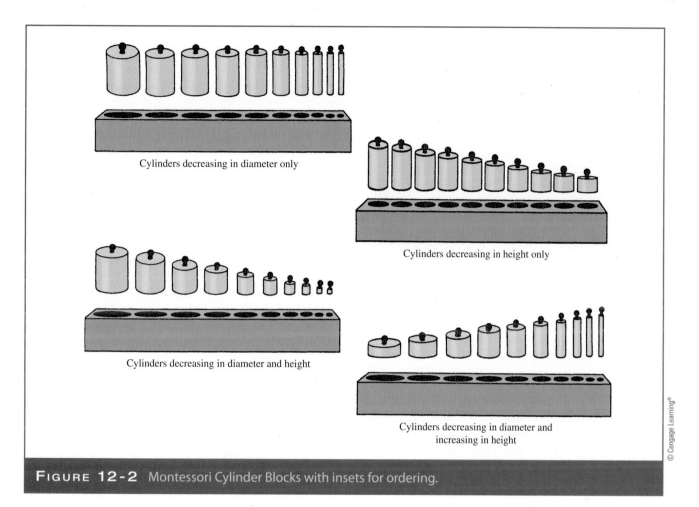

Cylinders decreasing in diameter only

Cylinders decreasing in height only

Cylinders decreasing in diameter and height

Cylinders decreasing in diameter and increasing in height

© Cengage Learning®

FIGURE 12-2 Montessori Cylinder Blocks with insets for ordering.

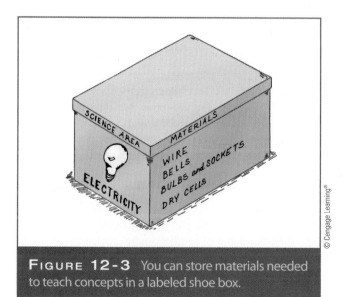

© Cengage Learning®

FIGURE 12-3 You can store materials needed to teach concepts in a labeled shoe box.

The Outdoor Classroom. Children need to spend more time outdoors in the natural environment (Nelson, 2012; Rivkin, 2014). The outdoors is a primary play area for children, where they can institute their own activities. They not only get exercise, they can do the same activities done inside

outdoors. Outdoors is an area where child-initiated curriculum can emerge. Weather and space permitting, gardening can take place outdoors (Starbuck, Olthof, & Midden, 2002). Children can select what to plant and take responsibility for caring for the plants. Children can search for insects, collect rocks, and play with sand and dirt.

 COMMON CORE STATE STANDARDS

12-1b The Math Learning Center

Materials in the math center should be neatly organized and displayed. Place the materials in containers on low shelves where the students can readily access them. Be sure that students clearly understand the procedures for removing, using, and replacing materials. Sometimes a specialized center (e.g., for measurement or classification) can add to the excitement of learning (see **Photos 12-1** and **12-2**).

Materials can be rotated according to the children's needs and interests and to keep their attention engaged. When new materials are introduced, the teacher should allow opportunities for children to explore them before the materials are used for adult-guided activities.

Math centers can also focus on specific concepts when they are being introduced. Focused centers can be set up for

PHOTO 12-1 An example of a carefully organized shelf.

any of the skills and concepts in the text. Math centers can be set up relative to available space and furnishings. A center might be a set of shelves with an adjacent table and chairs or carpeted area (Photo 12-1), a small table with a few different materials each day, or a space on the floor where math materials are placed. In one primary classroom, a math "bed" was installed. A blackboard was at one end, and shelves for books and materials were at the other end: a comfortable and inviting math center.

The math center should be available to every child, every day. Too frequently, the math center is open only to children who finish their workbook and other reproducible paper assignments. Unfortunately, the children who do not finish their paper-and-pencil work are probably most in need of experiences with concrete manipulative materials. If workbooks are required, then, after they have been introduced,

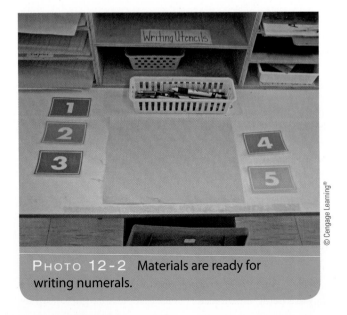

PHOTO 12-2 Materials are ready for writing numerals.

put them on a special shelf in the math center, and let the children who are ready select them from among the other materials available.

Many teachers, especially in the primary grades, feel pressured to follow the textbook and teach group math lessons without using manipulatives to introduce concepts as described in this text. A compromise can be found that is beneficial for both students and teacher. For example, one first-grade teacher, feeling discouraged with the progress her students were making in mathematics, decided to try a new approach: She took the objectives for the text assigned to her class and found developmentally appropriate activities that correlated with each one. She selected the activities from early childhood resources (as referenced in each chapter in this text) and assembled the necessary materials. She introduced each concept to the whole class and then divided the class into small groups to work with the concrete materials. The children felt more satisfied, performed their tasks with enthusiasm, and even commented on how much fun it was not to have to write! The teacher had time to circulate and help individual children. A positive side effect emerged from the opportunity to "talk" math: The children's language was extended, and unclear points were clarified. Peer tutoring developed naturally—to the advantage of both the tutors and those who needed help. The games and manipulatives were available for further use during the children's free time. The teacher's enthusiasm and the enthusiasm of the students were picked up by the other first-grade teachers and the principal. The teacher was asked to in-service the other first-grade teachers so that they could adopt the same system.

12-1c The Science Learning Center

You know that the interests of children stem from the kinds of learning materials and experiences available to them. One way to provide stimulating explorations is by setting up learning centers appropriate for an individual child or for a small group of children. As children work in centers, they learn how to learn on their own in a planned environment. In this way, instruction is individualized, and children have time to explore science materials.

The several different types of science learning centers are characterized by different purposes and modes of operation. The basic types of centers can be labeled as discovery, open learning, inquiry learning, and science interest.

Discovery Center. The word *discovery* implies that some action will be taken on materials and that questions and comments about what is happening take place. All is not quiet in a discovery center. So it should be located away from listening and literacy centers. Discovery centers can be located on large tables, desks against a wall, or any roomy spot. Mobile discovery centers made of trays, shoe boxes, or baskets can simply be picked up and taken to a designated

Materials	Procedure	Properties to Observe	Extensions
Several varying sizes of paper or plastic bags	Hold the bags open and describe what you see inside. Hold the bag closed and squeeze it. Do you feel anything? Try it again with a different bag.	Air can be felt even when it cannot be seen.	Try this activity with balloons. Ask children what happens to the air when the balloon is flat.
Balloons	Blow up a balloon. Hold the mouth of the balloon shut with your fingers. Open your fingers slightly and let some air out. What do you hear? Do your fingers feel anything?	Air can make noise and be felt.	Use flutes, recorders, or whistles to demonstrate how air can make different types of noise.
Paper and a stapler	Fold the paper accordion style and staple the end to make a fan. What do you feel when you wave the fan near your face?	Air can be moved and felt.	Use a fan or look outside on a windy day to observe how air moves and how air can move other things.

© Cengage Learning®

FIGURE 12-4 Using activity trays to observe the properties of air.

spot on the floor. An area rug makes a good place to work without taking up too much space.

In **Figure 12-4**, activity trays are used to explore concepts about air. As with any learning center, the size of your center area and ages of the children must be taken into account. For the three activity trays described in Figure 12-4, the teacher should use two trays with 5-year-olds and (initially) one tray with younger children.

Open Learning Center. The science center in an open classroom encourages creativity and contains an abundance of manipulative materials, most of which are homemade. Using minimum directions, the child might be asked to "invent something" with these materials. Guidance is provided in the way of helpful suggestions or questions as the children pursue and tinker with their invention.

An example of an open center is a sink-and-float center. In this center, reinforcing the sink-and-float concept is the central objective. The center contains a plastic tub half full of water and a box of familiar materials. On the whiteboard are the questions "What will float?" and "What will sink?" With no further direction, the children explore the questions with the materials.

Teacher evaluation is not formal; rather, the teacher visits the center and satisfies any concerns about children's progress. The teacher might find children making piles of things that do and do not float or trying to sink something that they thought would float. Some teachers suggest that the children communicate what happened at the center by drawing or by writing a few sentences.

Inquiry Learning Center. A more directed discovery approach focuses on a science concept or topic and contains materials to be manipulated by the children, directions for the investigation, and open-ended questions to be asked at the end of the inquiry. The objective is not to reinforce a concept, but to engage the child in problem solving beyond what is already known in order to gain new insights.

At an inquiry center, the child might find directions that say, "Using the materials in this box, find a way to light the bulb" or "What kinds of materials are attracted to magnets?" Science concepts are turned into questions that are placed on activity cards. There might be a single task or a series of tasks that a primary-age child can complete in 15–30 minutes.

It would be foolish to send children to an inquiry center without adequate preparation. Discuss directions, procedures, and task cards with the children before beginning center work. The children are expected to achieve a desired learning outcome. So, if things do not go smoothly, ask yourself: Were the directions clear? Did the children know where to begin and end? Did they know what to do when they were finished? Is the center appropriate for the age group? Did the first group using the center know how to restore the materials for the next group?

Science Interest Center. Science interest corners, tables, and centers are popular in many schools. This interest center reinforces, enriches, and supplements ongoing programs with materials that stimulate children's interest. The primary goal of the center is to motivate children to want to learn more about the subject at the center.

As a general rule, children are not required to visit this center, and no formal evaluation of their activities is recorded. Many times, the center repeats a lesson exploration. For example, if the class has done the "Thinking Like a Geologist" lesson described in Chapter 11, some children might want to try scratching minerals to test hardness or classifying the available rocks. Filmstrips, storybooks, and resource books on rocks and minerals should be available for the children to explore. Children could practice their measuring skills by using string to measure an assortment of

What is the purpose or objective?

Who will be using this learning center?

What are the concepts children should learn?

What are the skills children should learn?

What activities will take place?

What materials need to be available?

What are the learning objectives?

How will children's progress be evaluated?

© Cengage Learning®

FIGURE 12-5 Questions to ask when planning a learning center.

objects or become acquainted with a balance scale by comparing the weight of different rocks.

Plan Your Center. State learning center objectives in such a way that you know what you want the child to learn. Be aware of your children's developmental level. You can avoid inadvertently creating busywork for students by taking steps to carefully plan the concepts to be developed at the center. Start by writing a sentence that communicates what the child is expected to learn at the center. Children must be able to participate in the activities and methods independently. Evaluate the center by asking yourself: Is the center effective in achieving my objectives? How can the center be improved? **Figure 12-5** suggests a guide to planning a learning center.

12-1d Selecting Math Materials

In a classroom, each child has her individual and age-appropriate needs in mathematics. Every school and classroom includes children who are at various levels of concept development. Children should be provided with a wide array of math materials and the time to explore them freely.

In Chapter 1, three considerations regarding selection of math and science materials were discussed:

- The materials should be sturdy and versatile.
- The materials should fit the outcome objectives selected.
- The materials should fit the developmental levels of the children.

In addition, the following should be considered:

- The materials should be safe.
- The materials should be easily supervised.

- The materials should be free of gender, ethnic, age, and socioeconomic bias.
- Book illustrations and content and drawings, photos, and other materials should include depictions of members of diverse cultures in nonstereotyped dress and engaged in authentic activities.

When selecting materials, versatility is important; that is, can the materials be used on a regular basis for teaching a variety of concepts? For example, unit blocks, Unifix Cubes, and Multilinks fit this criterion. No material should be a health hazard. Avoid anything made from a toxic material and anything with sharp edges or small parts or pieces that can lodge in noses or ears or be swallowed.

When taking over a new classroom or at the end of each year in a current classroom, take an inventory of materials. Note their condition: Are parts missing? Do materials need mending or replacement? Are there materials for all concepts in the program and for naturalistic, informal, and adult-guided experiences? Are both indoor and outdoor materials and equipment in good condition? With this information, determine what is on hand and what needs to be purchased. In preprimary, when children have shorter attention spans, it is recommended that a variety of small sets of materials (enough for two or three children to share at one time) be purchased. In the primary grades, start with a classroom set of Unifix materials. These materials are among the most versatile because they can be used for teaching almost every primary mathematics concept. Many accessories are available, and you can select activities from the numerous resources already mentioned in this text. Gradually add base-10 blocks, fraction materials, and other manipulatives.

Another source of materials is the pool of parents, who can donate recycle materials. Ask parents to save egg cartons, buttons, boxes and other containers, bottle caps, yarn, ribbon, and other materials that can be used in the math program. Parents might also donate inexpensive items such as toothpicks, golf tees, playing cards, funnels, measuring cups, and so on. Lumber companies might donate scrap lumber. Restaurant supply companies will often sell teachers trays, various-sized containers, and the like at low prices. Try to convince your principal to let you spend your share of supply money on concrete manipulative materials and supplies for making two-dimensional manipulatives rather than on workbooks and copy paper. Resources for ideas for teacher-made materials are listed at the end of each unit. You can also view or request many catalogs online.

12-1e Selecting Science Materials

Providing materials that encourage children to "mess around" and explore is the responsibility of the teacher. At the center, children use the process skills to observe, investigate, classify, and perhaps hypothesize. Because this learning is not accidental, planning must go into setting up

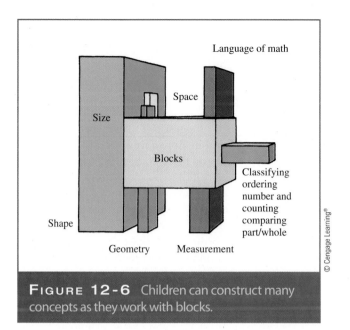

Size

Language of math

Space

Shape

Blocks

Classifying ordering number and counting comparing part/whole

Geometry   Measurement

© Cengage Learning®

FIGURE 12-6 Children can construct many concepts as they work with blocks.

centers and selecting materials. After completing the planning guide suggested in **Figure 12-6**, consider the following criteria in selecting and arranging materials.

1. *Are the materials open ended?* Can they be used in more than one way? For example, water play provides the opportunity to explore measuring or floating.

2. *Are the materials designed for action?* In science, children do something to materials to make something else happen. If substances are to be dissolved, which will offer the best example: salt, flour, or pudding mix?

3. *Are the materials arranged to encourage communication among children?* If appropriate, place materials to create cooperation and conversation. Arrange materials in categories such as pitchers of water in one section of the center, substances to be tested in another, and spoons and dishes for mixing in another. Children quickly learn to cooperate and communicate to complete the activity.

4. *Is there a variety of materials?* If the center is to be used over an extended period, some children will visit it many times. A variety of materials will prevent overexposure to the exploration.

5. *Do the materials encourage "What if …" statements?* The sink-and-float activity described in the open classroom learning center invites children to predict what will happen if they try to float a marble, toothpick, or sponge.

6. *Are the materials appropriate for the maturity of the children?* Consider the maturity level of the class. Select materials that the children can handle safely and effectively.

7. *Do the materials allow for individual differences such as ability, interest, working space, and style?*

After considering floating and sinking, some children will begin to consider size and other characteristics of the available objects. Have objects with a variety of textures and features available.

8. *How much direction do the materials require?* In giving directions, consider the age of the children. Although 4- and 5-year-olds might receive directions from a cassette recording, 3-year-olds (and some 4-year-olds) respond best to personal directions.

9. *Do the materials stress process skills?* Process skills are the fundamental skills that are emphasized in science explorations with young children. These skills will come naturally from manipulating materials. However, a variety of appropriate materials is required for this to happen.

10. *Are the materials culturally nonbiased?* Where appropriate, materials should illustrate authentic nonbiased dress and activities.

Sensory Learning Center. Children have a sensible approach to the world around them. The approach that they use is as basic to science as it is natural to young children. Use the type of center you prefer to give children an opportunity to taste, smell, touch, observe, and hear their environment.

Thinking Like a Criminologist. Skin prints are a way to take a closer look at the skin children live in. They enjoy examining their fingertips, taking their own fingerprints, and thinking like a criminologist at this center. Because a criminologist investigates crimes by analyzing clues in a systematic way, studying fingerprints is an important part of this job.

You will need one No. 2 pencil, white scratch paper, plain paper, a handheld lens, and a damp paper towel at this station. Show children how to rub soft pencil lead onto a sheet of paper and pick up a good smudge with one finger. Then they carefully pick up the smudge with a piece of clear tape, pull it away, and press the fingerprint onto a clean paper.

Begin by having students make a set of their own fingerprints on a sheet of clean paper. If someone makes a mistake, simply peel off the tape and start over. Then create a classroom mystery for your students to solve. Ask, "Who was the last person to use the pencil sharpener?" Each group that visits the center can be a group of suspects. Prepare prints in advance; then show prints that were found on the pencil sharpener. Have the children use the handheld lens to compare their prints to the set belonging to the "criminal."

Integrate fingerprinting into art by letting the children use ink pads to make prints from their hands or fingers. Children can bring the prints to life by adding legs, arms, and other features. Fingerprint stories can be developed, and you may even want to include toe prints as a homework assignment. You could go further and classify fingerprints into three basic patterns: whorl, arch, and loop. Refer to the further readings list for resources.

Do You Hear What I Hear? Walk in the hallway with a recorder, and record five interesting sounds. Bring the recording back to the classroom, provide earphones, and have the children draw a picture of the sounds that they hear. Children enjoy using recorders. Let them take turns recording sounds during recess, assemblies, or the lunch period. Challenge them to record unusual sounds, and infer what is making the sounds. Add further interest to this center by sending a recorder home with a child to record "home sounds." As children identify the home sounds at the center, have them compare and contrast the sounds in their own homes and write a story about the sounds and how they are created.

The recorder also makes a good listening center for a variety of recordings. Many of them should be stories. Children will enjoy illustrating the stories. Some will enjoy recording a story of their own for use in the center or as background for plays, puppet shows, or radio programs.

Red, Yellow, and Blue. The object of this center is to mix the primary colors and to observe and record the results. Have the children record the color that results from dropping the correct amounts of color into the correct container.

Smells, Smells, Smells. Gather small amounts of familiar substances with distinctive odors, such as coffee, popcorn, orange extract, hot chocolate, onions, apples, and peanut butter. Put the items in jars, shoe boxes, plastic sandwich bags, or loosely tied brown paper bags—whichever seems appropriate—and leave small holes in the containers so that the odors can escape. As children take turns smelling the containers, ask them to describe the various odors and guess what might be producing these distinctive smells. Make a duplicate set of containers, and ask the children to match the ones that smell alike. Be sure to show children the safe way to smell an unknown substance: They should gently fan the air between their noses and the container with one hand and breathe normally. The scent will come to them.

Apple or Potato? Spread vegetable pieces on a plate for children to taste. They will have to work in pairs. One puts on a blindfold, holds her nose, and tries to guess what she is tasting. The other child keeps a record by writing down what the vegetable piece really is and what his partner thinks it is. Then the children trade places, redo the test, and compare their scores.

The children will be surprised that they made a lot of wrong guesses. This is because it is hard to tell one food from another of similar texture. The secret lies inside the nose. Tongues tell only if something is sweet, sour, salty, or bitter; the rest of the information comes from the odor of the food. Lead children to the conclusion that they would have a hard time tasting without their sense of smell.

Tasting liquids that children drink frequently is fun. Pour some milk, orange juice, water, soda, or other popular drinks into paper cups or clean milk cartons, and provide clean straws for tasting. Have the children describe the taste and guess what it might be. Some children will enjoy drawing a picture of their favorite flavor. A sip of water or bite of bread between tastings helps clear their palates.

12-1f Technology

Technology resource suggestions have been inserted throughout the text and in Appendix B. Ideally, each classroom should have two or three computers, several tablets, and a Smart board where children can take turns exploring a variety of software, apps, and online resources. There should also be time for searching the Internet for information and using e-mail to communicate with others regarding problems to solve and information to share. Many early childhood and science and mathematics journals have software reviews in every issue, as well as frequent reports from teachers describing how they and their students use technology. Further suggestions are included later in the chapter.

Although computers have long been an important vehicle for mathematics instruction (Cross, Woods, & Schweingruber, 2009), other technology adaptations for young children are growing, as described in previous chapters. For example, today's young child may be observed doing searches on the computer and talking, texting, and taking and sending photos with her cell phone. Those adults who did not grow up using technology have a lot to learn to keep up with today's children.

Children from pre-K to grade 12 use many types of technology in classrooms. From PBS Kids, children can explore engineering math and science with the *Curious George Discovery Guide*. Kits that provide ideas and resources can be obtained from the Sesame Street website and the Electric Company website. Interactive whiteboards provide young children with many exciting learning experiences (Lisenbee, 2009). High school students are solving algebra problems on their smart phones (Davis, 2010), and educators are developing lessons for elementary students adapted to cell phones (Manzo, 2010). Everhart (2009) describes how YouTube can be incorporated into science lessons. Digital cameras are popular classroom tools, beginning in preschool. For example, Marinak, Strickland, and Keat (2010) describe a preschool photo narration project. Second graders collected information in the zoo, using digital cameras (Davison, 2009). Technology is spreading rapidly into homes and schools.

12-1g Materials That Help Children with Special Needs

Gargiulo and Kilgo (2014) provide suggestions for materials that support the learning of children with disabilities. Self-correcting materials, as suggested in previous chapters, can be especially effective for children with disabilities. Many Montessori materials are self-correcting. Computer software and app games may provide immediate feedback.

Teacher-made materials can have flaps or windows that reveal the correct answer. Children with physical or multiple disabilities can be provided with battery or electronic materials that operate by means of switches. Some can be operated by a puff of air or a head movement.

Materials should also provide for cultural diversity. They should reflect the students' cultures, languages, communities, and disabilities. According to de Melendez and Beck (2013), multicultural planning is child centered, developmentally based, and culturally responsive. Considerations include the children's individual and cultural characteristics, language, social and emotional development, cognitive development, and physical and motor capabilities. Stereotypes should be avoided. Media, pictures, manipulatives, and books should not promote bias toward any group, but should promote respect for diversity. For example, languages besides English should be represented in literature, songs, and rhymes and used in the classroom. Ethnic artifacts should be used. Accommodations should be made for children with special needs.

12-2 STANDARDS AND ACTION OVERVIEW

As discussed in Chapter 1, action in mathematics and science involves hands-on problem solving and inquiry. Students need to engage in science and engineering practices such as observation and data collection and analysis. Essential to mathematics are five process standards: problem solving, reasoning and proof, communication, connections, and representations (Koestler, Felton, Bieda, & Otten, 2013). This section of the chapter provides an overview of the kinds of activities that should be observed in action in early childhood classrooms. It focuses on the interrelationship of blocks, woodworking, songs, action games, problem solving, outdoor activities, technology, and culturally relevant activities that meet the affective, cognitive, and psychomotor learning needs of the young child. The emphasis is on active learning both indoors and outdoors.

Math and science go on all the time in the developmentally appropriate classroom for young children. The block builder, like any engineer, builds her building so that it will stand up and serve a planned function. The young carpenter measures wood and swings his hammer to get the most power when he hits the nail. Children do fingerplays and action songs and explore the outdoors while they apply math and science concepts. As children move into concrete operations, math and science in action include more complex group games and activities and the introduction of team sports and preplanned building and science projects.

Children continue to be active learners in the primary grades—a fact from research based on Piagetian theory. Unfortunately, the opportunities for active learning, such as block building and outdoor explorations, are not provided or considered in curriculum plans for primary-age children; this is a mistake. Remember, primary-age children are still concrete operation thinkers who learn to understand the world around them through actively engaging in explorations.

Block play and outdoor explorations provide children with many opportunities to investigate, test, and change objects. From these interactions, children build their own model of the world. (Refer to concept development in Chapters 1 and 2 to refresh your memory.)

A math lesson that meets the NCTM standards should include the following factors (Burrill, 1997): manipulatives, cooperative groups, a teacher who is a facilitator and a guide, the use of technology, opportunities to write, and strong connections to the children's world. Activities that meet these criteria can provide a program that will avoid the Math Curse (Scieszka & Smith, 1995). As described in Chapter 1, math and science in action includes hands-on projects for both individual and group work. Curriculum should emerge from children's interests (Wien, 2014; Shillady, 2013). STEM and STEAM projects proceed from children's interests and questions. Both individuals and groups of two or more can organize their work using the K-W-L-D model (Shaw, Chambless, Chessin, Price, & Beardain, 1997). *K* involves recording what is known from studying the problem to be solved. *W* stands for what I (we) want to find out, that is, identifying the question. The *L* step involves recording what the student or group of students has learned. In the final *D* step, the answer is stated and defended, and the process of problem solving is described: what we (I) did. An important aspect of a problem-solving approach to math and science is allowing plenty of time for students to think through and discuss their solution processes. Even in the midst of lively discussion, a long pause in the conversation may be needed for students to reflect on the problems so that they can create their own unique solutions.

12-2a Blocks

Blocks, especially unit blocks, are probably the play material most used by young children and most essential to their development. Unfortunately, blocks are seldom seen in classrooms beyond the kindergarten level, even though they have the potential to function as valuable concept-building materials for primary children. Research reported by Wolfgang, Stannard, and Jones (2001) indicates that young children's block play performance during preschool is a predictor of mathematics achievement in middle school and high school.

Unit blocks celebrated their 100th birthday in 2013 (Tunk, 2013). There are many other types of construction toys that provide for application of math and science concepts and skills. Tunk (2013) lists several such as Duplos, Bristle Blocks, large hollow blocks, and Legos. Children apply basic concepts as they explore the relationships among the various sizes and shapes in a set of unit blocks (Figure 12-6). They note that two of one size may equal one of another: Some are longer and some shorter; some are square; some are rectangular; others are triangular; and still others are curved. They are working with fractions and parts and wholes. MacDonald (2001) lists 29 mathematics and 20 science concepts and skills that children can construct and apply when building with unit blocks. Furthermore, block play enhances concepts and skills in art, literacy, physical development, social studies, and socioemotional development (MacDonald, 2001).

The block area needs plenty of space. Neatly organize the blocks and the small vehicles, people dolls, and animals that enhance the accompanying dramatic play activities on low shelves where the children can easily reach them. Mark shelves with outlines of each block shape so that the children can return the blocks to the proper place (and practice some one-to-one correspondence). Start the year with a small, easy-to-handle set. As time goes by, introduce more blocks and more shapes. Facilitate exploration by asking questions and making comments. For example, Mr. Sanchez notes that Trang Fung has used all square blocks in her structure, whereas Sara has developed her structure with larger units. Mr. Sanchez says, "It looks like each of you has your favorite-sized blocks."

Blocks can be purchased in sets of various sizes. Each set has a variety of shapes and sizes. The basic unit is a brick-shaped rectangle that is $1 \times 2\frac{3}{4} \times 5\frac{1}{2}$ inches. The variety of shapes and sizes is listed in **Figure 12-7**. Unit blocks should be made of good, strong, hard wood with beveled edges, so that they will not wear down or splinter. They should be smoothly sanded. The sizes must be precise so that building can be done effectively. Unit block sets are very expensive, but with good care they last for many years. Keep them dry and free of dust. Occasionally they should be oiled or waxed.

At the beginning stage, the child may just handle the blocks and carry them from place to place. At the second stage, the children make rows and lines of blocks. At the third stage, children build bridges. At the fourth stage, children make simple enclosures. At the fifth stage, the children make patterns that may be balanced and symmetric. At the sixth stage, the children name the structures and use them for dramatic play. At the last stage, the children make structures that represent familiar buildings, such as their own home or even their whole city.

Children enjoy using other types of building materials besides unit blocks. Many preschools have large, hollow wood blocks. At a lower cost, there are cardboard blocks. Cardboard boxes can enhance the imaginative activity of young children. Large boxes can be the focus of walking around, climbing in, and climbing over. Boxes can be moved about and combined in many different ways, providing experiences with weight, size, shape, and volume. Sheets and blankets can add to the variety of structures. Blocks and boxes provide a rich opportunity for math in action.

Name	Nursery	Kgn. and Primary
Square	40	80
Unit	96	192
Double unit	48	96
Quadruple unit	16	32
Pillar	24	48
Half pillar	24	48
Small triangle	24	48
Large triangle	24	48
Small column	16	32
Large column	8	16
Ramp	16	32
Ellipse		8
Curve	8	16
¼ circle		8
Large switch and gothic door		4
Small switch		4
Large buttress		4
½ arch and small buttress		4
Arch and ½ circle		4
Roofboard		24
Number of shapes	12	23
Number of pieces	344	760

FIGURE 12-7 Childcraft block sets.

© Cengage Learning®

12-2b Blocks: Science and Engineering

Block building and play are a part of science and engineering. The very nature of building a structure requires that children deal with the processes of science and engineering as discussed in Chapter 2. As children build, they compare, classify, predict, and interpret problems. Scientific thinking is stimulated as children discover and invent new forms, expand experiences, explore major conceptual ideas in science and engineering, measure, and work with space, change, and pattern.

Blocks Encourage Thinking. Blocks force children to distinguish, classify, and sort. This can be seen as a group of second graders learns the different properties of blocks by recreating a field trip to the zoo. As they plan and build the zoo, they deal with the fact that each block has different qualities. They consider size, shape, weight, thickness, width, and length. As construction progresses, the blocks become fulcrums and levers. Guiding questions such as "Can you make a ramp for unloading the rhinoceros?" and "Where will you put the access road for delivering food to the animals?" will help children focus on an aspect of construction. Some children create zoo animals, workers, and visitors to dramatize a day at the zoo.

Allow time for children to verbalize why they are arranging the zoo in a particular way. This will encourage children to share their problem-solving strategy and will help them clarify their thinking. By observing the children at play, you will also gain insight into their thought processes.

Blocks: Balance, Predictions, Interactions, and Movement. One emphasis in science is interactions within systems. In block building, the blocks form a system that is kept in equilibrium through balance. As children build, they work with a cause-and-effect approach to predict stress and to keep the forces of gravity from tumbling their structure. The idea that each part added to the structure contributes to the whole is constantly reinforced as children maintain its stability.

Balancing blocks is an effective way to explore cause and effect. By seeing the reaction of what they do, children begin to learn about causation. The following ideas emphasize action and cause and effect.

1. *Dominoes.* Children develop spatial relationships as they predict what will happen to an arrangement of dominoes. Ask, "Can you arrange the dominoes in such a way that they will all be knocked down?"

2. *Construct and roll.* Arrange plastic bottles or blocks in a variety of ways, and have the children try to knock them over with a ball. This bowling-like game encourages children to keep score and to establish a correspondence between the way blocks are arranged and how the ball is rolled. Ask: "What action caused the blocks to fall down? What action started the ball moving? Did the ball knock down every bottle that fell? If not, what made them fall?"

3. *Pendulum release.* In a pendulum game, a ball moves without being pushed; it is released. Children structure space as they place blocks in a position to be knocked down by the pendulum bob. Have children predict, "If the ball pendulum is pulled back and released, will it knock over the block?"

    Pendulums can be made life-sized by securing one end of a length of cotton string to the ceiling and attaching a weighted bob to the other end. Weighted bobs for the pendulum can be made by tying a plastic pill vial filled with sand to the cotton string. However, a smaller model may be more practical. Try this first and then tell the children how to expand to a life-sized model. One end of a length of cotton string or fish line must be attached to a stable support that allows for a swinging motion. A simple effective pendulum can be constructed by placing an eye screw into a board, suspending the board between the backs of two chairs, and attaching the string with the pendulum bob. Children can then sit on the floor and explore the action of the pendulum.

4. *Inclines.* In incline activities, the ball moves when released. Exactly where the ball goes is determined by manipulating the incline and the ball. Have children change the incline in different ways to control what happens to the ball. Children will enjoy creating games such as catching the ball with a cup, racing different-sized balls down the incline, and measuring how far the ball travels DeVries and Sales (2011) describe children's work with ramps and pathways.

5. *Buttons and bobby pins.* The object of this tilt game is to jiggle a button from start to finish without letting it fall off of the board or through a hole. The button or ball is guided by tilting and wiggling the board. To make the game, cut several holes in cardboard, and rub the board with a piece of waxed paper. Position bobby pins with the raised side up on the board, mark a start and finish, and begin the game.

Ramps and Pathways. Children can create ramps and pathways from cove molding, using a variety of supports to change speed and directions as the marbles or toy cars shoot down the pathway (Devries & Sales, 2011). PVC pipe or paper towel rolls can also be used for tunnels. The challenge is for children to invent ways to make a marble fall down a series of ramps and/or tunnels and make the trip as long as possible. Have the children glue wooden strips as obstacles. Then have them adjust their obstacles as they try out the marble. Ask, "Can you think of a way to slow down the marble?" (You might want to introduce the concept of friction.)

Balance and action can be seen as children assemble plastic ramps and chutes with commercial toys, such as Marbleworks. Children gain a familiarity with concepts such as gravity, acceleration, and momentum, and they can observe the relationship between time and speed when they design and create a maze of movement by fitting pieces together. To further introduce children to the principle of cause and effect, ask, "What action starts the marble moving?" Then have children predict how the marble will move. Creating different pathways and exploring how the marble moves on them can be exciting.

Complex block and marble sets seem to fascinate young children. With these sets, children arrange wooden sections to allow marbles to travel through holes and grooved blocks of different lengths. Children enjoy controlling the movement of the marble down the construction and creating changes that determine the direction and speed of the marble. Children can make their own marble runs from decorative molding available in paneling supply stores. The track can be nailed onto boards, taped down, or held for observing the movement of marbles (some will move at breakneck speeds). Have your students add a tunnel, try different types of balls, and find ways to use friction to slow down the marbles.

Straw and Pipe Cleaner Construction. Constructions introduce children to the conditions and limitations of space. They learn to bridge space with appropriately sized blocks and objects and to enclose space in different ways. The following ideas involve creating your own construction set with straws.

Use large straws for straw construction, and connect them with string, pipe cleaners, or paper clips. String is the most difficult to use, but makes the most permanent construction. Simply stick the string in one end of the straw and then suck on the other end. The string will be drawn through.

You will have to form a triangle with three straws. A triangle is the only shape made with straws that is rigid enough for building. If you are using string as a connector, tie the ends together to form a triangle, or thread three straws on one string to form the triangle.

Pipe cleaners as connectors are another method for building with straws. Push a pipe cleaner halfway into the end of one straw, and then slip another straw over the other end of the pipe cleaner. Double up the pipe cleaners for a tighter fit. Children can twist and turn this construction in many ways.

Many teachers recommend paper clips as ideal connectors in straw building. Open a paper clip, bend out the two ends, and slip each end into a straw. Paper clips are rigid and allow for complex building. You might have to add as many as three paper clips to give the structure strength. Paper clips may also be chained for a flexible joint between two straws. Challenge children to think and construct. Ask: "How tall a structure can you make? Why did your structure collapse? Can you make a bridge?"

When the straw frame stands by itself, test it. Ask, "Can you think of a way to test the strength of your structure?" Place a paper clip through a paper cup and hang it somewhere on the straw structure. Ask: "How many paper cups can your structure support? How many paper clips will make the framework?"

Block City. Blocks in the classroom provide many opportunities for children to integrate basic reading and writing, science, math skills and concepts, and social studies into the construction process. Opportunities for integration abound as children explore the busy life of a block city. See the photo of the city made of boxes.

Mr. Wang's second-grade children created a city of blocks (**Photo 12-3**). Buildings had to be accurate in the city, and each child builder represented herself in the daily

PHOTO 12-3 **The class builds a model of their town, using block boxes.**

acting out of city life. The block building sessions were preceded by class discussion as the children planned the daily block activities. Accessories (labeled boxes of food, clothing, computers, typewriters, and the like) were constructed from a variety of materials. Children played the roles of shopkeepers, bankers, and other workers. They made decisions such as where the people in the block city would get their money.

When the children had to put out an imaginary fire, they immediately saw a problem. How would they get water to the blaze? This discovery led to an investigation of how water gets into hydrants, utility covers, and water pipes. The children responded to the emergency by adding plastic tubing to the city as well as wire for electricity and telephones.

Not only was the city becoming more realistic, it was becoming less magical. Children no longer thought that water magically appeared when the water faucet was turned on. They knew that a system of pipes carried the water. In fact, the workings of a city in general became less magical. Many common misconceptions were dispelled, and an understanding of how a city functions began to develop. Second graders built New York City (Benedis-Grab, 2010). They learned about building materials. They applied concepts of size, shape, measurement, and time.

The Edible Village. Mrs. Moore's first-grade students integrated the study of their neighborhood with block building. After determining the different sections of the neighborhood and buildings they needed to create, each child was assigned a building. The class created their neighborhood with blocks made of graham crackers. They used flattened caramels for roadways and lollipops for streetlights. Coconut spread over white icing gave the illusion of snow.

The students mixed yellow and green food coloring into icing to create differently colored buildings. Recipes for icing provided opportunities to use measurements and follow directions in sequence. Writing about the creation of the village and what might be happening within graham cracker walls became a springboard for discussion.

Children made decisions about what should and should not be included in the village. They determined the authenticity of buildings and building size. This activity is especially appropriate for primary-age children. Children in this age group are able to incorporate more detail and can be exposed to another's viewpoint. For example, the teacher asked, "How will the people know that school is open?" Children began asking each other, "Do we need a hospital? What about a gas station?"

If your city or town is located near a river or lake, be sure to include it in construction. Paper straw bridges could be added, and the geography of your area explored. You will find that as the children develop questions, they are motivated to find the answers because they need to know something for construction of the city. Thus, the block experience also becomes a first research experience for them.

12-2c Woodworking

Most young children enjoy working with wood. Woodworking provides hands-on experience with measurement, balance, power, and spatial and size relationships. Children use informal measurement as they check to see whether they have a piece of wood that is the one they need and if they have a nail that is the correct length. As children move into the primary level, they can apply standard measurement: "I will need 12 pieces of 12 × 8-inch plywood for my birdhouse." The more advanced primary children can follow simple instructions and use patterns to make projects.

For effective woodworking, the classroom should have a sturdy workbench, good-quality real tools, and assorted pieces of soft wood. The workbench should be large enough for at least two children to work at the same time. Woodworking must always be closely supervised. Workbenches designed for children can be purchased from the major school supply companies, or a large old tree stump can be used.

The basic components of a high-quality tool set for 4- and 5-year-olds are illustrated in **Figure 12-8**. Older children can use a greater variety of tools. The tools should be easily accessible when in use, but kept in a locked closet or on a high shelf when not in use. Beginners do best with short nails with large heads.

Soft wood, such as pine, is easy for children to work with. When introducing sawing, the wood should be put in a vise so that it will be steady and the child's hands will not be in the line of the saw.

Experienced woodworkers enjoy creating projects using odds and ends with their wood. Wheels can be made from bottle caps and windows from plastic lids. Scraps of cloth or ribbon can be glued on to the wood. Children can apply their math vocabulary as they explain their finished projects.

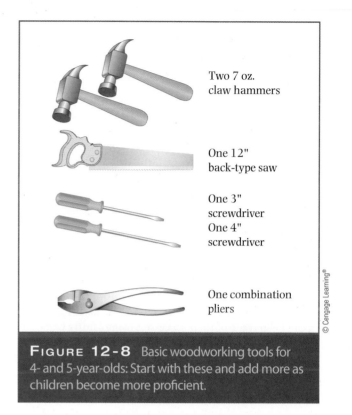

Two 7 oz. claw hammers

One 12" back-type saw

One 3" screwdriver
One 4" screwdriver

One combination pliers

© Cengage Learning®

FIGURE 12-8 Basic woodworking tools for 4- and 5-year-olds: Start with these and add more as children become more proficient.

12-2d Math Games

As described in Chapter 7, board games provide children with opportunities for counting and one-to-one correspondence. They also provide opportunities for developing social skills, such as cooperation and following rules.

Young children enjoy playing games. Some 4-year-olds and most 5-year-olds enjoy playing board games. For the preschooler, games should be simple with a minimum of rules. As children get older, they enjoy creating their own board games. The rules are often flexible and change frequently. They may make play money, applying their knowledge of money and cards that tell how many jumps they can make. Scores are kept and totals added up.

Board games provide an excellent way to teach math. Candyland, Numberland Counting Game, Chutes and Ladders, Fraction Brothers Circus, Memory, Picture Dominoes, Picture Nines (a domino game), Candyland Bingo, Triominos, Connect Four, Count-a-Color, Farm Lotto, and other bingo and lotto boxed games can be purchased. Board game patterns can be obtained from early childhood publications and Internet sites. For more advanced children, basic concepts can be practiced using board games such as Multiplication/Division Quizmo, Addition/Subtraction Mathfacts Game, Multiplication/Division Mathfacts Game, UNO, UNO Dominoes, Yahtzee, and IMMAWhiz Math Games. Games that help children learn money concepts are Monopoly, Pay the Cashier, and Count Your Change.

Trend Enterprise's Number Bingo Game can be purchased from Walmart. Lakeshore has several math Bingo games such as Addition, Money, Subtraction, and Time. Lakeshore has interactive science and math software and science folder games. Hatch carries several math and science games. Didax carries a collection of math games.

Other basic board games were described in Chapter 7. Card games that primary grade children enjoy include those suggested by Kamii (see Chapter 8) and those that are perennial favorites such as Go Fish, Concentration, Crazy Eights, Old Maid, Flinch, Solitaire, and Fantan. Look through catalogs (hard copy and online), and examine games at exhibitors' displays when you attend professional meetings. A vast selection is available. Marilyn Burns (2009) provides instructions for four math games for primary grade students.

Young children enjoy bowling games and games that involve aiming. Dropping clothespins into a container or throwing beanbags through a hole or into a container are appropriate for young children. Once they learn the game, they can keep track of their successes, using Unifix Cubes or making tally marks to keep score.

Outdoors or in the gym, children can have races. They could estimate how far they can throw a ball, a beanbag, or a paper plate. Primary children can measure with a yardstick and compare their estimates with their actual throwing distances.

Primary children enjoy jumping rope. They enjoy jumping to jingles such as "Mabel, Mabel." During the primary years, children are in the stage of industry versus inferiority. The struggle between these forces leads them into a natural interest in competitive activities, such as the games listed earlier, and into team sports and races. Adults must find ways for each of the children to achieve so that they do not experience inferiority feelings. Primary children enjoy races that give them practice in time and distance relationships. Hurdle jumping can begin with high and low jumps and then move into standard measures of height. Balls, beanbags, or Frisbees can be thrown and the distances compared and measured. Team sports require scorekeeping and an understanding of *more*, *less*, and ordinal relations (e.g., who is up first, second, etc.).

Primary grade children also enjoy math puzzlers and brainteasers that give them practice in problem solving. Some of these types of problems were introduced in Chapter 1. The following are additional examples:

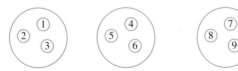

Move one so each set has a sum of 15.

Magic Triangles. Write the numbers 1 through 6 in the circles of the triangle shown in the following figure in such a way as to have a total of 9 (or 10 or 11 or 12) on each side.

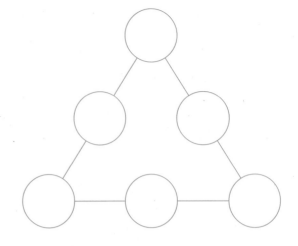

Totals of Nine

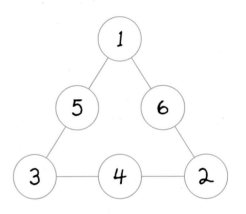

One Solution

The Lady and the Tiger. How many different squares can you count?

How many different triangles can you count?

Your Number. Ask someone to think of a number but keep it secret. Now tell him to double the number, add eight to the result, divide by two, and subtract the original number. Then have him write down the answer, but tell him not to show it to you until you predict the answer. The answer will always be four.

Young children enjoy games. Board, target, and action games offer them opportunities to apply math concepts. Through observation of children playing games, adults can obtain information regarding a child's development of math skills and concepts. Each issue of *Teaching Children Mathematics* includes a thematic section called "Math by the Month" that poses problems for elementary students beginning with kindergarten through grade 2. For example, in December 2009/January 2010 (Columba & Waddell), the theme was "A treasure trove of triangles." Four problems were presented: One focused on finding triangles in a quilt; another was a geoboard activity; a third focused on drawing as many triangles as possible on centimeter grid paper in 30 seconds; and the fourth involved sorting pattern blocks.

Fingerplays and Action Songs. Many fingerplays and action songs include the application of math concepts. Children may have to hear the song or fingerplay several times before they join in. If the teacher keeps repeating it, the students will gradually learn and participate. Favorite fingerplays are "Five Little Monkeys Jumping on the Bed" and "Five Little Ducks Swimming in a Pond." A longtime favorite song is "Johnny Works with One Hammer." Children particularly enjoy counting rhymes (Arenson, 1998). Two examples are as follows:

One potato,
Two potato,
Three potato,
Four;
Five potato,

Six potato,
Seven potato,
More.

Here is the beehive (fist closed),
Where are the bees?
Hidden away where nobody sees,
Soon they come creeping out of the hive,
[Open fingers one at a time.]
One! Two! Three! Four! Five!

Fingerplays and action songs help children learn math concepts through body actions.

Math in the Environment. The outdoors provides many opportunities for children's mathematics applications. Children can count the number of windows they can see from the playground. They can do informal measurements of playground equipment and distances across the playground. They can measure shadows at different times of the day. Trailblazers (2010) provide opportunities for children to create math trails in their environment. Children and/or teachers devise a series of directions that include math concepts, such as the following:

1. Walk to the front door. Count how many steps you took."

2. "Go out the door and walk to the church. Stop at the church. Count the number of windows in the front of the church."

3. "Walk by the park. How many swings do you see?"

4. "Look at the fence around the park. Which shapes do you see?"

A first-grade unit on the rain forest provided many mathematics applications (Thornton, Dee, Damkoehler, Gehrenbeck, & Jones, 1995). The study of the rain forest provided opportunities to advance the students' number sense as they created a sense of the space that the rain forest occupied, built a classroom rain forest, and used related problem-solving experiences. The students kept journals, made graphs, and did estimating.

Solving Mathematics Problems. A critical activity in mathematics is problem solving, as detailed in Chapter 1. Many examples of children's problem-solving approaches can be found in *Teaching Children Mathematics* journal articles. The *Navigation* series on problem solving and reasoning provides examples of problems to be solved (see Findell et al., 2004; Greenes et al., 2003; Small et al., 2004). Prekindergartners and kindergartners can be provided with problems involving number relationships, patterning, nonstandard measurement, and simple data analysis (Greenes et al., 2003). First graders can work with algebraic relationships, geometric relationships, data graphing, and measurement (Findell et al., 2004). Second graders can move on to more complex problems in number, algebra, geometry, measurement, and reasoning about data relationships (Small et al., 2004). Beginning problem solvers use drawings and/or manipulatives to reach solutions, whereas more advanced students gradually invent numerical processes.

NGSS

12-2e Science in Action: The Outdoors

Virtually all outdoors is science. This is where children can become a part of the natural world. Whether you use the outdoor environment around you to extend and enhance indoor science lessons or design lessons that focus on available outdoor resources, your students will benefit from the experience.

Children will be enthusiastic about exploring the "real" world. After all, "The real thing is worth a thousand pictures." Although this variation on the old saying—and many of the suggestions for implementing outdoor learning—overlap with field trip experiences, most of the learning strategies suggested here can also be done in an urban setting. Schoolyards, sidewalks, vacant lots, or any strip of ground can be an area for outdoor learning. The important thing is to get your students outdoors and engage them in challenging learning.

It is important to prepare the classroom and school grounds for science exploration (Ashbrook, August 29, 2013). Tools should be available indoors and out for examining and exploring both environments. Magnifiers are always fascinating for young children, even 2-year-olds. Measuring tools should always be available such as chain links, rulers, bathroom scales, and measuring cups. Egg cartons can be used to store collections such as seeds or pebbles. Tools for exploring water such as eyedroppers, turkey basters, a hose, sponges, and clear plastic tubing. Paper and pencils should be available for children to record their observations. Duties such as "Water plants" and "Feed the fish" should be included on the jobs chart.

Specific plans for outdoor learning will help ensure a successful experience. The following suggestions include teaching strategies that focus on specific science learnings. Refer to Chapters 10 and 11 and the last section of this chapter for more outdoor and environmental education ideas.

Engineering and Design. In the sandbox or with outdoor blocks and boards and other materials, children may want to build a building or a road or a bridge. It is important to define the problem and develop a model such as a drawing to give direction to solving the problem. Outdoors, small clipboards and pencils should be available.

Science and Art. Natural materials can be used for art (Ashbrook, November 3, 2013). Fall leaves can be examined, used for rubbings, sorted, and compared. Children can draw in sand, make designs with rocks and pebbles, and make structures with twigs and sticks. In nice weather, children can draw and paint outdoor scenes.

Animal Study Activities. Animal homes, habits, and behaviors fascinate children. To begin a successful outdoor experience, assess the previous experiences, skills, and attention spans of your students. Then, review the teacher preparation and management suggestions at the end of this section ("Planning for Outdoor Learning") and begin.

Animal Homes. Involve children in the study of animal homes. First discuss, "Where might an animal live?" Then, plan a field trip to look for animal homes. When planning a trip, keep in mind that most animals make their homes on southern slopes (sunny and warm). When you find a home, examine the area for tracks (**Figure 12-9**). Make a cast of the tracks and determine if the home is in use. Ask, "How can we tell whether an animal lives here?" (One way is to look for signs such as food scraps and activity around the entrance.) Discuss possible reasons for the selection of this particular location for an animal home, and speculate on the possible enemies and living habits of the occupant.

Finding Insects. Insects can be hard to find, but signs of their presence are common. The paper nest of a hornet or mud nest of a wasp can be found on buildings, rocks, or tree branches. Be careful: If the nests are occupied, the owners may sting.

The presence of bark beetles can be seen by the "tunnel" left when they strip bark from logs. Most children are familiar with ant nests and know how to find them. Fallen logs are good locations for observing insects in the winter. The insects are usually sluggish, and the stinging types can be more easily observed.

Follow animal home observations with discussion. Ask questions such as these: "What have we learned about the kinds of animals that live around our school? What are their needs?" Pick one animal to focus on. Have children write about what one of the animals is thinking as it prepares a home.

A Different Type of Home. The next time you see a swollen, tumor-like bulge on the stem, flower head, stalk, or root of a plant, you might be looking at a unique insect home known as a *gall*. The gall has a hard outer wall and contains a food supply from the plant tissue. Have your students search for galls growing on flowers, bushes, or trees. Lead the children to discover that certain types of galls are found on specific plants. For example, a gall found on a Canada goldenrod (*Solidago canadensis*) is caused by a small, brown-winged fly. This fly (*Eurosta solidaginis*) forms a gall only on the Canada goldenrod (**Figure 12-10**).

Children will enjoy dramatizing the life of a gall insect. Say: "Pretend you are tiny and helpless. Find a place where you can be safe." Have the children pull jackets over their heads to simulate how protected the insect feels. Make a large papier-mâché gall for children to crawl into. Furnish it with a battery-powered light, and children will enjoy crawling in to read, write poems, or turn the light off and simply speculate about what it would be like to be a gall insect inside its home.

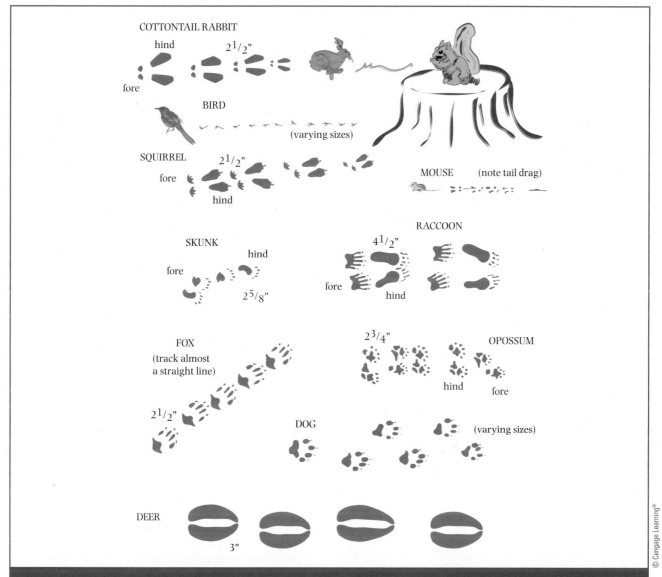

COTTONTAIL RABBIT
hind
2^1/$_2$"
fore
BIRD
(varying sizes)
SQUIRREL
fore
2^1/$_2$"
hind
MOUSE   (note tail drag)
SKUNK
hind
fore
2^5/$_8$"
RACCOON
4^1/$_2$"
fore
hind
FOX
(track almost
a straight line)
2^1/$_2$"
2^3/$_4$"
OPOSSUM
hind
fore
(varying sizes)
DOG
DEER
3"

© Cengage Learning®

FIGURE 12-9 "You can identify an animal by the tracks that you see."

Interview a Spider. Children enjoy becoming reporters and interviewing various wildlife. After discussing what a reporter does and the techniques of interviewing, teams of children can decide on an animal they want to interview.

Birds, Birds, Birds. A bird feeder is a good place to begin observing birds. If you do not have a suitable tree near your school, make your own with limbs or cornstalks tied together and propped up to provide perches and shelter. You will be providing birds with much needed food, and as the birds come to eat, children will have a chance to observe them and their activities at close range.

Children will enjoy making seasonal ornaments and garlands for an outdoor holiday tree. Also, use ground feeders or seed dispensers as added attractions for the birds. To decorate a tree, have students string foods that appeal to a wide range of birds. Give them cubes of cheese, popcorn, raisins, and peanuts (in shells). To attract fruit-eating song-birds, add dried fruits to the strings.

Plain peanuts in their shells appeal to both insect- and seed-eating birds; so hang them on fishing line or skewer them on galvanized wire and attach the line to the tree. Then, watch the antics of birds such as blue jays as they break open the shells.

Instruct children to keep a notebook of which foods various birds most like to eat. If you prefer, feed birds in aluminum TV dinner trays. Mount the trays on a board and puncture them so that excess moisture can drain out. Fill the different compartments in the trays with cracked corn, sunflower seeds, commercial birdseed, and fruit. Then, watch as the birds come to feed, and ask questions that help students focus on the differences in the birds' feeding habits.

FIGURE 12-10 A gall is a different type of insect home.

FIGURE 12-11 "Describe your plant as it appears today."

"Which birds prefer to eat on the ground? Do all of the birds eat seeds? Which like fruit the best?"

Have children begin a class (and personal) list of the birds that visit your feeder. With a little practice, children might be beginning a lifelong hobby and interest. You need to be familiar with the birds in your area that will most likely appear at the feeder. Each bird has its own specific habits, food preferences, and actions. Take the children on a field trip, and compare birds seen with the birds that visit the schoolyard feeder. (Refer to the latter part of this chapter for additional bird activities.)

My Wild Plant. Observing a wild plant and learning as much as possible through observation makes a good long-term activity for spring. Visit a vacant lot or school parking lot with the children, and try to find a spot not likely to be mowed, paved, or interfered with during spring months. Or contact your school maintenance personnel, and ask them to leave a small section of the schoolyard untouched for a month.

Have each child select one wild plant as her own for close study. A label with the child's name on it can be taped around the stems of the plant she selects. Encourage children

to begin a plant notebook to make entries about their plant (**Figure 12-11**). For example:

1. "Describe the plant as it appears today."
2. "Measure everything you can with a tape measure."
3. "Count all plant parts. Does the plant have an odor?"
4. "What textures did you find on the plant?" (You might be able to record these with crayon rubbings.)
5. "Does your plant make any sounds?"
6. "What other plants are the nearest neighbors of yours?"
7. "Do any animals live on or visit your plant?"

During subsequent visits, determine how the plant has grown and changed. Decide what effect the plant has on other plants and animals living nearby, and determine what is good or bad about this plant. Encourage children to make drawings and to take photographs so that they will be able to share the story of their plant with others. Then, predict what the plant and growing site will be like in one year.

Hugging a Tree. A variation of selecting a special plant is to have children work in pairs to explore a tree. Blindfold one of the partners. Have the other partner lead the blindfolded one to a tree. Give the children time to touch, smell, and hug the tree. Then bring the children back to a starting point, take the blindfold off, and ask, "Can you find the tree that you hugged?" Children will enjoy finding a special tree to hug; some might even want to whisper a secret to the tree.

What's for Dinner? Tell the children, "Go home tonight, and list everything you have for dinner." The next day, have

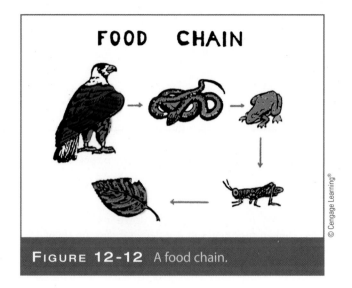

FIGURE **12-12** A food chain.

© Cengage Learning®

children work in groups to discuss the dinner menu and analyze where their food comes from. Help children trace every food back to a plant; for example, milk to cow to grass. Have reference books available for children to consult. Encourage the children to reach the conclusion that all animals and people need food and that we all depend on plants for food. Ask, "Do the plants need people and animals?" After a lively discussion, point out the decay of animal life that nourishes plants. Then, create a food chain for your bulletin board by using yarn to connect pictures of animals, plants, soil, and rocks. Add the sun, and have children create their own food chains to hang from a hanger (**Figure 12-12**).

Check the Weather. Children can put on their rain or snow gear and observe the weather. It may be raining or snowing, sunny or cloudy, hot or cold. Daily observations can be recorded.

Scavenger Hunts and Other 10-Minute Activities. Scavenger hunts are an excellent way to challenge children while focusing their attention on the task at hand. Make up a set of file cards they can take out with them. Each card should have a challenge on it. For example:

- Find a seed.
- Find three pieces of litter.
- Find something a bird uses for nesting material.
- Find something red.
- Find something a squirrel would eat.
- Find something that makes its own food.
- Find something that shows signs of erosion.
- Find something that shows change.
- Find a bird's feather.

Caution the children to collect only small quantities of the item on their card or not to collect at all if they will damage something. In this case, the child can write a description of what he sees. Pass out the cards, and tell the individuals or teams that they have 10 minutes to meet the challenge. Discuss the findings back in the classroom.

Circle Game. If the ground is dry, sit in a circle and pass an object such as a rock, leaf, or twig around the circle. As each child touches the object, he or she must say something that is observed about the object. Say, "You will need to listen and not repeat an observation made by anyone else." Remember, observations are made with the senses. Do not accept inferences or predictions.

While you are still in the circle, move the children apart, so they do not touch each other, and ask them to close their eyes and explore the area around them with just their hands (and bare feet, if the weather is nice). Then, ask them to describe or write the textures that they felt.

Outdoor Learning and Writing Experiences. Writing, drawing, and dictating can be integrated with outdoor learning experiences. Here are a few suggestions.

- Write poems about something that was observed during an outdoor experience.
- Write a story about a living thing in the outdoors that has the power to speak to the humans that come to visit its outdoor area. What might the living thing say? What questions might it ask you?
- Write and draw posters that describe outdoor experiences.
- Keep a written log of outdoor activities.
- Write a short play about the outdoor trip.
- Write letters to someone about one aspect of the outdoor experience.
- Dictate stories about an incident or observation made during the outdoor experience.
- Write how you would feel if you were a plant and it didn't rain for a long time.

Planning for Outdoor Learning. Taking children outdoors can be a challenge if you are not prepared. To ensure the greatest value from this experience, teachers of all age groups should consider the following:

1. Think about your purpose for conducting outdoor experiences (**Photo 12-4**). How will children benefit? What type of preparation do the children need before they go outdoors?

2. What are the logistics? Will you walk, drive, or ride in cars or a bus? What type of clothing is needed? Should you take snacks and lunch? Are there people to contact? What are the water and toilet facilities? How much help do you need?

3. Which concepts will be developed (**Photo 12-5**)? What do you hope to accomplish?

4. Have you planned what you will be teaching before the experience, during the activity, and after the experience?

PHOTO 12-4 A field trip provides an opportunity for a firsthand multisensory nature experience.

5. How much talking do you really need to do?
6. How will you evaluate the experience?
7. What types of follow-up learning will be provided? What subjects can you integrate into the experience?

PHOTO 12-5 This is part of the field trip.

Attention Grabbers. Devices for grabbing the attention of a group can be physical, such as pulling out a surprise object from your bag when you want to discuss a topic. Here are some subtle attention grabbers:

1. Look intently at an object to focus group attention on the same object.
2. Have children remind you of tasks, carry various items, assist with the activity, and lead in other tasks. This participation helps keep their attention.
3. Lower your voice when you want to make a point; this works well in the classroom and outdoors.
4. Change your position. Sit down with the children when they begin to wander, and regroup them.
5. Give the children specific items to look for or match, notes to take, or specific jobs. Children tend to lose interest if they do not have a task. Provide the children with small notebooks or clipboards.

Additional Management Strategies. Although you might be proficient at managing children indoors, the outdoors can be quite a different matter. Here are a few tips.

1. Before the outdoor experience, set up a firm set of rules (as you do indoors). As you know, relaxing rules is far easier than tightening them. However, hurting and frightening animals, crushing plants, and littering should not be tolerated.
2. When children become too active, try an attention grabber or initiate an activity designed to give children a chance to run. For example, "Run to the big pine tree and back to me." Relays with rocks as batons will also expend excess energy.
3. Have a prearranged attention signal for activities that require wandering. A whistle, bell, or hand signals work well.
4. When one child is talking and others desperately want your attention, place your hand on their hand to let them know that you recognize them.
5. Let different children enjoy leading the adventure. Occasionally, remove yourself from the line, take a different place in line, and go in a different direction. In this way, you lead the group in a new direction with different children directly behind you.
6. Play Follow the Leader with you as the leader as you guide the line where you want it to go. If there is snow on the ground, have the children walk like wolves: Wolves walk along a trail in single file, putting their feet in the footprints of the wolf ahead of them. If you are at the zoo, try walking to the next exhibit like the animal you have just been observing would walk.
7. Be flexible. If something is not working, just change the activity. Later, you can analyze why something was not working the way you had planned.

Exciting outdoor activities do not happen by chance. Begin by planning carefully what you want the children to learn. Then teach the lesson, and evaluate the children's learning and your preparation. You will be off to a good start as an outdoor science educator.

12-2f Technology

Relevant technology has been suggested throughout this text. More online software and apps and are becoming increasingly available. Some of these are listed in Appendix B. The Magic School Bus series is still excellent. The Magic School Bus science series is available in books, videos, and on YouTube, and the TV series is now available on DVD from Amazon. Children ages 6–10 will enjoy accompanying Ms. Frizzle and her class on a field trip to the sandy beaches and the ocean's depths. The program also includes games, experiments, and a treasure hunt.

Exciting adventures await students when they use the Internet, which provides opportunities for teachers to share ideas while students expand their knowledge. For example, a science teacher in Virginia whose students were interested in comparing Atlantic coast shells with shells found in other parts of the world assisted them in connecting with schools in other countries through the Internet (Holden, 1996). The students made contact through e-mail and exchanged beach materials. Today Skype can be used for face-to-face long-distance connections. Another teacher focused on mathematical thinking by having her students investigate pet ownership around the world through the Internet (Lynes, 1997). The students applied several standards areas: problem solving, communication, reasoning, and connections. The Global Schoolhouse provides access to collaborative projects and communication tools (classroom conferencing, mailing lists, and discussion boards). Teachers had students use digital cameras and whiteboards to demonstrate solutions to fraction problems (Canada, 2009). Primary grade students integrated concrete and virtual manipulatives (Rosen & Hoffman, 2009). Students can take virtual field trips on the PBS Learning Media website.

Instructional Technology in Action. Instructional technology offers many opportunities for children to learn more about the world around them than would be possible in the confines of the classroom or schoolyard. Numerous software programs are available for young children that encourage their critical thinking and problem solving. For example, young children can plan towns, roads, parks, and more by using *Stickybear Town Builder* (for grades K–3) or *SimTown* (ages 8 to 12). *Sammy's Science House* offers pre-K to grade 2 children a gadget builder as well as opportunities to sort and classify plants and animals, to sequence events in a filmlike fashion, and to explore different weather conditions. Millie's Math House teaches basic math concepts such as number, shapes, sizes, quantities, patterns, and sequencing; and NCTM's

Illuminations connects to many resources such as *Thinkfinity*, which provides lesson plans and links to videos. The Internet offers opportunities for students to interact with other students—and even scientists—from around the world, to see images otherwise inaccessible, and to play educational games.

Exploring Math and Science with Technology at Home. The resources listed in most chapters are available for parental purchase, online downloading, or interaction. Hand calculators may be explored at home, using the same types of activities suggested in Chapter 8. Also, children's TV channel websites such as *PBS Kids, Noggin,* and *Disney* have many online activities using the characters that are familiar to children from their daily television viewing. At the *Sesame Street* site, children can practice counting with the Count's Number of the Day activities or Journey to Ernie for problem solving with matching and pattern recognition. At the *Mr. Rogers' Neighborhood* site are simple recipes for cooking and projects such as making a bird feeder or a rocket ship. *Bill Nye the Science Guy* includes home science labs in the areas of planets, physical science, and life science. In addition, Animal Planet, Nova, and National Geographic offer informative programs on television. On the Lawrence Hall of Science Kidsite are activities such as "Measure Yourself" and "How Old Is a Penny?" The Family Math Site activities can be downloaded, such as *"Mixtures"* for young children and "The Balloon Ride" for older children.

Technology for Young Children

Finding the Right Tech Tools

"Kathy Schrock guides educators through the process of building a personal learning network and organizing a constant flow of information." (Piehler, 2013). The first step in keeping up is establishing a network. Kathy Schrock uses Twitter as her network. Her followers are trusted professionals who send her URLs. She uses Google+ as her social network. For professional connections, she uses LinkedIn. If you don't want to tweet, you can use Twitter Search for specific topics or enter the topic you want in your search engine.

Professional journals provide lists of apps. For example *Teaching Children Mathematics,* September 2012, provided the following list of the top four apps for classroom iPads:

1. *Zoom.* Version 2.1. A number line game.

2. *Slice It!* Version 1.3.0. Area visualization

3. *Rocket Math.* Free version 1.8. Telling time, handling money, identifying three-dimensional shapes.

4. *Coin Math.* Free. A coin learning game.

Other resources: Pinterest; BestAppsforKids; Common Sense Media; and Education.com, Inc.

C. Piehler, C. (2013, February 28). Finding the right tech tools is easy, if you know where to look. *T.H.E. Journal.* http://thejournal.com.

12-2g Culturally Relevant Mathematics and Science

The first NCTM (2000) principle is that of equity. "Excellence in mathematics education requires equity—high expectations and strong support of all students" (p. 12). Respect for and accommodation to differences are essential to instruction in both mathematics and science.

In Chapter 1, ethnomathematics—the natural mathematics that children learn in their culture—was described. Information regarding ethnomathematics can be obtained from the International Study Group on Ethnomathematics website (Eglash, 2001). It is essential to discover and build on the mathematics that children bring to school. It is also necessary to use culturally relevant materials and activities. For example, many of the books suggested throughout this text reflect cultural diversity (see especially Chapter 6 and Appendix B). Some books are written in English but focus on other cultures. For example, in the book *Round Is a Mooncake* (Thong, 2000), a young girl seeks out shapes in a Chinese American setting. In *Feast for Ten* (Falwell, 1993), an African American family is followed while shopping for, cooking, serving, and eating a meal. Books are also written in other languages as translations of English-language classics or as stories written originally in other languages. Books in Spanish are increasing in number and are reviewed yearly in *Science and Children* and frequently in *Young Children*. Advice on selecting mathematics-related books in Spanish is the subject of an article by Jacobs, Bennett, and Bullock (2000).

Culturally relevant mathematics and science can be integrated with social studies. Internet activities such as those just described can provide opportunities to learn about other geographic areas and their cultures while obtaining science knowledge and applying mathematics knowledge. Upper grade or younger advanced students can study and compare the mathematical systems of other cultures such as Native American, Roman, and Egyptian. They can compare calendars of various cultures, such as Chinese, Jewish, and Muslim (Zaslavsky, 2001). White (2001) describes how first graders explored geometry by comparing fabrics from different cultures.

12-3 FAMILY INVOLVEMENT IN MATH AND SCIENCE BEGINS AT HOME

The home is the first educational setting. Children's interest in math and in science begins at home (Crawford, Heaton, Heslop, & Kixmiller, 2013). Learning happens on a daily basis in the home: Children learn as they cook, set the table, sort laundry, pour sand and water, build with blocks, observe ants, watch birds, or take a walk in the backyard, neighborhood, or the park. Teachers of young children are in a unique position to help families make good use of these at-home learning opportunities. This part of the chapter provides guidelines for parents and other family members as teachers. It focuses on specific suggestions for emphasizing science and math as vehicles for family learning.

Parents and other family members need to understand that children are eager to learn and can learn if provided with developmentally appropriate experiences. As teachers of young children, you can assist parents in recognizing that they do not need to go overboard purchasing expensive materials when multitudes of learning opportunities center on everyday activities using resources naturally present in the environment.

Encourage family members to find the math and science in their homes. A large part of a child's time is spent in preschool or elementary school, but the majority of time is still spent outside the classroom. Every day at home is filled with opportunities for children to explore and ask questions that encourage their thinking. It should be stressed that family entertainment does not have to be passive, such as watching TV. Activities that incorporate daily routines such as cooking, playing games, doing simple projects, finding materials to bring to school, and exploring the lives of living creatures and plants are opportunities for discovery, science and math, and family fun. Crawford, Heaton, Heslop, and Kixmiller (2013) suggest activities and resources for science in the home in the major science areas of physical science, life science, earth and space science, and engineering, technology and applications of science.

12-3a Getting the Family Involved

Changes in our economy and lifestyles have resulted in a multitude of family configurations that were rare or nonexistent in the past. A large percentage of mothers of young children work either to boost the family income or because they are the principal breadwinners, so they are not as available as their predecessors were. Fathers work longer hours, sometimes holding down two jobs, and are also less able than in the past to participate in school-based activities. Family involvement in education has changed from the view that parents could be active participants only by coming to school and assisting with classroom activities and attending parent meetings and conferences. These are still important activities, but involvement has been expanded to include all family members and caregivers and to focus on opening lines of communication. Families are now provided with home learning tasks that can be performed as part of everyday living. Further, the use of home visits as a means for developing a good relationship with families is moving up from prekindergarten into the elementary school. The home visitor can model math and science activities in the home, suggest home materials that can promote math and science concepts, and explain how parents can boost children's math and science achievement. Research indicates that family involvement influences math achievement (Cross, Woods, &

Schweingruber, 2009; Zadeh, Farnia, & Ungerleider, 2010). Children's prekindergarten experiences relate to school achievement. Teachers need to build on this knowledge. The following are suggestions for getting families involved and engaging them in their roles as teachers.

A first step could be the publication of a newsletter that could be sent home each month telling about the past month's events and including information about upcoming activities (see **Figure 12-13** for a sample). Future activities could be described and/or sent in the form of a monthly calendar. Children can contribute to the newsletter. They can draw pictures and dictate, write news stories describing their experiences at school, or both. Two or three children can contribute to each newsletter. Suggested home activities

---

Kindergarten News

Published by Mr. Jones's Class *Carver School*
October 1, 2011

School Gets Off to a Good Start

The day after Labor Day, the children started kindergarten. Eight children came each day to get acquainted with the room and find out what we do in kindergarten. Several children have contributed descriptions of what they liked best about coming to kindergarten.

José: I like being bigger than the 4-year-old classes.
Mimi: I like painting and playing house.
Ronny: My favorite was drawing and writing with markers on big paper and playing with trucks and blocks.
Nina: I liked finding my new friend Marcus.

Buddy the Bunny Joins Us

Last week, we had a late arrival in our class. Mr. Ortiz, who manages a pet store at the mall, brought us a black-and-white rabbit with a cage and a supply of food. The class discussed a number of names. The majority voted for the name Buddy ("'cause he will be our best friend"). Buddy is very friendly and enjoys fresh vegetables. If your child asks to bring a carrot or a little piece of lettuce to school, please send it, if possible. The children are taking turns bringing treats for Buddy.

The Month Ahead

We are looking forward to fall. We are reading the outdoor temperature every morning and recording the data on a graph. We watch each day for the leaves to change. Our observations are written and drawn in our daily class journal. We are planning a walk around the block to collect samples of the leaves that fall from the trees. We will report next month on what we see and what we find.

© Cengage Learning®

FIGURE 12-13 Sample classroom newsletter.

---

may be included in the newsletter or sent home as a separate booklet. See the NAEYC publication *Family Friendly Communication for Early Childhood Programs* (Diffily & Morrison, 1996).

Getting parents or other family members to school for a meeting can be difficult. However, they need to become acquainted with the activities, the environment, their child's teacher, and the families of other students. Meetings should provide important information and involve active experiences that will give families an understanding of appropriate educational experiences that can be followed up in the home.

The students should be actively involved in the planning, so that their excitement and enthusiasm for the event will spill over to their parents. A program that has shown a great deal of success is Family Math (Coates & Stenmark, 1997; Lachance, 2007; Stenmark, Thompson, & Cossey, 1986) and Family Science (Petrinjak, 2011). Parents come to school and do math and science activities with their children. They are then provided with instructions for follow-up activities they can do at home. Math and science could be combined in one family night. Another procedure is to hold a Science and/or Math Fun Day (Carey, 1990; O'Rorke, 2013). For a Fun Day, several activities are set up in a large area, such as a gym or cafeteria. Families can be invited to take part as volunteer helpers and as active participants with their children. By having the Fun Day extend over several hours, busy people can more likely find a time when they can join in. See other resources listed at the end of this chapter.

Families can also be asked to send recyclable materials to school, as needed. The items listed in **Figure 12-14** as aids to learning math and science at home are also useful at school. Each child can bring a pack of small brown paper lunch bags to school at the beginning of the year; then, if an item is needed, the children can draw and/or write the name of the item on the bag, take it home, and ask their parents to put the item in the bag to take to school. Do not be concerned if the younger children write symbols that are not conventional pictures or words; they will know what it is and be able to read the symbol to adults.

Family members who have the time may volunteer to assist in the classroom. Those who are not free during the day or who prefer not to be involved in the classroom are often delighted to make games and other materials at home. There should always be an open invitation for family members to visit school.

Parents or other major caregivers need to meet with their child's teacher in one-to-one conferences to exchange information about children's activities and progress. At these times, teacher and parent or other family member (and even the child) can review the student's portfolio of work and discuss goals for the future. At the same time, family members can describe what they have been doing at home with the child and relate any home events that may be affecting the child's behavior.

From the Kitchen

egg cartons
cereal boxes and other empty food boxes
margarine tubs
milk cartons
milk jugs
plastic lids
pumpkin seeds
nuts
nutshells
straws
dry peas, beans, rice
coffee can and lids
other food and juice cans
baby food jars
potato chip cans
frozen food cartons
yogurt, cottage cheese,
    sour cream, or dip containers
milk bottle lids
individual small cereal boxes
soft drink bottle caps
plastic holder (soft drink six-pack carrier)
paper plates
coffee grounds
plastic bottles or jugs (soap, bleach, etc.)
plastic or metal tops or lids
Styrofoam™ meat plates (trays)
plastic bag twists
cardboard rolls (paper towels, foil, etc.)
kitchen scales
plastic forks, spoons
cleaned and dried bones

From Outside

pebbles	bird feathers
rocks and stones	acorns
twigs, sticks, bark	animal teeth
leaves and weeds	insects
pinecones and nuts	mosses
seeds	abandoned nests
corn kernels and husks	nonpoisonous plants
soybeans	
flowers	
clay, mud, dirt, sand	
seashells	

From All Around the House

sponges
magazines with pictures
catalogs (general, seed, etc.)
old crayons
shoe boxes and other small boxes (i.e., bar soap,
    toothpaste, aspirin, tape, etc.)
other cardboard boxes
    (not corrugated)
corrugated cardboard
cardboard tablet backs
scraps of wallpaper, carpeting
Contac® paper
toothbrushes (for spattering paint)
lumber scraps
gift wrap (used or scraps)
gift wrap ribbon and bows
old greeting cards (pictures)
newspapers
jewelry
wire
clothesline
clocks
watches
small appliances
rubber or plastic hose
plastic tubing
plastic tubs
nails and screws
wood scraps
tools

From Sewing Scraps

buttons
snaps
fabric
felt
thread
yarn
lace
ribbon
trim
rickrack
spools

FIGURE 12-14 Math and science materials found at home.

Homework becomes an important type of activity in the primary grades. Children can work their way into the more formal homework activities by bringing things requested from home as a part of their prekindergarten and kindergarten experiences. These activities help them to develop responsibility and accustom parents to supporting classroom instruction. Homework should always be an extension of what has been taught at school. It may involve bringing some material to school, doing a simple project, or obtaining some information from a newspaper, magazine, reference book, or the Internet. Be sure that all the information needed to guide the child to complete the assignment is included in the instructions. Assignments for young children should be something that can be easily completed in 10–15 minutes. Even kindergarten teachers are being pressured to provide homework assignments. These assignments should be interactive, requiring a parent or sibling to assist. **Figure 12-15** is an example of an activity that works very well with kindergartners. Articles by Burton and Baum (2009), Kliman (1999), and Kline (1999) provide ideas for home math support and activities. The February 1998 issue of *Teaching Children Mathematics* and the January 2003 and February 2012 issues of *Science and Children* focus on parent and community involvement (Edge, 1998; Getting Families Involved, 2012; Parental involvement, 2003).

An increasingly popular method for promoting developmentally appropriate at-home learning activities involves putting together small kits of materials that children can check out and take home for two or three days (Ashbrook, 2012; Czerniak, 1994; Merenda, 1995; Seo & Bruk, 2003; Freudenberg, 2012). Each kit includes materials and instructions for a home activity and some means for parents and children to return a report on the outcome along with the kit. Many of the activities suggested later in the chapter could be made into take-home kits.

Resources are available on the Internet that teachers can download to share with families or that families with Internet connections can download themselves. Government sites, such as the U.S. Department of Education (DOE) have many excellent resources that can be downloaded free of charge in both English and Spanish. The DOE site booklet *Helping Your Child Learn Science* (2005) provides families with children ages 3 to 10 with information, tools, and activities they can use in the home and community to help their child develop an interest in the sciences and learn about the world around them. This series of publications includes *Helping Your Preschool Child* and many more titles. The Lawrence Hall of Science at the University of California Berkeley is the site for Equals and Family Math. Activities can be downloaded and activity books purchased.

Family visits to museums provide a rich experience. The North Museum of Natural History and Science in Lancaster, Pennsylvania, has a monthly informal science program for 3- to 5-year-olds and their grandparents (Wahlberg, 2007). Preschoolers and grandparents share hands-on exploratory activities. University science departments may offer planetarium shows and special Saturday science activity experiences. During the summer, Weber State University in Ogden, Utah, science faculty present a science in the park program at locations where free lunch is provided for young children.

Take-Home Activity

Hello Family!

We have been working with groups of the amounts 0 to 10. *Ten Black Dots* is one of the books we are using to relate literature and math.

What can you do with ten black dots? This is a question we have worked on. In the book, rhymes suggest answers such as:

1. One dot can make a sun or a moon when day is done.
2. Two dots can make the eyes of a fox or the eyes of keys that open locks.

We have been working with black dots in class. Now it's time to do a job at home.

Home Job

1. Talk to your child about how dots can be used to make a picture. Make a list of ideas. Ten black dots are included below.

2. Have your child draw a picture including one or more black dots. Have the child write or dictate for you one or two sentences about the picture. A page is attached for writing and drawing.

Based on Ten Black Dots (Crews, 1986); created by Rosalind Charlesworth.

FIGURE 12-15 Ten Black Dots take-home activity.

12-3b Guidelines for Families as Teachers at Home

Many families have questions about how they can provide learning experiences at home. They need to be reassured that naturalistic and informal experiences are at the heart of home learning. All during early childhood, play is the major vehicle for learning, both at school and at home. Exploration and discovery through play allow children to construct concepts. Adults should be encouraged to be positive models for their children. If adults are enthusiastic learners, their children are more likely to be enthusiastic learners too. Parents often feel uncomfortable with math. Michael Shaughnessy (2010) offers six Do's for families and their math students:

1. Be positive.
2. Link mathematics with daily life.
3. Make mathematics fun.
4. Learn about mathematics-related careers.
5. Have high expectations for your children.
6. Support homework—don't do it for your children.

Advise parents to visit the Family Resource page at the NCTM website.

Families can provide a close relationship where exploration is encouraged and where one-to-one conversation can enrich the young child's math and science language development. Adults and older children must be cautioned to be patient and to allow young children the opportunity to explore, reflect, and construct concepts. They need to understand that children learn through repetition. Children do the same activities over and over before they assimilate what the experience has to offer and feel confident in their understandings. Families also need to realize that children learn through concrete experiences. They need to learn how to use simple household items and waste materials as the focus for learning.

Provide examples of naturalistic, informal, and adult-guided home learning experiences. *Naturalistic experiences* are those in which a concept is applied in an everyday activity, such as sorting laundry, counting out tableware, following an ant trail in the backyard, or watching the clock to get to an appointment on time. *Informal experiences* take place when the alert adult finds a way to involve the child in an activity, such as asking the child to set the table, measure out cooking ingredients, learn his telephone number, and count the money in his piggy bank. The adult can also sing a song or chant a rhyme on the spur of the moment and provide materials the child can use on her own (such as blocks, sets of dishes, construction materials, and the like). *Adult-guided activities* usually are not appropriate before age 3. Adults need to take care that, when they introduce adult-guided activities, they do not pressure the child if he seems uninterested or not ready. Suggest that adults pull back and try again in two or three

weeks. Emphasize that children need time to explore materials before adults present preplanned questions or problems to them. Hansen (2005) describes daily learning opportunities with art, food, bath, blocks, chores, games, books, and other home activities. Primary grade children can be helped with their homework as adults provide hints and ask open-ended questions that support the children's thinking processes and enable them to arrive at their own problem solutions.

12-3c Math and Science in the Home, Yard, Neighborhood, and Park

Many math and science activities can be done in the home, backyard, neighborhood, park, or even on a vacation trip. Any of the following activities could be included in a home newsletter, activity booklet, or monthly calendar. Activities begin with daily home routines and then move into other areas.

Daily Routines. Families should be encouraged to emphasize the skills of science as they go about their daily routines. Here are some examples:

1. As laundry is sorted and socks are matched, talk about the differences and similarities in the articles. Then fold the clothes, and put them in the correct places. Ask, "Where do the pants go? Where shall we put the T-shirts?" Even small children will begin the process of classification as they note the differences in characteristics.

2. Children can examine their bodies and compare themselves to animals in a concrete way. They have five toes on each foot, but a horse does not. When a family takes a trip to a farm or a duck pond, the differences and similarities in animal feet can be noted. Ask: "How many toes do you have? How are your toes different from a duck's? Why do you think a duck has a web between its toes?" Activities like this help children be aware of differences in animals and offer opportunities to discuss why an animal is structured in a certain way. They can measure the parts with string or yarn and compare the lengths.

3. When kitchen utensils are returned to drawers after washing or food is put away after a shopping trip, discuss why they go where they do. Say: "Where shall we put the spoons? Should the crackers go in the cupboard or the refrigerator?" Some parents might want to lay items such as spoons, spatulas, or cups on the table and see how many ways children can devise to group items: for example, things you eat with, things you cook with, things you drink with, and so on.

4. Begin a bottle cap collection for classifying, counting, and crafts. Have children sort caps by size, color, and function. Trace around the caps to make designs. Then, paste the caps on cardboard, and paint it.

5. Collect scraps of wood, and make things with the wood. Give children a hammer and some nails and say, "Let's make something with this wood." When the wood sculpture is completed, name it and propose a function.

6. As children work with tools (e.g., a hammer, screwdriver, tape measure) and various types of screws, bolts, and nails, ask: "What do we do with this? How is this tool used?" If something needs to be fixed, let the children help fix the item. Children enjoy tightening and loosening screws in a board. Simply begin the screws in a board, and let children practice the type of motion needed to operate a screwdriver. This is the beginning of engineering.

7. Begin a button collection for classifying, counting, and crafts. Have children sort buttons by size, color, and number of holes. Trace around the buttons to make designs. Paste the buttons on cardboard, and paint them. Graph the button attributes.

8. Bedtime story time can also include math. Laura Bilodeau Overdecks's books *Bedtime Math: A Fun Excuse to Stay Up Late.* (2013) and *Bedtime Math: This Time, It's Personal* (2014) include bedtime problems at three levels (Wee ones, Little kids, and Big kids), all with humorous themes and illustrations. The problems are designed to be done in the head, no pencil and paper needed. Laura has a nonprofit, Bedtime Math, that sends out suggested math problems by daily email.

Cooking with Children. Cooking offers many opportunities for parents to provide children with practical applications of both science and math. When someone is cooking, the child can measure the ingredients, observe them as they change form during cooking (or mixing), and taste the final product.

Children should be given as much responsibility for the food preparation as possible. This might include shopping for the food; washing; possibly cutting (carefully supervised, of course); reading and following the recipe; baking, cooking, or freezing; setting the food on the table; and cleaning up. The more the parent does, the less the child learns.

Try making an easy pizza. You will need English muffins, tomato sauce, oregano, mozzarella cheese slices, and meat or mushrooms. Spread half of the muffin with a tablespoon of tomato sauce. Add a pinch of oregano. Put meat or mushroom on the sauce and then add a layer of cheese. Place the little pizza on a cookie sheet and bake for 10 minutes at 425°.

Children enjoy getting creative with food. Create Bugs on a Log by spreading peanut butter on pieces of celery. Top off the "log" with raisin "bugs."

Make Summer Slush. Freeze a favorite fruit juice in ice cube trays. After the cubes are hard, place them in the blender, and blend. Add extra juice if needed for a slushy consistency.

Save the seeds from a jack-o'-lantern or a Thanksgiving pumpkin pie. Clean them thoroughly, and dip them in a solution of salt water (1 tablespoon salt in 1½ cups of water). Drain off the water, and spread the seeds on an ungreased cookie sheet. Bake at 350°. Stir every 5 minutes to be sure that they dry out and toast lightly on all sides. When lightly toasted, remove from oven, cool, crack, and eat.

Curious George's favorite is to spread a banana with peanut butter and roll it in ground nuts or wheat germ. Also fun to make with peanut butter are Kid Feeders. Bird feeders made with peanut butter on pinecones can be made the same day children make Kid Feeders. Quarter an apple and spread peanut butter on the cut sides. Roll the apple slices in one or more of the following: wheat germ, raisins, coconut, ground nuts, or sesame seeds.

Math and Science Activities Here and There. The following are a selection of home math and science activities. For more ideas, see the resources listed at the end of the chapter.

1. **Find the Numerals.** Using a newspaper page of grocery advertisements, find and mark numbers that are alike; for example, "Find all the fours." The child with well-developed motor skills can cut out the numerals and glue those that are alike on separate sheets of paper to make a number book.

2. **A Monthly Caterpillar.** Cut out and number one circle for each day of the month. Make a caterpillar head from one additional circle. Tape the head to the refrigerator or cabinet door. Each day, add the appropriately numbered circle. Point to and count the numbers.

3. **Traveling Numerals.** When driving or walking along highways and streets, have the child watch for numerals to identify. Note the article "Let's take a road trip" (Hildebrandt, Biglan, & Budd, 2013) that suggest games to play with license plate numbers and other numerals in the environment. The suggestions range from numeral recognition to more complex problems.

4. **Snack Shapes.** Cut sandwiches into circles, squares, rectangles, and/or triangles. Buy crackers in a variety of shapes.

5. **Fraction Food.** When the parent or the child is cutting foods (especially bananas or carrots), suggest that the foods be cut in two pieces (halves), three pieces (thirds), and so on. Introduce fraction vocabulary.

6. **How Many?** Play counting games, such as: "How many doorknobs in this room?" "How many legs on the kitchen chairs?" "How many numbers on the microwave?"

7. **Measure Things.** Encourage the child to describe the size of things using comparison words: *big (-ger, -gest), small (-er, -est), tall (-er, -est), short (-er, -est), wide (-r, -st), narrow (-er, -est)*, and the like. Keep a

record of the child's height and weight with a wall measurement poster so that the numbers can be checked at any time. Compare the children's measurements with their siblings', friends', and adults'. Have the younger child do informal measurements of things in the house and outdoors, using paper clips, toothpicks, body parts (such as hands or feet), string, and so on. Have the older (primary level) child use a clearly labeled ruler.

8. **Learn About Money.** Play simple games. For example, play store using objects such as empty food containers or the child's toys. Mark each item with a price tag in an amount that is understandable at the child's developmental level: in pennies for younger children and in larger amounts for older children. Work with pennies at first, and have the child count out the number of pennies needed to buy an item. When the child is successful with pennies, introduce the nickel as equal to five pennies. Price some items above 5¢, and have the child work with pennies and nickels. Go on to dimes, quarters, and dollars when the child is ready. The older children enjoy Monopoly. Look through the newspaper for grocery ads. Have the child make up a dinner menu using the ads, figure out the cost of the needed groceries, and add up the total cost.

9. **Growing Things.** Children enjoy caring for and observing their own plants as they grow. Bean seeds usually grow fast and do well under any circumstances. Place three bean seeds in a plastic bag with air holes or in a plastic cup along with a wet paper towel. This will allow the roots and stems to be observed. Keep a record of the plants' growth. Point out the roots, stems, and leaves. Keep the paper towel wet.

10. **Bathtub Fun.** Keep a supply of safe plastic containers and plastic boats in the bathroom. Let the child explore these materials during bath time.

11. **Freezing and Melting.** Put ice or snow in a bowl, and place it in a warm place. Watch it melt. Then take the water in the bowl, and freeze it outside or in the refrigerator. Have the child describe what he observes.

12. **Eye Spy.** Encourage both observational and questioning skills. Take turns describing objects in the room and have the other person(s) guess what it is by asking up to 20 questions.

12-3d Math and Science in Nature

The outdoors affords many opportunities for family activities that center on nature. Whether in urban, suburban, or small-town settings, the outdoors affords rich opportunities for observation and interaction. STEM in the park is a weekend event that can be organized (Bledsoe, 2012). Stations can be set up for various age and grade levels.

Who Invited the Ants? Encourage families to use their backyard as a resource for teaching science. Many of the activities found in previous units are appropriate for use in the home. Select topics that are relevant to family life, and suggest them to parents. For example, the following suggestions turn uninvited picnic visitors into a family science exploration.

You will need a spoonful of tuna, a spoonful of honey, and a piece of fruit for this activity. Ask: "What would ants eat if you invited them to a family picnic? Let's have a picnic for the ants in our backyard." Then let the fun begin. However, a few cautions should be noted. Ants belong to the same family as bees and wasps (some ants sting). They have strong jaws, and their bites can hurt a lot, so be very careful when dealing with ants.

To begin explorations, go on an anthill hunt, usually a small pile of dirt with a hole in the middle of it. Or if you spot any ants, follow them back to their home. If this does not work, any bare patch of ground will be fine for observing ants.

Arrange the food on the ground (1 foot apart). Put the honey on a leaf, and place the leaf, tuna, and fruit directly on the ground. Observe closely. Ask: "Which kind of food do the ants go to first? Do you think the ants go to their favorite food or to the food closest to them? Do all of the ants choose the same food?"

Observe ant behavior by asking, "Do the ants carry the food back to the anthill, or eat it on the spot?" Sometimes ants act like messenger ants. When they find food, they go back to the nest and tell the others. Then everybody comes to your picnic.

This activity extends to the sense of smell. Ask: "How do you think that the ants know where to find the food? Can they see the food? Can they hear the food?" Explain that as the ant runs to tell about the picnic, it leaves a scent trail for the other ants to follow.

Scent Trails. Which member of the ant family can smell the best? Make a scent trail on your lawn by placing drops of extract on pieces of cut-up sponge. Create trails using several distinctive scents, such as peppermint, cinnamon, or lemon. See if ants can find and follow the trail. Mixing extract with water and spraying it with a spray bottle in a trail pattern on the ground also works well.

Families will enjoy learning more about their picnic visitors. Most of the ants that we see are worker ants. Their job is to build and maintain the nest and to find food for the colony. Soldier ants live up to their name by defending the anthill against invaders. There is only one queen ant. She rules the nest and lays the eggs that populate the colony. Some queen ants can live 15 years.

There are a variety of ants with interesting habits and lifestyles to discover. For example, some ants even keep tiny insects called aphids to produce a sweet juice for them. The ants milk the aphids for the sweet juice in much the same way that cows are milked. Another kind of ant farmer chews up leaves and spreads them out so that an edible fungus will grow. Some worker honey pot ants use their second stomach to store honeydew. They get so fat with honeydew that they hang in their nest like honey pots. Other ants take the honeydew from them when they are hungry.

NGSS

12-3e Feed the Birds in the Backyard or Park

To help the children recognize different kinds of birds—and to find differences in birds' sizes, shapes, feeding styles, and food preferences—create your own bird-feeding program. In addition to the suggestions for learning about birds found in the second section of this chapter, make beef suet (hard fat from around the kidneys and loins) to help keep up the birds' energy by maintaining their body temperature. Ask a butcher for suet that is short and not stringy (stringy suet is hard for the birds to eat and does not melt down smoothly).

You can offer suet to the birds in many ways. Try putting it in a soap dish attached to a tree limb with chicken wire, or hang it in an onion bag or lobster bait bag. Or make suet ornaments with grapefruit rinds or coconut shells. To do so, chop the suet (or put it through a meat grinder) and then melt it in a double boiler. Pour the liquid suet into the rinds or shells to which you have already attached wire or string hangers, and set the containers aside in a cool place until the suet hardens. Then, hang them on your tree.

How about a bottle cap suet log? Simply nail bottle caps to one side of a dead bough. Pour melted suet into the caps and set the bough aside until the suet hardens. Woodpeckers and other medium-sized birds will gather around to eat from the suet log.

Or, make attractive suet pinecones. Melt the suet, and spoon it over the pinecones (to which you have already attached string or wire). Sprinkle the cones with millet, push sunflower seeds down into the cone's scales, and spoon more warm suet over the cones to secure the seeds. Place the cones on waxed paper and refrigerate until firm. Later, hang the cones from the tree as a snack for small birds, such as chickadees.

Peanut butter mixture makes great food for birds too because peanuts have high nutritional content, and mixtures made with them can be spread on tree bark, placed in the holes of a log or a bottle cap feeder, or hung from pinecones. But before giving the peanut butter to birds, be sure to mix cornmeal into it (1 cup of peanut butter to 5 cups cornmeal). This will make the peanut butter mixture easier for the birds

FIGURE 12-16 *"What kind of food do you think birds feed their young?"*

to swallow. Birds can choke on peanut butter when it is not mixed with anything.

Try mounting a whole ear of dried corn in a conspicuous place, perhaps by nailing it to a post. Then have the children predict which birds will be able to eat the corn (**Figure 12-16**). (Only birds with large beaks will be able to crack the whole kernels of corn).

A Family Bird Walk. A bird walk will heighten the observational skills of everyone involved. Families can look for birds that:

- Hop when they move on the ground.
- Peck at the ground.
- Hold their heads to one side and appear to be listening to something in the ground.
- Flap their wings a lot when they fly.
- Glide and hardly move their wings.
- Climb on the side of trees.
- Fly alone.
- Fly with many other birds.
- Make a lot of noise.
- Eat alone.
- Blend in well with the grass, trees, or sky.
- Swim in the pond.

Select a favorite bird, and find out as much as you can about it. This could be a family project. Use birdcall audiotapes or videotapes to identify the birds you have seen and heard on the bird walk. Children will enjoy creating bird stories, art projects, and puzzles as well as reading more about the birds they have observed. For helpful information on identifying birds and creating a backyard habitat, see Burke (1983), Cook (1978), Cosgrove (1976), and Kress (1985).

BRAIN CONNECTION

PROMOTING BRAIN DEVELOPMENT

Early brain development is dependent on cognitive and emotional and social stimulation (see Early Brain and Child Development special issue of *Zero to Three*, 2013). Scientists are focusing much study on children's early math development (Neergaard, 2013). Good number sense fluency at entry to first grade predicts later success in mathematics. Teaching young children math vocabulary (Chapter 6) by

attaching it to real-life things and experiences is believed to be a major activity for parents to stimulate child brain development. From birth, parents should talk with their child, using words for magnitude, numbers, distance, shapes, and so on. "You have **five** fingers," "I'll tickle your toes, **one, two, three, four, five**," "The dog is **big**," "Grandma lives **10 miles** away."

Early brain and child development. (2013), Zero to Three *[special issue], 44(1); L. Neergaard,* Math skills: What scientists can teach parents about kids' developing minds, *Huffington Post, March 25, 2013, www.huffingtonpost.com.*

SUMMARY

12-1 Overview of Materials and Environment

Stimulating science and math lessons do not happen by accident. The materials selected to teach science and math—and the format in which they are presented—are essential for successful explorations. Whether materials are purchased or scrounged, they must be flexible and appropriate to the developmental age of the child and the type of science and math learning required.

Basic Math and Science Materials. Basic groups of materials are the junk box, commercial materials, kits, and math manipulatives. Organized storage is essential.

The Math Learning Center. The math center may focus on a specific concept or be open ended. Discussion is essential element. If a textbook is required, the math center should provide hands-on parallel experiences.

The Science Learning Center. Learning centers are designed and used to meet specific teaching objectives, and they must be evaluated in terms of their effectiveness. Varieties include the discovery center, the open learning center, the inquiry center, and the interest center.

Selecting Math Materials. Materials should be versatile. Both commercial and donated recyclables can support math learning.

Selecting Science Materials. Ten suggestions for selecting science materials are listed. Science materials should support diversity.

12-2 Standards and Action Overview

"Math and science in action" means children exploring the environment, which they do through woodworking, block constructing, game playing, problem solving, and exploring the outdoor areas in their environment. The phrase also means children saying, singing, and acting out math and science language and concepts.

Blocks. When children make block-building decisions, they are thinking like scientists and engineers. They focus on a problem and use the thinking skills of math and science to

arrive at a solution or conclusions. Block building and other indoor and outdoor explorations give children an opportunity to learn by manipulating and acting on their environment as they build their own model of the world.

Woodworking. Woodworking is another constructive activity for young engineers.

Math Games. Games provide opportunities for practicing skills and concepts. Games also provide experiences is turn-taking, following rules, and cooperating.

Science in Action: The Outdoors. The outdoor environment can be used to extend and enhance indoor lessons or as a specific place for engaging children in challenging learning. Suggestions have been given about how to work directly with outdoor learning, as well as strategies for focusing children's attention on outdoor learning and encouraging higher-level math and science thinking. Once children learn how to study the outdoors, they will enjoy the fascinating world around them.

Technology. Technology provides increasing opportunities for children to learn about the world and to apply science and mathematics skills and concepts through software applications and through the broad domain opened up by the Internet.

Culturally Relevant Mathematics and Science. Equity is an essential principle of mathematics and science instruction. Focusing on children's cultural mathematics and science and comparisons with the mathematics and science of other cultures shows respect for diversity.

12-3 Family Involvement in Math and Science Begins at Home

Science and mathematics can provide many opportunities for informal family sharing. Family members can encourage children to explore, ask questions, and think about the world around them.

Guidelines for Families as Teachers at Home. A single guiding question from an adult can turn a daily routine into a learning experience. There are many resources available to help families learn how to incorporate math and science into daily activities.

Math and Science in the Home, Yard, Neighborhood, and Park. As children cook, observe, sort, investigate, construct, and explore software and the Internet, they are using the skills needed to learn science and mathematics. All around there are rich sources of math and science experiences families can use to enrich children's math and science knowledge and skills.

Math and Science in Nature. Birds, ants, rocks, trees, shells, and other outdoor inhabitants make ideal subjects for observation and exploration.

Feed the Birds in Backyard or Park. Birds are attracted to pine cones covered with peanut butter and birdseed. A bird walk can focus observation on the neighborhood birds. Rocks can be collected on a walk.

FURTHER READING AND RESOURCES

Ashbook, P. (2003). *Science is simple: Over 250 activities for preschoolers.* Beltsville, MD: Gryphon House.

Blake, R. W., Jr., Frederick, J. A., Haines, S., & Lee, S. C. (2010). *Inside-out: Environmental science in the classroom and the field, Grades 3–8.* Reston, VA: NSTA Press.

Churchman, S. (2006). *Bringing math home: A parent's guide to elementary school math: Games, activities, projects.* Chicago: Zephyr Press.

Colker, L. J. (2005). *The cooking book.* Washington, DC: National Association for the Education of Young Children.

Cook, D. (2006). *Family fun. Cooking with kids.* New York: Disney Enterprises.

Environments that engage and inspire young learners. (2013). [Focus Section]. *Young Children, 68*(4), 6.

Faulk, J., & Evanshen, P. (2013). Linking the primary classroom environment to learning. *Young Children, 68*(4), 40–45.

Franco, B. (n.d.). *Counting caterpillars and other math poems.* New York: Scholastic

Hirsch, E. (Ed.). (1996). *The block book (3rd ed.).* Washington, DC: National Association for the Education of Young Children.

Hoot, J. L., & Szente, J. (2010). *The earth is our home: Children caring for the environment.* Olney, MD: Association for Childhood Education International.

Johnson, E. (2009). *How kids can have fun in the kitchen: A first cookbook for children.* Frederick, MD: Publishamerica, Inc.

Maynard, C. (2006). *Science fun at home.* New York: DK Children.

Ogu, U., & Schmidt, A. R. (2013). The natural playscape project: A real-world study with kindergartners. *Young Children, 68*(4), 32–39.

Pollman, M. J. (2010). *Blocks and beyond.* Baltimore, MD: Brookes.

Ritz, W. C. (Ed.). (2007). *A head start on science.* Arlington, VA: NSTA Press.

Technology and young children. [Focus Section]. (2012) *Young children, 67*(3).

Williams, K. C., & Veomett, G. E. (2007). *Launching learners in science, Pre-K–5.* Thousand Oaks, CA: Corwin.

The Wisdom of Nature. (2010). Rifton, NY: Community Playthings and World Forum Foundation.

REFERENCES

Arenson, R. (Illus.). (1998). *One, two, skip a few! First number rhymes.* New York: Barefoot Books.

Ashbrook, P. (2012). Send-home science. *Science and Children, 49*(6), 26–27.

Ashbrook, P. (2013, August 29). Preparing the classroom and school grounds for science exploration. *Early Years.* http://nstacommunities.org/blog.

Ashbrook, P. (2013, November 3). Fall changes in trees bring science and art together. *Early Years.* http://nstacommunities.org/blog.

Benedis-Grab, G. (2010). The built environment. *Science and Children, 47*(6), 22–26.

Bledsoe, K. (2012). STEM day in the park. *Science and Children, 49*(6), 65–69.

Burke, K. (1983). *How to attract birds.* San Francisco: Ortho Books. (A well-illustrated book with an informative text about providing food, water, and nest sites for both Eastern and western birds.)

Burns, M. (2009). 4 win–win math games. *Instructor, 118*(5) (March–April).

Burrill, G. (1997). Show me the math! *NCTM News Bulletin, 3*(April).

Burton, M., & Baum, A. C. (2009). Engage families in meaningful mathematics. *Teaching Children Mathematics, 16*(1), 12–15.

Canada, D. (2009). Fraction photo frenzy. *Teaching Children Mathematics, 15*(9), 552–557.

Carey, J. H. (1990). Science fun: Have a field day in the gym. *Science and Children, 28*(2), 16–19.

Coates, G. D., & Stenmark, J. K. (1997). *Family math for young children.* Berkeley, CA: Lawrence Hall of Science.

Columba, L., & Waddell, L. (2009/2010). A treasure trove of triangles. *Teaching Children Mathematics, 16*(5), 272.

Cook, B. C. (1978). *Invite a bird to dinner.* New York: Lathrop.

Cosgrove, I. (1976). *My recipes are for the birds.* New York: Doubleday.

Crawford, E. O., Heaton, E. T., Heslop K., & Kixmiller, K. (2013). Science learning in out-of-school time. In A. Shillady (Ed.), *Exploring Science* (pp. 55–60). Washington, DC: National Association for the Education of Young Children.

Crews, D. (1986). *Ten black dots*. New York: Mulberry.

Cross, C. T., Woods, T. A., & Schweingruber, H. (Eds.). (2009). *Mathematics learning in early childhood*. Washington, DC: National Academies Press.

Czerniak, C. M. (1994). Backpack science. *Science and Children, 32*(1), 46–47.

Davis, M. R. (2010). Solving algebra on smartphones. *Education Week, 29*(6), 20–23. www.edweek.org.

Davison, S. (2009). A picture is worth a thousand words. *Science and Children, 46*(5), 36–39.

de Melendez, W. R., & Beck, V. (2013). *Teaching young children in multicultural classrooms*, 4th ed. Belmont, CA: Wadsworth Cengage Learning.

DeVries, R., & Sales, C. (2011). *Ramps and pathways*. Washington, DC: National Association for the Education of Young Children.

Diffily, D., & Morrison, K. (Eds.). (1996). *Family-friendly communication for early childhood programs*. Washington, DC: National Association for the Education of Young Children.

Edge, D. (Ed.). (1998). Beyond the classroom: Linking mathematics learning with parents, communities, and business and industry [Special issue]. *Teaching Children Mathematics, 4*(6).

Eglash, R. (2001). News from the net: The international study group on ethnomathematics. *Teaching Children Mathematics, 7*(6), 336.

Everhart, J. (2009). YouTube in the science classroom. *Science and Children, 46*(9), 32–35.

Fallwell, C. (1993). *Feast for 10*. New York: Clarion.

Findell, C. R., Cavanagh, M., Dacey, L., Greenes, C. E., Sheffield, L. J., & Small, M. (2004). *Navigating through problem solving and reasoning in grade 1*. Reston, VA: National Council of Teachers of Mathematics.

Freudenberg, K. (2012). Science sacks. *Science and Children, 26*(6), 37–41.

Gargiulo, R., & Kilgo, J. (2014). *Young children with special needs*, 4th ed. Belmont, CA: Wadsworth Cengage Learning.

Getting families involved. (2012). [Focus Issue]. *Science and Children, 49*(6).

Greenes, C. E., Dacey, L., Cavanagh, M., Findell, C. R., Sheffield, L. J., & Small, M. (2003). *Navigating through problem solving and reasoning in prekindergarten–kindergarten*. Reston, VA: National Council of Teachers of Mathematics.

Hansen, L.E. (2005). ABC's of early math experiences. *Teaching Children Mathematics, 12*(4), 208–212.

Hildebrandt, M. E., Biglan, B., & Budd, L. (2013). Let's take a road trip. *Teaching Children Mathematics, 19*(9), 548.

Holden, J. C. (1996). The science exchange program. *Science and Children, 34*(3), 20–21.

Jacobs, V. R., Bennett, T. R., & Bullock, C. (2000). Selecting books in Spanish to teach mathematics. *Teaching Children Mathematics, 6*(9), 582–587.

Kliman, M. (1999). Parents and children doing mathematics at home. *Teaching Children Mathematics, 6*(3), 140–146.

Kline, K. (1999). Helping at home. *Teaching Children Mathematics, 5*(8), 456–460.

Koestler, C., Felton, M . D., Bieda, K. N., & Otten, S. (2013). *Connecting the NCTM process standards & the CCSSM practices*. Reston, VA: National Council of Teacher of Mathematics.

Kress, S. W. (1985). *The Audubon Society guide to attracting birds*. New York: Scribner's.

Lachance, A. (2007). Family math nights: Collaborative celebrations of mathematical learning. *Teaching Children Mathematics, 13*(8), 404–408.

Lissenbee, P. (2009). Whiteboards and Websites; Digital tools for the early childhood curriculum. *Young Children, 64*(6), 92–95.

Lynes, K. (1997). Tech time: Mining mathematics through the Internet! *Teaching Children Mathematics, 3*(7), 394–396.

MacDonald, S. (2001). *Block play: The complete guide to learning and playing with blocks*. Beltsville, MD: Gryphon House.

Manzo, K. K. (2010). Educators struggle to design mobile-learning content. *Education Week, 29*(26) 28–29. www.edweek.org.

Marinak, B. A., Strickland, M. J., & Keat, J. B. (2010). Using photo-narration to support all learners. *Young Children, 65*(5), 32–38.

McNeil, N. M., & Uttal, D. H. (2009). Rethinking the use of concrete materials in learning: Perspectives from development and education. *Child Development Perspectives, 3*(3), 137–139.

Merenda, R. C. (1995). A book, a bed, a bag: Interactive homework for "10." *Teaching Children Mathematics, 1*(5), 262–266.

National Council of Teachers of Mathematics. (2000). *Principles and standards for school mathematics*. Reston, VA: Author.

Neergaard, L. (2013, March 25). Math skills: What scientists can teach parents about kids' developing minds. *Huffington Post*. www.huffingtonpost.com.

Nelson, E. (2012). *What is the outdoor classroom?* http://www.communityplaythings.com.

Overdeck, L. (2013). *Bedtime Math: A fun excuse to stay up late.* New York: Macmillan.

Overdeck, L. (2014). *Bedtime Math: This time, it's personal.* New York: Macmillan.

Parental involvement: A key factor of science success [Focus issue]. (2003). *Science and Children, 40*(4).

Petrinjak, L. Making a night of science. (2011, February 3). *NSTA Reports, 22*(6), 1, 4.

Piehler, C. (2013, February 28). Finding the right tech tools is easy, if you know where to look. *T.H.E. Journal.* http://thejournal.com.

Rivkin, M. S. (2014). *The great outdoors: Advocating for natural spaces for young children*, rev. ed. Washington, DC: National Association for the Education of Young Children.

Rosen, D., & Hoffman, J. (2009). Integrating concrete and virtual manipulatives. *Young Children, 64*(3), 26–33.

Scieszka, J., & Smith, L. (1995). *Math curse.* New York: Viking.

Seo, K., & Bruk, S. J. (2003). Promoting young children's mathematical learning through a new twist on homework. *Teaching Children Mathematics, 10*(1), 26–31.

Shaughnessy, J. M. (2010). Support for parents and families: Helping your math students. *NCTM Summing Up* (December), 1–2.

Shaw, G. M., Chambless, M. S., Chessin, D. R., Price, V., & Beardain, G. (1997). Cooperative problem solving: Using K-W-D-L as an organizational technique. *Teaching Children Mathematics, 3*, 482–486.

Shillady, A. (Ed.) (2013). *Exploring science.* Washington, DC: National Association for the Education of Young Children.

Small, M., Sheffield, L. J., Cavanagh, M., Dacey, L., Findell, C. R., & Greenes, C. E. (2004). *Navigating through problem solving and reasoning in grade 2.* Reston, VA: National Council of Teachers of Mathematics.

Starbuck, S., Olthof, M. & Midden, K. (2002). *Why garden?* Retrieved April 17, 2012, from Community Playthings .com.

Stenmark, D. D., Thompson, V., & Cossey, R. (1986). *Family math.* Berkeley, CA: University of California Press.

Thong, R. (2000). *Round is a mooncake.* San Francisco: Chronicle Books.

Thornton, C. A., Dee, D., Damkoehler, D. D., Gehrenbeck, H., & Jones, G. A. (1995). The children's rain forest. *Teaching Children Mathematics, 2*(3), 144–148.

Trailblazers. (2010). *Teaching Children Mathematics* (March). www.nctm.org.

Tunk, K. W. (2013). Happy 100th birthday, Unit blocks! *Young Children, 68*(5), 82–87.

Wahlberg, E. D. (2007). Grands are grand: A cross-generational learning experience at the North Museum of Natural History and Science. In R. E. Yager (Ed.), *Using the national science education standards for improving science education in nonschool settings.* Reston, VA: NSTA, 167–177.

White, D. Y. (2001). Kenta, kilts, and kimonos: Exploring cultures and mathematics through fabrics. *Teaching Children Mathematics, 7*(6), 354–359.

Wien, A. (2014). *The power of emergent curriculum.* Washington, DC: National Association for the Education of Young Children.

Wolfgang, C. H., Stannard, L. L., & Jones, I. (2001). Block play performance among preschoolers as a predictor of later school achievement in mathematics. *Journal of Research in Childhood Education, 15*(2), 173–180.

Zadeh, Y. Z., Farnia, F., & Ungerleider. (2010). How home enrichment mediates the relationship between maternal education and children's achievement in reading and math. *Early Education and Development, 21*(4), 568–594.

Zaslavsky, C. (2001). Developing number sense: What can other cultures tell us? *Teaching Children Mathematics, 7*(6), 312–319.

APPENDIX A

CONTENTS

SENSORIMOTOR: LEVEL 1

1A   Sensorimotor

Age 2 months

General Development

Method: Interview.

Skills: Perceptual/motor.

Materials: Familiar object or toy, such as a rattle.

Procedures/Evaluations:

1. Talk to the infant. Notice whether he seems to attend and respond (by looking at you, making sounds, and/or changing facial expression).

2. Hold a familiar object within the infant's reach. Note whether he reaches out for it.

3. Move the object through the air across the infant's line of vision. He should follow it with his eyes.

4. Hand the small toy to the infant. He should hold it for two to three seconds.

1B   Sensorimotor

Age 4 months

General Development

Method: Observation.

Skills: Perceptual/motor.

Materials: Assortment of appropriate infant toys.

Procedures/Evaluations:

1. Note each time you offer the infant a toy. Does she usually grab hold of it?

2. Place the infant where it is possible for her to observe the surroundings (such as in an infant seat) in a situation where there is a lot of activity. Note whether her eyes follow the activity and if she seems to be interested and curious.

1C   Sensorimotor

Age 6 months

General Development

Method: Interview and observation.

Skills: Perceptual/motor.

Materials: Several nontoxic objects or toys, including the infant's favorite toy.

Procedures/Evaluations:

1. One by one, hand the infant a series of nontoxic objects. Note how many of his senses he uses for exploring the objects. He should be using eyes, mouth, and hands.

2. Place yourself out of the infant's line of vision. Call out to him. Note whether he turns his head toward your voice.

3. When the infant drops an object, note whether he picks it up again.

4. When the infant is eating, notice whether he can hold his bottle in both hands by himself.

5. Show the infant his favorite toy. Slowly move the toy to a hiding place. Note whether the infant follows with his eyes as the toy is hidden.

1D   Sensorimotor
Age 12 months
General Development

Method: Interview and observation.

Skills: Perceptual/motor and receptive language.

Materials: Two bells or rattles; two blocks or other small objects; two clear plastic cups; pillow or empty box; a cookie, if desired.

Procedures/Evaluations:

1. Note whether the infant will imitate you when you perform the following activities (for each task, provide the infant with a duplicate set of materials).

   A. Shake a bell (or a rattle).

   B. Play peek-a-boo by placing your open palms in front of your eyes.

   C. Put a block (or other small object) into a cup; take it out of the cup, and place it next to the cup.

2. Partially hide a familiar toy or a cookie under a pillow or a box as the child watches. Note whether the infant searches for it.

3. Note whether the infant is creeping, crawling, pulling up to her feet, trying to walk, or is actually walking.

4. Note whether the infant responds to the following verbal commands:

   A. "No, No."

   B. "Give me the (name of object)."

SENSORIMOTOR: LEVEL 2

2A   Sensorimotor
Ages 12–18 months
General Development

Method: Interview and observation.

Skills: Perceptual/motor and receptive language.

Materials: Several safe containers and a supply of safe, nontoxic objects.

Procedures/Evaluations:

1. Give the child several containers and the supply of small objects. Note whether she fills the containers with objects and dumps them out repeatedly.

2. Tell the child, "**Point to your head (eyes, foot, stomach).**"

3. Hide a familiar object completely. Note whether the child searches for it.

2B   Sensorimotor
Ages 18–24 months
General Development

Method: Interview and observation.

Skills: Perceptual/motor and receptive and expressive language.

Materials: Child's own toys (or other assortment provided by you, such as a ball, toy dog, toy car, blocks, baby bottle, doll, and the like).

Procedures/Evaluations:

1. During playtime observations, note whether the child is beginning to organize objects in rows and put similar objects together in groups.

2. Ask the child to point to familiar objects. "**Point to the ball (chair, doll, car).**"

3. Note whether the child begins to name the parts of her body (usually two parts at 18 months).

PREOPERATIONAL: LEVEL 3

3A*   Preoperational
Ages 2–3
One-to-One Correspondence: see Chapter 3 for task

3B   Preoperational
Ages 2–3
Number Sense and Counting: Chapter 3

Method: Interview.

Skill: Child understands the concept of "twoness" and can rational-count at least two objects.

Materials: Ten counters (cube blocks, Unifix Cubes, or other objects).

Procedures:

1. Ask, "How old are you?"

2. Give the child two objects. Ask, "**How many (name of objects) are there?**" If the child succeeds, try three objects. Go on as far as the child can go.

Evaluation:

1. May hold up appropriate number of fingers or answer "two" or "three."

2. Should be able to rational-count two objects (or possibly recognize two without counting).

3C   **Preoperational**

        Ages 2–3

Logic and Classifying, Informal Sorting: Chapter 3

Method: Observation and informal interviewing.

Skill: While playing, the child groups toys by various criteria such as color, shape, size, class name, and so on.

Materials: Assortment of normal toys for 2- to 3-year-olds.

Procedure: As the child plays, note whether toys are grouped by classification criteria (see Chapter 3). Say, **"Show me the red blocks. Which car is the biggest? Find some square blocks."**

Evaluation: The child should naturally group by similarities, should be able to group objects by at least one or two colors, and should be able to find objects from the same class.

3D   **Preoperational**

        Ages 2–3

Comparing, Informal Measurement: Chapter 3

Method: Interview.

Skill: Child can respond to comparison terms applied to familiar objects.

Materials: Pairs of objects that vary on comparative criteria, such as

large–small	cold–hot
heavy–light	fat–skinny
long–short	higher–lower

Procedure: Show the child the pairs of objects one pair at a time. Tell the child, **"Point to the big (ball). Point to the small, or little, (ball)."** Continue with other pairs of objects and object concept words.

Evaluation: Note how many of the objects the child can identify correctly.

3E   **Preoperational**

        Ages 2–3

Comparing, Number: Chapter 3

Method: Interview.

Skill: Shown a set of one and six or more, the child can identify which set has more.

Materials: Twenty counters (e.g., pennies, Unifix Cubes, cube blocks).

Procedure: Place two groups of objects in front of the child: one group with a set of one object and one group with a set of six or more. Ask, **"Which has more (object name)? Point to the one with more."**

Evaluation: Note whether the child identifies the group that contains more.

3F   **Preoperational**

        Ages 2–3

Shape, Matching: Chapter 4

Method: Interview.

Skill: Child can match an object or cutout shape to another of the same size and shape.

Materials: Attribute blocks or shape cutouts; one red circle, square, and triangle; one green circle, square, and triangle. All should be the same relative size.

Procedure: Place the three green shapes in front of the child. One at a time, show the child each of the red shapes and tell the child, Say, **"Find a green shape that is the same as this red one."**

Evaluation: The child should be able to make all three matches.

3G*   **Preoperational**

        Ages 2–3

Space, Position: see Chapter 4 for task

3H*   **Preoperational**

        Ages 2–3

Parts and Wholes, Missing Parts: see Chapter 4 for task

3I   **Preoperational**

        Ages 2–3

Ordering, Size: Chapter 5

Method: Interview.

Skill: Child can order three objects that vary in one size dimension.

Materials: Three objects of the same shape that vary in one size dimension, such as diameter.

Paper towel rolls can be cut into proportional lengths (heights) for this task. More objects can be available in reserve to be used for more difficult seriation tasks.

Procedure: Say, **"Watch what I do."** Line up the objects in order from fattest to thinnest (longest to shortest, tallest to shortest). **"Now I'll mix them up."** (Do so.) **"Put them in a row like I did."** If the child does the task with three objects, try it with five.

Evaluation: Note whether the objects are placed in a correct sequence.

3J   Preoperational
Ages 2–3

Measuring, Volume: Chapter 5

Method: Observation.

Skill: Child shows an understanding that different containers hold different amounts.

Materials: A large container filled with small objects such as small blocks, paper clips, table tennis balls, or teddy-bear counters or with a substance such as water, rice, or legumes; several different size small containers for pouring.

Procedure: Let the children experiment with filling and pouring. Note any behavior that indicates they recognize that different containers hold different amounts.

Evaluation: Children should experiment, filling containers and pouring back into the large container, pouring into larger small containers, and into smaller containers. Note behaviors such as whether they line up smaller containers and fill each from a larger container or fill a larger container, using a smaller one.

PREOPERATIONAL: LEVEL 4

4A   Preoperational
Ages 2–3

One-to-One Correspondence, Same Things/Related Things: Chapter 3

Method: Interview.

Skills:

1. Child can match, in one-to-one correspondence, pairs of objects that are alike.

2. Child can match, in one-to-one correspondence, pairs of objects that are related but not alike.

Materials:

1. Four different pairs of matching objects (such as two toy cars, two small plastic animals, two coins, two blocks).

2. Two groups of four related objects such as four cups and four saucers, four cowboys and four horses, four flowers and four flowerpots, four hats and four heads.

Procedures:

1. Matching like pairs. Place the objects in front of the child in a random array. Say, **"Find the things that belong together."** If there is no response, pick up one. Say, **"Find one like this."** When the match is made, say, **"Find some other things that belong together."** If there is no spontaneous response, continue to select objects, and ask the child to find the one like each.

2. Matching related pairs. Place two related groups of four in front of the child in a random array. Say, **"Find a cup for each saucer (or a cowboy for each horse)."**

Evaluations:

1. Note whether the child matches spontaneously and if he makes an organized pattern (such as placing the pairs side by side or in a row).

2. Note whether the child is organized and uses a pattern for placing the objects (such as placing the objects in two matching rows).

4B   Preoperational
Ages 3–4

Number Sense and Counting, Rote and Rational: Chapter 3

Method: Interview.

Skill: Child can rote-count and rational-count.

Materials: Twenty counters (e.g., cube blocks, pennies, Unifix Cubes).

Procedure: First have the child rote-count: **"Count for me. Start with one and count."** If the child hesitates, say, **"One, two, _____. What comes next?"** Then ask, **"How old are you?"** Finally, place four counters in front of the child. **"Count the (objects). How many (_____) are there?"** If the child cannot count four items, try two or three. If she counts four easily, put out more counters, and ask her to count as many as she can.

Evaluation: Note whether she can rote-count more than five and rational-count at least five items. When she rational-counts more than four, she should keep track of each item by touching each methodically or moving those counted to the side.

4C   Preoperational
Ages 3–4

Logic and Classifying, Object Sorting: Chapter 3

Method: Interview.

Skill: Child can sort objects into groups, using logical criteria.

Materials: Twelve objects: two red, two blue, two green, two yellow, two orange, two purple. There should be at least five kinds of objects; for example:

Color	Object 1	Object 2
red	block	car
blue	ball	cup
green	comb	car
yellow	block	bead
orange	comb	cup
purple	bead	ribbon

In addition, you will need 6 to 10 small containers (bowls or boxes).

Procedure: Place the 12 objects in random array in front of the child. Provide him with the containers. Say, **"Put the toys that belong together in a bowl (box). Use as many bowls (boxes) as you need."**

Evaluation: Note whether the child uses any specific criteria as he makes his groups.

4D* **Preoperational**

      Ages 3–4

Comparing, Number: see Chapter 3 for task

4E* **Preoperational**

      Ages 3–4

Shape, Identification: see Chapter 4 for task

4F* **Preoperational**

      Ages 3–4

Space, Position: see Chapter 4 for task

4G* **Preoperational**

      Ages 3–6

Rote-counting: see Chapter 3 for task

4H* **Preoperational**

      Ages 3–6

Rational-counting: see Chapter 3 for task

4I* **Preoperational**

      Ages 3–6

Time, Identify Clock or Watch: see Chapter 5 for task

4J* **Preoperational**

      Ages 3–6

Symbols, Recognition: see Chapter 7 for task

5A **Preoperational**

      Ages 4–5

One-to-One Correspondence, Same Things/Related Things: Chapter 3

Do tasks in 4A (1 and 2), using more pairs of objects.

5B **Preoperational**

      Ages 4–5

Number Sense and Counting, Rote and Rational: Chapter 3

See 4B, 4G, and 4H.

5C **Preoperational**

      Ages 4–5

Comparing, Number: Chapter 3

Method: Interview.

Skill: The child can compare the amounts in groups up to five and label the ones that are more, less, and fewer.

Materials: Ten counters (e.g., chips, inch cubes, Unifix Cubes).

Procedure: Present the following groups for comparison in sequence:

    1 versus 5

    4 versus 1

    2 versus 5

    3 versus 2

    5 versus 4

Each time a pair of groups is presented, ask, **"Does one group have more?"** If the answer is yes, say, **"Point to the group that has more."** Then ask, **"How do you know that group has more?"** If the child responds correctly to *more,* present the pairs again, using *less* and *fewer.*

Evaluation: Note for which comparisons the child responds correctly. Can she give a logical reason for her choices (such as "Four is more than one" or "I counted them")? Does she place them in one-to-one correspondence?

5D* **Preoperational**

      Ages 4–5

Comparing, Informal Measurement: see Chapter 3 for task

5E* **Preoperational**

      Ages 4–5

Shape, Geometric Shape Recognition: see Chapter 4 for task

5F*   **Preoperational**

      Ages 4–5

Parts and Wholes, Parts of a Whole: see Chapter 4 for task

5G*   **Preoperational**

      Ages 4–5

Ordering, Sequential/Ordinal Number: see Chapter 5 for task

5H*   **Preoperational**

      Ages 4–5

Time, Labeling, and Sequence: see Chapter 5 for task

5I   **Preoperational**

      Ages 4–5

Practical Activities, Money: Chapter 6

Method: Observation and interview.

Skill: Child understands that money is exchanged for goods and services and can identify nickel, dime, penny, and dollar bill.

Materials:

1. Play money and store props for dramatic play.
2. Nickel, dime, penny, and dollar bill.

Procedure:

1. Set up play money and props for dramatic play as described in Chapter 6. Observe the child, and note whether he demonstrates some concept of exchanging money for goods and services and of giving and receiving change.
2. Show the child a nickel, dime, penny, and dollar bill. Say, **"Tell me the name of each of these."**

Evaluation: Note the child's knowledge of money during dramatic play and note which, if any, of the pieces of money he recognizes.

The following tasks can be presented first between ages 4 and 5 and then repeated as the child's concepts and skills grow and expand.

5J*   **Preoperational**

      Ages 4–6

Logic and Classifying, Free Sort: see Chapter 3 for task

5K*   **Preoperational**

      Ages 4–6

Logic and Classifying, Clue Sort: see Chapter 3 for task

5L*   **Preoperational**

      Ages 4–6

Symbols, Sequencing: see Chapter 7 for task

5M   **Preoperational**

      Ages 4–5

Naturalistic and Informal Activities

Method: Observation.

Skill: Child can demonstrate a knowledge of math concepts and skills during naturalistic and informal activities.

Materials: Math center (three-dimensional and two-dimensional materials), sand/water/legume pouring table, dramatic play props, unit blocks and accessories, cooking center, math concept books.

Procedure: Develop a recording system and keep a record of behaviors such as the following:

- Chooses to work in the math center.
- Selects math concept books to look at.
- Chooses to work in the cooking center.
- Selects working with sand, water, or legumes.
- Can give each person one napkin, one glass of juice, and so on.
- Spontaneously counts objects or people.
- While playing, spontaneously separates objects or pictures into logical groups.
- Spontaneously uses comparison words (e.g., This one is *bigger*).
- Chooses to build with blocks.
- Knows the parts of people and objects.
- Demonstrates a knowledge of *first, biggest, heaviest,* and other order concepts.
- Does informal measurement such as identifying hot and cold, a bigger container and a smaller container, and so on.
- Evidences a concept of time (What do we do next? Is it time for lunch?).
- Points out number symbols in the environment.
- Uses the language of math (whether he or she understands the concepts or not).

Evaluation: Child should show an increase in frequency of these behaviors as the year progresses.

PREOPERATIONAL: LEVEL 6

6A*   **Preoperational**

      Ages 5–6

One-to-One Correspondence: see Chapter 3 for task

6B   **Preoperational**

      Ages 5–6

Number Sense and Counting, Rote and Rational: Chapter 3

Method: Interview.

Skill: Child can rote and rational-count.

Materials: Fifty counters (e.g., chips, cube blocks, Unifix Cubes).

Procedures:

1. Rote-counting. Say, "**Count for me as far as you can.**" If the child hesitates, prompt with "**One, two, … what's next?**"

2. Rational-counting. Present the child with 20 objects. Ask, "**How many (objects) are there? Count them for me.**"

Evaluation:

1. *Rote.* By age 5, the child should be able to count to 10 or more; by age 6, to 20 or more. Note whether any number names are missed or repeated.

2. *Rational.* Note the degree of accuracy and organization. Does she place the objects to ensure that no object is counted more than once or that no object is missed? Note how far she goes without making a mistake. Does she repeat any number names? Skip any? By age 6, she should be able to go beyond 10 objects with accuracy.

6C **Preoperational**

Ages 5–6

Shape, Recognition and Reproduction: Chapter 4

Method: Interview.

Skill #1: Identify shapes, Task 4E.

Skill #2: Child can identify shapes in the environment.

Materials: Natural environment.

Procedure: Say: "**Look around the room. Find as many shapes as you can. Which things are square shapes? Circles? Rectangles? Triangles?**"

Evaluation: Note how observant the child is. Does she note the obvious shapes, such as windows, doors, and tables? Does she look beyond the obvious? How many shapes and which shapes is she able to find?

Skill #3: Child will reproduce shapes by copying.

Materials: Shape cards (as in Task 4E); plain white paper; a choice of pencils, crayons, and markers.

Procedure:

1. COPY THE CIRCLE.

2. COPY THE SQUARE.

3. COPY THE TRIANGLE.

Evaluation: Note how closely each reproduction resembles its model. Is the circle complete and round? Does the square have four sides and square corners? Does the triangle have three straight sides and pointed corners?

6D* **Preoperational**

Ages 5–6

Parts and Wholes, Parts of Sets: see Chapter 4 for task

6E **Preoperational**

Ages 5–6

Ordering, Size, and Amount: Chapter 5

Method: Interview.

Skills: Child can order 10 objects that vary in one criteria and five sets with amounts from one to five.

Materials:

1. *Size.* Ten objects or cutouts that vary in size, length, height, or width. An example for length is shown below.

——— —— ——— ———— ————

———————— ——————————

—————————— ———— ————————

2. *Amount.* Five sets of objects consisting of one, two, three, four, and five objects each.

Procedures:

1. *Size.* Place the ten objects or cutouts in front of the child in a random arrangement. Say, "**Find the (biggest, longest, tallest, or widest). Put them all in a row from _____ to _____.**"

2. Amount. Place the five sets in front of the child in a random arrangement. Say, "**Put these in order from the smallest bunch (group) to the largest bunch (group).**"

Evaluations:

1. *Size.* Preoperational children will usually get the two extremes but may mix up the in-between sizes. Putting 10 objects in the correct order would be an indication that the child is entering concrete operations.

2. *Amount.* Most 5-year-olds can order the five sets. If they order them easily, try some larger amounts.

6F **Preoperational**

Ages 5–6

Measurement; Length, Weight, and Time: Chapter 5

Method: Interview.

Skills: Child can explain the function of a ruler, discriminate larger from heavier, identify clocks, and explain their function.

Materials:

1. *Length.* A foot ruler.
2. *Weight.* A plastic golf ball and a marble or other pair of objects where the larger is the lighter.
3. *Time.* A clock (with a conventional face).

Procedures:

1. Show the child the rules. Ask, "**What is this? What do we do with it? Show me how it is used.**"
2. Give the child the two objects, one in each hand. Ask, "**Which is bigger? Which is heavier? Why is the small (object) heavier?**"
3. Show the child the clock. "**What is this? Why do we have it? Tell me how it works.**"

Evaluation: Note how many details the child can give about each of the measuring instruments. Is she accurate? Can she tell which of the objects is heavier? Can she provide a reason for the lighter being larger and the smaller heavier?

6G   Preoperational

Ages 5–6

Practical Activities, Money: Chapter 6

Method: Interview.

Skill: Child can recognize money and tell which pieces of money will buy more.

Materials:

1. Pictures of coins, bills, and other similar items.
2. Selection of pennies, nickels, dimes, and quarters.

Procedures:

1. Show the child the pictures. Say, "**Find the pictures of money.**" After he has found the pictures of money, ask, "**What is the name of this?**" as you point to each picture of money.
2. Put the coins in front of the child. Ask, "**Which will buy the most? If you have these five pennies** (put five pennies in one pile), **and I want two cents for a piece of candy, how many pennies will you have to give me for the candy?**"

Evaluation: Note which picture of money the child can identify. Note whether he knows which coins are worth the most. Many young children equate worth and size and thus think a nickel will buy more than a dime.

Check back to 5J, 5K, and 5L; then go on to the next tasks. The following tasks can be presented first between ages 5 and 6 and then repeated as the child's concepts and skills grow and expand.

6H*   Preoperational/Concrete

Ages 5–7

Ordering, Double Seriation: see Chapter 5 for task

6I*   Preoperational/Concrete

Ages 5–7

Ordering, Patterning: see Chapter 5 for task

6J*   Preoperational

Ages 5 and older

Symbols, One More Than: see Chapter 7 for task

6K*   Preoperational/Concrete

Ages 5–7

Sets and Symbols, Write/Reproduce Numerals: see Chapter 7 for task

6L*   Preoperational/Concrete

Ages 5–7

Sets and Symbols, Match Sets to Symbols: see Chapter 7 for task

6M*   Preoperational/Concrete

Ages 5–7

Sets and Symbols, Match Symbols to Sets: see Chapter 7 for task

6N   Preoperational/Concrete

Ages 5–6

Naturalistic and Informal Activities: Chapters 1–Chapter 7

Method: Observation.

Skill: Child demonstrates a knowledge of math concepts and skills during naturalistic and informal activities.

Materials: See Task 5M.

Procedure: See Task 5M. Add the following behaviors to your list.

■ Demonstrates an understanding of *more than, the same amount,* and *less than* by responding appropriately to questions such as, "Do we have the same number of children as we have chairs?"

■ Can match a set to a symbol and a symbol to a set (e.g., if the daily attendance total says 22, he can get 22 napkins for snack).

- Can do applied concrete whole number operations (e.g., if four children plan to draw and two more children join them, he knows that there are now six children; or if he has three friends and eight cars to play with, he figures out that each friend can use two cars).

Evaluation: Child should show an increase in frequency of these behaviors as the year progresses.

MATH LANGUAGE: LEVEL 7

By the time the child is between 5½ and 6½ years of age, she should be using most of the words listed in Chapter 6. The following tasks can be used to find out which words the child uses in an open-ended situation. Show each picture individually. Say, **"I have some pictures to show you. Here is the first one. Tell me about it."** For each picture, tape-record or write down the child's responses. Later, list all the math words. Compare this with the list of math words she uses in class.

CONCRETE OPERATIONS: LEVEL 8

The following tasks are all indicators of the child's cognitive developmental level. The child who can accomplish all these tasks should be ready for the primary-level instruction described in Section 5.

8A   **Concrete Operations**

        Ages 6–7

Conservation of Number: Chapter 1

Method: Interview.

Skill: Child can solve the number conservation problem.

Materials: Twenty chips, blocks, or coins, all the same size, shape, and color.

Procedure: Set up a row of nine objects. Then proceed through the following four tasks.

1. **"Make a row just like this one"** (point to yours).

Child	☐ ☐ ☐ ☐ ☐ ☐ ☐ ☐ ☐
Adult	☐ ☐ ☐ ☐ ☐ ☐ ☐ ☐ ☐

   "Does one row have more blocks (chips, coins), or do they both have the same amount? How do you know?" If child agrees to equality, go on to the next tasks.

2. **"Now watch what I do."** (Push yours together.)

Child	☐ ☐ ☐ ☐ ☐ ☐ ☐ ☐ ☐
Adult	☐ ☐ ☐ ☐ ☐ ☐ ☐ ☐ ☐

"**Does one row have more blocks, or do they both have the same amount? Why?**" (If the child says one row has more, then say, "**Make them have the same amount again.**") (If the child says they have the same amount, tell him, "**Line them up like they were before I moved them.**") Go on to Task 3 and Task 4 following the same steps.

3. Task 4

   Child ⬜ ⬜ ⬜ ⬜ ⬜ ⬜ ⬜ ⬜
   _____
   Adult ⬜ ⬜ ⬜ ⬜   ⬜ ⬜ ⬜ ⬜

4. Task 4

   Child ⬜ ⬜ ⬜ ⬜ ⬜ ⬜ ⬜ ⬜
   _____
   Adult   ⬜ ⬜ ⬜ ⬜ ⬜ ⬜ ⬜ ⬜

Evaluation: If the child is unable to do Task 1 (one-to-one correspondence), do not proceed any further. He needs to work further on this concept and needs time for development. If he succeeds with Task 1, go on to 2, 3, and 4. Note which of the following categories fit his responses.

Nonconserver 1. Indicates longer rows have more but cannot give a logical reason (e.g., the child may say, "I don't know," "My mother says so," or gives no answer).

Nonconserver 2. Indicates longer rows have more and gives logical reasons, such as "It's longer," "The long row has more," and the like.

Transitional. Says both rows still have the same amount but has to check by counting or placing in one-to-one correspondence.

Conserver. Completely sure that both rows still have the same amount. May say, "You just moved them."

8B   **Concrete Operations**

           Ages 6–7

Symbols and Sets, Matching and Writing: Chapter 7

Method: Interview.

Skill: Child can match sets to symbols and write symbols.

Materials: Cards with numerals 0 to 20, a supply of counters, paper, and writing implements.

Procedures:

1. Present the child with sets of counters. Start with amounts under 10. If the child can do these, go on to the teens. Say, "**Match the numbers to the sets.**"

2. Put the numeral cards and counters away. Give the child a piece of paper and a choice of writing instruments. "**Write as many numbers as you can. Start with zero.**"

Evaluation: Note how high the child can go in matching sets and symbols and in writing numerals.

8C   **Concrete Operations**

           Ages 6–7

Multiple Classification: Chapter 7

Method: Interview.

Skill: Child can group shapes by more than one criterion.

Materials: Make 36 cardboard shapes:

1. Four squares (one each red, yellow, blue, and green).

2. Four triangles (one each red, yellow, blue, and green).

3. Four circles (one each red, yellow, blue, and green).

4. Make three sets of each in three sizes.

Procedure: Place all the shapes in a random array in front of the child. Say, "**Divide (sort, pile) these shapes into groups any way you want to.**" After the child has sorted on one attribute (shape, color, or size) say, "**Now divide (sort, pile) them another way.**" The preoperational child will normally refuse to conceptualize another way of grouping.

Evaluation: The preoperational child will center on the first sort and will not try another criterion. The concrete operations child will sort by color, shape, and size.

8D   **Concrete Operations**

           Ages 6–7

Class Inclusion: Chapter 7

Method: Interview.

Skill: Child can perceive that there are classes within classes.

Materials: Make a set of materials using objects, cutouts, or pictures of objects, such as the following:

1. Twelve wooden beads of the same size and shape that differ only in color (e.g., four red and eight blue).

2. Twelve pictures of flowers: eight tulips and four daisies.

3. Twelve pictures of animals: eight dogs and four cats.

Procedure: Place the objects (pictures) in front of the child in random order. Say, "**Put the (object name) together that are the same.**" Then after the child has grouped into two subcategories ask, "**Are there more (wooden beads, flowers, animals) or more (blue beads, tulips, or dogs)?**" Have the child compare the overall class or category with the larger subclass.

Evaluation: The preoperational child will have difficulty conceptualizing parts and wholes of sets at the same time.

CONCRETE OPERATIONS: LEVEL 9

9A*   **Concrete Operations**

           Ages 6–8

Addition, Combining Sets up to 10: see Chapter 8 for task

9B*   **Concrete Operations**

    Ages 6–8

Subtraction, Sets of 10 and Less: see Chapter 8 for task

9C   **Concrete Operations**

    Ages 6–8

Addition and Subtraction, Understanding Notation: Chapter 8

Method: Interview or small group.

Skill: Child understands the connection between notation and concrete problems.

Materials: Counters (e.g., chips, Unifix Cubes, cube blocks), pencil, and paper.

Procedure: Each child should have a supply of counters, pencils, and paper. Say, **"Take three red (name of counter). Now, put two green (name of counter) with the three red. Write a number sentence that tells what you did."** When the child is finished, say, **"Put the three red and green (counters) back. Take out six yellow (counters). Separate three of the yellow (counters) from the six. Write a number sentence that tells what you did."** Continue with more addition and subtraction problems. Written story problems could be given to children who know how to read.

Evaluation: Note whether the children are able to use the correct notation, that is, 3 + 2 = 5 and 6 − 3 = 3.

9D   **Concrete Operations**

    Ages 6–8

Addition and Subtraction, Create Problems: Chapter 8

Method: Interview or small group.

Skill: Given a number sentence, the child can create a problem.

Materials: Counters (e.g., chips, Unifix Cubes, cube blocks), pencil, and paper.

Procedure: Give the children the number sentences below. Tell them to make up a story to go with each sentence, using their counters to represent the characters in the story. Non-readers/nonwriters can dictate their stories; reader/writers can write the stories themselves. Number sentences:

1.   3 + 5 = 8
2.   6 − 4 = 2

Evaluation: Note whether the dictated or written problem relates correctly to the number sentence.

9E   **Concrete Operations**

    Ages 6–8

Addition and Subtraction, Translating Symbols into Concrete Actions: Chapter 8

Method: Interview or small group.

Skill: The child can translate written problems into concrete actions.

Materials: Counters (e.g., chips, Unifix Cubes, cube blocks), pencil, paper, and several addition and subtraction problems.

Problems:

1.	9 − 4	6.	6 − 3
2.	4 + 5	7.	4 − 1
3.	3 + 2	8.	2 + 6
4.	8 − 6	9.	5 + 3
5.	1 + 7	10.	7 − 2

Procedure: Give each child a supply of counters, a pencil, and paper with one or more written problems like those above. It is best to give the problems one at a time the first time. Then give more as the children become more proficient. Point to the first problem, if there is more than one. Say, **"Look at this problem. Show me the problem with (counters). Now, write the answer. Read the problem and the answer to me."** If the children do this one correctly, have them continue on their own. Ask them to show you if there are any problems they can do without the cubes.

Evaluation: Note whether the children do the problems correctly and especially whether they are accurate in translating the signs. For example, for problem 1, a child might take nine counters and then take four more, ignoring the "minus" sign. Some children might be able to tell you, for example, that 2 + 6 = 8 but not be able to show you with the counters. This behavior indicates the children have learned to use the symbols in a rote fashion but do not understand the concepts that the symbols stand for.

9F*   **Concrete Operations**

    Ages 7–8

Multiplication, Readiness: see Chapter 8 for task

9G   **Concrete Operations**

    Ages 7–8

Multiplication, The Process: Chapter 8

Method: Interview.

Skill: Child understands the process of multiplication.

Materials: Counters (e.g., chips, Unifix Cubes, cube blocks), pencil, and paper.

4.   Show the child patterns of counters, such as:

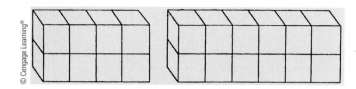

© Cengage Learning®

For each pattern, say, "Write an equation (or number sentence) that tells about this pattern."

5. "With your (counters), show me two times two." (Try 3 × 4, 5 × 2, etc.).

Evaluation:

1. Note whether the child writes (a) 2 × 4 = 8 or 4 × 2 = 8 (b) 2 × 6 = 12 or 6 × 2 = 12. It is not uncommon for a child to write 3 × 4 = 12 for the second equation. This response would indicate she has memorized 3 times 4 equals 12 without a basic understanding of the multiplication concept.

2. For 2 × 2, the child should make two groups of two; for 3 × 4, three groups of four; for 5 × 2, five groups of two. Some children will reverse the numbers, such as two groups of five for the last problem. Other children may just make two groups, such as a group of five and a group of two for 5 × 2.

9H   Concrete Operations

Ages 7–8

Multiplication, Using Symbols: Chapter 8

Method: Interview.

Skill: Child can solve written multiplication problems.

Materials: Counters (e.g., chips, Unifix Cubes, cube blocks), pencil, and paper.

Procedure: One at a time, give the child written multiplication problems. Tell her, "**Work out the problem with counters, and write down the answer.**"

Evaluation: Note whether the child makes the appropriate number of sets of the right amount. Note whether the child does the correct operation. Sometimes children will forget and add instead of multiply. That is, a child might write 3 × 2 = 5.

9I*   Concrete Operations

Ages 7–8

Division, Basic Concept: see Chapter 8 for task

9J   Concrete Operations

Ages 7–8

Division, Symbols: Chapter 8

Method: Interview.

Skill: Child understands the use of symbols in division problems.

Materials: Counters (e.g., chips, Unifix Cubes, cube blocks), pencil, and paper.

Procedure: Give the child a division story problem. For example: "**Chan has eight bean seeds. He wants to plant two in each small pot. How many pots will he need?**" Next, tell the child, "**Read the problem and solve it. Write the number sentence for the problem on your paper.**"

Evaluation: Note whether the child can write the correct number sentence. If she can't do the problem from memory, does she figure out that she can use her counters or draw a picture to assist in finding the answer?

9K*   Concrete Operations

Ages 6–8

Patterns, Extension in Three Dimensions: see Chapter 8 for task

9L   Concrete Operations

Ages 7–8

Patterns, Creation: Chapter 8

Method: Interview.

Skill: Child can create patterns using discrete objects.

Materials: Concrete objects such as chips, Unifix Cubes, or cube blocks.

Procedure: Tell the child, "**Using your (counters), make your own pattern as you have done with pattern starters I have given you.**" When the child is finished, say, "**Tell me about your pattern.**"

Evaluation: Note whether the child has actually developed a repeated pattern and if she is able to describe the pattern in words.

9M*   Concrete Operations

Ages 7–9

Patterns, Number Multiples: see Chapter 8 for task

9N*   Concrete Operations

Ages 6–8

Fractions, Equivalent Parts: see Chapter 8 for task

9O*   Concrete Operations

Ages 6–8

Fractions, One-Half of a Group: see Chapter 8 for task

9P*   Concrete Operations

Ages 7–8

Place Value, Groups of 10: see Chapter 9 for task

9Q* **Concrete Operations**

Ages 7–8

Place Value, Grouping to Identify an Amount: see Chapter 9 for task

9R **Concrete Operations**

Ages 7–8

Place Value, Symbols to Concrete Representations: Chapter 9

Method: Interview or small group.

Skill: Child can translate from written numerals to concrete representations.

Materials: Base-ten blocks or similar material (e.g., Unifix Cubes, sticks, or straws and rubber bands for bundling); 8 or 10 cards, each with a double-digit number written on it (e.g., 38, 72, 45, 83, 27, 96, 51, 50).

Procedure: Say, **"Using your base-10 blocks, make groups for each numeral."** After each group has been constructed, say, **"Tell me how you know that you have (number)."**

Evaluation: Note whether the child constructs the correct amount of 10s and units and can explain accurately how the construction is represented by the numeral.

9S **Concrete Operations**

Geometry, Graphs, Charts, and Tables: Chapter 9

See the prerequisite concepts and skills in Chapters 4, 5, and 7 and Assessment Tasks 3F, 3G, 4E, 5E, and 6C.

9T **Concrete Operations**

Measurement with Standard Units: Chapter 9

See prerequisite concepts in Chapter 5 and Assessment Tasks 3J, 4I, 5H, 5I, level 7, 8A, and 8B.

9U **Concrete Operations**

Ages 6, 7, 8

Solving Problems: Chapter 8

Method: Provide the students with problems such as can be found in the resource lists at the end of Chapter 1.

Skill: Developing problem solutions.

Materials: Pencils and paper, counters (if needed), and problems.

Procedure: Provide the students with oral and written problem versions, such as the following: *Four little piggies run out to play. Two piggies jump in a mud puddle and get muddy feet. The other two piggies just stick their snouts in the mud.* Ask, "How many muddy feet and muddy snouts are there all together?"

Evaluation: Note the procedures used by the students. Do they draw the pigs and count out the feet and snouts? Do they use counters for the pig parts? Do they use tally marks? Do they write out the numerals and add?

9V **Concrete Operations**

Writing Problems: Chapter 6

Method: Observation, interview; review of children's written products.

Skill: Children can write and/or draw their own problems and solutions to problems presented to them in their math journals. They can also record their general feelings about mathematics and their descriptions of what they have learned.

Materials: Notebook and writing tools (pencils, pens, crayons, felt-tip pens).

Procedure: Students should have regular daily opportunities to record their mathematics experiences in their math journals. The journals might contain solutions to problems they have identified and problems derived from class work, such as from literature selections. They can also be encouraged to record how they are feeling about mathematics and explain what they are learning.

Evaluation: Have the students read their entries to you and review what they have produced. Look for evidence of their mathematical thinking and their approach to problem solving. Also, look for their feelings about math and their view of what they know. Note growth in written expression and organization of illustrated problem solutions. Discuss with the children entries they choose to select for inclusion in their portfolio.

REFERENCES AND RESOURCES
General Resources

Baroody, A. J. (1988). *Children's mathematical thinking.* New York: Teachers College Press. (Includes many examples of children's common mistakes and misconceptions.)

Bray, W. S. (2014). How to leverage the potential of mathematical errors. *Teaching Children Mathematics, 19*(7), 424–431. (Using children's mistakes to advance their understanding)

Bredekamp, S., & Rosegrant, T. (Eds.). (1995). *Reaching potentials: Transforming early childhood curriculum and assessment* (Vol. 2). Washington, DC: National Association for the Education of Young Children. (Defines appropriate assessment strategies for young children)

Copley, J. V. (1999). Assessing mathematical understanding of the young child. In *Mathematics in the early years* (pp. 182–188). Reston, VA: National Council of Teachers of Mathematics, and Washington, DC: National Association for the Education of Young Children. (Provides an overview of early childhood mathematics assessment)

Evan-Moor. (2006). *Math assessment tasks. Quick check activities.* Monterey, CA: Author. (Paper-and-pencil and pictorial assessments)

Glanfield, F., Bush, W. S., & Stenmark, J. K. (Eds.). (2003). *Mathematics assessment: A practical handbook.* Reston, VA: National Council of Teachers of Mathematics.

Huniker, D. (Ed.). (2006). *Prekindergarten–grade 2 mathematics assessment sampler.* Reston, VA: National Council of Teachers of Mathematics. (Assessment tasks and guidelines for evaluation of student responses)

Larson, M., & Leinwand, S. (2013). Prepare for more realistic results, *Teaching Children Mathematics, 19*(9), 533–535. (With new standards, assessment results may be lower with new tests.)

Mindes, G. (2007). *Assessing young children* (3rd ed.). Clifton Park, NY: Cengage Delmar Learning. (Overview of early childhood assessment)

National Council of Teachers of Mathematics. (2000). *Principles and standards for school mathematics.* Reston, VA: Author.

National Governors Association Center for Best Practices, Council of Chief State School Officers. (2010). *Common Core State Standards—Mathematics.* Washington, DC: National Governors Association Center for Best Practices, Council of Chief State School Officers.

Richardson, K. (1984). *Developing number concepts using Unifix Cubes.* Menlo Park, CA: Addison-Wesley.

(Each chapter ends with a section on analyzing and assessing children's needs.)

Schwartz, S. (2013). *Implementing the Common Core State Standards through mathematical problems solving: K–2.* Reston, VA: National Council of Teachers of Mathematics.

Webb, N. L. (1993). (Ed.). *Assessment in the mathematics classroom: 1993 yearbook.* Reston, VA: National Council of Teachers of Mathematics. (Contains a series of chapters relevant to assessment in general and relative to grade level and specific skill areas.)

Zorin, B., Hunsader, P. D., & Thompson, D. R. (2013). Assessments: Numbers, contexts, graphics, and assumptions, *Teaching Children Mathematics, 19*(8), 480–488.

Kathy Richardson Materials

Kathy Richardson's materials always take an assessment approach.

Richardson, K. (1990). *A look at children's thinking: Videos for K–2 mathematics.* Norman, OK: Educational Enrichment.

Richardson, K. (1999). *Developing number concepts: Addition and subtraction.* White Plains, NY: Seymour.

Richardson, K. (1999). *Developing number concepts: Counting, comparing and pattern.* White Plains, NY: Seymour.

Richardson, K. (1999). *Developing number concepts: Place value, multiplication and division.* White Plains, NY: Seymour.

Richardson, K. (1999). *Developing number concepts: Planning guide.* White Plains, NY: Seymour.

* Tasks that have been used as samples in the text.

APPENDIX B

CHILDREN'S BOOKS, MAGAZINES AND TECHNOLOGY RESOURCES WITH MATH AND SCIENCE CONCEPTS

CONTENTS*

BIBLIOGRAPHY FOR ADULT REFERENCE

Note: See Chapter 6.

Bell, C.V. (2013). Sharing beans with friends. *Teaching Children Mathematics, 20*(4), 238-244.

Columba, L. (2013). So, here's the story. *Teaching Children Mathematics, 19*(6), 374-381.

Ducolon, C. K. (2000). Quality literature as a springboard to problem solving. *Teaching Children Mathematics, 6*(7), 442–446.

Fulwiler, B.R. (2011). *Writing In Science In Action*. Portsmouth, NH: Heinnemann.

Jacobs, V. R., Bennet, T. R., & Bullock, C. (2000). Selecting books in Spanish to teach mathematics. *Teaching Children Mathematics, 6*(9), 582–587.

Kazemi, E., & Hintz, A. (2014). *Intentional talk: How to structure and lead productive mathematical discussions*. Portland, ME: Stenhouse.

Marston, J.L., Muir, T., & Livy, S. (2013). Can we really count on Frank? *Teaching Children Mathematics, 19*(7), 440-448.

Outstanding science trade books for children. *Science and Children*. (Published yearly)

Picture Perfect Science Lessons. Arlington, VA: NSTA Press.

Rice, D. C., Dudley, A. P., & Williams, C. S. (2001). How do you choose science trade books? *Science and Children, 38*(6), 18–22.

Robillard, M. (2012). Picture-perfect science lessons and More picture prefect sciene lessons. Arlington, VA: NSTA Press.

Royce, A.R., Morgan, M, & Ansberry, K. (2012). *Teaching science through trade books*. Arlington, VA: NSTA Press.

Thiessen, D. (Ed.). (2004). *Exploring mathematics through literature*. Reston, VA: National Council for Teachers of Mathematics.

Whitin, D. J., & Whitin, P. (2004). *New visions for linking literature and mathematics*. Urbana, IL: National Council of Teachers of English, and Reston, VA: National Council of Teachers of Mathematics.

Wilburne, J.M., Keat, J.B., &Napoli, M. (2011). *Cowboys count, Monkeys measure and princesses problem solve*. Baltimore, MD: Brookes.

See end-of-chapter references and monthly reviews in *Teaching Children Mathematics* and *Science and Children*.

FUNDAMENTAL CONCEPTS

One-to-One Correspondence

Jocelyn, M. (1999). *Hannah and the seven dresses*. East Rutherford, NJ: Penguin Putnam **3, 5**.

Marzollo, J. (1994). *Ten cats have hats*. Jefferson City, MO: Scholastic Professional; **3**

Slobodkina, E. (1968). *Se venden gorras*. New York: Harper; **3, 9**.

Slobodkina, E. (1976). *Caps for sale*. New York: Scholastic Books (Ages 3–6); **3, 6**.

The three bears. (1973). New York: Golden Press (Ages 2–5); **3 , 5**.

The three billy goats gruff. (1968). New York: Grosset & Dunlap (Ages 2–5); **3**.

Wade, L. (1998). *The Cheerios play book*. New York: Simon & Schuster; **3**.

Number Sense and Counting

Many of the books listed in this section include ordinal numbers. Most also include number symbols.

Aker, S. (1990). *What comes in 2's, 3's, and 4's?* New York: Simon & Schuster (Ages 4–6); **3**.

Anno, M. (1982). *Anno's counting house*. New York: Philomel (Ages 4–7); **3**.

Anno, M. (1986). *Anno's counting book*. New York: Harper-Collins (Ages 4–6); **3**.

Aurego, J., & Dewey, A. (1989). *Five little ducks*. New York: Crown; **3**.

Baker, K. (1994). *Count to ten with big fat hen*. San Diego: Harcourt Brace Voyager; **3**.

Ballart, E. (1992). *Let's count*. Charlottsville, VA: Thomasson- Grant; **3, 9**.

Bang, M. (1983). *Ten, nine, eight*. New York: Greenwillow (Ages 3–5); **3**.

Blumenthal, N. (1989). *Count-a-saurus*. New York: Four Winds Press (Ages 3–6); **3**.

Boynton, S. (1978). *Hippos go berserk*. Chicago: Recycled Paper Press (Ages 3–6); **3, 11, 7, 8**.

Brusca, M. C., & Wilson, T. (1995). *Tres amigos: Un cuento para cantar* [Three friends: A counting book]. New York: Holt, Rinehart, & Winston; **3**.

Carle, E. (1968). *1, 2, 3 to the zoo*. New York: Scholastic Books; **3**.

Carle, E. (1969). *The very hungry caterpillar*. Mountain View, CA: Collins & World (Ages 3–5); **3, 5, 7**.

Carle, E. (2005). *10 little rubber ducks*. New York: Harper Collins; **3**.

Carter, D. A. (1988). *How many bugs in a box?* New York: Simon & Schuster (Ages 3–6); **3**.

Cave, K. (2003). *One child, one seed: A South African counting book*. New York: Henry Holt; **3**.

Christelow, E. (1989). *Five little monkeys jumping on the bed*. New York: Clarion; **3**.

Christelow, E. (1991). *Five little monkeys sitting in a tree*. New York: Clarion; **3**.

Compog, I. (2011), Diez perritos (Ten little puppies). New York: Scholastic. **3**.

Crews, D. (1985). *Ten black dots, revised*. New York: Greenwillow (Ages 4–6); **3**.

Cutler, D. S. (1991). *One hundred monkeys*. New York: Simon & Schuster (Ages 3–6); **3**.

Dingles. M. (2003).*Number 4 shop at the store (Numero 4 Vamas de compras a la tienda)*. New Jersey: Dingles. **3**

Dunbar, J. (1990). *Ten little mice*. San Diego, CA: Harcourt Brace Jovanovich (Ages 3–6); **3**.

Elkin, B. (1968, 1971). *Six foolish fishermen*. New York: Scholastic Books (Ages 3–6); **3, 10**.

Elkin, B., & Kratky, L. J. (Trans.). (1986). *Seis pescadores disparatados* [Six foolish fishermen]. Chicago: Children's Press; **3**.

Elya, S. M. (2002). *Eight animals on the town*. New York: Penguin (Integrates Spanish vocabulary); **3**.

Falwell, C. (1993). *Feast for 10*. New York: Clarion; **3**.

Feelings, M. (1976). *Moja means one: Swahili counting book*. New York: Dial (Ages 3–6); **3**.

Five Tumbling Tigers . (2010). New York: Scholastic. **3.**

Flemming, D. (1992). *Count!*. New York: Holt; **9.**

Friskey, M. (1946). *Chicken little count to ten*. New York: Harcourt, Brace (Ages 3–8); **3, 7.**

Frith, M. (1973). *I'll teach my dog 100 words*. New York: Random House (Ages 3–6); 3

Gag, W. (1928, 1956, 1977). *Millions of cats*. New York: Coward-McCann (Ages 3–5); **3, 6.**

Getty Museum. (n.d.). *1 to 10 and back again: A Getty Museum counting book*. Los Angeles: Author; **3,7.**

Gibson, R. (1998). *I can count*. London: Usborne Playtime; **3, 7.**

Grindley, S. (1996). *Four black puppies*. Cambridge, MA: Candlewick Press; **3.**

Grossman, V. (1991). *Ten little rabbits*. San Francisco: Chronicle Books (Ages 3–6); **3.**

Himmelman, J. (2010). *10 Little hot dogs*. Tarrytown, NY: Pinwheel Books. 3

Hudson, C. W. (1987). *Afro-bets 1, 2, 3 book*. Orange, NJ: Just Us Productions; **3, 7.**

Keats, E. J. (1972). *Over in the meadow*. New York: Scholastic Books (Ages 3–5); **3.**

Krebs, L. (2003). *We all went on safari. A counting journey through Tanzania*. Cambridge, MA: Barefoot Books (Includes information on Masai, Tansanian wildlife, and Swahili vocabulary); **3, 10.**

Leedy, L. (1985). *A number of dragons*. New York: Holiday House (Ages 1–3); **3.**

Lester, H. (2001). *Score one for the sloths*. New York: Scholastic Books. **3.**

Lowell, S. (1992). *The three little javelinas*. New York: Scholastic Books; **3.**

MacDonald, S. (2000). *Look whooo's counting*. New York: Scholastic Books; **3.**

McGrath, B. B. (1994). *The m&m's counting book*. Watertown, MA: Charlesbridge; **3, 5, 8.**

Merriam, E. (1996). *12 ways to get to 11*. New York: Aladdin Paperbacks. **3, 8.**

Micklethwait, L. (1993). *I spy two eyes: Numbers in art*. Fairfield, NJ: Greenwillow; **3.**

Moerbeek, K., & Dijs, C. (1988). *Six brave explorers*. Los Angeles: Price Stern Sloan (Ages 4–6); **3.**

Mora, P. (1996). *Uno, dos, tres (one two, three)*. New York: Clarion. **3.**

Moss, L. (1995). *Zin! Zin! Zin! A violin*. New York: Scholastic Books **3,6.**

Most, B. (1990). *Four and twenty dinosaurs*. New York: Voyager Books. **3, 10, 11.**

Novak, M, (2005). *Too many bunnies*. New Milford, CT: Roaring Brook Press. **3.**

Parish, S. (1998). *1, 2, 3 of Australian wildlife*. Archerfield BC, Queensland, Australia: Steve Parish; **3 9, 10.**

Roth, C. (1999). *Ten clean pigs, ten dirty pigs*. New York: North-South Books; **3.**

Ryan, P. M., & Pallotta, J. (1996). *The crayon counting book*. Watertown, MA: Charlesbridge; **3.**

Sayre, A. P., & Sayre, J. (2003). *One is a snail, ten is a crab*. Cambridge, MA: Candlewick Press; **3.**

Scarry, R. (1975). *Best counting book ever*. New York: Random House (Ages 2–8); **3, 5.**

Sendak, M. (1975). *Seven little monsters*. New York: Scholastic Books; **3.**

Seuss, Dr. (1938). *The 500 hats of Bartholomew Cubbins*. Eau Claire, WI: Hale (Ages 3–7); **3.**

Seuss, Dr. (1960). *One fish, two fish, red fish, blue fish*. New York: Random House (Ages 3–7); **3, 5, 6.**

Sheppard, J. (1990). *The right number of elephants*. New York: Harper-Collins (Ages 4–6); **3.**

Shulman, M. (2002). *I'll take a dozen*. New York: Bagel Books. **3.**

Slobodkina, E. (1940, 1947, 1968). *Caps for sale*. New York: Young Scott; **3, 9.**

Slobodkina, E. (1940, 1947, 1968; translation 1995). *Se venden gorras*. New York: Harper Arco Iris; **3, 9.**

Steiner, C. (1960). *Ten in a family*. New York: Knopf (Ages 3–5); **3.**

Thorne-Thomsen, K., & Rocheleau, P. (1999). *A Shaker's dozen counting book*. San Francisco: Chronicle Books; **3, 9.**

Thornhill, J. (1989). *The wildlife 1-2-3: A nature counting book*. New York: Simon & Schuster (Ages 3–6); **3.**

Tucker, K. (2003). *The seven Chinese sisters*. New York: Scholastic; **3, 5.**

Ungerer, T. (1962). *The three robbers*. New York: Antheum (Ages 3–5); **3.**

Von Noorden, D. (1994). *The lifesize animal counting book*. New York: Dorling Kindersley; **3, 4.**

Weill, C. (2012), *Count me in!: a parade of numbers in English and Spanish*. El Paso, TX: Inco Puntos Press. **3, 5.**

Wildsmith, B. (1965). *Brian Wildsmith's 1, 2, 3's*. New York: Franklin Watts (Ages 3–5); **3.**

Wildsmith, B. (1996). *¿Cuantos animals hay?* New York: Star Bright Books; **3.**

Wilson, K., & Rankin, J. (2003). *A frog in the bog*. New York: Scholastic Books; **3.**

Zaslavsky, C. (1999). *Count on your fingers African style*. New York: Writers & Readers; **3.**

Classification

Cabrera, J. (1997). *Cat's colors*. New York: Puffin; **3.**

Fiammenghi, G. (1999). *A collection for Kate*. New York: Kane; **3.**

Hill, E. (1982). *What does what?* Los Angeles: Price/Stern/Sloan (Ages 2–4); **3.**

Hoban, T. (1978). *Is it red? Is it yellow? Is it blue?* New York: Greenwillow (Ages 2–5); **3.**

Hughes, S. (1986). *Colors*. New York: Lothrop (Ages 2–4); **3.**

Wildsmith B. (1967). *Brian Wildsmith's wild animals*. New York: Franklin Watts (Ages 3–8); **3, 5, 7, 10.**

Wildsmith, B. (1968). *Brian Wildsmith's fishes*. New York: Franklin Watts (Ages 3–8); **3, 5, 7, 10.**

Winthrop, E. (1986). *Shoes*. New York: Harper & Row (Ages 3–7); **3, 7.**

Comparing

Bourgeois, P., & Clark, B. (1987). *Big Sarah's little boots*. New York: Scholastic Books (Ages 3–5); **3.**

Brenner, B. (1966). *Mr. Tall and Mr. Small*. Menlo Park, CA: Addison-Wesley (Ages 4–7); **3, 5, 7, 10.**

Broger, A., & Kalow, G. (1977). *Good morning whale*. New York: Macmillan (Ages 3–6); **3, 5, 7, 10.**

Carle, E. (1977). *The grouchy ladybug*. New York: Crowell (Ages 3–5); **3, 5, 7.**

Eastman, P. D. (1973). *Big dog, little dog*. New York: Random House (Ages 3–4); **3, 5, 7.**

Gordon, M. (1986). *Opposites*. Morristown, NJ: Silver-Burdett (Ages 3–5); **3.**

Graham, A., & Wood, W. (1991). *Angus thought he was big*. Hicksville, NY: Macmillan (Ages 3–5); **3.**

Hoban, T. (1972). *Push pull, empty full*. New York: Macmillan (Ages 3–5); **3.**

Hughes, S. (1985). *Noises*. New York: Lothrop (Ages 1–2); **3, 5, 7.**

Lewis, J. (1963). *The tortoise and the hare*. Chicago: Whitman (Ages 4–8); **3, 5.**

Lionni, L. (1968). *The biggest house in the world*. New York: Pantheon (Ages 2–6); **3, 5, 7.**

McMillan, B. (1986). *Becca backward, Becca forward*. New York: Lothrop (Ages 3–6); **3.**

Miller, N. (1990). *Emmett's snowball*. New York: Henry Holt (K–3 and above); **3, 5, 7, 9.**

Most, B. (1989). *The littlest dinosaurs*. New York: Harcourt Brace; **3.**

Novak, M. (2005). *Too many bunnies*. New Milford, CT: Roaring Book Press; **3.**

Presland, J. (1975). *Same and different*. Purton Wilts, England: Child's Play (Ages 4–7); **3.**

Scarry, R. (1976). *Short and tall*. New York: Golden Press (Ages 2–7); **3.**

Scarry, R. (1986). *Big and little: A book of opposites*. Racine, WI: Western (Ages 3–7); **3.**

Shapiro, L. (1978). *Pop-up opposites*. Los Angeles: Price/Stern/Sloan (Ages 3–5); **3.**

Early Geometry

Shape

Anno, M. (1991). *Anno's math games III*. New York: Philomel (K–6); **4, 7, 9.**

Budney, B. (1954). *A kiss is round*. New York: Lothrop, Lee, & Shepard (Ages 2–6); **4.**

Carle, E. (1974). *My very first book of shapes*. New York: Crowell (Ages 3–6); **4.**

Dodds, D. A. (1994). *The shape of things*. Cambridge, MA: Candlewick Press; **4.**

Ehlert, L. (1990). *Color farm*. New York: Harper-Collins; **4, 6, 7.**

Emberley, E. (1961). *A wing on a flea: A book about shapes*. Boston: Little, Brown (Ages 5–8); **4.**

Emberley, E. (1970). *Ed Emberley's drawing book of animals*. Boston: Little, Brown (Ages 6–8); **4.**

Emberley, E. (1972). *Ed Emberley's drawing book: Make a world*. Boston: Little, Brown (Ages 6–8); **4.**

Emberley, E. (1995). *El ala de la polilla: Un libro de figuras* [The wing on a flea: A book about shapes]. New York: Scholastic Books; **4.**

Hefter, R. (1976). *The strawberry book of shapes*. New York: Weekly Reader Books (Ages 3–7); **4.**

Hewavisenti, L. (1991). *Shapes and solids*. Chicago: FranklinWatts; **4, 9.**

Hoban, T. (1974). *Circles, triangles, and squares*. New York: Macmillan (Ages 5–8); **4.**

Hoban, T. (1983). *Round and round and round*. New York: Greenwillow (Ages 3–6); **4.**

Hoban, T. (1986). *Shapes, shapes, shapes*. New York: Greenwillow (Ages 3–7); **4.**

Hoban, T. (1997). *Look book*. New York: Morrow Junior Books; **4.**

Hoban, T. (2000). *Cubes, cones, cylinders, and spheres*. New York: HarperCollins; **4.**

MacKinnon, D. (1992). *What shape?* New York: Dial; **4.**

MacKinnon, D., & Sieveking, A. (2000). *Eye spy shapes: A peephole book*. Watertown, MA: Charlesbridge; **4.**

Rau, D. M. (2002). *A star in my orange: Looking for nature's shapes*. Brookfield, CT: Millbrook Press; **4.**

Shapes: Circle; Square; Triangle (3 books). (1992). New York: Books for Young Readers (Ages 3–6); **4**.

Sullivan, J. (1963). *Round is a pancake*. New York: Holt, Rinehart, & Winston (Ages 3–5); **4**.

Supraner, R. (1975). *Draw me a square, draw me a triangle, & draw me a circle*. New York: Simon & Schuster/Nutmeg (Ages 3–6); **4**.

Teulade, P. (1999). *El más bonito de todos regalos del mundo* [The most beautiful gift in the world]. Barcelona, Spain: Editorial Corimbo; **4**.

Thong, R. (2000). *Round is a mooncake: A book of shapes*. San Francisco: Chronicle Books; **4**.

Space

Barton, B. (1981). *Building a house*. New York: Greenwillow (Ages 4–7); **4, 5**.

Berenstain, S., & Berenstain, J. (1968). *Inside, outside, upside down*. New York: Random House (Ages 3–7); **4**.

Brown, M. (1949). *Two little trains*. New York: Scott, Foresman (Ages 2–4); **4, 6**.

Carle, E. (1972). *The secret birthday message*. New York: Crowell (Ages 3–7); **4**.

Hill, E. (1980). *Where's Spot?* New York: Putnam's (Ages 2–4); **4**.

Lionni, L. (1983). *Where?* New York: Pantheon (Ages 2–3); **4**.

Maestro, B., & Maestro, G. (1976). *Where is my friend?* New York: Crown (Ages 2–4); **4**.

Martin, B., Jr. (1971). *Going up, going down*. New York: Holt, Rinehart, & Winston (Ages 6–8); **3, 4**.

Russo, M. (1986). *The line up book*. New York: Greenwillow (Ages 3–5); **4**.

Teulade, P. (1999). *El más bonito de todos regalos del mundo* [The most beautiful gift in the world]. Barcelona, Spain: Editorial Corimbo; **4**.

Parts and Wholes

Axworthy, A. (Illus.). (1998). *Guess what I am*. Cambridge, MA: Candlewick Press; **4**.

Burton, M. R. (1988). *Tail Toes Eyes Ears Nose*. New York: Harper Trophy; **4, 5, 7**.

Campbell, R. (1982, 30th anniversary edition). *Dear zoo*. New York: Simon and Schuster Children's Publishing.

Carle, E. (1987). *Do you want to be my friend?* New York: Harper Trophy; **4**.

Dubov, C. S. (1986). *Alexsandra, where are your toes?* New York: St. Martin's Press (Ages 1½–3); **4, 5, 7**.

Dubov, C. S. (1986). *Alexsandra, where is your nose?* New York: St. Martin's Press (Ages 1½–3); **4, 5, 7**.

Hutchins, P., & Marcuse, A. (Trans.) (1994). *Llaman a la puerta* [The doorbell rang]. New York: Mulberry; **4, 8**.

Luciana, B., & Tharlet, E. (2000). *How will we get to the beach?* New York: North-South Books; **4, 9**.

Mathews, L. (1979). *Gator pie*. New York: Scholastic Books (Ages 4–7); **4, 7**.

Language

Arenson, R. (Illus.). (1989). *One, two, skip a few: First number rhymes*. Brooklyn, NY: Barefoot Poetry Collections; **6**.

Bemelmans, L. (1969). *Madeline*. New York: Viking (Ages 4–7); **3, 6, 5**.

Duvoisin, R. (1974). *Petunia takes a trip*. New York: Knopf/Pinwheel (Ages 4–7); **3, 6, 5, 7, 10**.

Figueredo, D. H. (2000). *Big snowball fight*. New York: Lee & Low Books; **6**.

Hoff, S. (1959). *Julius*. New York: Harper & Row (Ages 4–7); **6, 5, 7, 10**.

Mathematics in the kitchen, Mathematics at the farm, Mathematics in buildings, Mathematics on the playground, Mathematics in the circus ring. (1978). Milwaukee: MacDonald–Raintree (Ages 3–7); **6**.

McKellar, S. (1993). *Counting rhymes*. New York: Dorling Kindersley; **6, 8**.

Orozco, J. (1997). *Diez deditos* [Ten little fingers]. New York: Scholastic Books; **6**.

Shelby, A. (1990). *We keep a store*. New York: Orchard Books; **6**.

Umansky, K., & Fisher, C. (1999). *Nonsense counting rhymes*. Oxford: Oxford University Press; **6**.

APPLICATION OF FUNDAMENTAL CONCEPTS

Ordering, Seriation, and Patterning

Aker, S. (1990). *What comes in 2's, 3's, & 4's?* New York: Aladdin; **5, 7**.

Asbjörsen, P. C., & Moe, J. E. (1957). *The three billy goats gruff*. New York: Harcourt, Brace, Jovanovich (Ages 2–5); **3, 6, 5**.

Brett, J. (1987). *Goldilocks and the three bears*. New York: Dodd, Mead (Ages 3–5); **5, 7**.

Clements, A. (1992). *Mother Earth's counting book*. New York: Simon & Schuster (Ages 5 and up); **7, 8**.

Hoban, T. (1992). *Look up, look down*. New York: Greenwillow (Ages 5–8); **5**.

Maestro, B., & Maestro, G. (1977). *Harriet goes to the circus*. New York: Crown (Ages 5–8); **5, 7, 10.**

Mahy, M. (1987). *17 kings and 42 elephants*. New York: Dial (Ages 2–6); **3, 5, 7, 10.**

Martin, B., Jr. (1963). *One, two, three, four*. New York: Holt, Rinehart, & Winston (Ages 5–7); **3, 5.**

Martin, B., Jr. (1970). *Monday, Monday, I like Monday*. New York: Holt, Rinehart, & Winston (Ages 5–8); **5.**

Measurement

Volume, Weight, and Length

Allen, P. (1983). *Who sank the boat?* New York: Coward (Ages 3–5); **5.**

Anderson, L. C. (1983). *The wonderful shrinking shirt*. Niles, IL: Whitman (Ages 3–5); **5.**

Bennett, V. (1975). *My measure it book*. New York: Grosset & Dunlap (Ages 3–5); **5.**

Demi. (1997). *One grain of rice*. New York: Scholastic Books; **5.**

Faulkner, K. (2000). *So big! My first measuring book*. New York: Simon & Schuster; **5, 7.**

Henkes, K. (1995). *The biggest boy*. New York: Greenwillow; **5.**

Lionni, L. (1960). *Inch by inch*. New York: Astor-Honor (Ages 3–5); **5, 7.**

McMillan, B. (1987). *Step by step*. New York: Lothrop (Ages 3–6); **5.**

Myller, R. (1972). *How big is a foot?* New York: Atheneum (Ages 6–8); **5, 9.**

Parkinson, K. (1986). *The enormous turnip*. Niles, IL: Whitman (Ages 4–7); **5, 9, 10.**

Russo, M. (1986). *The lineup book*. New York: Greenwillow (Ages 2–4); **5.**

Schlein, M. (1954). *Heavy is a hippopotamus*. New York: Scott (Ages 3–6); **5, 7.**

Shapp, M., & Shapp, C. (1975). *Let's find out about what's light and what's heavy*. New York: Franklin Watts (Ages 6–8); **5, 9.**

Ward, L. (1952). *The biggest bear*. Boston: Houghton-Mifflin (Ages 3–5); **5.**

Zion, G. (1959). *The plant sitter*. New York: Harper & Row (Ages 3–6); **5.**

Time

Bancroft, H., & Van Gelde, R. G. (1963). *Animals in winter*. New York: Scholastic Books (Ages 3–6); **5, 9.**

Barrett, J. (1976). *Benjamin's 365 birthdays*. New York: Atheneum (Ages 3–6); **5.**

Berenstain, S., & Berenstain, J. (1973). *The bear's almanac*. New York: Random House (Ages 3–6); **5, 9.**

Bonne, R. (1961). *I know an old lady*. New York: Scholastic Books (Ages 3–5); **5.**

Brown, M. (1984). *Arthur's Christmas*. Boston: Little, Brown (Ages 6–8); **9.**

Brown, M. W. (1947). *Goodnight moon*. New York: Harper & Row (Ages 3–6); **5.**

Carle, E. (1977). *The very hungry caterpillar*. New York: Collins & World (Ages 3–5); **5, 7.**

Carle, E. (1993). *Today is Monday*. New York: Scholastic Books; **5.**

Carle, E., & Marcuse, A. E. (Trans.). (1994). *La oruga muy hambrienta* [The hungry caterpillar]. New York: Philomel; **5, 7.**

Carle, E., & Mlawer, T. (Trans.). (1996). *La mariquita malhumorada* [The grouchy ladybug]. New York: HarperCollins; **5, 7.**

Chalmers, M. (1988). *Easter parade*. New York: Harper (Ages 3–6); **5, 9.**

dePaola, T. (1986). *Merry Christmas, Strega Nona*. San Diego, CA: Harcourt, Brace (Ages 3–6); **5, 9.**

Duvoisin, R. (1956). *The house of four seasons*. New York: Lothrop, Lee, & Shepard (Ages 3–6); **5, 9.**

Flournoy, V. (1985). *Patchwork quilt*. New York: Dial (Ages 4–8); **5, 9.**

Hall, B. (1973). *What ever happens to baby animals?* New York: Golden Press (Ages 2–5); **5.**

Hauge, C., & Hauge, M. (1974). *Gingerbread man*. New York: Golden Press (Ages 2–5); **5.**

Hayes, S. (1986). *Happy Christmas Gemma*. New York: Lothrop (Ages 2–5); **5.**

Hooper, M. (1985). *Seven eggs*. New York: Harper & Row (Ages 3–5); **3, 5.**

Kelleritti, H. (1985). *Henry's Fourth of July*. New York: Greenwillow (Ages 3–6); **5.**

Kraus, R. (1972). *Milton the early riser*. New York: Prentice Hall (Ages 2–5); **5.**

Leslie, S. (1977). *Seasons*. New York: Platt & Munk (Ages 2–5); **5.**

McCully, E. A. (1985). *First snow*. New York: Warner (Ages 3–5); **5, 7.**

Miles, B. (1973). *A day of autumn*. New York: Random House (Ages 3–5); **5.**

Older, J. (2000). *Telling time*. Watertown, MA: Charlesbridge; **5, 9.**

Pearson, S. (1988). *My favorite time of year*. New York: Harper & Row (Ages 3–7); **5, 9, 10.**

Porter Productions. (1975). *My tell time book*. New York: Grosset & Dunlap (Ages 5–7); **5, 9.**

Prelutsky, J. (1984). *It's snowing! It's snowing!* New York: Greenwillow (Ages 4–7); **5, 7, 9, 11.**

Provensen, A., & Provensen, M. (1976). *A book of seasons.* New York: Random House (Ages 3–5); **5.**

Richards, K. (2000). *It's about time, Max!* New York: Kane Press; **5.**

Robison, A. (1973). *Pamela Jane's week.* Racine, WI: Whitman Books/Western (Ages 2–5); **5.**

Rockwell, A. (1985). *First comes spring.* New York: Crowell (Ages 2–6); **5, 7, 9, 11.**

Rutland, J. (1976). *Time.* New York: Grosset & Dunlap (Ages 2–7); **5, 9.**

Scarry, R. (1976). *All day long.* New York: Golden Press (Ages 3–6); **5, 9.**

Schlein, M. (1955). *It's about time.* New York: Young Scott (Ages 3–7) **5, 9.**

Schwerin, D. (1984). *The tomorrow book.* New York: Pantheon (Ages 3–6); **5.**

Todd, K. (1982). *Snow.* Reading, MA: Addison-Wesley (Ages 3–8); **5, 7, 9, 11.**

Tudor, T. (1957). *Around the year.* New York: Walck (Ages 3–5); **5.**

Tudor, T. (1977). *A time to keep: The Tasha Tudor book of holidays.* New York: Rand McNally (Ages 3–6); **5.**

Vincent, G. (1984). *Merry Christmas, Ernest & Celestine.* New York: Greenwillow (Ages 4–8); **5, 9.**

Wolff, A. (1984). *A year of birds.* New York: Dodd, Mead (Ages 3–6); **5, 7.**

Graphing

Dussling, J. (2003). *Math matters, fair is fair!* New York: Kane Press; **5, 9.**

Nagda, A. W., & Bickel, C. (2000). *Tiger math: Learning to graph from a baby tiger.* New York: Henry Holt; **5, 9.**

Practical Activities/Integration

Cohn, J. M., & Elliott, D. L. (1992). *Recycling for math.* Berkeley, CA: Educational Materials Associates (For teachers of kindergarten and up); **6.**

Lesser, C. (1999). *Spots: Counting creatures from sky to sea.* San Diego, CA: Harcourt Brace; **6.**

Shelby, A. (1990). *We keep a store.* New York: Orchard Books; **6.**

Wallace, N. E. (2000). *Paperwhite.* Boston, MA: Houghton-Mifflin; **6.**

Money

Asch, F. (1976). *Good lemonade.* Ontario, Canada: Nelson, Foster, & Scott (Ages 6–8); **9.**

Brenner, B. (1963). *The five pennies.* New York: Random House (Ages 6–7); **6, 9.**

Brisson, P. (1993). *Benny's pennies.* New York: Bantam Doubleday; **6, 7, 9.**

deRubertis, B. (1999). *Deena's lucky penny.* New York: Kane Press; **6, 9.**

Gill, S., & Tobola, D. (2000). *The big buck adventure.* Watertown, MA: Charlesbridge; **6, 9.**

Hoban, L. (1981). *Arthur's funny money.* New York: Harper & Row (Ages 4–7); **6, 9.**

Jenkins, Emily, (2012). *Lemonade in winter; a book about two children counting money.* New York: Random House/Schwartz & Wade. **6, 9.**

Kirn, A. (1969). *Two pesos for Catalina.* New York: Scholastic Books (Ages 6–8); **6, 9.**

Martin, B., Jr. (1963). *Ten pennies for candy.* New York: Holt, Rinehart, & Winston (Ages 5–7); **6, 9.**

Rockwell, A. (1984). *Our garage sale.* New York: Greenwillow (Ages 3–5); **6.**

Slobodkina, E. (1940, 1947, 1968). *Caps for sale.* New York: Young Scott; **3, 6, 9.**

Slobodkina, E. (1940, 1947, 1968; translation 1995). *Se venden gorras.* New York: Harper Arco Iris; **3, 6, 9.**

Thornburgh, R. (1999). *Count on Pablo.* New York: Kane; **6, 7, 9.**

Food

Note: See also Chapter 6

Brown, M. (1947). *Stone soup.* New York: Scribner's (Ages 3–5); **6, 9.**

Carle, E. (1970). *Pancakes, pancakes.* New York: Knopf (Ages 3–5); **6.**

deRubertis, B. (2006). *La limonada de Lulu.* New York: Kane Press; **6, 9.**

Ehlert, L. (1987). *Growing vegetable soup.* San Diego, CA: Harcourt, Brace, Jovanovich (Ages 3–6); **6, 9.**

Fleming, D. (1992). *Lunch.* New York: Henry Holt; **6.**

Hoban, R. (1964). *Bread and jam for Frances.* New York: Scholastic Books (Ages 3–7); **6.**

McCloskey, R. (1948). *Blueberries for Sal.* New York: Viking (Ages 3–6); **6.**

Norquist, S. (1985). *Pancake pie.* New York: Morrow (Ages 4–8); **6, 9.**

Sendak, M. (1962). *Chicken soup with rice.* New York: Harper & Row (Ages 3–5); **6.**

Sendak, M. (1970). *In the night kitchen.* New York: Harper & Row (Ages 4–6); **6, 9.**

Seymour, P. (1981). *Food.* Los Angeles: Intervisual Communications (Ages 2–5); **6.**

Thayer, J. (1961). *The blueberry pie elf.* Edinburgh, Scotland: Oliver & Boyd (Ages 4–7); **6, 9.**

Cookbooks

Can be adapted to all ages.

Ault, R. (1974). *Kids are natural cooks*. Boston: Houghton-Mifflin; **6, 9**.

Better Homes and Gardens new junior cookbook. (1979). Des Moines, IA: Meredith; **6, 9**.

Colker, L. J. (2005). *The cooking book*. Washington, DC: National Association for the Education of Young Children. **6, 9**.

Kementz, J. (1985). *The fun of cooking*. New York: Knopf. **6, 9**.

Pratt, D. (1998). *Hey kids, you're cookin' now: A global awareness cooking adventure*. Available from http://www.amazon.com **6. 9**.

Rothstein, G. L. (1994). *From soup to nuts: Multicultural cooking activities and recipes*. New York: Scholastic Books; **6, 9**.

Sesame Street cookbook. (1978). New York: Platt & Munk; **6, 9**.

Shepard, E. H. (1993). *Winnie-the-Pooh's teatime cookbook*. Available from http://www.amazon.com **6, 9**.

Walker, B., & Williams, G. (1995). *Little house cookbook*. Available from http://www.amazon.com **6, 9**.

Warner, P. (1999). *Healthy snacks for kids (Nitty Gritty Cookbooks)*. Available from http://www.amazon.com **6, 9**.

Williamson, S., & Williamson, Z. (1992). *Kids cook! Fabulous food for the whole family*. Charlotte, VT: Williamson; **6, 9**.

Science

Hall, Z. (1994). *It's pumpkin time!* New York: Scholastic Books; **5, 7, 10**.

Helman, A. (1996). *1 2 3 Moose: A Pacific Northwest counting book*. Seattle, WA: Sasquatch Books; **3, 4, 5, 6, 7**.

Kusugak, M. A. (1996). *My Arctic 1, 2, 3*. Toronto, Ontario, Canada: Annick Press; **3, 4, 5, 6, 7**.

Pallotta, J. (1992). *The icky bug counting book*. Watertown, MA: Charlesbridge; **3, 4, 5, 6, 7**.

Stevens, J., & Crummel, S. S. (1999). *Cook-a-doodle-do*. New York: Harcourt Brace; **6**.

Thornhill, J. (1989). *The wildlife 1-2-3: A nature counting book*. New York: Simon & Schuster; **3, 4, 5, 6, 7**.

Toft, K. M., & Sheather, A. (1998). *One less fish*. Watertown, MA: Charlesbridge; **3**.

Wadsworth, G. (1997). *One on a web*. Watertown, MA: Charlesbridge; **3, 4, 5, 6, 7**.

Wadsworth, G. (1999). *One tiger growls*. Watertown, MA: Charlesbridge; **3, 4, 5, 6, 7**.

SYMBOLS AND HIGHER-LEVEL ACTIVITIES

Groups and Symbols

Aker, S. (1990). *What comes in 2's, 3's, & 4's?* New York: Aladdin; **17, 23, 24, 25**.

Alain (Bruslein, A.). (1964). *One, two, three going to sea*. New York: Scholastic Books (Ages 5–7); **23, 24, 25, 27**.

Anno, M. (1977). *Anno's counting book*. New York: Crowell (Ages 5–7); **5, 7**.

Balet, J. B. (1959). *The five Rollatinis*. Philadelphia: Lippincott (Ages 4–7); **7**.

Chang, A. (2000). *Grandfather counts*. New York: Lee & Low Books; **7**.

Cuyler, M. (2000). *100th day worries*. New York: Simon & Schuster; **7**.

Duvoisin, R. (1955). *1000 Christmas beards*. New York: Knopf (Ages 3–7); **7**.

Duvoisin, R. (1955). *Two lonely ducks*. New York: Knopf (Ages 4–7); **5, 7**.

Federico, H. (1963). *The golden happy book of numbers*. New York: Golden Press (Ages 3–7); **7**.

Franco, B. (1999). *The tortoise who bragged: A Chinese tale with trigrams*. Sunnyvale, CA: Stokes; **7**.

Francoise (Seignobosc, F.) (1951). *Jean-Marie counts her sheep*. New York: Scribner's (Ages 3–6); **7**.

Friskey, M. (1940). *Seven diving ducks*. New York: McKay (Ages 4–6); **7**.

Garne, S. T. (1992). *One white sail*. New York: Green Tiger Press (Ages 5–8); **7**.

Getty Museum. (n.d.). *1 to 10 and back again: A Getty Museum counting book*. Los Angeles: Author; **3, 7**.

Gibson, R. (1998). *I can count*. London: Usborne Playtime; **3, 7**.

Gollub, M. (2000). *Ten Oni drummers*. New York: Lee & Low; **7**.

Guettier, B. (1999). *The father who had ten children*. East Rutherford, NJ: Dial/Penguin; **7**.

Hoban, T. (1987). *Letters & 99 cents*. New York: Greenwillow (Ages 4–8); **7, 9**.

Hudson, C. W. (1987). *Afro-bets 1, 2, 3 book*. Orange, NJ: Just Us Productions; **3, 7**.

Hulme, J. N. (1993). *Sea squares*. New York: Hyperion; **3, 7**.

Johnson, S. T. (1998). *City by numbers*. New York: Viking/Penguin; **7**.

Keats, E. J. (1971). *Over in the meadow*. New York: Scholastic Books (Ages 3–5); **7**.

Kherdian, D., & Hogrogian, N. (1990). *The cat's midsummer jamboree*. New York: Philomel (Ages 5–8); **7**.

LeSeig, T. (1974). *Whacky Wednesday*. New York: Random House (Ages 5–8); **25**.

Merriam, E. (1993). *12 ways to get to 11*. New York: Aladdin; **7**.

Miller, V. (2002). *Ten red apples: A Bartholomew Bear counting book*. Cambridge, MA: Candlewick; **7**.

Numbers: Match-up flip book. (1984). St. Paul, MN: Trend (Ages 4–8); **7**.

Suen, A. (2000). *100 day*. New York: Lee & Low Books; **7**.

Thaler, M. (1991). *Seven little hippos*. Old Tappan, NJ: Simon & Schuster (Ages 5–8); **7**.

Werner, S., & Forss, S. (2011). *Bugs by the numbers*. Maplewood, NJ: Blue Apple Books. **7**.

Zaslavsky, C. (1999). *Count on your fingers African style*. New York: Writers & Readers; **7**.

MATHEMATICS CONCEPTS AND ACTIVITIES FOR THE PRIMARY GRADES

As already noted, many of the books listed are appropriate for preprimary and primary children. Many books that are read-along books for the younger children become books for individual reading for older children. A few additional titles are included here.

Aber, & Allen, J. Carrie. *Esta a la altura*. Kane Press (Measuring). **9**.

Ada, A.F. (2002). I love Saturdays y Domingos. New York: Atheneum. **9**.

Adler, D.A. (2011). *Mystery math: A first book of algebra*. New York: Holiday House. **9**.

Barry, D. (1994). *The Rajah's rice: A mathematical folktale from India*. New York: Freeman; **9**.

Base, G. (2006). *Uno's garden*. Time Warner (K–8); **8, 9**.

Belov, R. (1971). *Money, money, money*. New York: Scholastic Books (Ages 6–8); **9**.

Basher & Green, D. (2011). *Algebra and geometry*. New York: Kingfisher. **9**.

Boynton, S. (1987). *Hippos go berserk*. Chicago: Recycled Paper Press; **9**.

Branco, B., & Salerno, S. (2003). *Mathematickles*. Riverside, NJ: Simon & Schuster; **9**.

Bruce, S., & Billin-Frye, P. (Illus.). ¡*Todos ganan!* New York: Kane Press (Division); **8**.

Bruchac, J., & London, J. (1992). *Thirteen moons on turtle's back: A Native American year of moons*. New York: Philomel; **9**.

Calmenson, S., & Cole, J. (1998). *Get well gators!* New York: Morrow Junior Books; **8**.

Cave, K., & Riddel, C. (1992). *Out for the count: A counting adventure*. New York: Simon & Schuster (Ages 6–8); **8, 9**.

Cobb, A. (2000). *The long wait*. New York: Kane Press; **9**.

Dahl, M. (2006). *Know your number series* (6 books). Mankato, MN: Picture Window Books; **8, 9**.

Dahl, R. (1990). *Esio trot*. New York: Viking (Ages 7–8); **9**.

Darwin, S., Grout, B., & McCoy, D. (Eds.). (1992). *How do octopi eat pizza pie?* Alexandria, VA: Time-Life for Children (Ages 6–9); **8, 9**.

Darwin, S., Grout, B., & McCoy, D. (Eds.). (1992). *Look both ways*. Alexandria, VA: Time-Life for Children (Ages 6–9); **8, 9**.

Driscoll, L. (2003). *The blast off kid*. New York: Kane Press; **8**.

Eboch, C. (2007). *Science measurements: How heavy? How long? How hot?* Mankato, MN: Picture Window Books; **9**.

Friskey, M. (1963). *Mystery of the farmer's three fives*. Chicago: Children's Press (Ages 6–8); **8**.

Gibson, R. (1998). *I can count*. London: Usborne Playtime; **9**.

Gill, S., & Tobolo, D. (2000). *The big buck adventure*. Watertown, MA: Charlesbridge; **9**.

Gifford, S. (2003). *Piece=part=portion*. New York: Tricyle Press. **8**.

Ghigna, C. (2013). *Veo al otono ((I see Fall)*. No. Mankato, MN: Picture Window Books. **9**.

Gom, T. (2006). *Spring is here (Llego la Primavera)*. San Francisco: Chronicle Books. **9**.

Gordon, J. R. (1991). *Six sleepy sheep*. Honesdale, PA: Boyds Mill Press (Ages 6–8); **8**.

Harper, D. (1998). *Telling time with big mama cat*. San Diego, CA: Harcourt Brace; **9**.

Hawkins, C. (1984). *Take away monsters*. New York: Putnam's (Ages 3–5); **7, 8**.

Heide, F. P. (1994). *The bigness contest*. Boston: Little, Brown; **9**.

Hewavisenti, L. (1991). *Measuring*. Chicago: Franklin Watts; **9**.

Hindley, J. (1994). *The wheeling and whirling-around book.* Cambridge, MA: Candlewick Press; **9.**

Hoban, T. (1998). *More, fewer, less.* New York: Greenwillow; **9.**

Hulme, J. N. (1995). *Counting by kangaroos: A multiplication concept book.* New York: Scientific American Books; **8.**

Jocelyn, M. (2000). *Hannah's collections.* East Rutherford, NJ: Putnam; **8, 9.**

Johnson, J. (1995). *How big is a whale?* Skokie, IL: Rand McNally; **9, 10.**

Johnson, J. (1995). *How fast is a cheetah?* Skokie, IL: Rand McNally; **9, 10.**

Kopp, J. (2000). *Math on the menu: Real-life problem solving for grades 3–5.* Berkeley, CA: Lawrence Hall of Science; **8, 9.**

Krudwig, V. L. (1998). *Cucumber soup.* Golden, CO: Fulcrum; **5, 9.**

Leedy, L. (1994). *Fraction action.* New York: Holiday House; **8.**

Lewis, J.P.(2012). *Edgar Allen Poe's Pie.* New York: HMH books for young readers. **8, 9.**

Lewis, J. P. (2002). *Arithme-tickle.* Orlando, FL: Harcourt; **8.**

Llewellyn, C. (1992). *My first book of time.* New York: Dorling Kindersley; **9.**

Long, E, (2012). *The Wing Wing brothers math spectacular!* New York: Holiday House. **8.**

Lowery, , L.F. (2012). *How tall was Milton?* Arlington, VA: NSTAKids. **9.**

Maestro, B. (1993). *The story of money.* New York: Clarion Books (Ages 6–9); **9.**

Maestro, B. (1999). *The story of clocks and calendars: Marking a millennium.* New York: Lothrop, Lee, & Shepard Books; **9.**

Martin, B., Jr. (1963). *Five is five.* New York: Holt, Rinehart, & Winston (Ages 6–8); **7, 8.**

Martin, B., Jr. (1964). *Delight in number.* New York: Holt, Rinehart, & Winston (Ages 6–8); **3, 8, 9.**

Martin, B., Jr. (1964). *Four threes are twelve.* New York: Holt, Rinehart, & Winston (Ages 6–8); **8.**

Martin, B., Jr. (1964). *If you can count to ten.* New York: Holt, Rinehart, & Winston (Ages 6–8); **8.**

Martin, B., Jr. (1971). *Number patterns make sense.* New York: Holt, Rinehart, & Winston (Ages 8–9); **8, 9.**

McMillan, B. (1991). *Eating fractions.* Jefferson City, MO: Scholastic Book Services (Ages 6–9); **8.**

Merriam. E. (1993). *12 ways to get to 11.* New York: Aladdin; **7, 8.**

Mollel, T. M. (1999). *My rows and piles of coins.* New York: Clarion Books; **9.**

Morgan, R. (1997). *In the next three seconds.* New York: Lodestar; **9.**

Morgan, S. (1994). *The world of shapes, squares, and cubes.* New York: Thomson Learning; **9.**

Morris, A. (1995). *Shoes, shoes, shoes.* New York: Lothrop, Lee & Shepard; **9.**

Murphy, S. J. (1997). *The best vacation ever.* New York: HarperCollins; **8.**

Murphy, S. J. (2005). *Same old horse.* New York: Harper Collins (Ages 6 and up); **9.**

Murphy, S. J., & Remkiewicz, F. (2003). *Less than zero.* New York: HarperCollins; **8.**

Nagda, A. W., & Bickel, C. (2000). *Tiger math: Learning to graph from a baby tiger.* New York: Holt; **9.**

Nagda, A. W., & Bickel, C. (2002). *Chimp math.* New York: Holt; **8.**

Napoli, D. J., & Tchen, R. (2001). *How hungry are you?* New York: Simon & Schuster; **8.**

Neuschwander, C. (1998). *Amanda Bean's amazing dream—a mathematical story.* New York: Scholastic Books; **8.**

O'Donnell, E. L., & Schmidt, K. L. (1991). *The twelve days of summer.* New York: Morrow (Ages 6–8); **8.**

Older, J. (2000). *Telling time.* Watertown, MA: Charlesbridge; **9.**

Pilegad, V. W., & Debon, N. (2003). *The warlord's puppeteers.* Gretna, LA: Pelican; **8, 9.**

Pinczes, E. J. (1993). *One hundred hungry ants.* New York: Scholastic Books; **9.**

Remkiewicz, F. (2002). *Arithmetickle.* Orlando, FL: Voyager Books. **8.**

Reys, M. & Reys, H. A. (2012). *Felez Navidad, Jorge el Curioso (Merry Christmas, Curious George).* New York: Houghton Mifflin Harcourt. **9.**

Richards, K. (2006). *¡Ya era hora, Max!* New York: Kane Press; **9.**

Schertle, A. (1987). *Jeremy Bean's St. Patrick's Day.* New York: Morrow (Ages 5–8); **5, 9.**

Schleim, M. (1972). *Moon months and sun days.* Reading, MA: Young Scott (Ages 6–8); **5, 9.**

Schwartz, D., & Kellogg, S. (2003). *Millions to measure.* New York: HarperCollins; **9.**

Schwartz, D. M. (1985). *How much is a million.* New York: Scholastic Books; **9.**

Schwartz, D. M. (1989). *If you made a million.* New York: Scholastic Books; **9.**

Scienszka, J., & Smith, L. (1995). *Math curse.* New York: Viking; **8.**

Sharman, L. (1994). *The amazing book of shapes*. New York: Dorling Kindersley; **9.**

Tang, G. (2002). *Mathematics strategies that multiply: The best of times*. New York: Scholastic Books; **8.**

Tompert, A. (1990). *Grandfather Tang's story*. New York: Crown; **9.**

Viorst, J. (1978). *Alexander who used to be rich last Sunday*. New York: Alladin; **8, 9.**

Viorst, J. (1992). *Sunday morning*. New York: Atheneum (Ages 6–8); **9.**

Weston, M. (1992). *Bea's four bears*. New York: Clarion Books (Ages 6–8); **8.**

Williams, S. (2001). *Dinnertime!* San Diego, CA: Harcourt; **8.**

Yates, P. (2005). *Ten little mummies: An Egyptian counting book*. East Rutherford, NJ: Penguin Putnam; **9.**

Ye, T. (1998). *Weighing the elephant*. Buffalo, NY: Annick Press; **9.**

BOOKS THAT SUPPORT SCIENCE INVESTIGATIONS

See the reviews and articles in each issue of *Teaching Children Mathematics* and *Science and Children*. Each year's March issue of *Science and Children* includes a section on the year's outstanding trade books in both English and Spanish.

Series

Cole, J. (1997). *El autobus magico* [The magic school bus]. New York: Scholastic Books (Grades 2–4); **10, 11.**

Delafosse, C., & Jeunesse, G. (1998). *Yo observo: Los animales marinos; Los animales bajo tierra; Las casas de los insectos; Los dinosaurios* [I see: Marine animals; Animals underground; Insects' houses; Dinosaurs]. Madrid, Spain: Ediciones SM (Ages 5–8); **5, 7, 10.**

Falk, J. H., & Rosenberg, K. S. (1999). *Bite-sized science*. Chicago: Chicago Review (Grades K–3; recommended for family activities); **4, 5, 7, 11.**

Glesecke, E. (1999). *Outside my window: Birds, trees, flowers, and mammals*. Portsmouth, NH: Heinemann (Ages 4–8); **5, 7, 10.**

Willis, S. (1999). *How, why and what series in Spanish on floating, weight, moon phases, rain, flight, time, distance, speed for grades 2–4*. New York: Franklin Watts; **10, 11.**

Reviews

Outstanding science trade books for students K–12. *Science and Children* (Published yearly).

Schon, I. Libros de ciencias en Español. *Science and Children* (Published yearly).

Life Science

Animals

Aranega, S., & Portell, J. (1999). *El elefante* [Elephant]. Barcelona, Spain: La Galera (Grades 1–3); **10.**

Arnold, C. (1987). *A Kangaroo's World; A Koala's World*. New York: Morrow (Ages 7–10); **10.**

Arnold, C. (1996). *Bats*. New York: Morrow (Grades 1–3); **7, 10.**

Arnold, C. (1996). *Fox*. New York: Morrow (Grades 2–5); **10.**

Arnosky, J. (1986). *Deer at the brook*. New York: Lothrop (Ages 1–6); **5, 7, 10.**

Arnosky, J. (1987). *Raccoons and ripe corn*. New York: Lothrop (Ages 3–6); **5, 7, 10.**

Arnosky, J. (1994). *All about alligators*. New York: Scholastic Books (Grades K–3); **4, 5, 7, 10.**

Arnosky, J. (1995). *All about owls*. New York: Scholastic Books (Grades K–3); **4, 5, 7, 10.**

Banks, M. (1990). *Animals of the night*. New York: Scribner (Ages 4–6); **5, 7, 10.**

Baredes, C. F., & Lotersztain, I. (2004). *Por que es tan guapo el pavo real? Y otras estrategias de los animales para tener hijos* [Why are peacocks so handsome? And other strategies of animals to have babies]. Argentina: Iamique (Ages 8–11); **4, 5, 7, 10.**

Baredes, C. F., & Lotersztain, I. (2006). *Por que es trompudo el elefante? Y otras curiosidades de los animales a la hora de comer* [Why is the elephant's nose so long? And other animal curiosities at meal time]. Argentina: Iamique (Ages 8–11); **4, 5, 7, 10.**

Baredes, C. F., & Lotersztain, I. (2006). *Por que se rayo la cebra? Y otras armas curiosas que tienen los animales para no ser devorados* [Why do zebras have stripes? And weapons that animals have to defend themselves]. Argentina: Iamique (Ages 8–11); **4, 5, 7, 10.**

Bilgrami, S. (2002). *Incredible animal discovery*. New York: Sterling (Ages 4–8); **4, 5, 7, 10.**

Bilgrami, S. (2003). *Animales increibles* [Incredible animal discovery]. Mexico City: Planeta (Ages 4–8); **4, 5, 7, 10.**

Bussolati, E. (1999). *Busca y encuentra* [Search and find]. Madrid, Spain: Editorial Edaf (Grades pre-K–1); **4, 5, 7, 10.**

Bussolati, E. (2000). *Los animales y sus crias* [Animals and their young]. Madrid, Spain: Editorial Edaf (Grades pre-K–1); **4, 5, 7, 10.**

Campbell, R. (2000). *Oscar en la granja* [Oh dear!]. Barcelona, Spain: Ediciones Elfos (Grades pre-K–1); **4, 5, 7, 10.**

Carle, E. (1987). *Have you seen my cat?* New York: Scholastic Books; **4, 5, 7, 10.**

Cole, S. (1985). *When the tide is low.* New York: Lothrop (Ages 3–9); **5, 7, 10.**

Cowcher, H. (1991). *Tigress.* New York: Garrar (Ages 4–8); **4, 5, 7, 10.**

Davis, K. (1999). *Quien salta?* [Who hops?]. Barcelona, Spain: Editorial Juventud (Grades pre-K–3); **4, 5, 7, 10.**

Diehl, J., & Plumb, D. (2000). *What's the difference? 10 animal look-alikes.* New York: Kingfisher (Grades K–4); **7, 10.**

Ehlert, L. (1990). *Feathers for lunch.* San Diego, CA: Harcourt Brace (Ages 4–7); **4, 5, 7, 10.**

Flack, M. (1930). *Angus and the ducks.* New York: Doubleday (Ages 3–6); **5, 7, 10.**

Fleming, D. (1993). *In the small, small pond.* New York: Holt (Ages 4–8); **4, 5, 7, 10.**

Fowler, A. (1992). *It's best to leave a snake alone.* Chicago: Children's Press **5, 7, 10.**

Fredericks, A. D. (2000). *Slugs.* Minneapolis, MN: Lerner (Grades K–6); **7, 10.**

Freeman, D. (1968/1976). *Corduroy.* New York: Viking/Penguin (Ages 3–6); **5, 7, 10.**

Gallagher, K. E. (2001). *The cottontail rabbits.* Minneapolis, MN: Lerner (Grades K–4); **7, 10.**

George, T. C. (2000). *Jellies: The life of jellyfish.* Brookfield, CT: Millbrook Press (Grades K–3); **7, 10.**

Gibbons, G. (1993). *Frogs.* New York: Holiday House (Grades pre-K–3); **4, 5, 7, 10.**

Gill, P. (1990). *Birds.* New York: Eagle Books (Ages 4–8); **5, 7, 10.**

Hickman, P. (1999). *My first look at: A new duck.* Niagara Falls, NY: Kids Can Press (Grades K–3); **7, 10.**

Hirschi, R. (1991). *Loon lake.* New York: Cobblehill (Ages 4–8); **5, 7, 10.**

Horenstein, H. (1999). *A is for . . .? A photographer's alphabet of animals.* New York: Harcourt Brace (Grades K–3); **7, 10.**

Horowitz, R. (2000). *Crab moon.* Cambridge, MA: Candlewick Press (Grades K–6); **10.**

James, S. (1991). *Dear Mr. Blueberry.* New York: McElderry (Ages 3–8) **4, 5, 7, 10, 11.**

Jango-Cohen, J. (2000). *Clinging sea horses.* Minneapolis, MN: Lerner (Grades K–4); **7, 10.**

Jenkins, M. (1999). *The emperor's egg.* Cambridge, MA: Candlewick Press (Grades K–6); **7, 10.**

Johnson, R. L. (2001). *A walk in the desert; A walk in the prairie; A walk in the rain forest.* Minneapolis, MN: Lerner (Grades K–8); **10.**

Johnson, S. A. (1982). *Inside an egg.* Minneapolis, MN: Lerner; **5, 7, 10.**

Johnston, G., & Cutchins, J. (1991). *Slippery babies: Young frogs, toads, and salamanders.* New York: Morrow (Ages 5–8); **5, 7, 10.**

Kalman, B., & Aloian M. (2006). *Muchos tipos de animals* [Many kinds of animals]. New York: Crabtree (Ages 5–9); **4, 5, 7, 10.**

Kalman, B., & Lundblad, K. (2006). *Animales ilamados peces* [Animals called fish]. New York: Crabtree (Ages 5–9); **4, 5, 7, 10.**

Kalman, B., & MacAulay, K. (2004). *Guinea pigs.* New York: Crabtree (Ages 7–8); **4, 5, 7, 10.**

Kalman, B., & MacAulay, K. (2006). *Los cobayos* [Guinea pigs]. New York: Crabtree (Ages 7–8); **4, 5, 7, 10.**

Kalman, B., & MacAulay, K. (2006). *Reptiles de todo tipo* [Reptiles of all kinds]. New York: Crabtree (Ages 5–9); **4, 5, 7, 10.**

Kalman, B., & Sjonger, R. (2004). *Hamsters.* New York: Crabtree (Ages 5–9); **4, 5, 7, 10.**

Kalman, B., & Sjonger, R. (2004). *Puppies.* New York: Crabtree (Ages 5–9); **4, 5, 7, 10.**

Kalman, B., & Sjonger, R. (2006). *Aves de todo tipo* [Birds of all kinds]. New York: Crabtree (Ages 5–9); **4, 5, 7, 10.**

Kalman, B., & Sjonger, R. (2006). *Los cachorros* [Puppies]. New York: Crabtree (Ages 5–9); **4, 5, 7, 10.**

Kalman, B., & Sjonger, R. (2006). *Los hamsters* [Hamsters]. New York: Crabtree (Ages 5–9); **4, 5, 7, 10.**

Kalman, B., & Walker, N. (2004). *Kittens.* New York: Crabtree (Ages 7–8); **4, 5, 7, 10.**

Kalman, B., & Walker, N. (2006). *Los gatitos* [Kittens]. New York: Crabtree (Ages 7–8); **4, 5, 7, 10.**

Koelling, C. (1978). *Whose house is this?* Los Angeles: Price/Stern/Sloan (Ages 3–5); **5, 7.**

Lewin, T., & Lewin, B. (1999). *Gorilla walk.* New York: Lothrop/HarperCollins (Grades K–6); **7, 10.**

Ling, M., & Atkinson, M. (1997). *The snake book.* New York: Dorling Kindersley (Grades 1 and up); **10.**

Lionni, L. (1963). *Swimmy.* New York: Pantheon (Ages 3–6); **5, 7, 10.**

London, J. (1999). *Baby whale's journey.* San Francisco: Chronicle Books (Grades K–3); **7, 10.**

Lowery, L.F. (2012). *What does an animal eat??* Arlington, VA: NSTAKids. **7, 10.**

Lowery, L.F. (2012). *What can animals do?* Arlington, VA: NSTAKids. **7, 10.**

Markle, S. (2004). *Crocodiles*. Minneapolis, MN: Lerner (Ages 7–9); **4, 5, 7, 10.**

Markle, S. (2004). *Great white sharks*. Minneapolis, MN: Lerner (Ages 7–9); **4, 5, 7, 10.**

Markle, S. (2004). *Lions*. Minneapolis, MN: Lerner (Ages 7–9); **4, 5, 7, 10.**

Markle, S. (2004). *Wolves*. Minneapolis, MN: Lerner (Ages 7–9); **4, 5, 7, 10.**

Markle, S. (2006). *Los Cocodrilos* [Crocodiles]. Minneapolis, MN: Lerner (Ages 7–9); **4, 5, 7, 10.**

Markle, S. (2006). *Los liones* [Lions]. Minneapolis, MN: Lerner (Ages 7–9); **4, 5, 7, 10.**

Markle, S. (2006). *Los lobos* [Wolves]. Minneapolis, MN: Lerner (Ages 7–9); **4, 5, 7, 10.**

Markle, S. (2006). *Los tiburones blancos* [Great white sharks]. Minneapolis, MN: Lerner (Ages 7–9); **4, 5, 7, 10.**

Markle, S. (2006). *Slippery, slimy baby frogs*. London: Walker Books for Young Readers (Ages 4–8); **4, 5, 7, 10.**

Mason, A. (2000). *Starting with science series: Living things*. Toronto, Ontario, Canada: Kids Can Press (Grades K–4); **7, 10.**

McCloskey, R. (1941/1976). *Make way for ducklings*. New York: Viking/Penguin (Ages 4–6); **5, 7, 10.**

McFarland, C. (1990). *Cows in the parlor: A visit to a dairy farm*. New York: Atheneum (Ages 5–8); **5, 7, 10.**

Mitsuko and Kamiko (A. Coll-Vinent, trans.). (1999). *El elefante* [Elephant]. Madrid, Spain: El Editorial Carimbo (Grades pre-K–1); **5, 7, 10.**

Mitsuko and Kamiko (A. Coll-Vinent, trans.). (1999). *El gato* [Cat]. Madrid, Spain: El Editorial Carimbo (Grades pre-K–1); **5, 7, 10.**

Murphy, J. (1993). *Backyard bear*. New York: Scholastic Books (Grades 2–4); **10.**

Netherton, J. (2000). *Red-eyed tree frogs*. Minneapolis, MN: Lerner (Grades K–4); **7, 10.**

Nicholson, D. (1987). *Wild boars*. Minneapolis, MN: Lerner (Ages 6–10); **10.**

Paladino, C. (1991). *Pomona: The birth of a penguin*. New York: Watts (Ages 5–8); **5, 7, 10.**

Pallotta, J. (1986). *The BIRD alphabet book*. Watertown, MA: Charlesbridge; **5, 10.**

Pallotta, J. (1989). *The yucky reptile alphabet book*. Watertown, MA: Charlesbridge; **4, 5, 10.**

Patent, D. H. (1987). *All about whales*. New York: Holiday House (Ages 6–9); **10.**

Patent, D. H. (1993). *Looking at penguins*. New York: Holiday House (Grades 1–3); **10.**

Patent, D. H. (1994). *Looking at bears*. New York: Holiday House (Grades 1–3); **10.**

Potter, B. (1902). *The tale of Peter Rabbit*. New York: Warne (Ages 4–6); **5, 7, 10.**

Robinson, C. (1999). *In the wild: Whales*. Portsmouth, NH: Heinemann (Grades 1–2);

Rotner, (2012). *Body actions*. New York: Holiday House. **10.**

Savage, S. (1992). *Making tracks*. New York: Lodestar (Ages 4–8); **5, 7, 10, 11.**

Savage, S. (2000). *What's the difference?: Birds*. Sydney, NSW, Australia: Steck Vaughn (Grades K–4); **7, 10.**

Sheldon, D. (1991). *The whales' song*. New York: Dial (Ages 4–8); **5, 7, 10.**

Simon, S. (1999). *Crocodiles & alligators*. New York: HarperCollins (Grades K–6); **7, 10.**

Souza, A. (1992). *Slinky snakes*. Minneapolis, MN: Carolrhoda; **10.**

Stanley, C. (1991). *Busy, busy squirrels*. New York: Cobblehill (Ages 4–8); **5, 7, 10, 11.**

Stuart, D. (1994). *Bats: Mysterious flyers of the night*. Minneapolis, MN: Carolrhoda (Grades 2–5); **10.**

Tagholm, S. (2000). *Animal lives: The rabbit*. New York: Kingfisher (GradesK-3) **7, 10.**

Weller, F. (1991). *I wonder if I'll see a whale*. New York: Philomel (Ages 4–8); **5, 7, 10.**

Wells, R. E. (1997). *What's faster than a speeding cheetah?* Morton Grove, IL: Whitman (Ages 7–9); **4, 5, 7, 10.**

Wells, R. E. (2006). *Hay algo mas rapido que un guepardo?* [What's faster than a speeding cheetah?] Barcelona, Spain: Juventud (Ages 7–9); **4, 5, 7, 10.**

Wildsmith, B. (1983). *The owl and the woodpecker*. New York: Oxford University Press (Ages 4–7); **4, 5, 7, 10.**

Yamashita, K. (1993). *Paws, wings, and hooves*. Minneapolis, MN: Lerner (Ages 6–8); **7, 10.**

Yolen, J. (1988). *Owl moon*. New York: Philomel (Grades pre- K–1); **4, 5, 7, 10.**

Bugs, Spiders, Bees, and Butterflies

Allen, J., & Humphries, T. (2000). *Are you a ladybug?* New York: Kingfisher Books (Grades K–4); **7, 10.**

Arnosky, J. (1996). *Crinkleroot's guide to knowing butterflies and moths*. New York: Simon & Schuster Books for Young Readers (Primary grades); **10.**

Berenstain, S., & Berenstain, J. (1962). *The big honey hunt*. New York: Random House (Ages 3–8); **21, 26, 34.**

Carle, E. (1969). *The very hungry caterpillar*. New York: Philomel (Ages 3–6); **5, 7, 10.**

Carle, E. (1977). *The grouchy ladybug*. New York: Crowell (Ages 3–6); **5, 7, 10.**

Carle, E. (1981). *The honeybee and the robber*. New York: Philomel (Ages 3–6); **5, 7, 10.**

Carle, E. (1984). *The very busy spider*. New York: Philomel (Ages 3–6); **5, 7, 10.**

Clay, P., & Clay, H. (1984). *Ants*. London: A & C Black; **5, 7, 10.**

Dallinger, J. (1981). *Spiders*. Minneapolis, MN: Lerner; **5, 7, 10.**

Facklam, M. (1996). *Creepy, crawly caterpillars*. Boston: Little, Brown (Grades 2–4); **10.**

Fleming, D. (1991). *In the tall, tall grass*. New York: Holt (Ages 4–8); **4, 5, 7, 10.**

Gibbons, G. (2012). *Ladybugs*. New York: Holiday House. **5, 7, 10.**

Guiberson, B. (1991). *Cactus hotel*. New York: Holt (Ages 4–8); **5, 7, 10, 11.**

Hall, M. C. (2006). *Arañas/Spiders* (Pebble Plus Bilingual). Mankato, MN: Capstone Press (Ages 4–7); **4, 5, 7, 10.**

Hall, M. C. (2006). *Grillos/Crickets* (Pebble Plus Bilingual). Mankato, MN: Capstone Press (Ages 4–7); **4, 5, 7, 10.**

Hall, M. C. (2006). *Hormigas/Ants* (Pebble Plus Bilingual). Mankato, MN: Capstone Press (Ages 4–7); **4, 5, 7, 10.**

Hall, M. C. (2006). *Mantis religiosas/Praying mantises* (Pebble Plus Bilingual). Mankato, MN: Capstone Press (Ages 4–7); **4, 5, 7, 10.**

Hall, M. C. (2006). *Mariquitas/Ladybugs* (Pebble Plus Bilingual). Mankato, MN: Capstone Press (Ages 4–7); **4, 5, 7, 10.**

Hall, M. C. (2006). *Saltamontes/Grasshoppers* (Pebble Plus Bilingual). Mankato, MN: Capstone Press (Ages 4–7); **4, 5, 7, 10.**

Hartley, K., Macro, C., & Taylor, P. (1999). *Bug books: Ant, bee, caterpillar, centipede, cockroach, grasshopper, ladybug, mosquito, snail, spider, termite, and worm*. Portsmouth, NH: Heinemann (Grades 2–3); **10.**

Fischer-Nagel, H & A, (1983). *Life of the honey bee*. Minneapolis, MN: Caroleroda.

Jeunesse, G., & de Hugo, P. (1998). *Los bichos de la casa* [House bugs]. Madrid, Spain: Ediciones SM (Grades 2–4); **10.**

Kneidel, S. S. (1993). *Creepy crawlies and the scientific method*. Washington, DC: National Science Teachers Association (Grades K–6); **7, 10.**

Overbeck, C. (1982). *Ants*. Minneapolis, MN: Lerner; **5, 7, 10.**

Pallotta, J. (1986). *The icky bug alphabet book*. Watertown, MA: Charlesbridge; **5, 7, 10.**

Pallotta, J. (1992). *The icky bug counting book*. Watertown, MA: Charlesbridge (Ages 4–8); **4, 5, 7, 10.**

Parker, N. W. (1987). *Bugs*. New York: Greenwillow (Ages 8–10); **10.**

Pinczes, E. J. (1993). *One hundred hungry ants*. New York: Scholastic Books; **5, 7, 10.**

Zemlicka, S. (2003). *From egg to butterfly*. Minneapolis, MN: Lerner (Ages 3–6) **5, 7, 10.**

Plants

Adler, D. A. (1999). *A picture book of George Washington Carver*. New York: Holiday House (Grades K–6); **7, 10.**

Bash, B. (1990). *Desert giant: The world of the saguaro cactus*. Boston: Little, Brown (Ages 5–8); **5, 7, 10, 11.**

Burns, D. L., & Burns, J. A. (1998). *Plant a garden in your sneaker*. Washington, DC: National Science Teachers Association (Grades 2–6); **10.**

Ehlert, L. (1991). *Red leaf, yellow leaf*. San Diego, CA: Harcourt Brace (Ages 4–8); **5, 7, 10, 11.**

Florian, D. (1991). *Vegetable garden*. New York: Harcourt Brace (Ages 3–5); **4, 5, 7, 10, 11.**

Gibbons, G. (1984). *The seasons of Arnold's apple tree*. San Diego, CA: Harcourt Brace (Ages 3–9); **5, 7, 10.**

Gibbons, G. (1991). *From seed to plant*. New York: Holiday House (Ages 5–8); **5, 7, 10.**

Gibbons, G. (1999). *The pumpkin book*. New York: Holiday House (Grades K–6); **7, 10.**

Hall, Z. (1994). *It's pumpkin time!* New York: Scholastic Books; **4, 5, 10.**

Hindley, J. (1990). *The tree*. New York: Clarkson Potter (Ages 6–12); **7, 10, 11.**

Hirschi, R. (1991). *Fall*. New York: Cobblehill (Ages 4–8); **21, 26, 34, 36.**

Hiscock, B. (1991). *The big tree*. New York: Atheneum (Ages 5–12); **5, 7, 10, 11.**

Johnson, R. L. (2001). *A walk in the desert; A walk in the prairie; A walk in the rain forest*. Minneapolis, MN: Lerner (Grades K–8); **10.**

Krauss, R. (1945). *The carrot seed*. New York: Harper & Row (Ages 3–5); **5, 6, 7, 8.**

Lowery, L.F. (2012). *How does a plant grow?* Arlington, VA: NSTAKids. **7, 10.**

Miller, D *Are trees alive?* New York: Walker & Company; **5, 7, 10, 11.**

Oechsli, H., & Oechsli, K. (1985). *In my garden: A child's gardening book*. New

York: Macmillan (Ages 5–9); **5, 7, 10.**

Ontario Science Centre. *Starting with science series: Plants*. Niagara Falls, NY: Kids Can Press (Grades K–4); **7, 10.**

Posada, M. (2000). *Dandelions: Stars in the grass*. Minneapolis, MN: Carolrhoda/Lerner (Grades K–3); **7, 10.**

Romanova, N. (1985). *Once there was a tree*. New York: Dial (Ages 3–9); **5, 7, 10.**

Silverstein, S. (1964). *The giving tree*. New York: Harper & Row (Ages 3–8); **5, 7, 10.**

Singer, M. (2006). *What stinks?* Plain City, OH: Darby Creek (Ages 9–12); **4, 5, 7, 10.**

Watts, B. (1990). *Tomato*. Morristown, NJ: Silver Burdett & Ginn (Ages 5–8) **5, 7, 10.**

Physical Science

Adler, D. A. (1999). *How tall, how short, how far away*. New York: Houghton-Mifflin (Grades K–3); **7, 10.**

Ardley, N. (1991). *The science book of air*. New York: Harcourt Brace (Ages 6–8); **5, 7, 10.**

Branley, F. (1996). *What makes a magnet?* New York: HarperCollins (Grades K–6); **7, 10.**

Brown, R. (1991). *The world that Jack built*. New York: Dutton (Ages 4–6); **5, 7, 10.**

Burton, V. L. (1939). *Mike Mulligan and his steam shovel*. Boston: Houghton-Mifflin (Ages 3–5); **5, 7.**

Carle, E. (1990). *Pancakes, pancakes!* New York: Scholastic Books; **4, 5, 10.**

dePaola, T. (1978). *The popcorn book*. New York: Scholastic Books; **5, 7, 10.**

Fowler, R. (1986). *Mr. Little's noisy boat*. New York: Grosset & Dunlap (Ages 5–9); **5, 7, 10.**

Graham, J. B. (1999). *Flicker flash*. New York: Houghton-Mifflin; **4, 5, 7, 10.**

Gourley, R. (2011). *First garden: the White House garden and how it grew*. New York: Clarion Books. **5, 7, 10.**

Hickman, P., & Stephens, P. (2000). *Animals in motion: How animals swim, jump, slither, and glide*. Niagara Falls, NY: Kids Can Press (Grades K–8); **7, 10.**

Hulme, J. (1991). *Sea squares*. New York: Hyperion (Ages 4–8); **5, 7, 10.**

Isadora, R. (1985). *I touch*. New York: Greenwillow (Ages 0–2); **5, 10.**

Kimiko (A. Coll-Vinent, trans.). (1999). *El avion* [Airplane]. Madrid, Spain: Editorial Corimbo (Grades pre-K–1); **4, 5, 7, 10, 11.**

Koningsburg, E. I. (1991). *Samuel Todd's book of great inventions*. New York: Atheneum (Ages 4–7); **5, 7, 10, 11.**

Lowery, L.F. (2012). *What makes different sounds?* Arlington, VA: NSTA Kids. **10.**

Morgan, E. (2012). *Next time you see a seashell*. Arlington, VA: NSTA Kids. **11.**

Murata, Michinori. (1993). *Science is all around you: Water and light*. Minneapolis, MN: Lerner (Ages 6–8); **7, 10.**

Nessmann, P. (2006). *El color* [Color]. Barcelona, Spain: Combel (Ages 8–10); **10.**

O'Leary, J. (2004). *El profesor Topo y sus máquinas* [Professor Mole's machines]. Barcelona, Spain: Combel (Ages 3–6); **10, 11.**

O'Leary, J. (2004). *Professor Mole's machines*. London: Tango Books (Ages 3–6); **10, 11.**

Ontario Science Centre. (2000). *Starting with science: Solids, liquids, and gases*. Niagara Falls, NY: Kids Can Press (Grades K–4); **7, 10.**

Piper, W. (1984). *The little engine that could*. New York: Putnam (Ages 3–5); **5, 7, 11.**

Pluckrose, H. (1986). *Think about hearing*. New York: Franklin Watts (Ages 4–8); **5, 7, 10, 11.**

Robbins, K. (1991). *Bridges*. New York: Dial (Ages 5–12); **5, 7, 10, 11.**

Rockwell, A. (1986). *Things that go*. New York: Dutton (Ages 3–5); **5, 7.**

Scarry, R. (1986). *Splish-Splash sounds*. Racine, WI: Western (Ages 3–7); **5, 7, 10.**

Taylor, K. (1992). *Flying start science series: Water; light; action; structure*. New York: Wiley (Ages 3–9); **4, 5, 10, 11.**

Wyler, R. (1986). *Science fun with toy boats and planes*. New York: Messner (Ages 5–9); **10, 11.**

EARTH AND SPACE SCIENCE

Adamson, T. K. (2006). *Júpiter/Jupiter* (Pebble Plus Bilingual). Mankato, MN: Capstone Press (Ages 4–7); **11.**

Adamson, T. K. (2006). *Marte/Mars* (Pebble Plus Bilingual). Mankato, MN: Capstone Press (Ages 4–7); **11.**

Adamson, T. K. (2006). *Mercurio/Mercury* (Pebble Plus Bilingual). Mankato, MN: Capstone Press (Ages 4–7); **11.**

Adamson, T. K. (2006). *Neptuno/Neptune* (Pebble Plus Bilingual). Mankato, MN: Capstone Press (Ages 4–7); **11.**

Adamson, T. K. (2006). *Plutòn/Pluto* (Pebble Plus Bilingual). Mankato, MN: Capstone Press (Ages 4–7); **11.**

Adamson, T. K. (2006). *Saturno/Saturn* (Pebble Plus Bilingual). Mankato, MN: Capstone Press (Ages 4–7); **11.**

Adamson, T. K. (2006). *La Tierra/Earth* (Pebble Plus Bilingual). Mankato, MN: Capstone Press (Ages 4–7); **11.**

Adamson, T. K. (2006). *Urano/Uranus* (Pebble Plus Bilingual). Mankato, MN: Capstone Press (Ages 4–7); **11.**

Adamson, T. K. (2006). *Venus/Venus* (Pebble Plus Bilingual). Mankato, MN: Capstone Press (Ages 4–7); **11.**

Aguilar.D.A. (2011). *13 planets: the latest view of the solar system.* Des Moines, IA: National Geographic Children's Books. **11.**

Aliki. (1990). *Fossils tell of long ago.* New York: HarperCollins (Ages 5–8); **5, 7, 11.**

Arion, P. (2012). *Los Planetas.* New York: Scholastic. **11.**

Arnold, C. (1987). *Trapped in tar: Fossils from the Ice Age.* New York: Clarion (Ages 7–10); **11.**

Baird, A. (1996). *The U.S. Space Camp book of astronauts.* New York: Morrow; **11.**

Barrett, J. (1978). *Cloudy with a chance of meatballs.* New York: Macmillan; **4, 5, 11.**

Barton, B. (1990). *Bones, bones, dinosaur bones.* New York: HarperCollins (Ages 5–7); **5, 7, 11.**

Bernhard, E. (2006). *La meteorologia* [Weather]. Barcelona, Spain: Combel (Ages 8–10); **11.**

Bilgrami, S. (2002). *Amazing dinosaur discovery.* New York: Sterling (Ages 4–8); **11.**

Bilgrami, S. (2003). *Dinosaurios increibles* [Amazing dinosaur discovery]. Mexico City: Planeta (Ages 4–8); **11.**

Branley, F. M. (1985). *Flash, crash, rumble, and roll.* New York: Crowell (Ages 5–7); **11.**

Branley, F. M. (1985). *Volcanoes.* New York: Crowell (Ages 6–8); **11.**

Branley, F. M. (1986). *Air is all around us.* New York: Crowell (Ages 3–6); **5, 7, 11.**

Branley, F. M. (1986). *Journey into a black hole.* New York: Crowell (Ages 8–10); **11.**

Branley, F. M. (1987). *The moon seems to change; The planets in our solar system; Rockets and satellites.* New York: Crowell (Ages 5–8); **11.**

Branley, F. M. (2000). *The international space station.* New York: Harper Trophy; **11.**

Carrick, C. (1983). *Patrick's dinosaurs.* New York: Clarion (Ages 4–8); **5, 7, 10, 11.**

Cole, J. (1987). *Evolution.* New York: Crowell (Ages 5–8); **10, 11.**

Cole, J. (1987). *The magic school bus inside the earth.* New York: Scholastic Books; **5, 7, 11.**

Cole, J. (1992). *The magic school bus on the ocean floor.* New York: Scholastic Books; **11.**

Dunphy, M. (1999). *Here is the African savanna.* New York: Hyperion (Grades K–6); **7, 11.**

Earle, S. A. (1999). *Hello, fish! Visiting the coral reef.* Washington, DC: National Geographic (Grades K–3); **7, 11.**

Everet, L. (2002). *Rocks, fossils, and arrowheads.* Minnetonka, MN: Northwind Press (Ages 7–11); **11.**

Hoban, T. (1990). *Shadows and reflections.* New York: Greenwillow (Ages 4–8) **7, 11.**

Holub, J. (2013*). Groundhog weather school: Fun facts about weather and groundhogs.* London: Puffin. **5, 7, 11.**

Kandoian, E. (1990). *Under the sun.* New York: Putnam (Ages 4–6); **7, 11.**

Keats, E. J. (1981). *Regards to the man in the moon.* New York: Four Winds (Ages 3–6); **5, 7, 11.**

Krupp, E. C. (2000). *The rainbow and you.* New York: HarperCollins (Grades K–4); **7, 11.**

Langley, A. (2001). *The Oxford first book of space.* New York: Oxford University Press (Grades K–4); **11.**

Lessem, D. (2005). *Sea giants of dinosaur time.* Minneapolis, MN: Lerner (Ages 7–9); **11.**

Lessem, D. (2006). *Gigantes marinos de la epoca de los dinosaurios* [Sea giants of dinosaur time]. Minneapolis, MN: Lerner (Ages 7–9); **11.**

Lewison, W. (1990). *Mud.* New York: Random House (Ages 5–8); **5, 7, 11.**

Lindbergh, R. (1998). *Que es el sol?* [What is the sun?] New York: Lectorum (Ages 5–7); **4, 5, 7, 11.**

Livingston, M. (1992). *Light and shadow.* New York: Holiday House (Ages 4–7); **5, 7, 11.**

Lye, K. (1987). *Deserts*. Morristown, NJ: Silver Burdett (Ages 8–14); **11.**

Maki, C. (1993). *Snowflakes, sugar, and salt*. New York: Lerner (Ages 6–8); **5, 7, 10, 11.**

Malnig, A. (1985). *Where the waves break: Life at the edge of the sea*. Minneapolis, MN: Carolrhoda (Ages 7–10); **11.**

McMillan, B. (1990). *One sun: A book of terse verse*. New York: Holiday House (Ages 5–8); **5, 7, 11.**

Morgan, E. (2012). *Next time you see a sunset*. Arlington, VA: NSTA Kids. **11.**

Most, B. (1991). *A dinosaur named after me*. San Diego, CA: Harcourt Brace (Ages 4–8); **5, 7, 11.**

Otto, C. (1992). *That sky, that rain*. New York: Harper (Ages 4–7); **5, 7, 11.**

Pallotta, J. (1986). *The ocean alphabet book*. Watertown, MA: Charlesbridge; **4, 5, 11.**

Parmall, P. (1991). *The rock*. New York: Macmillan (Ages 5–8); **5, 7, 11.**

Ressmeyer, R. (1992). *Astronaut to zodiac*. New York: Crown (Ages 5–12); **7, 11.**

Rocks and minerals. (1988). London: Natural History Museum (Ages 7–12); **11.**

Schlein, M. (1991). *Discovering dinosaur babies*. New York: Four Winds (Ages 6–9); **7, 11.**

Schmid, E. (1990). *The water's journey*. New York: North-South Books (Ages 6–8); **7, 11.**

Seymour, S. (1999). *Tornadoes*. New York: Morrow/ HarperCollins (Grades K–6); **7, 11.**

Souza, D. (1992). *Powerful waves*. Minneapolis, MN: Carolrhoda (Ages 6–12); **7, 11.**

Sqire, A. (2012). *Minerals*. New York: Scholastic. **11.**

Sqire, A. (2012). *Rocks*. New York: Scholastic. **11.**

Szilagyi, M. (1985). *Thunderstorms*. New York: Bradbury (Ages 3–9); **5, 7, 11.**

Thornhill, J. (1997). *Before & after: A book of nature timescapes*. Washington, DC: National Geographic (Ages 4–6); **4, 5, 7, 10, 11.**

Wade, H. (1977). *Sand*. Milwaukee, WI: Raintree (Ages 4–8); **5, 7, 11.**

Weimer, T. E. (1993). *Space songs for children*. Pittsburgh, PA: Pearce-Evetts (Ages 5–8); **5, 7.**

Environmental Science: Ecology, Nature, and Conservation

Allen, M. (1991). *Changes*. New York: Macmillan (Ages 4–7); **5, 7, 10, 11.**

Arnosky, A. (1991). *The empty lot*. Boston: Little, Brown (Ages 4–8); **5, 7, 10, 11.**

Bash, B. (1990). *Urban roosts: Where birds nest in the city*. Boston: Little, Brown (Ages 6–12); **7, 10, 11.**

Bruchac, J. (1992). *Native American animal stories*. Golden, CO: Fulcrum (Ages 5–8); **5, 7, 10.**

Cherry, L. (1990). *The great kapok tree: A tale of the Amazon rain forest*. New York: Gulliver (Ages 6–12); **7, 10, 11.**

Fernandes, K. (1991). *Zebo and the dirty planet*. Ontario, Canada: Firefly Books; **4, 11.**

George, W. (1991). *Fishing at Long Pond*. New York: Greenwillow (Ages 4–8); **5, 7, 10, 11.**

Glaser, L. (1997). *Compost! Growing gardens from your garbage*. Brookfield, CT: Millbrook (Ages 5–8); **4, 5, 7, 10, 11.**

Glaser, L. (2000). *Our big home: An earth poem*. Brookfield, CT: Millbrook Press (Grades K–3); **7, 11.**

Green, D. (2012). *Oceans making waves!* New York: Kingfisher. **11.**

Greenaway, T. (2001). *The water cycle*. Austin, TX: Steck-Vaughn (Ages 6–9) **4, 5, 7, 11.**

Greene, C. (1991). *Caring for our land*. Waltham, MA: Enslow (Ages 6–8); **4, 5, 7, 10, 11.**

Grupper, J. (1997). *Destination: Rainforest*. Washington, DC: National Geographic (Ages 6–9); **4, 5, 7, 10, 11.**

Harper, J. (2012). *Miss Mingo weathers the storm*. Somerville, MA: Candlewick. **4, 5, 7, 11.**

Hines, A. (1991). *Remember the butterflies*. New York: Dutton (Ages 4–7); **4, 5, 7, 10, 11.**

Kaner, E. (1999). *Animal defenses: How animals protect themselves*. Niagara Falls, NY: Kids Can Press (Grades K–3); **7, 11.**

Kuhn, D. (1990). *More than just a vegetable garden*. New York: Silver Press (Ages 6–8); **7, 10, 11.**

Leslie, C. (1991). *Nature all year long*. New York: Greenwillow (Ages 6–8); **7, 10, 11.**

Levine, S., & Grafton, A. (1992). *Projects for a healthy planet*. New York: Wiley (Ages 6–12); **7, 10, 11.**

Locker, T. (1991). *The land of the gray wolf*. New York: Dial (Ages 4–8); **5, 7, 10, 11.**

Lyon, G.E. (2011). *All the water in the world*. New York: Atheneum/Richard Jackson. **7, 11.**

Miller, D. S. (2000). *River of life*. New York: Clarion (Grades K–3); **7, 11.**

Moss, M. (2000). *This is the tree*. La Jolla, CA: Kane/ Miller (Grades K–3); **7, 11.**

Norsgaard, E. J. (1990). *Nature's great balancing act: In our own backyard*. New York: Cobblehill (Ages 7–12); **7, 10, 11.**

Osborne, M.P. (2012). *Pandas and other endangered species*. New York: Random House Books for Young People. **7, 11.**

Parnall, P. (1990). *Woodpile*. New York: Macmillan (Ages 5–8); **5, 7, 10, 11.**

Phillips, S. (2011). *Weather* (Mini Encyclopedia). Berkhamsted, Hertfordshire, UK: Make Believe Ideas. (also *Earth, Rocks, Space*, and *Sea*). **11.**

Russell, H. R. (1998). *Ten-minute field trips*. Washington, DC: National Science Teachers Association (Grades K–8); **26, 34.**

Rustad, M.E.H. (2011). *Animals in Fall: Preparing for Winter*. Millbrook Press, **7, 10.**

Sackett, E. (1991). *Danger on the African grassland*. Boston: Little, Brown (Ages 5–8); **5, 7, 10, 11.**

Sanders, S. R. (1999). *Crawdad creek*. Washington, DC: National Geographic (Grades K–6); **7, 11.**

Schuh, M. C. (2006). *El agua potable* [Drinking water] (Pebble Plus Bilingual). Mankato, MN: Capstone Press (Ages 4–7); **10, 11.**

Seibert, D. (1991). *Sierra*. New York: HarperCollins (Ages 5–8); **5, 7, 10, 11.**

Seibert, P. (1996). *Toad overload: A true tale of nature knocked off balance in Australia*. Danbury, CT: Millbrook Press (Ages 5–8); **4, 5, 7, 10, 11.**

Shetterly, S. H. (1999). *Shelterwood*. Gardiner, ME: Tilbury House (Grades K–6); **7, 11.**

Stiefel, C. (2010) *The forces of nature*. New York: Scholastic/The Weather Channel Kids. **11.**

Stock, C. (1991). *When the woods hum*. New York: Morrow (Ages 4–8); **4, 5, 7, 10, 11.**

Taylor, K., & Burton, J. (1993). *Forest life*. New York: Dorling Kindersley (Ages 7–12); **10, 11.**

Tresselt, A. (1992). *The gift of the tree*. New York: Lothrop, Lee & Shepard (Ages 5–8); **5, 7, 10, 11.**

Tweit, S. J. (1997). *City foxes*. Portland, OR: Graphic Arts Center (Ages 4–9); **4, 5, 7, 10, 11.**

Walker, K. (2010). *Paper (Recycling)*. New York: Benchmark Books. **11.**

Walker, K.(2011). *Rocks (Investigating Earth)*. New York: Benchmark Books. **11.**

Engineering Science

Beaty, A (2013). *Rosie Revere, Engineer*. Harry N. Abrams@abramskids. **11.**

Hunt, E., & Pantoya, M. (2013). *Designing dandelions*. Lubbock, TX: Texas Tech University Press. **11.**

Levine, S. (2004). *First science experiments: Mighty machines*. New Delhi, India: Sterling. **11.**

Reynolds, P.H., & Reynolds, P.A. (2010). *Water wonders*. Dedham, MA: FableVision Learning. **11.**

Rinker, S.D. & Lichtenheld, T. (2011), *Goodnight, goodnight, construction site*. San Francisco, CA: Chronicle Books. **7, 11.**

Rivera, E., & A. (2010). *Rocks, jeans and busy machines*. (no address, can be purchased from Amazon.com) Rivera Engineering. **11.**

Rooney, A. (2013). *Aerospace engineering and the principles of flight*. New York: Crabtree. **11.**

Rusch, E. (2012). *The mighty mars rovers: The incredible adventure of Spirit and Opportunity*. New York: HMH Books for Young Readers. **11.**

Snedden, R. (2013). *Environmental engineering*. New York: Crabtree. **11.**

Simon, S. (2011). *Let's try it out with towers and bridges*. Seymour Science Nook Book. barnesandnoble.com **11.**

Vancleave, J. (2007). *Janice Vancleave's Engineering for every kid*. Hoboken, NJ: Wiley **11.**

Young, C. (1990). *Castles, pyramids and palaces*. Tulsa, OK: E.D.C, Publishing. **11.**

CHILDREN'S PERIODICALS THAT EMPHASIZE MATH AND SCIENCE CONCEPTS

All Animals Magazine. Humane Society of the USA. www.humanesociety.org

Ask Magazine for kids 6-9. Explores arts and science. www.cricketmag.com

CLICK Magazine for Kids ages 3-6 *Cricket at www.cricketmag.com*

DynaMath and *SuperScience* and *Let's Find Out* [Monthly magazine (eight issues) with activities for elementary grades]. Scholastic, 1-800 SCHOLASTIC, magazinecs@scholastic.com a

Highlights at www.highlights.com

National Geographic Kids . Kids.nationalgeographc.com (Ages 5–12).

Odyssey (Magazine or kids 9-14). Cricket at www.cricketmag.com

Ranger Rick's Nature Magazine. http://www.nwf.org

Science Weekly. P.O. Box 70638, Chevy Chase, MD 20813-0638 (Ages 4–12). Scienceweekly.com

Sesame Street Magazine. Redan Publishing (Ages 2-7). Subscribe at www.redan.com

Wild Animal Baby [Monthly magazine (10 issues)]. National Wildlife Federation, www.shpnwf.org

Your Big Back Yard, National Wildlife Federation. Phone, 800-611-1599 (Ages 3–5) http://wwwnwf.org.

ONLINE TECHNOLOGY RESOURCES FOR CHILDREN

Apps and App Reviews

Apple Store. Many ngames for iPads, iPods and iPhones. Find at itunes.apple.com.

Common Sense Media. Commonsense.org. Reviews of movies, games, books and apps.

Education World. (monthly) iPad App Store and iPad App Reviews. Find at http://www.educationworld.com.

KIDS DISCOVER. *Plants, Simple Machines, Geology, and Matter.* http://www.kidsdiscover,com..

Shape Arts: Geometry Creations Reviewed in *Children's Technology* March 11, 2014. http://childrenstech.com.

Online Activities

Curious George Resources. Discovery Guide, Teacher's Guide, Family Activities Booklet, Curiosity Center Activities. Find at http://www.pbs.org

Design Squad Nation. Engineering projects. Find at http://pbskids.org

Discover Engineering. Hands-on activities and trips and destinations. Find at http://www.discovery.org.

Early Math. Nurturing early math: Infants and Toddlers, PreK & K, Grades 1& 2. Find at http://www.pbs.org.

Education World: Web site reviews. (monthly) Find at http://www.educationworld.com.

Engineering in Elementary (EiE). Engineering and technology lessons for children. Find at http://wwwmos.org/.

Engineering GoFor it! eGFI. Provides background information of engineering careers.

Funsciencedemos. Videos of many science concept demonstrations. Can be found on youtube.

The Graph Club 2.0 Online graphing tool. Tom Snyder Productions. www.tomsnyder.com.

Illuminations.nctm.org. Games, activities, problems.

Kahn Academy. http://www.khanacademy,org. K-12 activities congruent with CCSSM.

Nick jr. Math games, Numbers and shapes games. Find at http://www.nickjr.com.

PBS Teachers Mathline®. Videoclips for math and science. Find at http://pbs.org.

PBS Teachers STEM resources. Find at www.pbs.org.

Science Made Simple. Articles for kids, parents, and teachers. See at http://www.sciencemadesimple.com.

Science Magazine for Kids, *Earth for kids, Science for kids.* Pitara kids network. See at http://www.pitara.com.

Symbaloo. A site for connections to many NGSS curriculum resources. www.symbaloo.com

USDA healthy living sites. Activities for K and prek about food and the Food Plate. See letsmove.gov.

Software Resources

Broderbund at Riverdeep

Edmark (see Riverdeep)

Inspiration Software, Inc.

LCSI®

LeapFrog Enterprises, Inc.

LEGO® MINDSTORMS™

Lego Systems, Inc.

NASA

Neufeld Learning Systems, Inc.

Riverdeep-Edmark

(see Broderbund for address)

ROBOLAB

Scholastic, Inc.

School Zone Publishing Company

Sunburst/Tenth Planet

Tom Snyder Productions

Visions Technology

Wright Group

*Bold numbers that follow a listing indicate relevant chapters in this book.

GLOSSARY

A

abstract symbolic activities—activities that involve the manipulation of groups using number symbols.

accommodation—when new information that does not fit into an existing scheme is modified or a new scheme is made.

action symbols—symbols that tell what action to take, such as (+) or (×).

add (+)—to join groups.

adult-guided learning—learning in which the adult chooses the experience for the child and provides some direction to the child's actions.

algebra—at the preoperational level, algebraic thinking involves discovering and creating patterns.

algorithms—step-by-step procedures for solving problems.

amphibians—animals that live both on land and in water.

anthropomorphic—giving human shapes or characteristics to animals.

arbitrary units—units used in the third stage of measurement, where anything can be used as a unit of measure; extends through the latter part of the preoperational period.

assess—the first step in instruction; where are the children now in their development?

assessment—gathering information and evidence about student knowledge.

assimilation—fitting information into an existing scheme.

association—one of the criteria that can be used as a common feature to form a group (i.e., things that do a job together, come from the same place, or belong to a special person).

atmosphere—gaseous mass surrounding a star or planet; all of Earth's air.

authentic assessment—equitable assessment through the use of developmentally appropriate methods such as portfolios.

autonomy—achieving independent thinking, which is the aim of education.

awareness—the first stage in the learning cycle as adapted to early childhood education: a broad recognition of objects, people, events, and concepts that develops from experience.

axes—the names for the left side and bottom of a line graph.

B

balanced reading—a view that reading instruction should include a balance of phonics and whole language focus.

basic facts—number combinations that add up to 1 through 10.

biodegradable—capable of being readily decomposed by biological means.

C

camouflage—the appearance of an animal or insect that allows it to blend with its environment for protection.

cardinality—an understanding that the last number named is the amount in a group.

cardinal meaning—the last number counted is the amount in the group.

centration—the characteristic of preoperational children that causes them to focus on the most obvious aspects of what they perceive.

charts—means of visually depicting data.

checklist—a list of skills that can be dated as children accomplish them.

chemical change—a change in which substances mix and form something new.

choose objectives—after assessment, decide what the child should learn next.

circle—a continuous curved line.

classification—putting things from a larger group into smaller logical groups; systematically distributing a group of many items into smaller groups with similar characteristics; also known as *sorting*.

classifying—grouping or sorting according to properties such as size, shape, color, use, and so on.

class inclusion—one class may be included in another (beagles and poodles are included in the class of dogs).

class name—one of the criteria that can be used as a common feature to form a group (e.g., animals, furniture, people).

cognitive structure—the grouping of closely related facts and phenomena related to a concept.

color—one criterion that can be used to place things in a logical group.

common features—one of the criteria that can be used to form a group (e.g., all have doors, handles, points).

communicating—recording ideas, directions, and descriptions orally or in written form, such as pictures, maps, graphs, or journals so others can understand what you mean; one of the science process skills.

comparing—finding a relationship between two items or groups of items based on a specific characteristic or attribute; one of the science process skills.

comparisons—the second stage of measurement, which extends through the preoperational period; comparisons such as weight, length, and temperature are made.

computational fluency—computing with efficiency, accuracy, and flexibility.

concept application phase—after completing investigations and problem-solving experiences, taking the knowledge and applying it to a new situation; this phase expands the concept.

concept introduction phase—initial investigation and problem-solving experiences designed by the teacher and/or children to acquire knowledge of a topic; this phase provides opportunities to accommodate information.

concepts—the building blocks of knowledge; they allow for organizing and categorizing information.

conceptual subitizing—seeing number patterns within a group such as a large number of dots (usually more than five).

conclusions—statements that tell whether the original prediction or hypothesis was rejected.

concreteness—the degree to which materials approach reality.

concrete operations—the third period identified by Piaget, during which children attain conservation.

concrete whole number operations—solving simple addition, subtraction, division, and multiplication problems using concrete materials.

condensation—to pass into a denser form, as vapor into a liquid.

connections—the bridge between the informal mathematics learned out of school with the formalities of school mathematics; concrete materials can serve this function.

conservation—the ability to retain the original picture in the mind when material has been changed in its arrangement in space; also, the care and protection of natural resources.

constellations—a number of fixed stars arbitrarily considered a group, usually referred to by a name or number.

construct—as children explore their environment they build concepts

constructivism—the view that people build their own knowledge

contrived problems—problems devised by the teacher for which the teacher models a problem-solving procedure.

convergent questions and directions—having only one possible answer or activity.

counting—attaching number names to objects (rational counting) and reciting the names of the numerals in order from memory (rote counting).

cultural time—time that is fixed by clocks and calendars.

curiosity—a desire to learn or know.

curves—curved, but not straight, paths that connect two points.

cylinder—a three-dimensional figure with parallel circular bases.

D

data collection—recording information collected during observations.

descriptive lessons—lessons in which children mainly observe, interact, and describe their observations.

design technology—an area of engineering where math, science, and technology become integrated.

development—changes that take place as a result of growth and experience.

direction—in spatial relations, indicates "which way" (i.e., up, down, across).

discrepant event—an event that has an unexpected conclusion.

disequilibrium—occurs when children realize that they do not understand something they previously thought they understood.

distance—in spatial relations, indicates relative distance (e.g., near or far).

divergent questions and directions—provide opportunities for guessing and experimenting.

divide (÷)—to separate a whole into parts.

dividend—the amount to be broken into equal parts in the division operation.

divisor—the number of parts that a group is divided into in the division operation.

dramatic role-playing—taking on roles in pretend play.

duration—how long an event takes (e.g., minutes, days).

duration (time) words—clock (minutes, hours) and calendar (days, weeks) words.

E

ECE—Early Childhood Education.

ECSE—Early Childhood Special Education.

ELL(s)—English Language Learner(s).

embryo—rudimentary plant contained in a seed.

English units—units of measure customarily used in the United States (such as inches, feet, and yards).

environment—all the conditions, circumstances, and influences surrounding and affecting the development of an organism or group of organisms.

equality—when groups have the same amount.

equals—is the same in quantity, size, degree, or value.

equilibrium—is established when children have enough information to satisfy their curiosity and to create a new cognitive structure.

erosion—the removal of soil by water or wind.

estimation—making a sensible and reasonable guess regarding "how many" or "how much" without counting or measuring.

ethnomathematics—mathematics learned outside of school.

evaluate—find out whether an objective has been reached through observation or questioning.

evaporation—changing into vapor or the removal of moisture from milk, fruit, and so on.

exploration—the construction of personal meaning through sensory experiences with objects, people, events, or concepts.

exploration phase—the second stage in the learning cycle as adapted to early childhood education: the construction of personal meaning.

F

factors—the numbers operated on in multiplication.

Food Plate—developed by the United States Government, Department of Agriculture, it shows the five main food groups and the relative amounts present in a well-balanced diet.

formal operations—Piaget's final period, which extends from about age 11 through adulthood.

fossils—hardened remains of animal or plant life from a previous geological period.

fourths—the parts of a substance or a group when the substance or group is separated or divided into four equal parts.

fractions—an area of formal mathematics that grows out of an informal understanding of parts and wholes; during the primary grades, children learn about halves, fourths, and thirds (they also use terms such as *pieces, whole,* and *almost whole*).

function—one of the criteria that can be used as a common feature to form a group (i.e., all used for the same thing, such as eating or playing music).

G

general (time) words—words such as "time" and "age."

geoboard—a square board with headed screws or pegs sticking up at equal intervals; rubber bands are stretched between pegs to make a variety of shapes.

geologist—specialist in geology.

germinate—to start developing or growing; to begin sprouting.

glycerin—a thick, odorless, colorless liquid prepared from hydrolysis of fats and oils.

graphs—visual representations of two or more comparisons.

H

halves—the parts of a substance or a group after it is separated or divided into two equal parts.

haptic—relating to the sense of touch.

heuristics—questions that children generate when solving problems.

hierarchical classification—classes within classes, with a series developing larger and larger classes.

holistic evaluation—an evaluation in which a rubric is used to place portfolios in groups, such as strong, average, and weak.

hypothesis—a statement, based on observations, that can be tested by experiment; one of the science process skills.

I

IEP—Individualized Educational Plan.

IFSP—Individualized Family Service Plan.

igneous rocks—rocks formed through cooling of magma or lava.

inferring—basing on observations, but suggests more meaning about a situation than can be directly observed; one of the science process skills.

informal learning—learning experiences initiated by the adult as children engage in their everyday natural activities.

informal measurement—measurement done by comparison or by using nonstandard units (e.g., a shoe, a paper clip, a block).

inquiry—the third stage in the learning cycle; as adapted to early childhood education, learners compare their findings; a major focus of science process skill.

integrated curriculum—curriculum that integrates math, science, social studies, language arts, music and movement, and visual arts, usually through projects and/or thematic units.

intentional teaching—teaching that balances child-guided and adult-guided instruction.

invertebrates—animals that have no backbone or spinal column.

L

landfill—an area of land where garbage is stored, mainly items that cannot be recycled.

learning cycle—phases of learning used for curriculum development and as teaching strategies: exploration, concept development, concept application.

Lego/LOGO—a combination of LEGO bricks and LOGO programming that children can use to explore physics, technology, and mathematics.

length—in measurement, denotes how long, wide, or deep.

lens—a piece of glass, with two curved surfaces, that is used in a magnifier to enlarge images.

less than (<)—a group or quantity comparison term and symbol meaning a smaller amount, fewer, or to a smaller degree.

line—a connection between two points.

line graphs—graphs made on squared paper grids connecting data points.

logical grouping—groups whose members have a logical connection (such as number, color, shape, or class).

logico-mathematical knowledge—knowledge that enables us to organize and make sense out of the world, such as classification and number concepts.

LOGO—a computer language that can be applied to many geometric experiences.

M

magnifier—lens that enlarges the apparent size of an object.

manipulative materials—materials featuring parts and pieces that can be picked up and moved by the child in the process of problem solving.

material—one criterion that can be used to place items in a logical group (e.g., wood, plastic, glass).

mathematics learning disorder (MLD)—occurs in about 6% of school-age children who cannot remember basic facts and/or cannot carry out basic procedures.

measurement—assigning a number to things so they can be compared in terms of the same attribute.

measuring—quantitative descriptions made by an observer either directly through observation or indirectly with a unit of measure; one of the science process skills.

metamorphic rocks—rocks formed when sedimentary and igneous rocks are completely changed in form through pressure and heat.

metric units—measurement units based on groups of 10.

minerals—inorganic substances that occur naturally in the earth and have a consistent and distinctive set of physical properties.

more than (>)—a group or quantity comparison term and symbol .

multiple classification—classifying in terms of more than one criterion.

multiple intelligences—areas of strength identified by Howard Gardner.

N

naturalistic experiences—learning that occurs as children go about their daily activities.

Next Generation Science Standards (NGSS)—national expectations for what children will know and be able to do in the area of science.

nonroutine problems—problems that involve more than one step and do not follow a predictable pattern.

notation—number and operations symbols.

number—one of the criteria that can be used to form a group (e.g., pairs or other groups of the same amount).

number sense—the concept or understanding of number.

number sentences—sentences that symbolize an operation; for example, $3 + 4 = 7$ and $8 > 6$.

numerals—number symbols (i.e., 1, 2, 3, etc.).

O

object permanence—the realization that objects exist even when they are out of sight.

object recognition—the ability to identify objects, using previously acquired information such as color, shape, and size.

one more than—a concept basic to sequencing or ordering groups of amounts, each of which is one more than the other.

one-to-one correspondence—the recognition that one group has as many members as another.

ordering—putting items in a logical sequence.

organism—any living thing.

P

part(s)—things have parts (e.g., legs, doors, handles) and groups have parts (e.g., each child gets two cookies).

pattern—one criterion that can be used to place items in a logical group (e.g., stripes, dots, plaid).

patterning—making or discovering auditory, visual, and motor regularities.

perceptual subitizing—being able to state how many are in a group, without counting or grouping.

performance-based assessment—giving one or more students a task to do, which will indicate the student level of understanding of science concepts and thinking skills.

personal experience—the view of time held by young children (e.g., "When I was a baby . . .").

phonics—an approach to beginning reading that focuses on the elements of printed text, such as letters and sounds.

physical change—when the physical appearance of a substance changes, but it is not chemically altered.

physical knowledge—knowledge of things in their environment and their characteristics.

place value—pertains to an understanding that the same numeral represents different amounts, depending on its position.

plan experiences—deciding which strategies should be used to enable the child to accomplish instructional objectives.

play—the major medium through which children learn.

play stage—the first stage of measurement, during which children imitate adults and/or older children by using measurement tools such as rulers or measuring cups; this stage extends into the preoperational period.

points—introduced as small dots and later applied to making line graphs.

pollution—to make unclean or impure as in water, air, or soil.

portfolio—a purposeful collection of student work.

position—in spatial relations, an indication of "where" (e.g., on, off, under, over).

preconcepts—incomplete concepts that develop before true concepts.

predicting—making reasonable guesses or estimations based on observations and prior knowledge and experiences; one of the science process skills.

preoperational period—the second Piagetian developmental period, which extends from about age 2 to age 7.

preprimary or preschool/kindergarten—the period before children enter first grade.

primary—grades 1–3.

principles—basic rules that guide high-quality mathematics education.

problem solving—a major mathematics process standard, which involves application of the other four standards.

process skills—label for fundamental mathematics concepts such as classifying, comparing, and measuring when applied to science.

product—the result of a multiplication operation.

Q

quantities above 10—once children understand the base quantity of ten, they can move on to working with larger quantities.

quantity comparison—considering two groups of objects and deciding whether they have the same amount or if one group has more.

quotient—the result of the division operation.

R

RTI (Response to Intervention)—an intervention approach that follows specific intervention guidelines.

rational counting—attaching a number name to each object counted.

reasoning—the ability that enables children to draw logical conclusions, apply logical classification skills, justify problem solutions, and make sense out of mathematics and science.

record folder—a collection of anecdotal records and checklists.

rectangular prism—a three-dimensional figure with identical rectangular bases and four rectangular sides.

recycling—reusing existing materials.

regrouping—moving groups from one column of numbers to another.

relational symbols—indicate that quantities are related; for example, equal (=), less than (<) and more than (>).

relational (time) words—words such as "soon," "yesterday," "early," and so forth.

remainder—in division, the result may not come out with equal groups; there may be a remainder.

renaming—after a group has been moved using regrouping, the new number is renamed.

representation—demonstrating thought and understanding through oral and written language, physical gestures, drawings, and invented and conventional symbols.

representational thought—the ability to think through the solution to a problem before acting.

reptiles—a group of cold-blooded vertebrates that crawl on their bellies or creep on short, stubby legs.

resources—anything that can be used to fill a need; natural resources include coal, water, oil, gas, and so on.

reversibility—When the arrangement of material is changed, the mind's ability to reverse the process of change and visualize the original arrangement.

rote counting—reciting the names of the numerals in order from memory.

routine problems—problems that follow a predictable pattern.

rubrics—evaluation guides that show students' criteria for self-assessment.

S

scaffolding—assistance in learning from someone who is more mature.

sedimentary rocks—rocks formed from eroded rocks, sand, clay, silt, pebbles, and other stones.

select materials—deciding which materials should be used in order to carry out an instructional plan.

self-correcting materials—materials that the child can use independently by trial and error to solve a problem with little or no adult assistance.

self-regulation—active mental process of forming concepts.

senses—sight, touch, smell, hearing, and taste.

sensorimotor period—first cognitive developmental period identified by Piaget; extends from birth to about age 2.

sequence—time as related to the order of events.

seriation—according to Piaget, ordering that results from putting items in a logical sequence such as first to last.

shape—criterion that can be used to place items in a logical group (e.g., square, circular, triangular) and can be reproduced with geoboards or stencils.

signs—the tools of the mind, such as language, that we use for thinking.

size—a measurement term referring to volume, height, weight, and/or length.

skepticism—attitude whereby a person does not accept things easily on face value.

skip counting—counting using quantities and number symbols other than ones, such as "2-4-6-8 . . ." or "5-10-15 . . ."

social activity—time as viewed from the sequence of routine daily activities.

social knowledge—the knowledge created by people, such as rules of conduct.

sorting—the process of separating a larger group into two or more smaller groups; see *classification.*

special days—time as indicated by holidays and other special days.

specific (time) words—words that refer to a specific time, such as "morning" and "night."

sphere—a three-dimensional circular figure.

square—a shape with four equal sides and four corners.

stage one, object graphs—the first stage in graphing, which uses real objects such as cube blocks; usually two items are compared.

stage two, picture graphs—the second stage of graphing, where more than two categories may be compared and a more permanent record (such as pictures) may be kept.

stage three, square paper graphs—the third stage of graphing, where more than two categories may be compared and a more permanent record (such as using paper squares) may be kept.

standards—provide guidance as to what children should know and be able to do at different ages and stages.

standard units—units of measurement that are standardized (e.g., inches, centimeters, pounds, liters, miles) and that everyone agrees on; children begin to understand the need for standard units during the concrete operational period.

STEM—an integration of science, technology, engineering, and mathematics.

STEAM—an integration of STEM with the arts.

subitizing—knowing instantly how many is in a group, without counting.

subset—a smaller group within a larger group.

subtract (−)—separate a group into two smaller groups.

sum—the result of combining groups.

symbolic behaviors—behaviors that appear during representational play, as when children use materials to represent something else (e.g., sand for food).

symbolic level—the stage at which children have connected sets and symbols and can record the solutions to concrete problems using number symbols.

symmetry—correspondence of two sides of a figure on each side of a line.

T

tables—means of visually depicting data.

teach—do planned experiences with children.

teachable moment—a time when adults recognize that a child has chosen an activity that provides a time to insert instruction.

temperature—in measurement, denotes how hot or cold.

terrapins—North American freshwater or tidewater turtles.

texture—one of the criteria that can be used as a common feature to form a group (e.g., rough, smooth, hard, soft).

thematic units and projects—instructional methods that provide for the integration of math, science, and other content areas.

thirds—the parts of a substance or a group when the substance or group is separated or divided into three equal parts.

times (×)—the action term for multiplication.

tortoises—turtles that live on land.

total—the resulting group amount when groups are combined.

trading rules—establish what happens when numbers are regrouped.

triangle—a shape with three straight sides and three points.

triangular prism—a three-dimensional figure with identical triangular bases and three rectangular sides.

turtle—the name for the cursor when using LOGO language to solve geometry problems.

U

understanding—the basic premise of the CCSSM and NGSS standards; stands in opposition to just memorizing.

unit—a quantity chosen as a standard of measurement, which measurement must be made with the same unit to be accurate and comparable.

utilization—the fourth stage in the learning cycle as adapted to early childhood education: learners can apply and use their understandings in new settings and situations.

V

variable(s)—anything changeable.

virtual materials and activities—pictorial versions of concrete materials as depicted online.

volume—in measurement, denotes how much.

W

weather—the general condition of the atmosphere at a given time in regard to temperature, moisture, cloudiness, and so on.

webbing—strategy used to depict a variety of possible concepts and curricular experiences.

weight—in measurement, denotes how heavy.

whole number operations—addition, subtraction, multiplication, and division.

whole(s)—all of some object or a group of objects.

Z

zone of proximal development (ZPD)—the area between where the child is now operating independently and where the child might be able to operate with the assistance of an adult or a more mature peer.

INDEX

Note: page numbers followed by an "f" indicate figures; a "p" indicate photos; "t" indicate tables.